Books by Edward Streeter

DERE MABLE

DAILY EXCEPT SUNDAY

FATHER OF THE BRIDE

SKOAL SCANDINAVIA

MR. HOBBS' VACATION

MERRY CHRISTMAS,
    MR. BAXTER

MR. ROBBINS RIDES
    AGAIN

CHAIRMAN OF THE
    BORED

CHAIRMAN OF THE BORED

Edward Streeter

HARPER & BROTHERS, PUBLISHERS
New York

Contents

PART I   *Realization*

1

THE MORNING LETTERS HAD BEEN dictated. They were not particularly good letters—decidedly below par, in fact. Mr. Crombie prided himself on his ability to write clear, readable English, but there were days when his creative machinery seemed to be gummed up; days when sentences refused to end and went trailing on and on until he had forgotten how they began.

The sad truth was that he could no longer toss off one of Jane Marbury's dinner parties the way he used to. They were no Bohemian orgies, heaven knew. Quite the reverse. But their ritualistic stuffiness and impeccable refinement had an even more insidious way of creeping up on you unnoticed. The world of Jane Marbury was populated with Gentlemen. It was a nice old tradition, but for ordinary people like Mr. Crombie it required a degree of self-control which at times he found difficult to exercise.

In the morning, as he walked briskly from his apartment to the subway, the disciplined middle road was obviously the desirable way of life for all but morons. You knew what these dinners were like. It was just a matter of being braced for them. Two cocktails and that was that. Play with the wine.

You can't pour wine on top of hard liquor and expect to feel like a mountain brook the next morning. And then, above all, no brandy and no highballs after dinner—nothing.

That was all right for the early morning. The trouble was that two martinis caused a new character to come on the stage. Exit the morning Crombie, clean, wholesome man of iron; enter the evening Crombie, the *bon vivant*; Crombie, the droll, charming dinner companion; Crombie, the informed member of the after-dinner-coffee group. ("Crombie, have you heard this rumor about the Texacron crowd taking over Byers Steel?" "Well, that's quite a story, Joe. I do happen to know something about it—yes, a little brandy, thank you—it seems that Phil Adams of Texacron . . ."); Crombie, to whom every woman in the room liked to talk because he had understanding, lightly spiced with daring. ("Jane, dear, you have to face it sooner or later and you might just as well come to grips with the situation—thank you, Scotch, please, with soda.")

And the worst of it was that the evening Crombie was not just a weakling, reneging on rash post-breakfast commitments made by the morning Crombie. He had never even heard of the stuffed shirt and was therefore completely ignorant of the fellow's philosophy and views, nor could he care less.

There was nothing forgetful, however, about the morning Crombie. He knew and loved his wayward evening namesake, felt toward him as a father would toward a gay, irresponsible son from who he had dared expect too much. But there were times when he felt depressed about him and wondered if the fault had been his.

What it all added up to was that Mr. Crombie, the morning Crombie, had a slight hangover. Miss Parkinson was fully aware of this, but he didn't mind because Miss Parkinson justified such things on the grounds that anyone who worked as hard as he did was entitled to an occasional bisque.

Over a period of thirty-five years Miss Parkinson had never let him down. He often wondered how a person with such sympathetic understanding, such loyalty and intelligence could have escaped marriage. Perhaps it was the relationship between a man and his secretary which brought out these qualities. Perhaps as a wife she would have been like all other wives.

It disturbed him at times to realize that Miss Parkinson knew him a lot better than Jinny did, and that in a certain sense he was more relaxed with her than he was in his own home. He said things to her that he would never have dreamed of saying to Jinny; the rebellious thoughts that lie buried in the most devoted husbands. Jinny would have been forced to disagree or to capitulate, but Miss Parkinson, having no stake in the matter, no face to save, was free to understand and let it go at that.

It was strictly a one-way relationship and such things were not without advantages from the male point of view at least. Miss Parkinson knew everything about Mr. Crombie, but he could have written all he knew about her on the back of an envelope. All day long she was a captive audience, forced to listen to his jokes, his troubles and his perplexities, bound to smile appreciatively at his dictated quips, steering him with skilled anonymity through the maze of the daily routine. So impersonal was their relationship that he regarded her more as an extension of his ego than as an individual in her own right, yet he missed her dreadfully and complainingly on the rare occasions when she was absent.

"Do you want to start that memo for the Chicago office?" she asked as he riffled through the remaining papers on his desk.

"Oh Lord, do I have to tackle that this morning?" he asked.

"It can wait," she reassured him. "Is that all?"

"All I can find for the moment," said Mr. Crombie. "You'd

better hammer out that long one to Foster and Kerr as a draft, double spaced."

"I was going to," said Miss Parkinson. "By the way, I put a note on your desk about the spring outing. We ought to be setting a date and appointing a committee or we'll be in the same old last-minute jam."

"Good God," said Mr. Crombie, "we just survived one of those things."

"That was seven months ago," said Miss Parkinson.

"I can't tell you how I hate these spring outings. I don't think anybody really enjoys them and they cost more every year."

"Well, this is the last one you'll have to worry about," she said soothingly. "By the time the next one comes around you'll be retired and you can let someone else worry. I'll give you a memorandum showing you who was on the Arrangements Committee last year." She picked up her notebook and her three needle-sharp pencils and disappeared into her outer office.

Mr. Crombie sat staring at the pile of memoranda and reports on his desk blotter, her last words repeating themselves in his mind like a faulty phonograph record. "This is the last one. . . ." So calm, so matter of fact. "You can let someone else worry." He had scarcely expected Miss Parkinson to be burned on his funeral pyre, but after working together for the best part of both their business lives his retirement didn't have to be brought up as casually as if it concerned a proposed change in the bookkeeping department.

He had been much too busy to give this matter of retirement the thought that it obviously deserved. Crombie, Hamilton and Gardiner, the biggest (and best) investment-counsel company in the United States, had grown so fast since it was founded in the golden Twenties that his life had been spent running a losing race with time, which had left no room for the consideration of compulsory retirement, or what one was going to do with it when it happened, or anything else, for that matter.

And now Miss Parkinson, who in common decency should go at least slightly to pieces at the thought of his pulling out, had referred to it in the dead-pan manner of a stage butler announcing dinner. It was incredible. Crombie, Hamilton and Gardiner was his brainchild. If it had not been for him, Jack Hamilton and Minton Gardiner might still be sweating it out in some underwriting house or the trust department of a bank. Miss Parkinson had upset him so that for the moment he forgot they were both dead.

That did not alter the fact, however, that it was *he*, Graham Crombie, who had persuaded them to leave perfectly good jobs and join him in this new venture and that *he* was the one who had put it across. It was equally true that when the original firm had been incorporated ten years ago it was *he* who had set up the present pension plan and insisted that retirement be made compulsory at sixty-five for men and at sixty for women.

As a matter of fact, if he wanted to be completely honest with himself, it had never occurred to him that the rule would be applied to him. Perhaps it wouldn't be. Why jump at conclusions? But Miss Parkinson had taken it so for granted; as if it was common knowledge. Was it? It was not the sort of thing you could go around asking people about, but he wished he could talk to someone. Who fired the boss, anyway?

He consulted Miss Parkinson's neatly typed list of things that he should do that day. As he read over the items he found that he didn't want to do any of them—phone Carr about the Sinclair estate, phone Dodger, who had called him after he had left the previous evening, call his attorney, Joe Loomis, about the Harris mess, phone Pearson at the Bank.

Miss Parkinson had noted that he had called before Mr. Crombie arrived at the office. Was that an implied rebuke? The buzzer on the side of his desk sounded. He picked up the phone. It was Jinny.

"Yes, dear," he said, in the clipped tone which he always used when she phoned him at the office, just to indicate that he was in no mood for fooling around.

"Listen, I'm almost crazy. Jack Mayhew can't come to dinner tomorrow night and he's the only unattached man I know to pair off with Judy. You *must* know somebody—some widower."

"There aren't any widowers, darling, don't you know that by this time? Just widows."

"I know, but can't you be a *little* helpful?"

"Jinny, dear, I don't care *who* you have for Judy. She bores me stiff. Hire a gigolo. Let her sit by herself at a card table in the corner. I really don't *care*. There *are* no extra men, period. They're all dead. And don't act as if I had a private supply that I'm hiding in my desk. I'm terribly busy. See you tonight."

"I love dinners, but only when somebody else gives them," she moaned. "You're always busy. What are you doing?"

"Don't be difficult, dear. Good-by."

He replaced the receiver and immediately picked it up again and pressed the button that sounded a buzzer on Miss Parkinson's desk. "Get me Mr. Carr," he said.

"There's a lady here to see you. She says she wants to discuss her investments. That Mr. Woodhouse sent her."

"Can't you sick her on Gleason or Henry Buckley? I have a lot of things that ought to be done right away."

"No. She says Mr. Woodhouse told her that she was to talk to no one but you."

"Damn Woodhouse. Just because he has nothing to do . . ."

"She looks wealthy," said Miss Parkinson in a muffled voice.

"Oh, I suppose I must. Show her in. But see if you can't get Carr before we get started. What did you say her name was?"

"I didn't. It's Mrs. John K. Winters. She's a widow."

"Naturally," said Mr. Crombie.

A moment later Miss Parkinson opened the door to Mr. Crombie's office and ushered in a plump, rather pretty woman in her middle fifties. She was wearing deep and expensive mourning. Mr. Crombie rose and motioned to the chair beside his desk. "Won't you sit there, Mrs. Winters."

"So good of you, Mr. Crombie, to take time out to see me about my poor little affairs," she said, collapsing into the chair. "They seem awfully big to me, I can tell you. You see my poor, dear husband died about two months ago." She began pawing through her handbag for a handkerchief.

Miss Parkinson lingered in the doorway watching with hostile eyes. "Will you shut the door, please," said Mr. Crombie. "Oh yes, and cancel that call to Carr." Miss Parkinson sniffed audibly and closed the door.

2

THREE-QUARTERS OF AN HOUR later Mrs. Winters, dabbing at her eyes with a tiny handkerchief, emerged into the outer office. She was followed by Mr. Crombie, showing visible signs of strain. "Why don't you go back and see Mr. Woodhouse," he was suggesting.

"Talk things over with him. He knows the whole situation and he may see things differently than I do."

"Oh, I know what he'll say. You businessmen are all alike. Sell the apartment. Get rid of my faithful old servants. All you think of is money, money, money. There are other things in this world besides money."

"I'm sorry if I upset you," said Mr. Crombie, looking miserable, "but I had to tell you the truth as I see it. I'm sure things are going to turn out better than you think. And please come back if I can be of any help."

She didn't notice his outstretched hand and he watched her with troubled eyes as she walked, straight-backed, past Miss Parkinson's desk and disappeared down the corridor. She wouldn't come back. They never did.

"What's the matter?" asked Miss Parkinson. "No money?"

Mr. Crombie nodded. "Same old story. Husband had a huge salary and she spent it as fast as he brought it in. Big apartment, country place, servants; the usual setup. All he left her is a couple of hundred thousand life insurance."

"Oh baby, I wish he'd left it to me," said Miss Parkinson.

"You'd know what to do with it. She doesn't. She said there were other things in this world besides money. The trouble is she never had a chance to find out what they were."

"Poor thing," said Miss Parkinson cheerily. "Now look, I have a lot of things for you." She reminded Mr. Crombie of a squirrel who had been diligently gathering nuts while he frittered away his time. "I thought you were never going to get rid of her." Miss Parkinson regarded most of Mr. Crombie's clients as so many interruptions to the day's work.

She followed him back to his office, consulting her notebook. "Mrs. Crombie called. She said she had tried two extra men for dinner tomorrow night and neither of them could come. She says can't you blackjack some attractive young man from the office. And she says what kind of wine do you want?"

Not by the slightest inflection of her voice did Miss Parkinson deviate from her professional role as secretary, but the glance which she gave Mr. Crombie said plainly, "You poor, put-upon man. With the weight of the world on your shoulders you have to be dragged into this." Mr. Crombie, long an expert in interpreting Miss Parkinson's glances, was comforted.

"I'm just not going to go in for that," he said. "If I ask someone from the office, the whole place will have its ears up trying to figure out what's going on."

"Of course," murmured Miss Parkinson, with downcast eyes which said, "You'd think people with any common sense would know that."

"As for the wine—the wine—good Lord. Must I . . . ?"

"I know," said Miss Parkinson. "You're having roast beef. I suggested some of that red wine you served at the Whitman dinner last week. You must have some left. I ordered a case."

Mr. Crombie looked at her admiringly. "Thanks, pal," he said. "What else?"

"Well, let's see. Mr. Carr called again. Mr. Loomis returned your call. Mr. Pearson called again. I think you ought to get hold of Mr. Loomis. He's worried about something."

"Put in a call," said Mr. Crombie. "Anything else?"

Miss Parkinson shook her head and left for her desk. A few minutes later she reappeared. "Mr. Loomis has gone out," she said. "He'll call you first thing this afternoon. And by the way, don't forget that you're having lunch with that group from the J. B. Cottwell Company. They're meeting here at twelve."

"Good Lord, is that today?" said Mr. Crombie. "You were going to get me some information about the company."

"Don't you *ever* read my memos? Here," said Miss Parkinson, thumbing through the papers on his blotter. "Here it is. It's been there since yesterday."

"I guess I didn't see it," said Mr. Crombie, humbly.

"Well, it's certainly not complete, but it's all I could dig up. This business has been developed by young Partridge and that cute Mr. Applegate. You remember what it's about. They're trying to get the Cottwell Company to name us as investment counsel for their pension fund. The president, the exec and the treasurer are coming today to talk things over. They're meeting here at twelve so that you can show them the office. That's Mr. Partridge's bright idea. I've engaged a private dining room at the Sky Club for a quarter to one."

"But what does the Cottwell Company *do?* What are the *names* of these characters? How big is the pension fund? I'm not a mind reader. Half an hour from now I'm supposed to sell a bill of goods and nobody takes the trouble to tell me what it's all about. Where in hell are cute Mr. Partridge and cute Mr. Applegate? Why don't they brief me on this?"

"I talked to them both this morning," she said calmly. "Mr. Partridge is down at Wall Street and won't be back until twelve, but Mr. Applegate is all set to brief you. He phoned me while that woman was here. Just now he has an important customer with him. As a matter of fact, you have an officers' meeting right now. It shouldn't last more than fifteen minutes, though. I don't think there's anything special coming up. I'll have Mr. Applegate here at quarter to twelve. He can cover the ground easily before they show up."

Mr. Crombie glanced at his wrist watch. "I almost forgot about the officers' meeting. I don't like to keep those fellows waiting and I can never get them to go ahead without me."

The phone rang. Miss Parkinson answered it. "It's Mr. Dodger," she said, covering the mouthpiece. "He called last night, you remember."

"Tell him I've just left for a meeting," said Mr. Crombie. "I'll call him right after lunch."

Miss Parkinson raised her eyes to the ceiling and waited until Mr. Crombie was out of the room before removing her hand from the mouthpiece of the phone.

3

THEY WERE ALL SEATED AROUND
the long table in the new gray-paneled Broad Room. Bingham, head of bond investments, was holding forth on money
rates. So they hadn't waited for him after all!

Bingham paused as Mr. Crombie entered and took his seat
at the head of the table. "We thought you'd want us to go
ahead, Graham," said Mr. Gleason. "I asked Bingham to give
us a little rundown on this recent rise in money rates."

Gleason was the senior executive officer. Mr. Crombie
wished he wouldn't flout this in front of the younger officers
like a matador's cape. "Go right ahead," he said, with a re-
assuring gesture of his hand. "Sorry to be late."

Bingham resumed his exposition. What a dreary fellow he
was! Bonds and interest rates were boring enough on their
own, but Bingham could make them positively lethal. Mr.
Crombie gave up listening and began to study the faces
grouped around the table.

Did all these men realize that within a year and a half he,
Graham Crombie, the man who had put this show on the
road, was going to retire? Was he the only one who had not
taken that clause in the pension plan seriously? Of course he
was. Everyone else had been aware of his retirement date for
months. Their interest was not in him, however, but rather
in the degree of benefit that might accrue to each as a result of
his withdrawal.

Take Gleason, for instance, seated opposite him, thin-lipped and poker-faced, nervously folding and unfolding a piece of scratch paper; as senior vice-president you could be sure that he had been lying awake for months weighing his chances of succeeding to the top post. The odds were that at the moment he wasn't paying the slightest attention to what Bingham was saying, but was planning the changes that he would put into effect when, as and if he were made president.

In the middle of the table Tom Potter sat with his finger tips pressed together, listening, saying little. Potter was one of the best men in the organization, brilliant, sound of judgment, with a genius for handling difficult customers. Actually, he was the one who should take Mr. Crombie's place if the choice was made solely on merit. But in a large organization like Crombie, Hamilton and Gardiner it was so seldom that one could make these high-level decisions on merit alone.

If you gave Potter the job, Gleason would quit. Mr. Crombie felt sure of that. He had plenty of money. Mr. Crombie often wondered why he went on working as hard as he did. Undoubtedly it was because he wanted to be president. Gleason's loss would be a real one. He had qualities the company needed even if he didn't have Potter's touch with people.

Crawford, the economist, had started an argument with Bingham. This was routine. Whether it was Gleason or Potter who ultimately sat at the head of the table, you could be sure that Crawford and Bingham would continue their non-stop argument and that the younger executives, their faces set in expressions of attention, would go right on wondering how much the doctor was going to charge for Johnny's operation, how many more payments were due on the washing machine, or whether the old car would hang together for a few more months. And you could be equally sure that the affairs of Crombie, Hamilton and Gardiner would go rolling smoothly along in spite of the fact that there would no longer be a Crombie to guide them.

Once an organization passed a point in size (or was it a matter of momentum?) it suddenly became an entity in itself, bigger and stronger than the individuals who ran it. It was like one of those man-made satellites which ultimately detach themselves from the final booster rocket and take off on their own. He'd been the booster rocket and now . . . he looked at his wrist watch. Good Lord. It was a quarter to twelve!

"I must ask you gentlemen to excuse me," he said. "This is all very interesting, but I have some people coming in at twelve and I think it might be a good idea to find out something about them before they arrive." They laughed politely. Mr. Crombie's oversensitized ear picked up a slightly patronizing note. He hurried back to his office.

"Is that cute Mr. Applegate here?" he asked Miss Parkinson.

Miss Parkinson's fingers were flying over the keys with an effortlessness which told her life story.

"I just called Miss Newman," she said. "He'll be here in a minute. Mr. Reed called again and said *wouldn't* you try to call him before you went out to lunch. And Mr. Faxon at Cross and Black's called. He wants you to call him back as soon as you can."

"Listen," said Mr. Crombie. "In ten minutes a group of zombies are due to appear in this office. Nobody's had the thoughtfulness to tell me anything about them. All they want *me* to do is sell them something. And now *you* want me to start making a lot of phone calls."

Miss Parkinson recognized with annoyance the persecution tones in Mr. Crombie's voice. These executives sometimes acted like little boys being hounded to do their homework.

"I have to *tell* you, don't I?" she said, coldly. "If you don't make the calls that's up to you."

Mr. Crombie sighed. "Get me Reed," he said. "Oh, Applegate, come in, come in. Don't stand around out there. Tell me about these—these *people*—before they barge in. I haven't the slightest idea who they are or what they do."

Mr. Applegate was a thin, delicate-featured young man who obviously did not react well to pressure. At the moment he had the strained look of one about to part at the seams.

"I'm sorry, sir," he said, laying the palms of his hands on Mr. Crombie's desk and then removing them nervously, leaving two damp spots. "I had that Mrs. Ballinger with me for two hours. I still don't know what she wants. It seems she has a brother in Pittsburgh. . . ."

"Never mind Mrs. Ballinger," said Mr. Crombie, making a conscious effort not to shout. "Who are we taking out to lunch and what's it all about?"

"Oh, sir, I thought you knew. . . ."

"I tried to get Mr. Reed," said Miss Parkinson from the doorway. "He's in conference."

He ignored her and Mr. Applegate continued breathlessly, "The name of the company is the Cottwell Corporation. Partridge and I have been working on them for months to let us handle their pension-fund investments. I think they're just about ready to sign up. You see . . ."

"O.K. But what does the company *do?*"

Mr. Applegate looked pained. "The *Cottwell* Corporation, sir? Why it's the largest producer of metallurgic chemicals in the United States."

"Of *what?*"

"Metallurgic chemicals, sir. The company covers the whole field of chloral metallurgy. Probably the most revolutionary . . ."

Miss Parkinson put her head in the door. "Your guests are here, Mr. Crombie," she said in her best secretarial voice.

Mr. Partridge entered, closely followed by three men who looked to Mr. Crombie like television detectives. "Mr. Crombie," said Mr. Partridge, "I'd like to have you meet Mr. Rambaux, the president of the Cottwell Corporation."

Mr. Rambaux, who might have been a professional wrestler in his day, extended a hand like an outfielder's mitt. "T'meet-cha," he bellowed. Everything about Mr. Rambaux was big. "You certainly got a fancy setup here. Looks like—"

"And this is Mr. Abt," interrupted Mr. Partridge, indicating a tall, cadaverous man whose spectacle bows were so wide they looked like blinders. "Mr. Abt is executive vice-president of Cottwell. And this is the company treasurer, Mr. Brummer."

"Well," said Mr. Crombie, "it certainly is good to have you gentlemen with us. I've heard a lot about your company from Applegate and Partridge." Mr. Applegate looked surprised.

"Well, these two young fellows of yours have been barkin' at our heels so long we thought we better come in before they put the bite on us," roared Mr. Rambaux.

Everyone laughed heartily. Mr. Rambaux threw his arm across Mr. Partridge's shoulder. "No offense, Jack. No one appreciates a good salesman better than I do, though I'm nothin' but a lousy engineer."

"I'm glad to hear you say that," said Mr. Crombie, ambiguously. "These lads are good salesmen because they know what they're talking about. And they've got something to sell," he added as an afterthought. Conversation lagged.

"You've got nice offices here," said Mr. Abt in the uncertain voice of one who feels it necessary to register his presence by saying almost anything.

"I'll say he has," shouted Mr. Rambaux. "No wonder he has to charge so much for tellin' people what to do with their own money." Mr. Brummer and Mr. Abt laughed. Mr. Partridge and Mr. Applegate looked to Mr. Crombie for their cue.

"Before we go out to lunch," said Mr. Crombie, "I want to take you fellows on a little tour of the office and introduce you to a couple of our key men."

"Lead on, Macduff," said Mr. Rambaux. "I begin to get

hungry right after twelve o'clock. Got more to feed than you little fellows."

Laughing faithfully they filed through the outer office past Miss Parkinson's desk. "My secretary, Miss Parkinson—Mr. Rambaux, Mr. Abt and Mr. Dummer."

"Brummer," said Brummer.

"I beg your pardon," said Mr. Crombie. "I can foul up a man's name quicker than anyone I know. If it wasn't for Miss Parkinson doing all my thinking for me . . ."

"You're in," roared Mr. Rambaux, laying a paw on Miss Parkinson's shoulder. "Strike him for a raise after lunch." He winked so violently that it contracted the whole side of his face. Miss Parkinson flushed. Mr. Abt and Mr. Brummer laughed. The procession emerged into the wide corridor whose pastel-colored walls extended for a city block. As they passed each office, heads were raised from identical desks and appraising eyes swept the group.

"I don't see how these fellows ever find their own kennels again if they leave 'em to go to the boys' room," shouted Mr. Rambaux.

"These are the specialists," said Mr. Crombie with dignity, causing Partridge and Applegate to bit off a laugh in mid-air. "Our oil expert has that office we just passed. That man in there is our automotive expert. Next to him . . ."

"Don't you have a chemical man?" asked Mr. Rambaux.

Mr. Partridge seized the opportunity to say something. "Yes, indeed. One of the best in the country. He was to have been with us today but he's out, sick."

"Just as well," said Mr. Rambaux. "He probably don't know anythin' about metallurgic chemicals, anyway. Nobody does."

Mr. Crombie didn't feel that he was in any position to argue that point. "This corner office is where our vice-president, Myron Crawford, works. He's our economist. Myron, I want to introduce some good friends of ours."

Mr. Crawford, who had been immersed in a thick memorandum, replaced his look of annoyance with a cordial smile as he rose from his desk.

"Myron, these gentlemen are from the Cottwell Corporation with which we are all familiar." He introduced Messrs. Rambaux, Abt and Brummer. Mr. Crawford, who wasn't familiar at all, murmured genially and waited for a lead.

"I've always wondered what an economist did," said Mr. Rambaux. "I bet it has nothin' to do with economy."

Mr. Crawford smiled feebly. "An economist," he said, "is concerned with general business conditions and that's broad enough to include almost anything. He . . ."

"You're just the man I want to know," roared Mr. Rambaux. "What's the stock market going to do tomorrow? If I could find that out I'd sell my business and go to Miami. It's my personal opinion, and mind you I'm nothin' but a lousy engineer . . ."

"The short-range fluctuations of the market are outside Mr. Crawford's field," interposed Mr. Crombie, quickly. "We must push along now. I don't want you fellows hurried over lunch. Won't you join us, Myron?"

"Wish I could but I'm all tied up. Nice to see you, gentlemen."

"You know," said Mr. Rambaux as they rounded the corner and proceeded along the south side of the building, which was identical with the east side, "I never could see the sense in these fellows that spend their lives drawing graphs of what happened yesterday. We all know what happened yesterday and the chances are it was lousy. It's tomorrow we want to know about. Now I been following a man by the name of P. B. Parker out in Duluth. He has a system for telling when to buy and sell stocks. There's a man who could help you a lot in your business."

This was not exactly the direction in which Mr. Crombie had planned to lead the conversation. "Well, that's about it," he interrupted as they came to the end of the corridor. "I wanted you to meet Gleason and Bingham but I guess they're out. You've got an idea of our setup, though. Now we'll go back to my office, pick up our hats and coats and walk over to the Sky Club."

"Good," said Mr. Rambaux, as they reversed their direction and started back to Mr. Crombie's office at the other end of the block. "My stomach's beginning to rumble. Now look, Graham, I was telling you about this fellow P. B. Parker out in Duluth. You don't mind if I call you Graham, do you?"

"Not a bit," said Mr. Crombie, wondering what Mr. Rambaux' first name might be, but not caring much.

"Well this fellow P. B. Parker is a character you ought to look into. He's really got it, Graham. He hit 1929 smack on the nose. Bingo! And he's been right ever since. You ought to get in touch with him, Graham. You're in the business of putting people in at the bottom an' taking them out at the top an' old P.B.'s got the answers. Why he . . ."

"We're going to the Sky Club, Miss Parkinson," said Mr. Crombie.

"I know," she said. "Don't forget your meeting at a quarter to three."

"Come on, Graham," said Mr. Rambaux, taking Mr. Crombie's arm. "I want to tell you more about this P. B. Parker."

4

It was half-past two before Mr. Crombie returned to the office. Miss Parkinson followed him to his desk. He looked tired.

"How did it go?" she asked.

"Oh, all right I guess. Everything was left pretty much in the air. It was hard to tell who was selling who most of the time."

"Whom," she said. "I'm glad I didn't have to listen to that big grampus all during lunch. You must be exhausted. Now I *know* you have a meeting at quarter of three, but you really should make *some* of these phone calls. It's no use my telling people you're busy—they're busy, too, and if you're harder to get at than the Dalai Lama it doesn't impress them a bit. It just makes them sore."

"I know, I know," said Mr. Crombie humbly. "Oh how *well* I know how *right* you are. Don't let anyone in and I'll make as many calls as I can before the meeting."

Miss Parkinson smiled slightly. "Good," she said. As she turned to go back to her room she hesitated for an instant, looking down at the broad, bent shoulders encased in the gray herringbone coat. A stranger, observing this scene, might have supposed that she was going to pat them reassuringly, but she merely said, "I'll get Mr. Loomis first," and went out to her desk.

Mr. Crombie started to sign his mail. His buzzer sounded and he picked up the phone. It was Loomis. "God, Graham, what are you having over there, a convention or something? I've been trying to get you all day. Listen. About this Harris situation. Their lawyer was in this morning. I think we got everything straightened out. Now here's what . . ."

The conversation over, Mr. Crombie resumed signing letters. His buzzer summoned him to the phone once more. "Mr. Dodger is out of the office. I'm putting the other calls through," said Miss Parkinson.

He went on signing. The buzzer sounded off like an angry bee. He picked up the receiver. "Hello," he said.

"Hello," said a voice at the other end. There was a silence.

"Who's this?" asked Mr. Crombie.

"What do you mean 'who's this?' My secretary just dragged me out of a meeting because your secretary said you were calling and it was important. You're calling *me*."

"I'm sorry. My secretary is trying to clean up a string of calls that came in while I was out of the office. Who did you say this was?"

"I didn't say, but it happens to be Allen Pearson of the First. What did you have on your mind, Graham?"

"Why . . ." There was a moment's hesitation. "You called me originally. I was just returning your call."

"I called *you?*" Mr. Pearson was incredulous.

"Yes. My secretary says you called me twice this morning."

Pearson's voice became muffled. "Miss Belsam, did we call Crombie this morning?"

Mr. Crombie could hear Miss Belsam's nasal, defensive voice. "You asked me last night to call him the minute you came in this morning. He wasn't in yet. I called again in the middle of the morning."

"Well, I'm damned if I know what I wanted him for. Don't *you* know, Miss Belsam?"

Mr. Pearson's voice returned to the phone. "Graham? Sorry to keep you waiting. I can't remember for the life of me what I called you about. Nice to talk to you, though. Let's have lunch someday."

"I'd like to. I'll give you a ring."

"O.K. Good-by. By the way, don't forget you're sitting at our table at the Waldorf tonight."

"Looking forward to it, Allen."

Mr. Crombie snapped up Miss Parkinson's switch on the intercom. "Listen," he said. "For God's sake let me know who's coming in on the phone. I had a rough time with that idiot, Pearson. Nobody ever tells me anything."

He could almost hear her bristle. "I'm sorry, Mr. Crombie. He came in so fast I didn't have a chance. I don't think he has much to do." Miss Parkinson rated executives by the difficulty she had in getting them to take a call. Those who answered their own phones stood at the bottom of her list. "I'm getting Mr. Carr. The file on the Sinclair estate is on your desk."

"All right. Then come in and I'll give you a memo on my talk with Loomis. Oh, Lord, it's quarter of three. I've got that meeting with the Whitehouse people. Is Gleason going to be there?"

"Yes, sir. Gleason and Smathers, both; I told them you'd be a little late and to go right ahead. Mr. Gleason said that he and Smathers would get all the preliminaries out of the way and then you could enter with a flourish of trumpets."

"Oh, he did, did he? How thoughtful. Well, put in a call for Carr, then bring your book in."

She reappeared several minutes later. "Mr. Carr's in conference. His secretary will have him call you as soon as he gets back to his office."

"Oh, good God! Then I'll be in conference. All right. Let's go. Memo: Conversation with Joseph Loomis re: Estate of

Henrietta A. Harris. Mr. Loomis informed me this morning
that Martin Hart . . . Better look up his middle initial."

"L.," said Miss Parkinson.

"Of course, L. . . . of the firm of . . . of the firm of
. . ."

"Battersea, Carruthers, Hart, Swinnerton and Moore," said
Miss Parkinson.

"Of course. . . . which firm is representing the above
estate . . ." The phone rang. Mr. Crombie picked up the
receiver impatiently. "Hello. Oh, *hello*, Barnes. Of course.
Certainly. I understand. Naturally. We'd be only too glad. I'll
tell you what I'll do—I'll connect you with a young man in
our organization who handles the details of the account. Mr.
Partridge. I'm not trying to push you off on a junior, understand, but he may want to ask you some questions. How are
you otherwise? I know. It's been much too long. Look, why
don't you let me know when you're coming uptown so I can
take you to lunch? Do that, will you? Just a minute and I'll
connect you with Partridge."

Mr. Crombie clicked his phone rapidly to attract the operator, who apparently wasn't in a mood to be clicked at. He
placed his hand over the mouthpiece. "What the hell's the
matter with our switchboard?" he said to Miss Parkinson.

"New girl," said Miss Parkinson morosely.

"Why don't we fire her and get somebody who knows her
job?"

"There is no such person," said Miss Parkinson. "They all
have coffee poisoning."

"Well, one of these days I'm going to sound off and when
I do . . . Where *is* that worthless operator? Oh, excuse me,
is that you, Operator? Will you please put this call on Mr.
Partridge's wire? Thanks. And before you disconnect me, let
me speak to Mr. Partridge. Sam? This is Graham. I'm going
to introduce you to Mr. Barnes—Mr. Adolph Barnes. He's on

the wire (warningly) . . . a very good friend of ours as you well know. He's the attorney for the Banks estate, as you also know. He wants some information about the estate and I told him you had it all at your finger tips. There you are, Mr. Barnes. Not at all. Only sorry to have kept you waiting so long." He hung up.

"That fellow wants more service than any attorney in town," said Miss Parkinson.

"He's a grafting old skinflint," said Mr. Crombie. "Where were we?"

"You were saying, . . . which firm is representing the above estate."

"Right. On January second, Martin . . ."

"L.," murmured Miss Parkinson.

"Right. . . . Martin L." The phone rang. "I'm going nuts." Mr. Crombie snatched at the receiver and glanced at his wrist watch. "Hello. Oh, hello, Bert. Glad to hear your voice. How's everything in the Windy City? Fine, thank you —how's Mary? Good. Good. You're a lucky boy, Bert. Wish I'd seen her first. Hope the Chicago office is making a lot of money to offset our losses down here. What's that? I see. Oh, my, my . . . oh, I hope not . . . hmm . . . what a mess. Look. I'll tell you what I'll do—I'm going into a meeting in a few minutes and as soon as I come out I'll call you right back. You bet. Righto. Yes, indeed . . . soon as I come out. Let's have lunch together some day."

"Why did you ask your Chicago partner to have lunch with you?" asked Miss Parkinson looking at him curiously.

"I didn't," said Mr. Crombie indignantly.

"You did," said Miss Parkinson.

"God, he'll think I'm crazy. It's getting to be a reflex action."

She kept her eyes on her notebook. "The last thing you dictated was . . . on January second Martin L. . . ."

"Oh, yes. . . . Martin L. What's-his-name . . ."

"Hart," she said.

". . . Martin L. Hart called and demanded an accounting. He said that the executor, Mr. . . . Mr. . . ."

"George N. Peabody," said Miss Parkinson.

". . . Mr. George N. Peabody felt that the beneficiaries . . ." The phone rang.

"Let me take it," said Miss Parkinson, taking it. "Just a moment please."

She placed her hand over the mouthpiece. "You go to your meeting," she said. "This is a doomed memo. I'll call Loomis and get him to dictate it to me over the phone." She removed her hand from the phone. "Mr. Crombie's office. Thank you for waiting. Oh, Mr. Reed, I'm so sorry. He's just this moment left for a meeting."

Mr. Crombie reached for the receiver, but she shook her head. "I know. It's a shame, Mr. Reed. You've been trying to get him all day, haven't you? He's been hounded to death, Mr. Reed, he really has. Ever since this morning. Just in and out of meetings. Listen, Mr. Reed, isn't there *anything* I could do to help? This is Miss Parkinson. Just fine, thank you. Of course. Naturally. Oh, yes. You mean that pamphlet we sent out at Christmas? But of course. What is your aunt's name and address? Mrs. . . ."

But Mr. Crombie was on his way to the meeting with the Whitehouse people.

5

THE WHITEHOUSE FAMILY WOULD
have been easier to deal with had they not been so rich that
they could afford to consider money a vulgar commodity
which, like one's intestinal health, should never be discussed
in public. As a result of this sensitivity, the financial affairs of
each member of the family were carried on in an atmosphere
of secrecy comparable to Yale's Skull and Bones.

They were immensely proud of the monetary web which
they had spun and, in suggesting to Crombie, Hamilton and
Gardiner that it step into the investment picture, it had never
occurred to them that anyone would have the bad taste, to say
nothing of effrontery, to suggest simplification.

"But this is a large family, Mr. Gleason," the older Mr.
Whitehouse was saying as Mr. Crombie joined the meeting,
murmuring apologies and taking a conspicuously humble seat
in the corner. "The Estate Office must be maintained separately, as must that of the Holding Company. And then, as
you know, the Whitehouse Mills have large security holdings
which are also administered separately. Certainly the various
individual Funds must be kept separate."

Mr. Gleason turned to Mr. Crombie. "There are something
over six million dollars in the various accounts just mentioned
by Mr. Whitehouse. He has suggested that we make a flat
rate based on the total dollar amount, but that we administer

each fund separately. There are twelve separate accounts involved, of varying sizes. I've been pointing out that we don't believe they can be handled profitably for anything like the fee Mr. Whitehouse suggests."

Mr. Crombie nodded pleasantly, to indicate that he understood and was in agreement with everyone. "You fellows go right ahead," he said. "I'm sure you will work something out that will be fair and just to all concerned."

It was a good opportunity to watch Gleason and Smathers work on a tough one and the Whitehouses had a flair for making anything tough. Mr. Crombie regarded them as an opinionated, penny-pinching group of reactionaries, but six million was six million, no matter how you chopped it up.

He tried to concentrate on the discussion. Gradually, however, he lost the thread of the studiously polite argument and his thoughts wandered among the events of the day.

As usual, he searched for the things neglected. He hadn't done anything about that damned outing, for one thing. As a matter of fact, it was difficult for him to recall just what he *had* done. Days like this were apt to become a jumble in which eventually the primary objective was to keep afloat. How in the world did *anything* get done in the midst of such confusion? How had he ever created an organization like Crombie, Hamilton and Gardiner against such a background?

Perhaps in the old, beginning days, life had not been so hectic, so cut up. Perhaps it had been possible then to start a job and finish it. Or was this perpetual lack of time tied, by any chance, to the business of growing old? He liked to believe that he worked faster and more decisively today than he ever had in his life. Was it possible that he was merely fumbling and bumbling around, working fast, perhaps, but accomplishing little?

But, he reassured himself, didn't the younger executives also complain of their inability to bring anything to a conclusion in the face of increasing pressure. Hadn't something happened in the world of Big Business which had suddenly made demands on all executives that they were finding increasingly difficult to meet?

In the early days of the original partnership there had been only a few customers. The partners had worked hard to give each one of them the best service and the soundest advice of which they were capable. The measure of their success had been the number of new customers that were sent to them by the old. The firm grew slowly at first, then faster and faster, until it was no longer possible (regardless of what the Public Relations Department might claim) for the senior men to give each account the same individual attention. And even if there had been time, they no longer had the knowledge. The industrial world had become too big, too specialized for the general business practitioner.

That was it. It was size that licked you—not growing old. Size begat size automatically. It was the Chicago office, which had touched off the chain reaction. Mr. Crombie couldn't remember why they had opened it, but it had seemed logical at the time. Then, like shoots emerging from the roots of an old lilac bush, came the Boston office, the Detroit office and the Atlanta office.

It was the bigness, the unceasing straining for biggerness, which was causing executives to work in an atmosphere of frenzy a good part of the time, and which reduced the ablest of them on occasion to quivering jellies of frustration. Biggerness was synonymous with more; more customers, more prospects, more staff, more overhead, more telephone calls, more mail, more conferences, more memos to write, more memos to read, more silly demands on one's time from people whom you could ill afford to brush off, more of everything except more hours in the day.

Suddenly the idea of being retired seemed almost desirable.

It would be like a plane which, having been buffeted by storm, suddenly emerges into the calm clear air above the clouds. . . . Mr. Gleason's voice had become suddenly sharp and rasping. "It seems to me," he was saying, "that you are being somewhat unreasonable, Mr. Whitehouse. You not only want us to take on a large group of accounts . . ."

"Just a moment," interrupted Mr. Crombie. His voice was level but authoritative. They had forgotten that he was there and turned in his direction with surprised expressions. "I have known the Whitehouse family for many years. It has always been an ambition of this organization to do business with them. That is because they are the same kind of people we are and have the same point of view about things. I know Mr. Whitehouse well enough to be certain that the last thing he would want—the last thing he would *permit*—would be an arrangement that was not fair and equitable to all. He is too good a *businessman* to put himself into such a position."

Mr. Whitehouse bowed slightly to indicate that an unfair arrangement could only be made over his dead body. Mr. Gleason attempted to conceal his annoyance. Mr. Smathers tried to conceal himself by pushing his chair back among the shadows.

"Now, it has always seemed to me," continued Mr. Crombie, "that at any summit meeting of this kind—and this is a summit meeting (Mr. Whitehouse's smile indicated that he and Mr. Crombie were men who thought along the same lines)—it is the function of the participants to lay down broad policies and agree on intent. The details necessary to implement these decisions should be left to others who are accustomed to handling such matters. Don't you agree, Mr. Whitehouse?"

Mr. Whitehouse murmured something that Mr. Crombie chose to consider as assent. "I knew you would," he said. "Now you have indicated a desire to do business with us and

we most certainly want to do business with you. You've outlined your general plan of procedure. It seems to me that
the next step is to bring your auditor and our auditor together
to work out the details of a mutually profitable relationship.
This is not your sphere, or mine, Mr. Whitehouse—nor is it
Mr. Gleason's or Mr. Smathers'," he added. "This is an ac-
countants' job and I propose that Mr. Smathers arrange a
meeting between your accountant and ours tomorrow morning."

"Splendid idea," said Mr. Whitehouse. "You have a wonderful way of simplifying things, Crombie." He looked at his
watch. "I had no idea we'd talked so long. It was worth it,
though. We've ironed out a lot of things and I think final
arrangements should be very simple. I want to thank you and
Mr. Gleason for your consideration—and you, too, Mr.—er—
Smatters. If you'll excuse me now I must hurry along. I have
another meeting to which I am already late. . . ."

6

"You're a wonder," said Gleason
as they walked down the hall toward Mr. Crombie's office. "I
wouldn't have given that suave old chiseler stable room. What
do you think is going to happen tomorrow when Jim Baker
tangles with his accountant?"

"I don't know," said Mr. Crombie, "but at least we haven't
lost the business until then."

Miss Parkinson followed him to his desk. His scattered papers had been arranged into neat piles. "You have a number of phone calls to make. Some of them are important."

It occurred to Mr. Crombie that someday, when there was no Miss Parkinson to keep reminding him that there were a number of phone calls to be made, life might seem rather hollow.

"Here are a few letters that came in this afternoon which should be answered right away. You may want to dictate replies so that I can get at them the first thing in the morning —in case you're late."

"Just why would I be late?" asked Mr. Crombie, testily.

"Well, you're going to that dinner tonight at the Waldorf."

"I've decided not to go. I'm too tired."

"But you *have* to go. You're sitting at the Bank's table and you told Mr. Pearson just before you went into the meeting that you were looking forward to it."

"What's it all about?"

"I don't know, exactly; the International Economic something-or-other. Here's the invitation. The big gun is Sir Douglas Crowthers-Burt, whoever he may be. And here's your ticket. And here's the number of the Bank's special room. You're to meet there for cocktails at six-thirty."

She hesitated. "I hate to do this to you, but you told me to remind you that you wanted to go to the opening of Alice Quayle's exhibit at the Farquahar Galleries between five and seven."

"Who in hell is Alice Quayle?" There was a hysterical note in Mr. Crombie's voice.

"Why, you know—she's the would-be painter wife of Henry Richmond; the one who has the big account with us."

"I'm not going," said Mr. Crombie. "It's half-past four now. In a little over two hours I'm supposed to stagger into a smoke-filled room and be buddy-buddy with a lot of strangers. Let

Richmond take his account out. Let Alice Quayle show her etchings to anybody she wants. She's not going to show them to me today."

"I'm glad," said Miss Parkinson. "You had that dinner party last night, you've got another tomorrow night and you ought to get home now and get a little rest before you go out. I'll send flowers to Mrs. Richmond tomorrow with a card. She won't know you weren't there. I doubt if she'll know that she was. Now I'll try to get Mr. Cheney at the Chicago office while you finish signing the mail."

She returned in a few minutes. "He's gone for the day—playing squash at the La Salle Club if you ask me."

"Nuts," grunted Mr. Crombie, reading and signing.

"He'll call the first thing in the morning," she said. "It's like a game of tennis."

"You know," he said, laying down his pen, "there are moments when I wonder what a top executive really does in a place like this. I've been busy as a bird dog all day and what have I accomplished? Absolutely nothing. Phoning people who weren't there, sitting in meetings listening to other people talk, reading memoranda written by somebody else. The real work—the work that keeps the machine going—was all done by the younger men. I might just as well have stayed home."

"Nonsense," she said. "The younger men are taking care of the details. That's all. It's what they should be doing. You're the *leader* of this orchestra. Did you ever think of it that way? If you don't believe that's important, try letting it perform without a leader and see what happens. Your trouble is you want to play all the instruments too."

"I don't," he said. "That's silly."

"You do," she said, "and I don't blame you. This is your show. You put it together and you love it better than life. Why shouldn't you?"

This conversation was getting out of hand. "What about those letters you want me to dictate?"

"Listen. Why don't you forget them and the other calls and go home. Just finish signing your mail. The letters will keep and you can't reach anyone this time of day. It's quarter to five and in fifteen minutes you won't be able to get a taxi for love or money."

"I think I will," said Mr. Crombie. "Did Loomis give you that memorandum?"

"He did. It's all typed. It's on top of the pile to the right of your mail."

Mr. Crombie picked it up, wearily.

"Please don't read it now. I'm going, and that's what you should do, too."

7

HE OPENED THE DOOR TO THE apartment quietly. It was never locked. He hated fumbling around with a key as if he were entering a hotel bedroom. He wanted to be able to turn a knob and walk into his home as he had done all his early life when he had lived in Cleveland.

It was a high-ceilinged, old-fashioned apartment with plenty of room to move around and huge closets where one could store the memorabilia of two busy lives and then forget them forever. It had been their home for twenty-five years (something of a record for New York) and although all the

children were married, neither of them had ever considered
the idea of moving to a smaller place.

There were voices in the living room. Probably another
damn committee meeting. Mr. Crombie tossed his hat dis-
gustedly on the huge old settee in the hall. It had belonged to
Jinny's mother.

It was a funny thing about Jinny. She hated housekeeping
in any form. She couldn't cook and had no intention of learning. But when it came to organization, she was God's gift to
New York's interlocking committee world. She floated up into
chairmanships with the natural buoyancy of a cork. Ambitious
people might be envious of her, but they were seldom hostile.
They never felt the imprint of her meticulously shod feet on
their backs—she merely flashed past them.

She heard him in the front hall and came out to meet him.
After forty years the sight of her still gave him a pleasant feeling of excitement. Jinny was one of those women whose
beauty merely ripened and deepened as she grew older.
From her immaculately groomed, graying hair to her slim
ankles she was as trim as a jet liner, but the thing that struck
one most was not her beauty or her natural style but the
vitality which revealed itself in every movement of her body,
through her eyes, in the constantly changing expressions of
her face and in the vibrant quality of her husky voice.

"Darling," she said, "I'm so sorry. It's that hospital crowd
again. I planned to have them beaten into submission and out
of here before you came home. They just refuse to be beaten,
though. That old gargoyle, McCullough, is causing all the
trouble. Never mind. I'll tell them it's time to adjourn and
throw them out."

"No, don't," said Mr. Crombie. "I have to be at the Waldorf at six-thirty. I have that dinner tonight. I think I'll just
spread myself on the bed for a few minutes. Go ahead and
finish your meeting."

"Oh, Graham, I'd forgotten all about that horrible dinner. I was looking forward to a nice quiet evening together after that rout last night. Do you *have* to go?"

"Yes. The Bank has a table. They asked me two weeks ago and I said I would, just to please Allen Pearson."

"Why do you have to please Allen Pearson, dear? He doesn't keep an account with *you*. I should think he'd be the one to please *you*."

"Well, we do a lot of business together. I please him and he pleases me."

"I don't see why that doesn't cancel everything out and leave you both free to do as you want once in a while. Oh, I'll be so glad when you step out of the whole rat race and try living your own life for a change."

He looked at her in surprise. So here was another one calmly planning on his retirement without saying a word to him about it. They treated him as if he was a horse about to be turned out to pasture.

"Why do you look so surprised? Didn't you *know* you were going to retire? You're the one who invented the idea."

"I've been so busy I guess I hadn't thought much about it."

"Well, it's about time we began. We probably should have started long ago. But we can't very well go into it now. Go and get some rest. I'll go back and wrestle with Mrs. McCullough."

She kissed him lightly and turned back to the living room. Mr. Crombie walked down the hall to their bedroom, removed his coat and threw himself on the bed without taking off his shoes or turning back the spread—a cardinal sin as he well knew.

8

HE TRIED TO MAKE HIS MIND A blank. He had once read that Theodore Roosevelt, before making an important speech, would sit in a chair, make his mind a blank and sleep like a baby for fifteen minutes. All his life he had been striving to achieve this feat with quite opposite results. Due to some faulty mechanism in his mental control room, any attempt to blank out his mind immediately caused it to become a motion-picture screen across which passed an endless series of unrelated and unselected incidents, pleasant and unpleasant, which only responded to his efforts to shut them out by coming into sharper focus.

At the moment the very thought of composing himself for a fifteen-minute nap made him tense—gave him the feeling that, with so little time to rest, he must hurry. The events of the day began to flash past and in due course the scene appeared in which Miss Parkinson was assuring him that this was the last company outing he would have to worry about, because before the next one came around he would be out on his ear. She hadn't put it just that way, but it was obviously what she meant.

Why had Miss Parkinson's casual remark struck him like a blow? The trouble was, as he had just said to Jinny, he had been so busy handling other people's affairs that he had had no time for his own. Was that the real answer?

It might be nearer the truth to admit that he had never expected the rule to apply to *him*. He had been like a soldier charging across a field swept by machine-gun fire. Those singing bullets were meant for other men.

This was all his leaping mind needed to put on a brand-new scene. He was entering the Board Room. He recognized the principal department heads and the investment specialists. Gleason occupied the chair at the head of the table. "Graham," he said, as all eyes turned toward Mr. Crombie, "this is a revolt. We've just had a meeting and we've decided that no matter *what* the Pension Plan says you can't retire. This business *needs* you too much. We *all* need you, Graham. You're at the peak of your form and you've got to stay on. You're *drafted!*"

There were shouts of approval. Miss Parkinson, whom he had not noticed before, was crying and waving her notebook. Then this gratifying sequence was replaced by Jinny standing in the hall of the apartment. "I'll be so glad when you step out of this whole rat race."

They all took it for granted. There would be no revolt. The whole office had undoubtedly been discussing it for months. He suddenly felt sorry for himself.

How in the world was he going to finance retirement? Had anybody thought of that? No. And what was more, they cared less. He had spent the best part of his life building up a successful business and, now that they were all assured of their fat salaries, they were going to toss him out on a minor technicality, to starve or sell apples or whatever appealed to him in his new-found freedom.

He'd never saved much money. It had always come so easily that there had been no reason to suppose this pleasant condition would ever cease. Jinny had recently received some money from her father's estate. Thank Heaven for that, although it was no fortune. Rather decent of the old fellow, though, to expire so unselfishly at just the right moment.

Perhaps the company might give him a retaining fee as a consultant. He turned this idea over in his mind for several minutes. Then he remembered Sam Bunker. Sam had been one of the first to retire after the Pension Plan went into effect and they had retained him as a consultant partly because he had been one of the best market analysts in the Street and partly because, being unaccustomed at that time to compulsory retirement, it had seemed too brutal to push him out after all his years with the Company. There was no question that Bunker *had* been a great analyst, but as soon as he retired he seemed to lose touch with the current picture and based all his judgments on a past that had no application to the modern world.

That wasn't the heart of the trouble, however. The young fellows who were coming up behind him wouldn't have taken Bunker's advice had he been the Delphic Oracle. To have done so, quite obviously, would have meant that they were in *need* of advice. So the old fellow just became a damn nuisance, hanging around people's desks when they were busy. They had a dreadful time getting rid of him. Mr. Crombie dismissed the idea of being a consultant to his own company.

Perhaps the Company would grant him a supplemental pension. There was nothing to prevent it. Then he remembered Old Conrad. Old Conrad was an economist. He'd shown considerable promise in the early days, when Crombie, Hamilton and Gardiner was still a small partnership. But the man lacked drive. He just never *got* anywhere. Nice enough fellow—a gentleman and all that—but he lacked what it took.

One morning Miss Parkinson had come to him looking upset. "Mr. Conrad's outside," she said. "He's retiring next month, you know. He wants to see you about something in connection with his pension. I told him you were busy, but he said it was important." She shrugged, as much as to say, "What can you do with people like that?"

"Never too busy to see one of my boys," Mr. Crombie had

replied. He said it loud enough so that Conrad, standing in
the outer office, could hear. "Come in, Conrad. Come in.
Don't stand on ceremony in this office."

Old Conrad had shuffled in and sat down on the edge of
Mr. Crombie's leather-cushioned visitors' chair. He didn't
know what to do with his hands. Mr. Crombie had felt like
loaning him his hat so that he could turn it slowly while he
talked.

There had been an awkward silence. "Well, Conrad, I hear
you're about to retire," Mr. Crombie had said by way of a
self-starter.

"That's what I came to see you about, sir. I suppose you'll
think it's very impertinent of me, but my wife said I owed it
to my family to talk to you."

"You can always talk to me, Conrad. You know that. The
door to this office is never shut."

"I know, sir. And it's appreciated. But this is rather an unusual situation." He had hesitated, his fingers working nervously on the arms of the chair. "You see, sir, I've never had
what you might call a big salary, so that now, when I put my
pension and my social security together, it comes to only a
little over $3,000 a year. I might be able to live on that if it
wasn't for my wife. She's an invalid and needs quite a bit of
medical care."

Mr. Crombie remembered remorsefully the wave of irritation that had swept over him. It was not due to any lack of
sympathy, but rather because Old Conrad was about to present him with a dilemma for which he had no solution. It put
him in the position of having devised a pension plan so inadequate that men couldn't live on it.

"Do you own a home?" he asked, largely for something to
say.

"Yes, sir, in a way. There's a mortgage on it."

"How many children do you have?"

"Two, sir. They're married and I guess they can take care of themselves."

"Couldn't they help you out a little?"

"Oh, no, sir. They've got five kids between them and neither of them earns much. They just about make the grade and that's all. You know how it is."

Mr. Crombie had drummed thoughtfully on the desk with his finger tips. The trouble with Conrad was, and had always been, that he didn't have common sense or judgment or whatever it was. Pension plans had been created to *supplement* a man's savings, not to support him, without any further contribution on his part, for the rest of his life. Perhaps the whole pension idea was a mistake which merely sapped people's self-reliance and made them think the world owed them a living.

"Conrad," he had said, and he still remembered what a heel he had felt as he listened to his own words—but what other course could he have taken? The Plan was there, rigid, legalized, certainly not something which could be regulated like a water faucet. "I wish I could help. I hope you know that. But, as you are well aware, our plan is set up to give each employee a certain sum of money on retirement, based on years of service and salary. It's a hard and fast formula. Now, you're too good an economist to think that we can change that formula at will. If we did it for one, we'd have to do it for all and the whole Plan would be on the scrap pile. You understand that, don't you, Conrad?"

"Of course, sir. I shouldn't have spoken about it. It was my wife. I wish I hadn't." He fumbled uneasily with his chin.

"No, Conrad. Don't feel that way. I'm glad you did speak and I want you to explain to your wife just how this thing is set up. Have you ever thought about selling that house of yours and buying yourself a little place in some lovely spot like Vermont—a small house with some ground around it, where you could grow vegetables and keep a chicken or two?

"After people know you, you might even get a job in the local bank or the post office or something. This is a real challenge, Conrad—and I think you're going to be a lot happier because you worked it out yourself.

"I'm not saying good-by to you now. I'll see you before you go. But remember, this door is always open. You must keep in touch with your old friends."

That was obviously the exit line. They had both stood up. There were tears in Old Conrad's eyes. "Thank you, sir," he had said. "You've been more than kind to me. I'll never forget it." They shook hands and he walked out of the office.

No, there would be no supplemental pension. He'd follow his own advice. They'd move to some little place in the country and lead a quiet existence, dropping out of the New York life entirely. They'd . . .

Jinny opened the bedroom door and stuck her head in. "I hate to disturb you," she said, "but they've gone, taking Mrs. McCullough's body with them. If you expect to make that dinner you'd better step on it. I hope you had a good nap. You were snoring like a grampus. And for God sake don't lie on that spread with your shoes on."

9

IT WAS AFTER SEVEN WHEN HE AR-
rived at the Waldorf. It was too late to go to the Palm Room, where the Bank was dispensing cocktails. He went into the bar and ordered a double Scotch on the rocks. For the moment

it made him feel less like hiring a room and going to bed. Squaring his shoulders, he mounted the red-carpeted stairs to the lobby.

The tables in the great ballroom were crowded together so closely that he was scarcely able to squeeze between them. Even the bunting-draped boxes were filled with diners looking, in the distance, like figures in a waxworks. Three long tables filled the stage, rising one behind the other, suggesting a white linen waterfall. A few nervous headwaiters hovered over them, giving the final sixteenth-of-an-inch adjustment to a knife here, a napkin there. High up in the left-hand corner of the huge room an American flag fluttered wildly in the blast from a concealed blower.

Below the stage the orchestra leader stood rigid with uplifted baton, his eyes on a short flight of temporary steps leading from the floor of the ballroom to the left-hand corner of the stage. The first violins, their bows raised to precisely the same height, and the trap man, his drumsticks poised above his snare drum, watched the leader tensely. At the head of the steps, the maître d'hôtel peered down into the gloom, his right arm poised to give the signal.

The roar of voices died slowly away. All eyes were turned toward the stage. Women wearing new strapless evening dresses took advantage of the opportunity to glance nervously downward in order to be sure that they were not disclosing too much, or vice versa. Men used the moment to dispose of the elaborate and costly printed matter which had been placed beside each plate, by sliding it under the table.

Then the maître d'hôtel dropped his right arm, setting in motion a chain reaction. The orchestra leader lowered his baton. The bows of the first violinists descended as one. The trap man rolled his sticks smartly across the face of his drum. The stiff, military rhythm of "Pomp and Circumstance" filled the ballroom.

A white-tied, white-haired figure ascended the steps to the stage, emerging from the gloom like a swimmer from the sea. He was a huge man whose protruding stomach refused to be contained between the wings of his full-dress coat, giving it the appearance of a white blimp emerging from its hangar. Preceded by the maître d'hôtel, he walked stiff-legged across the stage, his face contorted with self-consciousness. At the end of the front table he was halted by a body block from the maître d'hôtel. Like a parade of uncertain penguins, the other VIP's followed behind him in single file.

It was a spectacle never to be forgotten. The strained silence was broken. Wasn't that Hoover? No. That was the Mayor. It couldn't be. It was ex-Commissioner Moses. There was Ben Gurion. What's his name? Which one? The one just leaning over to talk to that woman in the green dress. What a dress! Who did the program say *she* was?

The Chairman rose to announce that Miss Gwendolyn Somebody-or-other would sing "The Star-Spangled Banner," which she did in a series of piercing screams. As her last ear-splitter died among the bunting, the diners sank back onto their gold chairs and at the same moment the doors in the corners of the ballroom opened. Through them marched a regiment of red-coated waiters, proudly bearing tureens of scalding soup and piles of red-hot plates as if they were temple offerings. Lucullus, at the peak of his glory, never put on a better show. Gliding like lizards between the crowded tables, they dispensed their bounty with never a drop lost on an anxious neck. The roar of shouted urbanities gave way to the staccato clanking of soupspoons against china and the soft intake of turtle soup.

Mr. Crombie was sitting between Pearson and a man with John L. Lewis' eyebrows who had been silently breaking up hard-crusted rolls since the end of the national anthem. He now placed his face a few inches above his soup and attacked it furiously. Apparently he had not eaten for days. Pearson was talking to a bald man on his left.

"My name is Crombie," said Crombie to the roll buster.

"Badger," said Badger tersely, without interrupting the rhythmic rise and fall of his spoon.

Obviously nothing was going to develop out of that lead. Mr. Crombie sought a new opener. "I'm interested to hear Sir Henry speak tonight. I have always thought he was the best economist in England."

"Don't know anything about him," said Mr. Badger. "Don't even know what dinner this is. Pearson asked me. Had to come. Big line of credit." He finished his soup and relit a cigar which he had cached among the broken rolls on his butter plate. Apparently he regarded the conversation as over.

Mr. Crombie turned to Pearson, but he was still occupied with the person on his left.

"Quite a crowd," said a man across the table who also seemed bereft of human companionship.

"Yes," said Mr. Crombie gratefully. "I think a lot of people are interested to hear what Sir Henry is going to say."

"My wife saw him on TV last night. Terrible."

At that moment the military waiters burst through the doors once more, this time bearing great platters of larded beef. Mr. Badger wolfed his dinner in silence, retrieved his cigar from its nest among the broken rolls and stared morosely at the dais. "I don't know why I let myself in for a thing like this," he said, addressing no one in particular. "I guess it's because I like meat." He blew a thick cloud of cigar smoke at Mr. Crombie and stared at him curiously through the haze as if just seeing him for the first time.

"Wife's sick," he said.

"I'm sorry to hear that," said Mr. Crombie.

Mr. Badger nodded as if to say that it was all that could be expected, under the circumstances. "Kidneys," he said.

"I hope it's not serious," said Mr. Crombie. He was so glad to be in contact with the world once more that he was quite willing to explore Mr. Badger's home problems.

"Serious?" said Mr. Badger, showing signs of animation for the first time. "She just plain fell apart. That's how serious. Let me tell you, brother. . . ." He did, leading Mr. Crombie on a guided tour of Mrs. Badger's interior.

The red-coated waiters entered bearing glittering cakes of ice, lit from within with colored electric lights. The guests applauded.

"They thought it was her spleen," said Mr. Badger, applauding with the others.

The ice cream was eaten, the demitasse cups were filled. The Chairman rose and approached the podium with heavy dignity.

". . . couldn't keep anything on her stomach," said Mr. Badger.

"Quiet," said someone at the next table.

Mr. Badger frowned, shrugged and knocked his cigar ash onto the tablecloth.

The Chairman declared that because of the wealth of oratorical talent scheduled to follow, his role would be a brief one. A thousand pairs of lungs exhaled with relief. He then read for twenty minutes from a manuscript. No one paid any attention to him except the people on the dais who, in the face of a battery of searchlights, had no choice but to stare rigidly in his direction.

Two other speakers matched his performance, including the opening assurance about brevity. The diners, on whom the little gold chairs were beginning to make a lasting impression, passed from squirming to writhing.

Eventually the great Sir Henry rose ponderously to his feet amid thunderous applause, a goodly part of which was merely an expression of the diners' relief that the preliminary bouts were over. Matches flicked like fireflies as people lit fresh cigars and cigarettes; chairs creaked as they settled into less painful positions. There was always the chance that the main bout might be better.

Sir Henry glared about the room, his huge mustache bristling with aggression. He removed his wrist watch and placed it on the reading desk; a favorable sign. Removing his heavy-rimmed glasses, he told a humorous story in an accent so British as to be unintelligible for all practical purposes. It was greeted with gales of laughter. Looking somewhat surprised, as he hadn't thought much of the story when his speech had first been handed to him, Sir Henry replaced his glasses and picked up a thick manuscript from the reading desk with the air of one who has made the necessary concessions to levity and proposes to get on with things.

For several minutes the audience listened attentively, then, as the British accent became even harder to follow and the subject matter more difficult to understand, the weaker spirits began to drop out and resume their writhing.

Mr. Crombie half turned and draped his arm over the chair's gilt back to ease the pain. He found himself studying the rear hairdo of a woman seated a foot away from him at the next table. It was the first chance he had ever had to go into this sort of thing carefully and this was a particularly challenging example because of its unbelievable complexity.

He wondered what she did with it when she went to bed and if such a painstaking achievement was attached to a good-looking face. He shifted his chair several times in an attempt to satisfy himself on this point. In doing so he noticed that Mr. Badger's chair was vacant. The coward had sneaked out. Mr. Crombie was unaccountably annoyed. He glanced over his shoulder at Pearson. The latter was dozing, but as Mr. Crombie turned, his head came up and he smiled brightly and winked, for no obvious reason.

". . . and in conclusion," said Sir Henry. His next sentence was drowned out by the sound of many bodies suddenly straightening. It was as if a bell had rung, indicating the last lap. The great man finished amid excited applause from a thousand people who had not listened to a word he had said, but who, in their enthusiasm over the ending of their torture, almost drowned out his closing sentence. The Chairman came to the podium, but if he said anything his words were lost in the confusion as the diners rose, exchanged perfunctory farewells, and hurried from the ballroom, knowing that the hindmost must stand in line in the coatroom for a good fifteen minutes.

10

HE TOOK A TAXI TO 84TH STREET and Lexington Avenue and walked home from there to get some fresh air into his lungs before going to bed. Why, as that character had remarked at dinner, did people let themselves in for evenings like this?

There wouldn't be many more, so it was an academic question as far as he was concerned. He felt suddenly depressed, although he couldn't have told why. Then he recalled that strange scene with Miss Parkinson just before he left the office. She had said that he loved his business better than life. Perhaps she was right. Dinners at the Waldorf merely belonged to the over-all picture, you might be bored, but you were bored with a lot of things during the course of the day. The point was that they were part of a whole and the whole was good. Yes, Miss Parkinson had been right. He loved it all and he was going to miss it—even dinners at the Waldorf.

Jinny was in bed when he arrived at the apartment. He turned on the light in their little dressing room, hoping not to wake her up.

"Was it horrible, darling?" she asked sleepily.

"No, no. Not so bad," he said, hanging up his tuxedo carefully. "Very pleasant, as a matter of fact."

She watched him with an amused expression for several seconds, then turned her back to the light and went to sleep.

PART II   *Preparation*

1

IT WAS ONE OF THOSE HOT, HUMID nights in early September which descend on New York periodically like a stifling blanket. Every window in the apartment was open in the optimistic hope of inducing some vagrant breeze to enter. Through the deep, formless rumble of the City there emerged, like bubbles, a succession of small noises: a woman's laughter from the esplanade below, the bark of a dog in Carl Schurz Park, the roar of a westbound turbojet gaining altitude after its take-off from La Guardia, the banshee wail of a police car, the whine of a bus and, startlingly close, the prolonged, belligerent hoot of a tug approaching the Hell Gate bend.

Mr. Crombie sat by the window, his feet on a chair, the collar of his soft shirt open, looking apathetically across the eddying currents of the East River to the endless lights of Queens. From time to time he patted his face with a balled-up handkerchief and took a drink from a tall glass which stood on a table by his chair. Every gesture was a protest. The Voice of the City might be all right for fellows like Walt Whitman and Carl Sandburg, but it was getting on his nerves. To his

53

ears all it spoke of was the steaming millions surrounding him on every side. He was willing to love his neighbors within reason and under normal conditions, but not when they were steaming.

"What a dump to be stuck in on a night like this," he muttered. "No beginning. No end. Just a mass of hot flesh. Why do people do it?"

Mrs. Crombie was stretched out on the sofa reading. She had on one of these flimsy, feminine affairs which make almost any woman look cool if she can keep her nose powdered and her hair in place, and Mrs. Crombie was the kind of a woman who had no difficulty doing either. "What are you mumbling about, dear?" she asked, glancing at him over the top of her book.

It struck her that he looked a bit old. Perhaps it was because all men over sixty were apt to look old when the weather was hot and they sat around in that collapsed way, with their shirt collars open. Women of similar vintage looked the same way minus their girdles and bras, but men seemed able to achieve it without taking off anything but their coats and neckties. "I said New York was a dump," replied Mr. Crombie.

"The trouble with you is you make yourself hot fighting the heat. As a matter of fact, after you retire I don't see why we need be in New York at all during the hot weather. Why should we?"

There it was again, that casual reminder that in a few months (nine, to be exact) he would be out of the picture— washed up on the beach like a horseshoe crab. Here was something of tremendous importance to him and, with all due modesty, to his Company and his family, yet people treated it as casually as an impending vacation.

"Next June is a long way off," he said, crossly. "We may all be dead."

For the first time she realized that he did not want to face the day when he was no longer boss-man of Crombie, Hamilton and Gardiner. As a matter of fact, she did not want to, either. Over the years she had created a way of life that was both stimulating and satisfactory. She had no desire to change any part of it. But when the routine of men like Graham Crombie was broken, things were bound to change.

What in the world did retired men do with themselves all day? Did they just sit around the apartment trying to keep out of the way of the cleaning women and asking their wives where they were going every time they put on their hats? What *was* there for the poor things to do?

He had seldom been seriously ill, but on the rare occasions when he was, she had found it harder to cope with him as a convalescent than as a patient. During his periods of recovery he had spent his time observing her movements like an industrial engineer making a study of plant operations. This would be followed by a critique with specific suggestions for improving her efficiency.

She always missed him when he returned to the office, but her regrets were accompanied by a sigh of relief, for only then could she pick up the threads of her own life and start weaving them once more into the old familiar patterns. When he retired he would presumably be home most of the time. Was he going to try to run the house as if it were an office? Even if he didn't . . . ? She had never realized how much she valued her independence. Probably he did also. But how could two people be independent if they were falling over one another all the time?

No, no. There must be a more constructive solution than this; some more positive approach to the problem; something that wouldn't shatter her lovely, ordered existence.

"All right, so we may all be dead," she said. "Then we won't have to bother. But suppose we're not. Suppose we're alive. Then June will be on top of us before we know it. We just have to begin thinking about it instead of acting like a couple of ostriches."

"We're not acting like a couple of ostriches," he said. "I've been . . ."

"Of course we are. At the present moment I haven't the slightest idea what we're going to do after June first—and I doubt if you have, either."

Mr. Crombie was silent for some time, watching the shattered light reflections on the surface of the swift-flowing river. "No, I haven't," he admitted. "There's so little time in the day to think about anything. I suppose we *ought* to do some planning. We might travel a bit. We've never had a chance to see much of the world. Would you like to do some traveling?"

He looked so helpless. Traveling wasn't a bad idea, though. It was temporary. It didn't mean completely uprooting one's old life. On the other hand, wasn't it just evading the basic issue? Wasn't it just another way of burying one's head in the sand?

"But, Gray, we can't keep going round and round the world forever like a homeless satellite. So we travel and we get sick of it. Then what do we do?"

"I don't know," he said. "We're not going to have as much money to spend after I retire. That's another thing we must face. I suppose we ought to tackle the problem at the grassroots level. We're going to have to *simplify* our lives. Our job is to shake off the web of *things* we've woven around ourselves like a cocoon. We're all tangled up with property and possessions—obligations we don't seem to be able to duck. Somehow or other we're going to have to cut ourselves down to our new size."

Mrs. Crombie had an uneasy feeling that the conversation was not moving in the direction she had hoped. Experience had taught her, however, never to argue about generalities, which inevitably changed when they came up against the facts of life.

"I guess you're right," she said. "Our life has grown much too complex. Now why in the world—just for example—do you need *two* golf clubs? Adele Browning told me yesterday. . . ." The phone rang.

Mr. Crombie looked pained. "I wish Adele Browning would keep her long nose out of our business."

"I'll answer it," she said, the tension suddenly gone from her voice. "I think I know who it is. Hello. Oh, is that you, Jane dear? I was going to give you a ring. You weren't at Helen's today, so you don't know what happened at the meeting. That silly Mrs. Bonner . . . What? Oh, has Peg been talking to you? Well, then, you *do* know what happened—and probably a few things that didn't. Did you *ever* hear anything more ridiculous? No, I can't tomorrow, dear—tomorrow is one of my frenzy days. Hairdresser at nine, then that damn benefit meeting. I'm going to tell them quite bluntly to either make sense or run it themselves. Then guess who I'm lunching with?"

Shaking his head despairingly, Mr. Crombie rose from his chair, drained the melted ice from his glass and walked heavily toward the bedroom. He felt depressed and very, very tired. Life was such a buoyant thing to Jinny. Her days were so filled with interest—and he knew they would continue to be, no matter where they went or what kind of life they chose to lead. That was why he loved her and it was also why he was a little jealous of her.

2

A MONTH PASSED—THAT FRANTIC
month right after Labor Day when the business world, forgetful of past disappointments and rejuvenated by a brief scorching on distant beaches, sets out once more to scale the golden
heights.

All over New York in offices marked "Private," in littered
conference rooms, in taxis and over ash-strewn lunch tables,
busy men were preparing to become still busier. Mr. Crombie
had no time to talk or think about retirement, or anything else
other than the business of the moment. And as a result of all
this pother and to-do, he found himself at ten-twenty, one
cloudy October morning, strapped to a seat in a huge jet
plane about to be catapulted across the United States on his
way back to New York.

As the big engines were revved up, the plane trembled with
anticipation like a dog waiting for the front door to open and
release him into the fresh morning air. This sensation of
eagerness always transmitted itself to Mr. Crombie. The
take-off was his favorite flying moment. The odds were a
thousand to one—ten thousand to one—that the great plane
would rise into the air at the will of the pilot, but there had
been cases. . . . It added a light spicing of danger, like rid-
ing a bicycle "no hands."

And then, once up, he would be filled with a delicious calm
as the plane leveled off toward its distant goal. With a relax-

ing sigh he would loosen the safety belt and adjust the seat, secure in the knowledge that for a few blessed hours he could play hooky from the world.

On this occasion the seat beside him was happily empty. He was quite sure that there was no one on the plane that he knew. His dispatch case was filled with papers that he should read and had no intention of reading. For five hours he was going to do just as he damned well pleased.

The plane roared down the runway and was airborne. Below him the environs of San Francisco looked just as drab and uninteresting as those of any other city viewed from the air. The occasional creeks resembled stagnant ditches and the tiny automobiles, crawling antlike along the ruler-line roads, were merely parts of a standard landscape—something that could be ordered by the square yard from Sears Roebuck.

Then they nosed into a cloud bank and in a few moments burst forth into a world of blinding whiteness, domed by a blue of unbelievable purity; a world so unreal, so brilliantly dramatic, that it would not have been surprising to see, on a promontory of cloud, a massed choir made up of all races, creeds and colors singing "America." Mr. Crombie pulled a paperback from his attaché case titled *Street of Sin*.

For an hour or more he read with indifferent interest. Sin could be almost as dull as virtue at times. Tilting back his seat, he closed his eyes with that feeling of guiltless laziness which one can only experience when circumstances make it impossible to do anything else.

He dozed fitfully for half an hour and then found himself looking through half-closed eyes at the dazzling whiteness outside. Something was demanding admission into his torpid brain. Then it entered and banished his drowsiness.

When was he going to face up to what lay ahead? Another month had passed. Only eight more remained before he would find himself in a strange new world in which he would no longer be making business trips to the West Coast and living in luxurious hotel suites, all on the good old expense account. No longer would he spend his days adjusting the everlasting personal grievances of prima donnas. No longer would he be introduced as Graham Crombie of Crombie, Hamilton and Gardiner, but as Graham Crombie, period. He felt a tremor of panic.

In May he would be sixty-five. This was the statistic that was upsetting everything. He might, as he had said to Jinny, be dead by that time, but that was true for everyone. As far as he knew there was nothing the matter with him and there was no reason why he shouldn't live to be eighty. Why not assume that? You had to assume something in order to make plans. What was he going to do with these fifteen years? What sort of life would bring the greatest satisfactions to Jinny and to him? Of one thing he was sure. They were not going to spend them like two people sitting in a railway station waiting for the train, as so many of their older friends seemed to be doing.

Having decided that point on a broad, statesmanlike basis, the next problem was to determine just how he proposed to achieve this end. He had devoted his entire life to business. For forty-three years it had dominated every waking hour. Even on the golf links or while dining with friends or during their summer vacations he had never completely put it out of his mind. During the first years the goal had been money. Later it had been the game itself which had driven him. It was so essentially, fascinatingly real—as real as war and love.

We thought of ourselves as a sports-loving nation. We were, but the great American sport was business. Baseball claimed the honor, but that was hogwash. Of course there were a few true zealots, but for the most part baseball merely furnished a background patter for adolescents, a conversational take-off point for businessmen and a refuge for frustrated salesmen.

The average successful man lived in the world of business all his life. It absorbed him so completely that, with the passing of time, he came to consider it the only occupation worthy of he-men, and his attitude was apt to be slightly contemptuous toward those who earned their living in less frankly commercial fields; the artists, singers, writers, poets, antique dealers, horticulturists, lecturers, and the dancers—oh, very decidedly the dancers. As a businessman he might also be an omnivorous reader, a collector of pictures or antique furniture, an expert gardener, even a painter, but these were, and according to his code they must be, side issues, avocations, hobbies, which merely served to emphasize the diversity of his talents and the degree of his vitality.

There was nothing disparaging about all that. Business was what Americans liked to do and did superlatively well. Why should they do something else which they probably would not enjoy and would, therefore, do badly. It was difficult, however, for a man who was about to retire to leave a field which absorbed him and in which he had been so intensively trained, and enter suddenly into a new way of life.

Difficult or not that's what it amounted to. He'd seen men trying to avoid this sudden transition by clinging to the old, familiar things, but they were just kidding themselves. There was no such thing as half staying. You were either in or you were out.

The blonde hostess was bending over him. "Would you like a pillow, sir?"

"No, thanks," he said, shortly, annoyed at having his train of thought interrupted. Why did hostesses always give you that tenderly impersonal smile which was traditionally reserved for infants, the senile and the dying?

She managed to look hurt while continuing to smile. He wondered if hostesses stopped smiling when they were off duty. Someday a good-looking girl was going to create a sensation in the airline industry by playing the role dead pan.

He closed his eyes once more. There was no question about it. When a man retired he should make a clean break with his past life. Everyone had things that he'd always wanted to do if he only had the time. This was the moment to bring them out and dust them off.

Take his own case. He had always dreamed of a country place that he could groom until each blade of grass was under control, each weed banished, every dead leaf and twig removed. In the midst of this orderly Eden, shaded by two gigantic elms, there would be a white farmhouse with a central chimney, its fresh paint gleaming in the sunlight. Actually, what he was dreaming of was a setting that symbolized the antiseptic tidiness of his own office.

In his cellar (and he could hear his guests exclaiming in surprise as he led them down the cellar stairs—the immaculately clean cellar stairs) there would be a fully equipped woodworking shop. On its pine-paneled walls—each board of which he had prepared and put in place himself—the tools would hang in neat precision. Behind each hammer and chisel would be painted a black silhouette so that one could tell in a moment what belonged where and what was missing. Beside the workbench stood a half-finished corner cupboard.

"But, Graham, I didn't know you did this sort of thing."

"What beautiful work! It's so professional."

"Gray's always wanted to work with tools, my dear. I'll show you the other end of the cellar where he has his plumbing and electrical shop. Gray's done every bit of plumbing and electrical repair work in this house since the day we moved in." Even Mr. Crombie, sitting in a plane twenty thousand feet above the Rockies, was surprised at this disclosure.

Then they'd go out to see the brook, a feature which had suddenly appeared, cutting across the front lawn. You could cast a fly into it from the terrace. It burst forth from a stand of white birch like a ballet dancer leaping onto the stage, after which it rushed across the lawn and disappeared over the edge of a rock garden, in the midst of which its mountain-cool waters were contained momentarily in an oval swimming pool. Wasn't the whole picture becoming rather elaborate?

"Would you like a magazine, sir?" This time it was the brunette hostess, also smiling.

He shook his head, trying to hold his train of thought and at the same time smile back. The thing was growing contagious. "Oh, you look as if you needed *something* to read. I have the *Post, Ladies' Home Journal, Life, Look, Time. . . .*"

"No, thank you," said Mr. Crombie, firmly. "I attribute my success to the fact that I never learned to read." She looked puzzled and for a fraction of a second the smile threatened to disappear. Then, obviously concluding that this was just another high-powered businessman trying to horse around, she gave a mirthless laugh and turned to the man across the aisle who had been watching the calves of her legs attentively.

This time he was glad of the interruption. His trouble had always been that whenever he began daydreaming things seemed to get out of hand. Phantasy had no place in the picture now. This was for real, and simplicity must be the keynote. A tiny cottage with a magnificent view (that was free), a brook, if possible (also free), and lots of woods where he could wander in the afternoon with his dogs.

Dogs! Where had they come from? He had always yearned for one, but Jinny insisted that she wasn't going to have dogs tearing around the apartment and she stubbornly refused to curb one—a simple, homely chore which, for some reason or other, she considered revolting.

Now he could have dogs . . . dogs all over the place . . . dogs unlimited!

He'd raise them! That's what he'd do. He'd have a kennel.

And in the evening, when the fire was blazing in the great fireplace, the favored ones would lie stretched full length before it on the stone hearth like a scene in an old baronial castle.

It must be the kind of place that was alive with birds (as in the case of the brook and the view, also free). He had always had difficulty telling one bird from another and it irritated his orderly mind that this should be so. Now he would study them at his leisure until he knew them all—lying down or standing up.

He wouldn't stop at birds. He'd learn the trees, too. He already knew birches, maples and elms, but there must be dozens of others. He'd learn the whole world of forest and field, mosses and ferns, bushes and grasses, and all about the lives of the little creatures that lived in and among them. That was the trouble with America. We were losing our touch with nature. Here was a project to challenge the best in any man and who could tell where it might lead. "During the last years of his life, after he retired from business, Graham Crombie became an internationally known naturalist whose field books have become standard equipment for nature lovers. He is survived by . . ."

He opened his eyes and looked about him impatiently. What was the matter with him? Couldn't he even take a walk in the woods without starting a competition with John Kieran and Teal? He must be getting a Leonardo da Vinci complex or something.

His fellow passengers had sunk into a state of torpor so complete that he had the impression of being alone on the plane with a collection of waxworks. Even the hostesses had given up and were leaning against the monel-metal icebox, staring moodily at nothing. He was relieved to note that they were not smiling.

His eyes closed and the reel began to unwind once more.

He could see the cottage quite plainly now. It sat on a kind of natural terrace from which the ground sloped away steeply toward the valley and the village, which was almost hidden behind the trees except for the spire of the old church.

With the smooth technique of a seasoned movie fan he shifted the scene to a village street where white clapboard houses drowsed peacefully in the shade of ancient elms. They were the kind of houses that were sure to shelter sturdy New England characters—simple men of the old tradition who had never overcharged anyone in their lives (which, in Mr. Crombie's lexicon, meant that they undercharged, thus pleasantly reducing the cost of living). They were the kind of houses that might even shelter a few retired professors with whom one could sit before a fire at the end of the day discussing the meaning of life.

Taking a quick swing back to the cottage, he discovered a tiny library, paneled with boards two feet wide. A fire was crackling merrily in the fireplace. In Mr. Crombie's dream world it was always cold outdoors. In one corner, under a standing lamp, was his old leather chair, molded by usage into deep, inviting hollows. This was his sanctum sanctorum, where he would read and think. Ah, the sweet luxury of just sitting and thinking!

By the window, looking out over the valley, stood a table desk, its appointments precisely ordered. Here he would carry on his correspondence (letter writing was becoming a lost art in America) and keep his accounts in a bound book not unlike that used by Thomas Jefferson.

He would rise at six-thirty, walk down to the village for the paper and then, after a leisurely breakfast, he would closet himself like Samuel Pepys in his sunny, book-lined library and write and read through the quiet morning. Just before lunch he would go down to the village again for the mail. There he would spend a half hour on the veranda of the old post office, talking to the village characters, a book-worthy, homespun group.

In the afternoon he would work on the place, weeding the garden, rebuilding an old stone wall, sawing up wood for winter fires ("He's hard as a rock, my dear. Just amazing for his age"), and on rainy days he would be in his workshop repairing a broken chair, fixing a balky toaster, building a cabinet, the air fragrant with the smell of fresh-cut wood.

In the fall he would wander through the woods with his dogs, discovering rare ferns and fungi, identifying trees and bushes; reading the story which the forest told only to the initiated.

Around five-thirty, friends in worn tweeds (these must be the professors) would begin to drop in to smoke their battered pipes before the fireplace. There, relaxed by glasses of hot buttered rum, they would talk meaty talk, spiced with epigrams and garnished with wisdom.

He must have slept, for he suddenly became aware that the hostess was nudging him gingerly. She wanted to insert the rods of his tray rest into the arms of his seat. "Would you like a martini or whisky on the rocks?" she asked, and now her morning smile was tinctured with a slight leer.

"*Double* martini," he leered back. "If you have such a thing."

3

HE SAID NOTHING ABOUT THESE daydreams when he returned home. Ideas of such import must be disclosed gradually and only after careful thought. The thing to do was to let the concept simmer within him until he could see how it stood up against more familiar backgrounds than a jet plane floating on a limitless cloud-sea.

To his surprise he found the picture coming more sharply into focus each day. The white farmhouse was taking definite shape, a big red barn had edged its way onto a far corner of the property, as well as a covered bridge spanning a trout stream. The serenity of the setting was beginning to produce a kind of premature nostalgia.

Underneath this pastoral idyl, like the natural caldrons which bubble and rumble ceaselessly beneath Yellowstone Park's picnic-laden crust, was the ever-present and uneasy realization that his retirement date was running toward him as a landing field toward a descending airplane. He tried to alleviate the recurring feeling of panic by thinking of all the difficult and irritating things he would never have to cope with again once he was free (he tried to stress that word); the congested streets through which it was increasingly difficult to force a car and on whose sidewalks one was slowed to a toddle; the inability to find anyone to do simple little things like put up a shelf or fix a wall socket; the impossibility of getting taxis on rainy days; the sweltering, inhuman subways;

the exorbitant prices paid for slipshod, sullen service; and pigeons—never again to wade through flocks of feeding pigeons should be compensation enough for anyone.

Man had created, in the name of progress, a milieu so complex that it was becoming unlivable and he, for one, didn't propose to go on trying to live in it. The only thing he regretted was the necessity of resigning from the various boards and committees on which he had served for so many years. To do so would be to slam the door irrevocably on a world which, inconsistently enough, he was at heart reluctant to leave.

If you came right down to it, why was it necessary to resign? The farm (he had begun to think of it as "The Farm") was only three or four hours' drive from New York. His board meetings came on Tuesdays and Wednesdays. What more simple than to drive down on Monday afternoon and go back after lunch on Wednesday? This would give them two evenings a week to see their New York friends, go to the theater and generally keep in touch with things.

That might do a lot to reconcile Jinny to the idea. He had no way of knowing as yet how she was going to react to the life bucolic, but she had been born with a concrete spoon in her mouth and the chances were she was going to put up a battle. She loved the City. To her, the sound of a pneumatic drill was a lullaby and she reacted to carbon monoxide as others react to salt sea air. That was the real reason, had he chosen to admit it, why he was procrastinating about mentioning "The Farm." If, however, they came to New York each week, he would scarcely be asking her to change her way of life at all.

Spending two nights a week in a New York hotel would, of course, be expensive and inconvenient, involving reservations and suitcases and tips, and without any feeling of belonging. The answer to that was a hide-out, a *pied-à-terre*—in short, a room in which they could leave their city clothes and all the little things that would otherwise have to be toted back and forth each week. There must be hundreds of older people living in New York in apartments that were too big for them now that their children were married. They would be delighted, he felt sure, to rent a room and bath very cheaply.

It was a perfect plan. Mr. Crombie felt a great surge of relief now that the uncertainty of the future had been eliminated. As he reviewed the details of their new life it seemed incredible that Jinny wouldn't be just as enthusiastic as he was. What could she want or desire that it did not contain? For some instinctive reason, however, he put off telling her, waiting for just the right setting—waiting until every last piece was in place.

Mrs. Crombie, who could read him as old sailors read weather, noticed that he was looking alternately smug and worried. She said nothing, feeling sure that whatever was bothering him was bound to come out eventually and that it was better to let it do so unaided.

4

THEY WERE SITTING AT BREAKFAST, each hidden behind a newspaper. Mr. Crombie had finished the first page of the *Times* and turned to the obituaries, in his customary order.

"Anyone special dead?" asked Mrs. Crombie, flipping her paper over to David Lawrence. She left the obituaries to her husband. Weddings, divorces and columnists were her department.

"Not today," said Mr. Crombie, in the tone of one who opens an empty mailbox. He picked up the second section and turned to the financial pages.

"They bunch up," observed Mrs. Crombie, reassuringly. "You get a dry run like this and then all of a sudden we'll be attending funerals for a week."

"I know it. It would be better if they could be spread out more," he agreed. "The last one was Jack Carpenter. That must have been two months ago."

"Wasn't he just going to retire?"

"Yes. That's what we were talking about the other night at the Bentons'. I think the poor guy dreaded it so that he worried himself to death. He used to come in and talk to me about it. He didn't have the foggiest idea what he was going to do with himself and it was driving him nuts."

"Have you?"

This was it. They both knew it. Like two boxers coming out of their corners at the sound of the gong they circled cautiously, each one unwilling to commit.

"Yes," he said after a moment's hesitation. "Yes, I have."

She suddenly understood the moods that had puzzled her during the last few weeks. For forty years they had discussed their plans together while they were in the making. Now, at the most important crossroad of their lives, he had reached a decision without consulting her. It could mean only one thing. It was something she was not going to like and he knew it. She braced herself not to like it.

"But you've never said a word to me about it," she said.

That put him on the defensive. She had won the first round.

In the split second that their eyes met, hers questioning, his uncertain, apologetic, her mind raced through the possibilities.

It must be some new kind of life that was about to be sprung on her. Oh, God, not the edge of a California cliff with the Pacific rollers dashing themselves to pieces on the rocks below. Not Florida, dear God, nor Santa Fe, nor the Eastern Shore, nor Black Angus in Virginia. Not something, please, that would cause her to dismantle this lovely old apartment.

He leaned forward, resting his forearms on the table, his hands clasped as if in unconscious supplication. "I've been thinking about this for weeks," he said.

She nodded. "I know you have."

"This business of retirement is a serious thing—serious for both of us. I'm about to be ejected from a comfortable, mink-lined rut which I've been digging for forty years. We both are, for that matter. (Here it came.) Up to date our life has been like a familiar dance routine. No matter how fast the tempo of the music, our feet carried us along almost without help from our brains. We were not afraid of falling because we'd done these things so many times that balance was second nature."

She was about to make a wisecrack, but thought better of it and didn't interrupt. They were so used to one another that he hesitated for a moment to give her a chance. When it was not forthcoming he hurried on, encouraged.

"And now the tune is about to change. The *music* won't stop. It never does. But the tune and the tempo and the key must change and the choice of the new tune is up to us. Are we going to try to imitate the old one; trying harder each year and being less and less successful?"

"Not Florida," she said. She hadn't meant to.

He looked puzzled. "I don't know what you're talking about, but try not to be clever for a moment. I'm serious. I've come to the conclusion that we have to break with the past, to start a new life. . . ."

She glanced about the dining room, at the familiar, faded,

scenic wallpaper, the massive Georgian sideboard, the two big steel engravings of eighteenth-century English life. It was as if she were saying good-by to them already.

So strong was her feeling of crisis that it engulfed her and she only half heard him. . . .

". . . a place in the country . . . back among the hills . . . dogs . . . woods . . . a workshop . . . not so far from New York that we can't motor in occasionally . . ." She heard that. Well, at least it wasn't Florida or California, or Black Angus. ". . . even have a little room here in town where we could spend the night when I come in to meetings." She heard that, also.

As he saw the tension fade from her face he also relaxed and the words began to pour from him. The white house on the hill looking out across the valley, the village with its main street sloping down to an old covered bridge, the characters and the retired professors who would be their friends in a classless community, the clean white sweep of snow-covered countryside in winter . . .

While he talked her thoughts continued to race on ahead of him. New York was her life. The Cos Club, the committees, the theaters and music and, above all, the people—the new, exciting people as well as the old familiar ones; New York with all its crowds and noise, its impersonality and frustrations. She loved it because it was as aggressively alive as she was. She accepted it, not as something alien, but as part of herself.

He was saying, "New York is only for making money and I'm not sure even that isn't a fallacy. Given good, ordinary brains, I'm not sure you couldn't make just as much in Baton Rouge or Medicine Hat—and live a damn sight more comfortably while you're doing it.

"People *exist* in New York. No one thinks of it as a home, the way we used to think of Cleveland. It's too big. You could drop dead and if your friends didn't read the papers a lot of them wouldn't know about it for a year. And it's getting bigger every day."

"I hate to disagree with you, Gray, but I love every bit of it," she said. It was not a challenge, but a simple statement of fact. She refilled his coffee cup from a silver pot.

He looked at her quizzically for several seconds before replying. "I question whether in your heart you really love it as much as you think, Jinny. You've done an amazing job because you have brains and energy and judgment. You're wanted on every Tom, Dick and Harry's committee. The minute you land on a committee you're made chairman of it . . . and yet . . ."

"Darling," she said, "did it ever occur to you that I wouldn't do these things if I didn't want to? I love the city . . . and so do you."

It was so hard to argue with women. "I'm not so sure," he said. "You think you love New York because you've been successful in it, but I've always suspected that all this activity is largely a frantic attempt to find a crack in the concrete in which to grow roots."

"I couldn't agree with you less," she said, her voice flat but without irritation.

"I don't expect you to. But it sometimes seems to me that only a few specialized groups really fit into this place. The money-makers, of course. I mean money-*makers*, not money-earners—there's a big difference. And the professional people; the ones who are able to sink into an exclusive professional world small enough to make them feel at home. And the neurotically shy—the ones who like New York because they can wrap its bigness around them like a cloak. And then there's the party crowd—and of course, the underworld—both of which need size to live."

"Graham Crombie, those are just a lot of words. You love

this city just as much as I do. It's been our home for forty years. Where else could you have made such a success? You'd be bored to death in any other place inside of six months. And no matter what you call New York you can't call it boring."

"I didn't say it was boring. I said it was too impersonal, too lonely, too confused."

"I think you're so anxious to justify this country idea of yours that you've lost your sense of values. You've worked at high pressure ever since we were married. Now that it's about to be removed you want to roll for a while like a horse that's been ridden all day and has just been unsaddled. As soon as you've had a good roll I'll bet you'll want to be back."

"Doing what?" he asked, tonelessly.

In those two words he revealed to her what was behind his plan. He saw his world crumbling and he was fleeing from the rubble. Perhaps it was all that he *could* do at the moment—get away. But it seemed so unnecessarily irrevocable.

Few things were really irrevocable, however. They only sounded so at the moment of decision. Time was the great revoker. And at this crucial point in their lives, surely he was the one to make the decisions.

"I don't *know* what," she said. "I like to unload problems like that onto the future. Right now I guess it's your show. For forty years you've been living for other people. Now you're entitled to live for yourself. What was the wild metaphor you were using about dancing? Well, whatever it was, I think that now it is your privilege to call the tune."

"But you don't really *want* to go to the country?" he asked, anxiously.

"No, darling. Quite frankly I don't. There's no use being a hypocrite about it. But I do want you to be happy. I'm built so that I can be happy almost anywhere. And if we can have a little place in town to hang our hats once a week, that makes it all the better.

"There's one thing I'm certain of," she continued after a pause. "I don't want to spend the last years of our lives worrying about money. If we must simplify, let's do it *now* while we have the chance."

"That's why I want to get out of here and move to the country," he said.

"All right, darling." She felt slightly sick as she heard her own words. "If this country business is going to make you happy and help us to cut down expenses, then it's what I want. All I am going to insist on is that whatever kind of a place we live in, it must be small—something we can keep up with a minimum of effort; something completely modern where all I have to do is to push buttons. That's about all I'm capable of. You know me and housework."

He looked disappointed. "I'd hoped you'd want a lovely old farmhouse with big hand-hewn beams and wide floor boards," he said. "A house with the date over the door."

"As long as the machinery that runs it is new, it can be a log cabin."

"Do you think the whole idea is crazy?" He so obviously wanted her unqualified approval. She wanted to give it but couldn't.

"I'm not sure about that," she said, finally, pushing the toast crumbs beside her plate into a tiny pile. "I don't see how *you* can be either. All I'm saying is that since we've been married you have slaved for me and for your family. That sounds a bit grim, but once committed to Crombie, Hamilton and Gardiner you had no choice. You *had* to make a success of it. You did a wonderful job. Now we do have a choice and I want *you* to make it without regard to me or anybody else."

He interrupted her. "But whatever life we choose, *you* must be happy in it," he said. "You just said you couldn't be happy unless I was. That works both ways. To get the fullness out of any way of life, both people involved must be enthusiastic about it. Even the *indifference* of one of them will spoil the broth."

"How right you are," she said, "but as I just told you I can be happy almost anywhere. It just means that I must learn some new tricks. And if we're able to have a little place in New York, I can keep in touch with my friends here, too. I'd feel rather lost if we cut loose from everything."

Walking to the window, he stood looking down at a tug towing a string of barges against the current. He was silent so long that she wondered if she might have hurt him.

"Did I say something stupid, darling?"

He did not answer immediately and when he did his voice was slightly choked. "I was just thinking," he said, "that I married a great gal."

5

THEY HAD BOTH BEEN AWAKE FOR some time. Each was aware of this, but as often happened they lay quite still, absorbed in their own thoughts until the muted buzz of the alarm clock announced the official opening of the day.

"How many rooms are there going to be in this cottage?" she asked, plunging characteristically into the middle of the subject which was occupying her mind.

"You mean the country place? Gracious, I wouldn't have the slightest idea. Well, let's figure it out. It should have a living room with a big fireplace—you know, a crane and pots and all that sort of thing."

"I don't even care if it has a fireplace," she said, "as long as it has a good heating system that does its own thinking, and unlimited hot water. . . ."

". . . and a kitchen . . ."

"Of course, silly, and a roof and windows. I meant how many bedrooms?"

"Well," he said, "outside of our own I shouldn't think we'd want more than a small guest room. Just big enough to squeeze in two beds. That'll discourage people from camping on us indefinitely. We must keep this thing simple."

She was silent for several minutes. "I agree. But have you given any thought to the children?" she asked. "Obviously the greatest pleasure we're going to get out of a place in the country will be having our children and grandchildren visit us. Now we have, as you are perhaps aware, three married children, three in-laws and nine grandchildren. All right. How in the world can they come and visit us if we only have one small guest room?"

It was his turn to be silent. "What are you suggesting; that we have a house with room for fifteen guests?"

"Of course not. But just suppose, for instance, Sam and Linda arrive for the weekend with their four children. Where are you going to put them? On the floor?"

"That means a double room for Sam and Linda and some kind of dormitory for the four kids."

"That wouldn't do for long," she said. "In another year or so they'd need a room for the two little boys and another for the two girls. Even now they'd tear the place to pieces if you put them all in one room."

"I guess you're right. You'd have to have our room and three double guest rooms. That's four double bedrooms. Quite a cottage."

"It does sound big when you put it that way," she said, "but what's the use of living in the country if we can't see our children and grandchildren?"

"I know," said Mr. Crombie. "They don't have to be *big* bedrooms—double deckers for the kids. There's another thing I've been thinking about right along those lines—I hope we can get a place with a lot of woods and that sort of thing. None of these kids know anything about real country."

"Yes, and a swimming hole."

"That *would* be good," he said. "Well, we'd better plan on getting up. I'm not retired yet."

6

"I've been thinking about that room in New York," said Mrs. Crombie several nights later. "I checked with a few real-estate people today and they tell me the only one-room hide-outs in New York are either in sailors' boarding houses or hotels, which would be ghastly expensive, of course."

"How can the sailors afford them?" he asked.

"I mean the hotels, you goof," she said. "You also spoke about renting a room in someone's apartment, but I'd feel uncomfortable with a setup like that. No, I think it would be a lot better if we rented a tiny apartment somewhere with a living room and a bedroom. You can find those. Then we'd be independent and we could have a few friends in for cocktails once in a while without making them sit on the beds."

"It's a strange thing," he said, "how modern living centers more and more around the cocktail."

"You're a fine one to talk," she snorted.

"You may be right about an apartment," he said. "I'll tell you another thing. It would be nice to get something high up—something with sun and a view."

"I thought of that, too. A studio room. That would be the answer. Then we could invite everybody we knew without crushing them to death. I'll begin scouting around."

They ate in silence for some time, turning the idea over in their minds.

"You know something?" she said. "There probably will be times when we won't want to hurry back on Wednesday night." There was a note of hopeful excitement in her voice. "If that's so, we'll need a little kitchen; for boiling eggs and making ice cubes and that sort of thing."

"Why don't you see what you can find. Only don't go off the deep end. Let's keep it simple."

7

"WAIT TILL I SHOW YOU WHAT I've done," said Mrs. Crombie proudly. "You make the martinis and I'll have it ready for you when you come back."

When he returned to the living room, she had set up two card tables side by side. On them was spread a large map.

"This is the largest scale map of New England I could find," she said. "Now if we're going back to New York once a week we certainly don't want to be more than 150 miles away. It would be better if it was less than that. So I've drawn an arc from the Hudson to the Sound with a 150-mile radius. Somewhere along that line is where we dig for our new home."

He looked at her admiringly. "You should have taken over my business and let me bring up the children," he said.

"I think you'd have been awkward at it. Don't stir those things until they're nothing but water." He filled her glass. "Now I'll tell you what I did next. I marked all the places that you'd be willing to be seen dead in and I've dug up the names of the real-estate brokers in each one. Poor Lucy Pratt in Elliman's office has been doing nothing else all day. A lot she's going to get out of it."

"She can find us that little apartment and sell this one at a huge profit. What more does she want?"

"I told her that. Well, anyway, my suggestion is that we start up here in the northwest and work around to the Sound. We must educate ourselves before we buy. We'll just look and look and we won't make up our minds until we've seen the works. How does that strike you?"

"Terrific," he said. "We can do it weekends. Saturday nights we can stay in cute little inns. New England's top-heavy with cute little inns."

8

THE NEWS THAT THE CROMBIES were looking for a country house spread like a brush fire. The phone rang day and night. Real-estate brokers in towns they had never heard of assured them that their lists contained nothing but the kind of houses that people like the Crombies wanted. Just what kind they were was never made clear except that they were all little gems which probably would be snapped up before the Crombies got there. In the real-estate world people didn't "buy" property, they "snapped" at it.

The Crombies had never realized what desirable people they were. Friends phoned whom they had not heard from for years, inviting them for a weekend during which they would have a chance to look over one of New England's most charming and exclusive countrysides. Many had specific places in mind which were just coming on the market and which were such rare examples of eighteenth-century inconvenience that the Crombies were mad not to take an option just to hold them until they could come out and see them.

As time went on it became apparent to Mr. Crombie that all people who live in the country around New York are in a constant state of nervous anxiety about the future of their communities. Their eagerness to get "people like you to come out here" was flattering, but it was difficult to avoid the feeling that the whole area was probably on the skids.

There were times when it even occurred to them that the reason why some of these solicitous friends were so anxious to have them purchase adjacent property was to prevent a developer from building 150 shacks on it or to make sure that the tottering old manse which presently stood there was not converted into a roadhouse.

Just as they were settling into bed the phone would ring. "I hope I didn't wake you, my dear, but we hear you're looking for a country place and there's something coming on the market right near us that you'd go wild about. They're asking a terrific price but I can tell you in confidence that's just to keep undesirables away. People like you could have it for a song. The present owners have lived in it for years and they want someone to take over the old place who really understands and appreciates it."

"I can't figure out," said Mr. Crombie after being wakened by one of these calls, "why everybody that owns an old house is so certain that we understand and appreciate it before we've even seen it."

"I know," said Mrs. Crombie, "and why do they give a damn? Incidentally, how do you 'understand' an old house, anyway? I suppose if the roof falls in or the floors give way you just nod and say 'how delightfully typical.' This one is probably an old wreck, but I'm afraid we'd better go and see it. Sarah Perkins is awfully touchy."

"Touchy about what?" asked Mr. Crombie. "Because we don't pay a fortune to pick up a termite sanctuary that's probably an eyesore from their dining-room windows?"

But they went. They always went.

9

AND SO, GRADUALLY, THEY CREPT around Mrs. Crombie's arc, while a New England autumn turned the foliage from green to brilliant scarlet and orange and finally plucked all this beauty from the branches, leaf by leaf, and scattered it wantonly on the ground.

"It's a curious thing," said Mrs. Crombie, as they motored back to New York after a long and fruitless weekend, "that nobody seems to have built a house in Connecticut after 1800."

"Up to then there must have been a seventy-five-year building boom," he said. They drove through the Parkway traffic into the setting sun. "If you were looking at a new house," he observed finally, as if speaking to himself, "and you found a window an eighth of an inch out of line, you'd walk out and say the place was badly built, but if it's an *old* house, the more it looks as if it had been designed by a modern artist on a three-day binge the better it's supposed to be."

Week after week they carried on the search doggedly, climbing dozens of ladderlike stairs, the treads of which were so narrow that one had to walk like a duck when descending them in order to find a footing, poking their heads into bathrooms which had been squeezed into places where no bathroom should ever have been forced to go; admiring the grizzly do-it-yourself adaptations of hollow-eyed owners who frequently gave the impression that they were starving to death—desperately eager owners who pointed out views where there was no view and conveniences where there was no convenience.

"There must be *some* good places," moaned Mrs. Crombie as they crawled back to New York with the Sunday traffic. "*Somewhere* in New England there must be a house that's livable, a place that doesn't look as if the owners were camping in it. There must be one *new* house for sale, all gleaming with gadgets and not in the middle of a development."

"Do you suppose we're looking for something that isn't there?" he asked, jamming on the brakes as the traffic ahead came to a sudden stop.

"I'm beginning to think so," she said. He rather resented the cheeriness of her voice. "Listen, darling, if we don't come up with something next weekend, why don't we go into hibernation for the winter?"

"That's all right with me," he said. "One more try and out."

10

And that was when they found it. All Sunday morning they had shuttled back and forth among the hills with a glum real-estate agent who had nothing to show and knew it.

"Well, I guess that's it," said Mrs. Crombie, finally. "We're

going to hit the bad traffic if we don't start back soon." The
pale afternoon sun was approaching the treetops when Mr.
Barnhauser, the agent, suddenly turned his car off the main
road and they began to climb. "I can see," he said, "that you
folks want something different. I got a place that's really
unusual." Their hearts sank. When agents said that, it meant
something unusually awful.

"We ought to be getting home," said Mrs. Crombie, but
Mr. Barnhauser paid no attention.

They passed through a large tract of woods. The road
wound along the base of a hill.

"All that up there to the right is national forest," said Mr.
Barnhauser. "Up over the hill and for miles to the east."

Then they emerged from the woods, rounded a bend and
there it was. Three giant elms stood guard in front of the low
white farmhouse. To the west the land fell away in broad
meadows flanked on either side by woodland. A river ran
through the bottom of the valley and behind it the land rose
again in a range of purple hills, their tops already brushed by
the setting sun, their bases deep in shadow.

A roaring brook cut under a wooden bridge and burrowed
across a corner of the lawn. Hurrying to join the river, it disappeared around the corner of a huge red barn.

"It's it," cried Mr. Crombie excitedly. "Everything. Everything we planned."

A look of ecstasy lit up Mr. Barnhauser's bony face. "Sunset Hill," he said. "Wait till you see it inside."

It was a 1790 house, enlarged and restored by hands that
knew their business. The fireplace in the huge low-ceilinged
living room was at least twelve feet long. The little library
was paneled with two-foot boards.

"Beauty is you can move right in," said Mr. Barnhauser.
"Don't have to spend a nickel." It was really a steal, Mr. Barnhauser assured them.

//

"GRAHAM, YOU'LL NEVER SEE ANY-
thing like that again," she said as they drove back to New
York. "If we must move to the country it's just the size we
were looking for. It's a museum piece; beautifully located and
there's that charming little village—what was its name?—
Highfield, less than a mile away. And then there's a college
only fifteen miles west, Mr. Barnhauser told me—Middleburg
I think he said. A college town is sure to be filled with interesting people. And best of all, as far as I'm concerned, the
house seemed to have all the gadgets. Mr. Barnhauser said
they were in perfect order. Why don't we buy it, darling?"

This was exactly what Mr. Crombie would have said had
she shown indifference. Now the contrariness, which is the
basis of all successful married life, asserted itself. "Look here,"
he said. "I'm going to *retire*. We're going to have to live on
less money than we have now. We both agreed months ago
that we must *simplify* our lives.

"What we decided to do was to buy a *little* place in the
country and have a room in New York. Now you're proposing
to put a fortune into a great big house with a hundred acres
of land in a community you never saw before. It's crazy,
Jinny," but he knew those were only words. He was merely
acting as a brake to a vehicle which was already on its way to
an inevitable destination.

"I know," she said, "but we agreed that we had to have a place for the children and this house has just the number of double rooms we need and the *most* wonderful setting for children I ever saw. I'll admit the price is terrible, but I know you're going to get a much bigger price for our apartment than you ever dreamed of and you claim that living in the country is going to be so much cheaper than it is in the city."

"I'll make an offer," said Mr. Crombie vaguely.

"You'll lose it," she said. It interested him to note the anxiety in her voice. "Somebody'll jump at that lovely place like a trout. If you lose it, I'll give you fair warning. I'm going to stay right in the city."

"I'll make an offer," said Mr. Crombie, his jaw coming forward slightly.

12

Miss Goldfinch, the owner, turned down Mr. Crombie's offer with polite disdain.

"You've lost it," said Mrs. Crombie triumphantly. "Just as I said you would."

"All right. We've lost it," said Mr. Crombie, "and we live in the city. I'm not sure it wouldn't make more sense at our age."

She looked at him in bewilderment. Men complained that women were unpredictable.

"We'll just sit tight," he added and disappeared behind his newspaper.

Caught up in the strong current of New York's winter life, Mr. Crombie found it easy to postpone thinking about retirement and all things connected with it. They never heard anything further from Miss Goldfinch.

Christmas came and went, then New Year's Day. The matter of Mr. Crombie's successor had not yet been decided, although everybody seemed to assume it would be Gleason and had been acting accordingly for months. Mr. Crombie began to have the gnawing feeling of frustration that comes with postponing something you know must be done.

He called up George Gillespie and asked him to lunch with him at the Club. George had been retired almost a year. Like Mr. Crombie he had been the head of his own business. Above all he was a realist. There was no nonsense about George Gillespie. He said what he thought and he usually thought straight.

"So it's caught up with you, too," he said, when the waiter had taken their order. "I'll bet you wrote yourself out of a job just the way I did. That old clause about mandatory retirement at sixty-five—I put it in myself."

"So did I," said Mr. Crombie, "and I still think I was right."

"Of course you were right from the Company's point of view. But we were wrong from *our* point of view. Make retirement discretionary and every unimaginative old dodo in the shop wants to stay on. And the Board will be sorry for them because they never seem to have enough money to live on and there they'll be, like rocks in the middle of a stream; cantankerous old 'no' men, blocking promotion, sore because conditions are changing and worst of all quietly sabotaging new ideas at a time when every company's future depends on new ideas."

George Gillespie stared at his large, bony-fingered hands. They were becoming old man's hands, the veins showing and the skin loose on the backs. "No, Graham. I'm sorry to say that what's good for the Company isn't necessarily good for you and me."

"That's what I want to talk to you about," said Mr. Crombie. "Haven't you been happy since you retired?"

"Hell, no," said Gillespie. "Listen, Graham, I worked since the day I got out of college—forty-three years—not because I wanted to—at first, anyway—but because I had to. Then, like so many others, as I succeeded I began to like the racket more and more until at last work became a part of me."

"I guess it was more or less the same with me," said Mr. Crombie.

"It's nothing to be ashamed of," Gillespie continued, "but modern business involves such an intensive kind of conditioning for those who want to succeed that after a while nothing else is quite real.

"That's why, when you fling a man out of his job at sixty-five he's apt to sink, particularly if it's been a top job. Nobody wants him in the business world and he's been conditioned to look down his nose at anything outside of it."

"I know," said Mr. Crombie. "You'd think, though, that with all their experience the good men would be in demand after retirement. You'd think they'd be valuable at least in an advisory capacity."

"For the majority, the answer to that is 'nuts,'" said Gillespie, impatiently. "Sure, the specialists, the fellows who know things nobody else knows, the scientific boys—they're in demand, but not the general run of us. Take you, for instance: Who the hell wants a guy like you?" Mr. Crombie hoped the glum-looking man eating alone behind him hadn't overheard. "Or me, either," added Gillespie, generously. "What specific knowledge have you got? You had something else, Graham. You had the gift of success, which is getting other people to work for you, and getting people to believe in you. You're a salesman, Graham, not a technician. It's fellows like you that build the businesses and make the money, but your resale value is nil.

"No, when guys like us are out, we're out. If we'd stayed on, some of us might have done a good job for quite some time. But on the average it's a good thing from the Company's point of view to get rid of us at sixty-five."

"But lots of people have interests outside their businesses," protested Mr. Crombie, looking distressed. "You talk as if all businessmen were mentally muscle-bound. You had interests. A lot of them. Aren't you following them up?"

"The trouble is, Graham, fellows like us are too busy to really plan what we're going to do when we retire—too busy to get ready for it. Sure, I had interests, but I never developed them. They never got past the 'interests' state. For instance, I always wanted to travel, but I never thought it through—never planned it intelligently. So what happens. Three days after I pull out of business we get on board a floating hotel and away we go. Where? Anywhere. No need to tie ourselves down to schedules any more—we were going to take a year, go around the world, perhaps, but in our own time and in our own way. Hell, at the end of six months we never wanted to see another hotel. At the end of eight we never wanted to see each other. At the end of nine we came home.

"People who enjoy business and who have been lucky enough to be successful don't plan retirement, partly because we're too busy, partly because we don't want to believe that anybody else can do the job we've been doing, and so we hope we're going to be drafted to stay on—and then there's a third reason. It's the same one that applies to people who can't bring themselves to make a will. Retirement has always been synonymous with old age—with slowing down. The idea of slowing down makes people like us sick. Q.E.D.; just plow ahead until to your surprise and indignation some pension plan gives the signal and they pull the trap door on you."

"You talk as if you didn't like pension plans," said Mr. Crombie.

"Well, I wouldn't put it that way. They're giving people security in their old age that they never had before. But you can't have your cake and eat it, too. You have to pay for all that security somehow. You pay for it two ways. A pension plan can shackle a guy to a job. What happens if he works for a company with a pension plan for forty years and then gets an offer of a better job in another company? He can't carry his pension benefits with him the way a turtle lugs his shell around, and he can't afford to throw away all those accumulated benefits and start all over again at the bottom of the totem pole even though he might be getting a lot bigger salary. With taxes where they are, what chance has he to lay by anything?

"That applies more to old codgers like you and me than to the young fellows. They're smarter—bolder. When they get offered a big job they don't think about pension plans or salary any more. They think in terms of stock options and they've got confidence in themselves to make them good. You know all about that.

"The other way you pay for your damned security is having to get out when you're sixty-five. I suppose some are only too glad to have the excuse. But a lot of them aren't. Personally, I think we *ought* to be glad, in spite of the fact that I'm not. This little old world is changing faster than you and I can keep up with it. We had certain things drilled into us and we operated on those principles. These kids today wouldn't know what I'm talking about. They're opportunists, not from choice, but because they have to be. You can't set your course and steer by it any more. Business today is more like a slalom race where, in the middle of the run, somebody's changed the flags. You've either got to respond fast or you'll be out of the race. You and I are pulling out at the right time, Graham, even though we don't know it. This is no world for pontificating, pompous old men. It's a world for broken-field runners— a young man's world. The only trouble is it leaves me all dressed up with no place to go."

13

MR. CROMBIE RETURNED TO HIS office filled with gloomy doubts. Gillespie had thought he wanted to travel and look what happened. Suppose they bought the house in the country and found they didn't like it. Did he really want to garden? Did he really want to do things with his hands? How could he be sure he even wanted to live in the country? If he didn't, what in hell *did* he want?

Had the world gone past his generation the way George Gillespie said? Was he actually the leader of Crombie, Hamilton and Gardiner or was he just marking time in a big corner office while the kids took over, quietly and unofficially? Was he just puttering, attending meetings, telephoning about inconsequential things, preoccupied with details that didn't add up to anything? Weren't most of his friends in the higher echelons engaged in the same sort of ritual dance; solemn and impressive to the outside eye, perhaps, but behind the scenes weren't the cash crops harvested by younger men?

George Gillespie was right. The world had not only changed but it was changing so fast that even the young men

must be having trouble keeping pace with it. For almost the
first time in his life he had a feeling of not belonging. As he
looked around his familiar office it suddenly became, not so
much a headquarters from which to guide the destinies of a
business, but a sanctuary—a familiar, tight little sanctuary,
journeying like a missile through unexplored space.

Damn Gillespie for getting him into this frame of mind.
This was old men's thinking—defeatism. You had to keep
moving forward or you moved backward. That was the
trouble; he was about to move backward for the first time in
his life. He looked at his wrist watch. It was a quarter to five.
He decided to move home.

The curb was lined with groups of young men and women
waving at already occupied taxis. He didn't waste time competing with them, but merged with the human stream that
was flowing toward Grand Central. The great floor of the station was seething with people, all going in different directions, weaving, dodging, never touching. It was Mr. Crombie's
idea of what the inside of a molecule must look like with the
atoms all rushing about at tremendous speed without collid-
ing. Make it the Universe if you were in a more expansive
mood.

The subway platform was jammed, yet down the broad
stairs, like water running over the concrete spillway of a reservoir, people continued to flow and merge with the crowd at
the bottom, finding room where none existed. The express
rumbled in, already filled to bursting. The waiting crowd
tensed visibly like an animal preparing to spring. As the doors
opened a few passengers popped out like watermelon seeds
under pressure. As the last one struggled free the platform
crowd hurled itself at the openings.

To anyone who had never witnessed this scene it would
have seemed unlikely that another person could have squeezed
into any car. There was a composite sound of pain as the

irresistible force from the outside met the immovable bodies within. Then slowly, like X rays penetrating a steel plate, the outside bodies were absorbed into the inside mass until only a few were left with their feet on the platform while their shoulders pressed frantically inward in a desperate attempt to compress the mass another few inches and slide behind the closing doors. Be it ever so humble, there was no place like home.

Eventually the almost-made-its were removed by the poker-faced guards, the doors scraped shut over hundreds of tired backs and backsides, the brakes let go with a slight jolt and the long express slid out of the station as Mr. Crombie's local slid in on the opposite side.

He could remember the days, not so long ago, when a passenger who knew where to stand when the doors were opened might get a seat on the local if he was nimble. Such days belonged to the past, but the local wasn't quite as drastic as the express even yet.

As he clung to the squeaking enameled-iron strap, he passed the time by examining his fellow passengers. Tonight he saw them in a different light. These were the representatives of George Gillespie's new world. He stood among them, alien, alone, without a point of contact. Even his dress distinguished him from the others as if it had been a costume. Within his range of vision he was the only man with a tweed overcoat, a hat and a conventional worsted suit. In fact, as far as he could tell, he was the only man in the car whose coat and pants matched.

In the event of a violent revolution there was nothing in his clothes closet, no matter how old, which would not proclaim him for just what he was—an elderly man belonging to a disappearing class formerly referred to as gentlemen.

Even the words which had been used to type people for generations were becoming obsolete. The very meaning of

the word "gentleman" was becoming more and more difficult
to define and it was one which you used carefully. Women
had clung to "lady," but it had merely slid down the semantic
scale until it had displaced "woman." You called shop girls
"salesladies" now. Certainly no one would ever think of calling them "saleswomen." And you said, "Lady, you dropped
your glove." It would be hard to conceive of anyone saying,
"Gentleman, you dropped your wallet." Democracy preferred
"Mac."

He walked from the subway station to the apartment, still
vaguely depressed. They had a name for a retired educator.
They called him "Professor Emeritus." "Emeritus" was such
a flattering word. "Graham Crombie, president emeritus."
Wouldn't "emeritude" be much less trying than "retirement"?

Old John, the doorman of Mr. Crombie's apartment, was
returning to his post after having successfully inserted two
overdressed tenants into a taxi.

"Good evening," said Mr. Crombie cordially, sensing here
at last something comfortable and familiar in a world adrift.

"Good evening, sir," said John. "It's been a beautiful day."

"Hasn't it," said Mr. Crombie. "A little cold."

"Yes, sir, a little cold," said old John. "But I think it'll get
warmer."

"I think it will," said Mr. Crombie.

Life was back in its normal grooves before he reached the
elevator.

14

IT WAS MARCH. NEW YORK WAS the center of the annual struggle between spring and winter, with winter enjoying a slight advantage.

One day the air would be heavy with the damp, earthy smells of spring, although goodness knew where the earth was that sent them forth. A soft breeze, whispering of even better things to come, would blow up the river. Mr. Crombie on his way to the office would pause at the entrance to the apartment and scan the sky carefully.

"Do you think I need an overcoat, John?"

Old John, invited to participate in this problem by countless tenants, would also case the cloudless sky. "Well, now," he would say, thoughtfully, "you might and then if it gets warmer you might not." Years of experience had taught John to trim his sails in matters involving topcoats and umbrellas. In fact, it was prudent to keep them trimmed at all times. The rich had positive opinions and if you didn't watch out you found yourself on the wrong side.

15

IN THOUSANDS OF OFFICES THE AM-
bitious plans and projects of the preceding fall were either still
on the planning boards or had been virtually completed. In
the former case they would probably die stillborn, unmourned
except by their originators. The impact of the latter group had
not been nearly as world-shattering as had been anticipated.
In fact, the business year which was now within ninety days
of its demise had been surprisingly like all other business years
in the memory of living man.

At long last the finger had been put on Joe Gleason as Mr.
Crombie's successor. When the decision of the Board was
announced to the staff Mr. Crombie had hoped that it would
be a meaningful event in the history of Crombie, Hamilton
and Gardiner. He had been disappointed by the reaction.
Everyone had assumed for so long that Gleason would have
the job that several were sure Mr. Crombie had already announced it and regarded it as further proof of the boss's increasing senility.

He was also dismayed at the calmness with which the office took this final confirmation of his retirement. Only Miss
Parkinson seemed to be upset by it. She stood at his desk,
fumbling with the red morocco sheath that held his paper
knife and shears. "It's never going to be the same again," she
said. She continued to stare at the top of his desk for several

seconds, then turned and went out of the room. During the years to come he would remember the scene as the one completely sincere tribute to forty years of work.

Once Gleason's status had become official, Mr. Crombie began to hand over his accounts—the biggest and most important to Gleason, some of the more difficult ones to Tom Potter, the only man in the office who had been really hit by Gleason's appointment; others went to Bill Simonds and the younger men. The transfer was distressingly smooth. The customers all seemed to have known for months that Mr. Crombie was retiring. Their only anxiety had been as to who was going to take care of them when he was gone.

As the accounts were assigned, the younger men went after them like beagles on a fresh scent. Many of the old customers were startled by the sudden attention they were receiving. If they had had misgivings they were reassured, and one or two remarked that Crombie, Hamilton and Gardiner seemed to be taking a new lease on life.

Mr. Crombie had been uneasy about the responsibilities which his retirement was placing on the shoulders of some of the junior executives. They had not seemed sufficiently mature to reach high-level decisions. As he watched them pick up the reins and drive confidently away, however, he was astonished and somewhat shaken by their unsuspected ability. Yesterday they had been meek subordinates. The coming change seemed to affect them like a tonic and they became suddenly charged with ideas, many of which he secretly had to admit were better than any he had had for some time past.

One by one the little, time-consuming details of administration were transferred to other desks. Each day the neat pile of papers beside his blotter grew smaller. Instead of being relieved, he felt as the management of U.S. Steel would have felt if it saw the company's backlog of unfilled orders steadily diminishing.

The phone rang less constantly. People still came to his office, but many of them came now because they wanted a favorable introduction to Gleason, or because you never could tell what might happen until a person was really out and it did no harm to pay one's respects to the old boss before passing on to his successor's office.

"Who was that?" asked Mr. Crombie, as a familiar figure hurried by his door.

"That was Mr. Chauncey Brown," said Miss Parkinson.

Neither made any further comment because they were both thinking the same thing and they knew it. For thirty years Chauncey Brown had refused to talk to anyone except Mr. Crombie.

"I imagine he'll drop in on his way out," she said, as a mother would put her arm around the shoulder of a young child who has been spurned by his older playmates.

"Who?" asked Mr. Crombie, pretending.

"Mr. Brown," said Miss Parkinson.

16

He became restless and uneasy. All his life he had complained that the demands, crowding in on him each hour and minute of his waking day, were driving him into an early grave. Now he realized that pressure was as stimulating to him, as necessary to his well-being, as danger to a big-game hunter or trouble to a labor mediator.

He was only happy when he was bedeviled by constant interruptions, faced with an enormous correspondence which must be dealt with immediately, hounded by an insistent phone ringing just as he was rushing from the office for an appointment to which he was already late, wrestling with an impossibly crowded appointment pad and overpowered by the feeling that he was being whirled helplessly in a Gargantuan washing machine.

Of course, it was against all the tenets of executive efficiency for a top man to have such a crowded desk. He was a poor delegator. Everyone in the office knew it. It was a carry-over from the early days when the staff had been so small that he had been obliged to do almost everything himself if he wanted it done right (or at all). Later he rationalized his weakness by saying that a man could delegate work to a point where he only participated in the business by drawing his salary, but all he needed to do to prove the fallacy of this statement was to sit at Gleason's bare, efficient desk and watch him operate.

"Why don't you get rid of some of this stuff?" Miss Parkinson would ask as the hands of the desk clock passed the five-thirty mark. "Pass it on to someone else."

"All right, that's what I've been trying to do for years. Now I'm going to leave it to you. Whenever you see something that you think can be delegated, let me know."

That would silence her. She had been working beside him for so long that she knew that no one else had his personal touch, that no one else would take the pains to explain little things in words that inexperienced people could understand, that no one else could make the least-important customers feel that Crombie, Hamilton and Gardiner existed to serve them and them alone. The idea that the business could be conducted without his touch was something that had never occurred to her any more than it had to Mr. Crombie.

Every so often, at officers' meetings, he had been in the habit of making a little speech on desk cleaning. "Get rid of the unnecessary details. Let someone below you do them. Clear your desks of the unimportant things so you will have time to do some constructive thinking."

This was merely standard procedure—theory which he knew didn't work in practice, even while he preached it. When a man sat down at a bare desk to do constructive thinking, the odds were that he couldn't think of anything constructive to think about and that he would end up wondering with whom he was lunching or whether his son, Sam, was ever going to make enough money at architecture to support four children.

17

As "R" DAY DREW NEARER MR. Crombie began to realize more clearly what he was about to lose. Because he had built the business, because it was so much a part of him, it had never occurred to him that the deference he received from morning until night was for the job rather than its incumbent. This was not because he was egotistical; he had just never thought about it.

He had taken the deep-piled luxury of his big corner office for granted, as he had all the comfortable grooves in which his life was channeled. Now, as what the personnel men referred to as "the terminal date" drew near, things that he had

scarcely noticed up to this point suddenly began to acquire
new values; the familiar faces of the staff looking up and
smiling at him as he passed, the obsequiousness of headwaiters, the pride in the junior officers' voices when they introduced a prospective customer ("I want you to meet our
president, Mr. Crombie"), the requests to act as chairman of
committees, the tiny minutiae of everyday business life which,
like moisture particles, formed a fleecy cloud on which he
had been borne unheeding these many years.

The duties and obligations that he had complained of so
bitterly suddenly began to appear in a new light now that he
was about to be relieved of them. The great dinners at the
Waldorf at which his firm was always browbeaten into taking
a table or into helping some business associate to fill his, the
luncheons in the private dining rooms of exclusive clubs or
(depending on the tastes of the customer) in the more relaxed
atmosphere of "21," the night ball games in the Company's
box halfway between home plate and first, the noise and confusion of conventions, the flying business trips about the
country, the incessant committee and board meetings, the requests for favors which somehow must be granted, now
appeared to him nostalgically in the soft amber light of his setting sun.

So many of these activities had acquired an unrealized
social quality. The men with whom he had sat through the
years on charitable and commercial boards, who had worked
with him on club committees, and on groups appointed to
investigate and report on some hopeless muddle—had gradually become his friends. To some degree they had replaced
his college and prebusiness connections.

As long as he was the active head of a large, successful company nothing would change. It was becoming disturbingly evident, however, that on the day he retired his status would
suddenly shift from somebody to nobody: a person occupy-

ing no established place in the community, unwanted and un-
needed, not because people didn't like him, but because their
financial attachment was to Crombie, Hamilton and Gardiner,
the institution, rather than to Graham Crombie, the man.

He fought against the despondency that these thoughts
induced. He knew how irrational it was, how full of bathos
and self-pity. What was about to happen to him was normal
and proper, in his best interests as well as those of his company. He was moving into a life of greater self-expression
where, for the first time, he would be free to follow whatever
paths might interest him. But the black moods were hard to
dispel.

18

IN APRIL, AS THE FIRST SOFT
breezes of spring crept timidly through the shadowed canyons
of the City, Mr. Crombie lost his nerve and bought the Highfield house for the asking price. Well, Jinny had had her way.
As time passed he even began to believe that this move to the
country was something she had initiated and brought about.

"I suppose we ought to tell the children," he said at breakfast the following morning.

"I know we should. We must, of course. I sort of dread it."

"Why, for heaven's sake?"

"Oh, I don't know. The children have been so queer about
this whole idea of a country place. I was thinking about it last

night. When we first told them what we had in mind they scarcely made any comment. And from that day to this, not one of them has shown the least interest. It isn't like them."

"Now that you speak of it, that's right," said Mr. Crombie. "What do you suppose is the matter with them?"

"I don't know, but I suspect they think we've gone financially haywire and that their future inheritance is being poured quietly down the drain. It's just a hunch. Their reactions are so uniform that I'm sure they've talked this over among themselves and being very well-mannered children they've decided there's nothing they can do about it but keep still and hope we don't find any place we like."

Mr. Crombie laid down his paper irritably. "Listen, dear, we bought this place for *ourselves*—for you and me. We bought it after a lot of thought because you . . . because we both wanted to live in the country."

A pained look flitted across Mrs. Crombie's face. She started to say something, then stopped.

"We're swinging into the last lap," he continued, "and I want you to have what you want."

She wished he wouldn't keep referring to the "last lap" and the "last mile" all the time. She felt like the heroine of a cowboy ballad.

"Let the children fight about our money when we're gone. We've bought a beautiful place and if they don't like it they needn't come."

"Of course, darling. You couldn't be righter. But a place like that simply screams for grandchildren. You can't think of it entirely in terms of you and me."

"Well, why shouldn't there be grandchildren? There's a whole national forest right outside the kitchen door for them to get lost in and an enormous hay barn where they can break every bone in their bodies and a brook to fall into—what more do they want?"

"Oh, I'm sure they'll like it," she said. "It's just that every-one is so quiet about it."

"You're overtired. You always get apprehensive when you're overtired," he said. "Let's get the whole gang in and tell them about the place. They'll go for it like hot cakes."

19

A WEEK LATER MRS. CROMBIE succeeded in bringing all six members of the Crombie family together at dinner—a feat only made possible by the dismayed conviction on the part of all three families that the old folk had finally gone off the deep end. They assembled one Wednesday night like the scattered chieftains of a nomad tribe, gathering in the tents of the elders in response to a catastrophe.

Pat and Bud were the first to arrive. Pat was the oldest and Mr. Crombie's favorite, although he mistakenly supposed he had no favorites. Strikingly beautiful, blonde, of the type re-ferred to among the horse crowd as "clean-limbed," she showed no trace of her thirty-nine years or of bringing up three children in the midst of an inflation while at the same time taking a violently active part in the superthyroid life of Redding Ridge.

She had married Bud Lansing during the war, an equally extroverted lad compounded of dismaying energy and brash self-confidence, two qualities highly respected and rewarded

in his Madison Avenue habitat. The Lansings called themselves Liberal Democrats and were full of advanced ideas—
most of which, it seemed to Mr. Crombie, had to do with the
deployment of other people's money.

From the jungles of Westport came the Dexter Crombies.
Dexter, thirty-six, was an electronic engineer who lived in a
world completely incomprehensible to any but his associates.
In his moments of relaxation he read aloud the poems of William Butler Yeats to his wife, Elizabeth, who was an editor of
Motherhood Magazine and chairman of the Eastern chapter
of the Planned Parenthood Association. Mr. Crombie enjoyed
Dexter and Elizabeth although they always left him with a
slight feeling of inferiority.

Sam and Linda were late. The residents of Sneden's Landing made a cult of being late, refusing to be shackled by the
bonds of time. Sam and Linda represented the arts in the
Crombie clan. Sam was an architect and his wispy, mouselike
wife painted on porcelain and bore children.

As he made the drinks, Mr. Crombie let the measuring jig-
ger slop over a bit into each glass. In spite of his bold words
to Jinny, he sensed that this might not be a soft sale. And in
spite of his declared conviction that what he and Jinny did
was nobody's business but their own, he knew in his heart
that this was not so.

He had decided to play the announcement down and bring
it in casually after dinner. As a result the meal went off in
routine fashion, involving the usual violent sociological arguments between the Lansings and the Dexter Crombies. Eventually Verma, the colored maid, brought in the after-dinner
coffee. Mr. Crombie took advantage of a momentary lull.
"We bought the place in Highfield," he said, casually. "It's
called Sunset Hill." It seemed to him a direct, simple way of
approaching the subject and had the advantage of finality.

It was what they had been waiting for. He saw Pat glance

quickly at her husband. "You mean the one with the brook running across the front lawn that you told me about, Mother?"

Mrs. Crombie nodded. "It's so dreamy," she said. "I can't wait for you all to see it."

"How much?" It was Dexter who asked the crucial question, and typical of him, Mr. Crombie thought. Only an engineer would have approached it with such slide-rule bluntness.

"Well, I don't think that's anything I'd want to discuss," he said with what he hoped was quiet dignity, "but it was quite a bargain—quite a bargain."

They looked relieved.

"How far is it by car?" asked Sam.

"Well, it's a little over 150 miles from here," said Mr. Crombie, "but it's an easy drive."

"The grandchildren will just love it," said Mrs. Crombie, a shade too enthusiastically. "There are miles and miles of real forest right behind the house and a huge barn and we're going to put in a swimming pool." Mr. Crombie looked surprised. "We'll expect you every weekend. Some of you, anyway," she finished lamely.

"Listen, Mother, how do you think we're going to get the children up there over a weekend? Suppose we came up Friday night. Bud doesn't get out to Redding Ridge till about six o'clock. Before he's fed and we can get off, it would be seven. We'd get there around midnight and have to come home right after lunch Sunday."

"Isn't there any train?" asked Elizabeth. "Jamie gets carsick if he goes more than five miles."

"Yes, you can go to Middleburg. That's where the college is. We could meet you there. It's only fifteen miles away."

"The round trip would cost more than ten bucks, no matter how you go," said Pat. "How can anybody afford that?"

"Why should *you* talk? You're loaded. Try being an architect with four under five and you'll take off your shoes when you come in the house just to save them."

Mr. Crombie looked crushed. This was an angle neither of them had considered. "I'll pay for your gas or your train fare," he said.

"Oh, we'll come, Dad. Just don't expect us to do it often."

"If you really want to see us," said Dexter, "just invite us to spend the night in New York. We all *live* in the country. That's no treat to us. It's a night in the city we look forward to."

"Besides which we all work like pack mules every weekend on our own places," said Bud. "Every time we go away we find ourselves working on somebody else's place. That's all right for the somebody else but it doesn't do us any good."

Mr. Crombie had grown visibly smaller during this conversation. Now he drew himself up in his chair and his jaw protruded slightly. "Well, I hope you can come once in a while," he said. "Mother and I have decided we want to live in the country. We're going to put this apartment on the market."

"You're going to *what?*" There was unbelief in Pat's voice.

"Of course. We can't have two big places. We're just going to have a hole in the wall in New York to use when we come in for the theater and things like that."

"But where are *we* going to stay when we come in?" asked Sam. "As you know, I'm always here once or twice a week."

"And Bud and I always plan on one night a week during the winter."

"Where am I going when I work late in town?"

"I don't know," said Mr. Crombie unhappily. "I just don't know. Maybe you can use the hole in the wall when we're not there."

They dropped the subject. They were polite, much too polite. There was a trace of hostility in the air. At half-past nine Sam rose. "I have to be up at the crack of dawn," he said. "I think we'll be pushing along."

The others leaped to their feet. Mr. Crombie stood with them in the vestibule waiting for the elevator. Pat kissed him good-by. "Thanks for the dinner, Pops. And I'm glad you've found a place you like. It's your life and you're entitled to get all the fun out of it you can."

The elevator door closed on them and he and Mrs. Crombie were alone, very much alone.

They prepared for bed silently. Neither wanted to be the first to bring the evening up. Mr. Crombie tried to read, gave it up and snapped off his bed light.

"We seem to have made a mess of things," he said, address-ing his remarks to the darkness.

"Nonsense," she said. "Wait till they see it. They'll be fight-ing for beds. They just won't accept anything new in spite of the fact that they like to think of themselves as tomorrow's babies. We've got a lovely place. Now you just go to sleep and dream about it."

Hours later she listened to him snoring contentedly into his pillow while she lay staring at the reflection of the street lights on the ceiling, wondering, wondering.

20

MAY FOLLOWED APRIL AS IT AL-ways has, only this time it seemed to follow more quickly than usual.

"When," said Miss Parkinson, "are you going to start cleaning out your files and your desk drawers? You certainly don't want to lug all this junk home with you and you can't expect me to know what you want to throw away and what you want to keep."

"I assume by 'junk' you mean my personal correspondence and private papers," said Mr. Crombie coldly.

Miss Parkinson nodded.

"I promise you I'll get after it, or them, immediately."

"I thought you might do it this Saturday," she said. "You've been about to do it 'immediately' for a month."

"Saturday," he said, reaching for his pocket engagement book. "I think . . ."

"You have no engagements. Mrs. Crombie called me yesterday and I asked her."

"O.K., O.K.," he said, returning the book to his pocket. "You two seem to know more about my life than I do. Saturday it is. You'll be here, of course?"

"No, sir," she said firmly. "This is your show. Nobody can do it for you. I'm going to visit friends in New Jersey."

Mr. Crombie felt decidedly sorry for himself as he unlocked the entrance door of Crombie, Hamilton and Gardiner at ten o'clock the next Saturday morning. The great empty office reminded him unhappily of some dear, dead friend. The old familiar features were there but, without the life that ordinarily sparked them, they were rather gruesome. He walked quickly to his own office, closing the door after him to shut out the emptiness beyond. He was cross at Miss Parkinson as he thought of her kicking up her heels in some New Jersey suburb. He hoped it was a dump.

The row of files, painted to match the walls, confronted him with their grim challenge. Pulling open a drawer, he regarded its closely packed contents with dismay. Surely no man could have created all this correspondence in the course of a single lifetime—and there were five other drawers just as full as this one. He wondered whether he should give the whole works to Harvard. Would some sucker ever edit them? *The Letters of Graham Crombie* in five volumes. He might be a modern Pepys.

Perhaps he had better warm up by cleaning out his desk. Seating himself in his worn leather desk chair he pulled out the top middle drawer. It contained neatly sorted supplies of rubber bands, paper clips of various sizes, white scratch pads, a box of loose sheets headed "From the Office of Graham Crombie"—surely Miss Parkinson didn't expect him to go through the paper clips and discard the ones that were sprung.

Near the front of the drawer was a sheaf of miscellaneous calling cards. They represented the gleanings of a decade. He removed the limp rubber band that bound them together and regarded the top one curiously. "E. Townsend Wombeck, Universal Mortgage Company." Who in hell was E. Townsend Wombeck? He'd never even heard of the Universal Mortgage Company. Removing the card he dropped it into the wastebasket. Well, that was a beginning, anyway.

The next one was from "William Cullen Lowenstein, U.S. Management Corp." Was it possible that he was cleaning out the wrong desk? "The Rev. Ovid Sims, Denver, Colorado." "Marcus T. Bamburger, National Furniture Manufacturers' Association, Grand Rapids." He riffled through the remainder rapidly, seeking for at least one name that he could even dimly recall. Then, replacing the rubber band carefully, he tossed the lot into the basket. In the rear of the drawer was a box of his own business cards. He opened it and took one out. "Crombie, Hamilton and Gardiner, Investment Counselors. Graham Crombie, President." He started to put the box back in the drawer; then it occurred to him that in another four weeks these cards would be merely souvenirs, like his college diploma or his honorable-discharge certificate from the Army. He had more than enough in his wallet to last for a month.

Impulsively he hurled the box into the basket. So much for "Graham Crombie, President." Feeling like one who has committed a painless form of hara-kiri, he turned to the right-hand top drawer.

He and Miss Parkinson had always referred to this drawer as the Drug Department. Over the years any man is bound to have a few minor attacks of this or that. The remedy, usually purchased on his way back from lunch, eventually found its way into the Drug Department, there to remain forever after, for neither Miss Parkinson nor Mr. Crombie believed in throwing anything away that might conceivably be useful at some future time.

Now, mixed in with the sodium bicarbonate, Gelusel tablets, Tums, Alka Seltzer, milk of magnesia tablets and whatnot were mysterious bottles of pills bearing Dr. Bailey's name. He had no idea what they were for and there were seldom more than two or three pills missing from each bottle. Mr. Crombie could never remember to take pills. Just having them in his desk was apparently sufficient to cure whatever ailment was uppermost at the moment and once they had fulfilled this function they became part of the permanent collection.

Mixed among them were rolls of chlorophyll tablets. Almost inevitably when you were forced to drink cocktails before lunch in the name of business hospitality, the Company's most important and strait-laced customer was sure to drop in right after lunch and they always had noses like bird dogs.

In the farthest corner was an old safety razor, a tube of shaving cream and a package of blades. He took out the razor and examined it curiously. He had had it in college and carried it in his musette bag all through World War I. This was something to be kept by all means. The rest he scooped up and tossed into the basket.

Speculating on the cost of the unused drugs which he had thrown away in the course of a long life and how Thoreau

would have reacted to such a situation, he turned to the
drawer below. This Miss Parkinson referred to as the Odds
and Ends Department. Its contents largely consisted of gift
paperweights and letter openers bearing the names of the
donor companies. Both Miss Parkinson and Mr. Crombie
knew that none of them would ever, under any circumstances,
appear on the top of the desk, but as Miss Parkinson said, they
were obviously too expensive to throw away in cold blood. Both
felt instinctively that by putting them into storage for a suitable length of time the amenities would be satisfied and then
someday one could dispose of them without conscience interfering.

The trouble was that anything that went into the Odds and
Ends Department never came out. Well, the amenities had
been satisfied and they were going to come out now. Pulling
the wastebasket from under the desk, he dropped the contents
of the drawer into it one by one. It gave him a feeling of freedom. The last one, a heavy bronze disc, he held in his hand for
several minutes, thinking what a splendid noise it would make
if he sailed it through the window beside him. Then sanity
took over and he flung it into the basket with a satisfying
crash.

In the back of the drawer he discovered his Fortieth Reunion name plate and a faded photograph. He took out the
photograph and snapped on his desk light to examine it more
closely. It was the picture of one of his old girls, his first love
as far as he could remember.

Someone had sent it to him long after he married Jinny. He
hadn't seen it, or her, for years. Her head was thrown back and
she was laughing, just the way she used to laugh when she
was a kid in Cleveland. Gosh, she had been attractive! He'd
never had a chance against that curly-headed lump of muscles
she'd finally married. Well, he hoped she was happy with
him. Odd he'd never taken this picture home. He was about

to tear it up, but changed his mind. Taking an envelope from another drawer, he placed the photograph in it, sealed it and printed "Personal" across its face. Then he placed the envelope in the now almost empty Odds and Ends drawer. What he thought was going to become of it from that point on he could not have told.

The other drawers were filled with office supplies, check books and canceled checks. Miss Parkinson could certainly take care of all that. He wheeled his chair around and faced the files once more.

How could anyone possibly go through this endless accumulation of typed pages? He pulled out a folder at random. The first letter in it was a carbon copy: "Dear Joe, Sorry you can't make lunch on Thursday. I wanted you to meet Mike Huntley before you go back. Better luck next trip." It had been written eight years before. He could only remember Mike Huntley dimly and had entirely forgotten why he wanted Joe Ball to meet him. Well, that was one item that could be destroyed. He tore it up carefully. His eye fell on a series of folders marked "Projects 1954," "Projects 1955," "Projects 1956," etc. There was one for each year for at least two decades. He pulled out "Projects 1945" and started to read.

This stuff was good. Most of it consisted of copies of memos to various members of the staff, suggesting, decreeing, urging, wheedling. They were models of tact. "As you suggested at the officers' meeting yesterday . . ." Always let the other fellow think the idea is his. These ideas were tops. What in the world had become of them? Why hadn't they been put into effect? Or had they been and had they subsequently been quietly sabotaged?

He thought of all the effort that had gone into evolving them; the preliminary research, the conferences, the painful drafting and redrafting, until every word carried the meaning intended for it, the announcement to the staff, after which the majority of them were allowed to wither on the vine until all that was left was a carbon copy in a project file.

He thought of this process being duplicated in thousands of corporations throughout the country. They talked about the loss of man hours due to strikes. They should find a way of measuring the lost man hours due to abandoned projects.

One drawer was equipped with a special lock. This contained the top-secret stuff—the files marked "Private and Confidential." He unlocked it with a duplicate key which he kept among the abandoned ball-point pens in the top middle drawer of his desk and selected a file marked "Dunky Matter." It had to do with the disappearance of ten thousand dollars' worth of government bonds. The FBI had been in on the case and they strongly suspected a mouse of a man named Dunky in the Auditing Department. The bonds had turned up four or five years later wedged between a wall and a radiator in the Accounting Department. Unfortunately, poor Dunky had passed on to a less suspicious world in the meantime. Perhaps he never knew; Mr. Crombie hoped not.

He glanced at his wrist watch. It was almost one o'clock. How could he have spent three hours poking among these dusty fragments of an almost forgotten past, like an old crone hovering over a trash barrel? The question was whether to go to the Club and have lunch or stick on this job until it was finished. He would probably work more efficiently with a little food.

The big cocktail table in the main room of the Club was surrounded. That was the way it went. Some Saturdays there wouldn't be anyone in the place and the following week all the old-timers would assemble as if at the call of a soundless trumpet. He sat down next to Joe Backer, who was in the midst of a long dialect story, and rang the bell for the bar waiter.

It was almost three o'clock when he returned to the office,

feeling drowsy. It annoyed him to find the Confidential File drawer still open just as he had left it. Who did he think was coming in to close it? At the rear of the drawer was an open space behind the manila folders. He put his hand in and pulled out a pair of rubbers that had been missing for several years. It was hopeless. There was only one thing to do. Jettison the whole thing—lock, stock and barrel. Feverishly he began pulling out folders and tearing them up. His waste-basket filled quickly. He brought in one from Miss Parkinson's desk. Would she get a surprise when she came in Monday morning and found the filing cabinets empty!

His wrists grew tired. Tearing up files reminded him of a strongman who once came to a summer hotel where he went when he was a little boy and tore up telephone books. Miss Parkinson's basket overflowed. He let the pieces fall to the floor in an ever-growing mound. What was he accomplishing by all this conscientious demolition? What cleaning woman would ever want to read this stuff? He drew out half a dozen files and threw them on top of the heap untorn.

Now he was getting somewhere. With a mounting frenzy he emptied drawer after drawer. This was the way firemen must feel. He was standing knee deep in manila folders. Closing the last empty drawer with a bang, he pulled his chair back to his desk. Picking a sheet of paper from the floor, he found a red pencil and printed in large letters:

CLEANING WOMAN—PLEASE REMOVE

He laid it on top of the pile. It was too small. She would never see it. He would get one of the big graph sheets from Statistical and use the reverse side.

He stopped in the chartroom just off Statistical. This was Joe Hennessy's baby. The charts were mounted on hinged panels which you could flip over and examine like wallpaper samples. Joe had charted every possible situation he could think of; the price of barley since the American Revolution, the relationship between the cost of labor and corporate profits, the fluctuations of the cocoa market. It was the living world reduced to saw-toothed lines; weak lines attempting to keep up with strong ascending lines, then giving up in despair and sinking limply to the lower right-hand corner; competitive lines, battling savagely with one another across the charts; turbulent lines, suggesting a cross section of the Grand Tetons.

These things must cost a fortune to maintain and no one really looked at them except prospective customers—who were forced to. The man hours lost keeping up useless charts should be added to the time lost in the preparation of abandoned projects.

Picking up a piece of graph paper from one of the desks, he returned to his office and prepared a new notice for the cleaning woman.

As he surveyed the wreckage he was glad that it would all be picked up by Monday morning before Miss Parkinson came in. She would disapprove of such a careless disposal of important papers and insist on everything being reduced to confetti. He felt emotionally disturbed, as if he had thrown away a part of himself—unread. Perhaps it would be a good idea to walk home and settle back to normalcy before seeing Jinny.

He found himself passing the Club and decided to drop in just to check up on who was around. He felt the need to re-establish contact with the familiar. There was no use seeking companionship upstairs. The Saturday-afternoon bridge players were hard at work there and brooked no interruptions. He wandered to the bar, which was empty except for Freddie Wimple, who was seated at a table gazing moodily at the bartender who was polishing glasses at the other end of the room.

Thanks to the diligence of his ancestors, Freddie Wimple had never done a day's work in his life. Mr. Crombie had always considered him as more or less of a joke. Now his urge to talk to somebody, anybody, caused him to greet Freddie almost effusively.

"Have a drink?" he asked.

Freddie made a noise intended to indicate that he considered this a sound idea. They ordered two Scotch and sodas and sipped them silently for several minutes.

"Where you going this summer?" asked Freddie. He usually started all conversations with checkup questions of this nature.

"I'm retiring," said Mr. Crombie. "We've just bought a house in the country and we're going to be busy getting settled."

"Retiring?" asked Freddie, puzzled. "You mean from business?"

"Of course. Did you think I meant I was going to bed?"

"Congratulations," said Freddie, his voice animated for the first time. "Say, that's wonderful, isn't it? I'll bet you're tickled —just like getting out of jail, or something."

"Oh, I don't know. What's wrong with business?"

"Frightful waste of time, unless you got t'have the money. Everybody tryin' to sell things they can't get rid of to people who don't want 'em. Fearful rat race. People sittin' in conferences talkin' about things they don't understand. Writin' memos to each other nobody pays any attention to. [Mr. Crombie winced.] Thinkin' up new ways to be complicated just to impress somebody. Waste, waste, waste. All the business in the world could be done between ten in the morning and noon if people would cut out the waste."

"Oh, come now. You live on the earnings of business, don't you?"

Freddie ignored this as a silly question. "Well, you're well

out of it, Crombie. Lucky lad! Now you can begin kickin'
your heels an' raisin' hell. Might's well start now. Have another. . . ."

"No, thanks. I've got to be getting home."

"Only four o'clock."

"Some other time, thanks."

"Well, congratulations again. It must almost be worth
workin' all your life to have the fun of quittin'."

As Mr. Crombie walked up Park Avenue his step was once
more springy. Freddie Wimple had been just the medicine he
needed. In another month he would be free to kick his
heels and start raisin' hell.

21

MR. CROMBIE FOUND THAT WHEN
they were alone in the evening he had a tendency to go to
sleep right after dinner. It meant, of course, that he was working extremely hard at the office and was coming home exhausted, but that was something that no woman ever seemed
to understand. "Gray, why don't you go to bed? It's awfully
discouraging to sit here and watch a man sprawled in a chair
with his mouth open. You look like something that's been
freshly murdered."

He didn't ask how she could read a book and watch his
mouth at the same time, but merely shook himself and picked
up his book, unable to tell just where he had left off until he

had gone back and read several vaguely familiar pages. Sleepy as he was, he didn't want to go to bed, because he knew that after a few hours of drugged sleep he would be catapulted into consciousness once more, condemned to lie staring at the ceiling for the remainder of the night.

Of course at such times the obvious thing to do was to make his mind a blank and go back to sleep, a task which reminded him of a man rushing around an old house trying to keep the wind from seeping through loose windows. After a while some particularly worrisome thought would move in and he would cease to struggle. It used to be the office. Now, more and more frequently, it was the new house in the country that took command.

How in the world was he going to get the place cleaned? Could you hire people to clean houses for you in the country? Would Jinny ever find a small apartment in town? Or would he go bankrupt carrying their present apartment *and* the country place? How did he know that, when Jinny found a new apartment, they would be able to sell the one they were in? People didn't want a big barn of a place like this any more. The first thing he knew he'd be stuck with *three* places. He suddenly realized that he'd never gone into the water system in the new house. How did one go into a water system? He'd asked where the water came from and they had said an artesian well. What else should he have asked?

As a matter of fact, he'd never gone into anything at all in connection with the new house. Did it leak? Was it full of termites? Was the furnace any good? Was the place infested with rats? Were there mosquitoes in summer? These were all things a sensible man would have checked carefully before committing himself. All he had done was to hand the owner a check for what she asked.

A place like that would take two men to keep up and he was tackling it all by himself. He must be crazy. He felt all right now, but in five years he'd be seventy and men of seventy didn't go around chopping out underbrush and staggering around with armfuls of firewood.

He turned over violently, hoping that Jinny would hear him and say something, but her breathing only became more peacefully regular.

When they moved, part of the furniture would go to the country and part to the little apartment that Jinny hadn't found yet. How in the world were they going to divide all this stuff? And how were the movers going to know what went where? The whole thing really was a mess. He wondered what Jinny would say if he announced to her at breakfast that he was putting Sunset Hill on the market.

In the next bed she broke into a contented purr. She never really snored. The sound that she made was so relaxed, so far removed from Mr. Crombie's tortured world, that it infuriated him. It was as if she had dumped all their common cares and problems into his lap and gone on a vacation.

He turned on his bed light and arranged his pillows for reading, hoping that she would wake up. She didn't stir. He opened his book and read until his eyes, straying over the top of the book, noted the first ghostly light of dawn. It was more than he could take. Closing the book he snapped out the reading light and wriggled under the covers until only the top of his head was showing. In a few minutes he was asleep.

He was awakened by Jinny's hand shaking his shoulder. "Gray, you're going to be late again and get yourself into a lather the way you did yesterday."

He looked at her with sleep-heavy, appealing eyes. "Oh, no," he said. "Don't. I had just gotten to sleep. I didn't sleep a wink until a few minutes ago."

"Nonsense," she said, "you snored like a grampus all night." There was no use arguing. A man knew if he hadn't slept and it did no good to prove it to anyone. He swung his feet out of bed and after a moment or two padded unsteadily to the bathroom.

22

THE INEVITABLE DINNER TO THE
retiring president was over—at least his part in it was over. He
and Gleason and a few others had pulled out around midnight. The others were still sitting in the oak-paneled dining
room at the Club. There they would remain, drinking faster
and faster, talking louder and louder, until either their control
towers closed for the night or the silent, patient waiters removed the portable bar from the corner of the room.

Mr. Crombie entered the apartment quietly and placed
a bulky flannel-swathed object on the table. The idea of going
to bed was repugnant to him. He wanted a Scotch and soda.
God knew he didn't need it, but he was filled with a restless-
ness that only another highball could quell.

There was a note from Jinny on the hall table. "Hope the
dinner was all you deserve. Ice bucket and the necessary in
the library." That was so typical of Jinny. She knew just
when to do the right thing even though it didn't fit into her
woman's ideas. If more wives would realize that men and
women were quite different—as different as dogs and cats—
Reno would still be a small town.

He mixed himself a drink and let his body fall wearily into
the big leather chair in the library. After a few moments he
rose and picked up the flannel bag from the hall table. Un-
tying the drawstring he pulled out a large silver bowl which
he held up to the light so that he might read again the en-

graved signatures which covered its gleaming sides. Every
officer was there and, in addition, old "Jackal" Jones. That
had been a touch—having Jackal at the dinner. He had come
with Mr. Crombie from the Guaranty when Crombie, Hamilton and Gardiner was organized and had been his humble,
loyal slave for thirty-five years, asking nothing, giving all. He
turned the bowl so that the light from the table lamp lit up
the inscription:

> *To Graham Crombie*
> *who had the courage to put his*
> *dreams into action.*
> *This bowl is a symbol of the enduring esteem and affection*
> *of those privileged to have had a small part in the building*
> *of a great enterprise.*

The words brought into focus something that had been
bothering him all evening. Dinners like this marked a point in
time—a dividing point—when there was no longer anything
in common between the hosts and the honored guest. The
former were, in effect, dropping the pilot. He, his role completed, could only look backward. They, although they made
a brave pretense that this was also for them an evening of
nostalgia, were only concerned with the future. The pilot had
brought them through the narrow places. Now, for them, the
open sea lay ahead.

He would never forget it; the candlelight throwing everything outside the oval of faces into semidarkness; the long
table littered with bottles, glasses, silver ice bowls and crum-
pled napkins; the deep shadows on the faces of the diners;
everyone clapping and cheering as Gleason finished his speech
of presentation and handed Mr. Crombie the bowl; Tommy
Potter, who had wanted the top job so badly, rising, very
drunk, to make an impromptu speech and being pulled down
with laughter and much horseplay by Bingham and Joe

Loomis; the young account executives whose early, respectful reserve had been swept away by a reckless absorption of martinis and the Club's choicest wines, egging Tom Potter on, trying to show him by their enthusiasm that he was still their man and that they regarded Gleason as a stuffed shirt.

Mr. Crombie was on his feet, then, waiting for the din to subside; ready with his swan song. The first and last part of his speech had been a tremendous success. He was a natural storyteller and he had opened with two or three of his best efforts just to jar them into consciousness. He had never had a more receptive audience.

It was too bad after such a good start that he had dwelt so long on the early history of the Company. Reminiscences, which meant so much to him, were tales from the Dark Ages to most of these boys. Their risibles had been aroused by his stories and they had sat alert, at first, ready for fresh opportunities for laughter. Their responses gradually became formally polite until finally their faces froze into those masks of attention behind which men hide when they cease to listen and abandon themselves to their own thoughts or to their lack of them.

He was too old a hand to have fallen under the spell of his own words, but that is just what he had done. He had always made a point of watching the faces of his audience for signs of inattention, but tonight his eyes were turned back on other scenes. It was not until young Applegate (Miss Parkinson's "cute Mr. Applegate") fell off his chair that he came to his senses. He was still irritated at Gleason for rapping on his glass and calling the dinner sharply to order. He was quite able to control his own crew.

He had wound up the speech quickly and sat down. They gave him an ovation that constricted his throat so that he could not speak. There had been a dreadful moment when he thought he was going to cry. He chose to think that a good part of the enthusiasm was because they realized there would be no more speeches, but he knew in his heart that they liked him.

You didn't want to take these overtures too seriously, however. Of course a certain percentage of it was personal. The rest was for that idol of clay, the great god Boss.

The build-up of an executive was a highly developed technique. One moment you were the promising young man, permitted to sit, on occasion, in the councils of the elders, but unheeded and unnoticed; then, suddenly, a few men came out of an inner room smiling knowingly and sent for you. A few moments later you were a major executive.

Immediately the attitude of the whole world changed. Customers who had never spoken to you before stopped at your desk to ask your opinion on things you knew nothing about. Committees waited on you deferentially to ask you to join other committees. Corporation presidents asked you to lunch at the Downtown Association and the Brook Club in order to sound you out as to whether you would undertake some backbreaking philanthropic job.

Old jokes that you had trotted out previously and in vain at many a tongue-tied business lunch were suddenly received with overhearty laughter. Ideas that you had tried to sell for years were now adopted with acclaim. At Christmastime your home and your office were flooded with greetings from well-wishers. Tycoons from whom you had never been able to drag two words suddenly became shoulder-patting buddies.

It was heady stuff. It ruined some. Few came through the ordeal without being changed to some degree. The very care with which you must now weigh your words was bound to have some effect on one's character. Whereas yesterday people paid so little attention that you were apt to overstate in order to get your point across, now the very opposite was true. Small wonder that over the years the top-brass men grew taciturn.

Taciturnity wasn't as bad as pompousness, though, but few wholly escaped the latter either. Few went through the ordeal of success without acquiring some trace of what Miss Parkinson referred to as "boo boo boo." Gleason had more than a trace of "boo boo boo" and oddly enough one of the troubles with Tom Potter was that he had none at all and never would have. Perhaps just a dash of it was necessary in a top executive, just as a dash of overassurance was necessary in an actor. Perhaps the gap between executives and actors was not so great as people supposed.

He wondered how pompous he appeared to his staff and to the world. Heaven knew he didn't *feel* pompous. He might well have become so, however, had he not been flanked by Jinny and Miss Parkinson. It would be hard to imagine two more alert and enthusiastic deflators. He was glad Miss Parkinson had only a year to go before she also was retired. The most lonely person in any organization is the late Boss's secretary.

Gleason had taken her on, but quite obviously she never would be happy with him. With her old boss gone she only waited for retirement so that she could travel and read. At least that was what she had told him. It was hard to think of Miss Parkinson traveling or reading or doing anything, in fact, but sitting in the outer office taking care of him.

And how faithfully she had done that. How could he have survived those early years without her? How he had survived them even with her was something of a miracle.

What strange conceit, born of ignorance, had led him to believe that he was qualified to start an investment-counsel firm and lead it to success? He was not an investment expert. He was not even investment minded, if he wanted to be thoroughly honest with himself. How had he been able to sell the idea to Hamilton and Gardiner, who had forgotten more about securities than he ever knew? How had he

brought in those first accounts which had enabled them to
survive until a rising stock market paved the way to the top
ranks?

Perhaps it was because he was genuinely fond of most
people. He is sure of one thing—if you sincerely liked a man
you could be reasonably sure that he liked you. And the
reverse was equally true. If you didn't like him, the odds were
that he thoroughly reciprocated your feelings. And even if he
was one of your best customers no amount of backslapping
and mutual protestations of good fellowship could change
that fact and it was well to take it into your calculations.

He had also discovered early in life that men do not grow
up in quite the same way that women do. In spite of their
seeming maturity most of them remain little boys at heart.
That was why they responded so readily to conventions and
outings, fishing trips and poker clubs, reunions, old school
ties and outdoor cooking. This knowledge had been of inestimable value to him throughout his business life. It was one of
the factors which enabled him to mingle with men easily and
informally after a relatively short acquaintance, while others
were never able to get past the stage of stiff formality.

He was surprised to find that his highball glass was still half
full. He looked at his wrist watch. It was two-thirty. He heard
Jinny calling, "Gray, what's the matter with you? Have you
gone to sleep in there?"

"No, dear. Just thinking things over. I'll be in in a minute."

He heard her get out of bed and come down the hall. "Do
you know you've been sitting here almost two hours? How
did it come off?"

"They dropped the pilot," he said.

She looked at him, anxiously. "Come on now, darling. Get
some sleep in bed before it's time to get up."

23

Even if the sand on Jones Beach were to be removed a grain at a time, the ultimate moment must come when only one grain would remain. No matter how endless the days seem as we look ahead and count them by years, then months, then weeks, the last day will eventually creep up behind us and pounce with the unexpectedness of a panther springing from the branches of a tree.

"Well, boss, this is it. Gateway to freedom day," said Miss Parkinson. "I've given all your office mail to Mr. Gleason. There's some personal stuff here that you'll probably want to answer."

"While I have a secretary," he added, with the thin smile of a martyr who watches the faggots lighted about his feet but is determined to be a good sport about it.

She looked as if she were going to say something, then she compressed her lips into a thin straight line, sat down in the chair beside his desk and opened her notebook as she had done so many hundreds of times before.

The letters she had saved for him were mostly from business friends concerning his retirement. He replied to them all, lightly, confidently. They were good letters. He could confirm that by watching Miss Parkinson's sensitive face. He always knew when he was on the beat by the appreciative little smile that played around the corners of her mouth.

The phone rang. It was the first time it had rung that morning. Miss Parkinson picked up the receiver. "Mr. Garbotch to see you," she said, placing her hand automatically over the receiver. "He just wants to say good-by."

Mr. Crombie made a face.

"Typical of him," said Miss Parkinson, scornfully. "Do you want me to get rid of him?"

"No, he's a perfectly good customer. Tell him to come in."

Miss Parkinson went out and a moment later Mr. Garbotch entered, loud and overhearty. "Crombie, I can't believe it. This isn't going to be the same place without you. I'm not going to say good-by, though. We've been working together too long for that. I can't stay a minute. Just dropped in to wish you all kinds of luck."

Mr. Garbotch settled his immense body into the chair beside the desk. "No, sir. We've known each other too long to lose contact now. I'm going to keep in touch with you, Crombie. I value your views on market conditions more than those of anyone I know. That's not saying much, though, because any guy that can forecast the market today is Superman, I'm telling you." He looked belligerently around the room at the colored prints as if waiting for Mr. Crombie to contradict this statement.

"You know what I think? I think we're just starting the biggest boom in history. Let me have that pad a minute. I want to show you some figures." For the next half hour Mr. Garbotch contentedly filled page after page with figures, all demonstrating the fact that in six months the Dow Jones average would be a hundred points higher. Miss Parkinson entered and placed a note in front of Mr. Crombie.

"Oh, yes," exclaimed Mr. Crombie, raising his voice in order to penetrate Mr. Garbotch's statistic-laden consciousness, "Ralph Barton. You know Ralph Barton, Morris. Tell him to come in, Miss Parkinson."

"I've got to go," said Mr. Garbotch. "I'm late now. The point I want to make is this . . ." He was off again, tearing sheets from Mr. Crombie's pad and dropping them on the floor. Mr. Barton appeared in the doorway.

". . . department-store sales in the ten key cities," said Mr. Garbotch.

"Hello, Graham," said Mr. Barton. "I just can't believe it. I didn't come in to say good-by. You're going to be around and I'm going to keep in touch. . . ."

Mr. Garbotch, obviously annoyed by the interruption, tossed his last sheet of unfinished forecasts on the floor. "I gotta be going," he said, nodding to Mr. Barton. "Seeyasoon."

Mr. Crombie tried to accompany him to the door, but Garbotch had disappeared before he could round his desk. "I hope I didn't interrupt . . ." said Mr. Barton apologetically. "Miss Parkinson said to come right in."

"That's right," said Mr. Crombie, picking up Mr. Garbotch's litter. "You didn't interrupt a bit. Old Morris was just giving me a preview of tomorrow's financial page. How are you, anyway?"

"Well, I'm not so good," said Mr. Barton. "But I didn't come to talk about myself. I can't stay a minute. Just dropped in to congratulate you on your retirement, or commiserate you, or whatever you do when a guy's leaving the old treadmill."

"Well, I appreciate it," said Mr. Crombie. "Sorry to hear things aren't right with you, though. What's the trouble?"

"Oh, it's a lot of things, Graham. Part of it's me. My circulation isn't right. Ankles swell up. Doctors can't find out what the matter is."

Mr. Crombie, not knowing what to say, clicked his tongue sympathetically. Mr. Barton nodded. "Then *Mrs.* Barton's not very well. . . ."

"I'm sorry to hear that."

"Yes, she has dizzy spells," said Mr. Barton. "Can't tell

when they're going to hit her. One minute she'll be talking to
you about this and that, bright as a button. The next minute
she's on the floor. The doctors can't figure it out."

Mr. Crombie shook his head.

"You get these things when you get older," said Mr. Barton,
almost cheerfully. "I watched my father and mother go and I
want to tell you, Graham, I'll never forget it." He launched
into a harrowing account of the last ten gruesome years of his
parents' lives. Miss Parkinson appeared, eventually, and
placed a piece of paper in front of him. It said, "Miss Pankhurst is on the phone."

There was no "Miss Pankhurst." She was a figment of
Miss Parkinson's imagination, to be used for rescue work. Mr.
Crombie was now free to say, "Will you see if you can get her
to talk to Mr. Gleason? I don't want to be interrupted right
now," or "I'm afraid I'll have to take this. It's important. Tell
her I'll be with her in a moment."

He chose the latter alternative, to Mr. Barton's obvious
annoyance. "I'm sorry I didn't have time to finish," he said,
rising unwillingly. "It's an interesting story. Well, I must run.
You've made me late for an appointment as it is. All I wanted
to do was to congratulate you on your retirement, or maybe I
should commiserate you. Be seeing you."

"Mr. Gleason wants to come in when you are free," said
Miss Parkinson.

"I'll go to see him."

"No, please. He said for me not to tell you, but to let him
know when you were free, else you'd be coming to him." She
returned to her desk and in a few minutes Gleason appeared
in the doorway.

"I really feel like a traitor to do this, Graham, but you
made me promise to tell you if the staff was planning any little
whimsies, so I suppose I have to. I got it through the grapevine
that they're going to waylay you on your way out this after-

noon and give you three rousing huzzahs, or call for a speech or something."

Mr. Crombie's face was contorted with anguish. "Oh, *no*," he said, "they *can't*. I couldn't take it. *Please*."

"Nonsense," said Mr. Gleason. "They want to and they should. This company's losing something, Graham, and you're the only one that doesn't seem to realize it. What're you doing for lunch?"

"I'm sorry, Joe, I have a date."

"Well, there was nothing on my mind. Just thought we could break bread for once without talking business. Oh, well—there'll be plenty of other chances. I've got to get back now. Mr. Marston is coming in."

Nothing that Gleason could have said would have depressed Mr. Crombie more than the announcement that Marston was coming in to see him. For a quarter of a century Kendrick Marston had never discussed his ramified and complex affairs with anyone but Mr. Crombie. He rose from his desk and walked to the window. Fifteen stories below him the ceaseless traffic of Park Avenue moved north and south, halting with the long line of red lights, then resuming its antlike progress as the line turned green.

"They don't even wait for the king to die," he muttered. He walked to the outer office and took his hat from the rack. "I'm going to lunch," he said.

She looked up in surprise. "It's only twelve o'clock," she said.

"I know. I'm going early. Have an errand on the way."

"Where are you going to be? You have no luncheon date today?"

"I'm going home, if you have to know. For keeps. I can't take it." Then, seized by a sudden impulse, "I don't suppose you'd have lunch with me, would you? Last rites and all that sort of thing?"

She shook her head without looking at him. "Thanks a lot," she said. "We wouldn't know what to say to each other after all these years."

He reached out and touched the back of her thin hand with his finger tips. "I'll be seeing you," he said.

She could only nod as she watched his heavy frame pass through the door. Then she jumped up from her desk, went into his office and closed the door behind her.

The telephone rang five times and was silent.

PART III   *Hesitation*

1

MRS. CROMBIE SANK LIMPLY INTO
an armchair. The floor of the big, low-ceilinged living room of
Sunset Hill was filled from wall to wall with cartons, furniture, lamps without shades, shades without lamps and lumpy
packages. "Well," she said, "we're in."

"We sure are," said Mr. Crombie. "Up to our necks."

"Do you know something," she said, "there's a crack in that
ceiling."

But he was not listening. He had opened one of the cartons.
Seated on the floor he was examining its contents. "I haven't
seen a lot of this stuff for years," he said. "This is my old war
diary and here's the map I carried the day we went over the
top at Bois des Forges. Gosh, I'd forgotten all about this.
Listen. This was written right after the attack on the 26th of
September. 'Last night they moved the 75s right up behind
the Infantry's jumping-off place—wheel to wheel. At . . .' "

"For heaven's sake, Graham, haven't you got enough trouble
without starting to fight World War I all over again? Before
you begin emptying cartons and digging up your past, let's
get some of this truck out of the way so we can *walk* around

the room instead of climbing around it. Now those cartons over there are all books. Why don't you take them into your library? That will give us room to turn around at least."

"Why don't we mix a couple of martinis instead?" he suggested. "I've been working since eight o'clock this morning. I'm pooped."

"But it's only four o'clock. We have two hours work ahead of us. If we don't keep at it we'll never get straightened out."

Mr. Crombie groaned and picked up a carton of books. "Why do people insist on carting around a mountain of books they're never going to read again or never going to read period?" he said, staggering to the door.

"Don't talk to me. They're your books. You wouldn't part with one of them for money."

"In my present state of mind I'd part with everything I own for money—including my wife."

"That crack in the ceiling bothers me," she said. "I wonder why we didn't notice it before?"

2

IT HAD BEEN A TEMPESTUOUS three weeks. Mr. Crombie felt tired and worn. The old apartment on the river had been sold. The greater part of its contents, accumulated during thirty years of living in one place, had found its way to Sunset Hill, the balance had gone into storage until the little apartment in New York, which they had also bought, was ready for occupancy.

Never in all his years of active business life had he toiled so hard, so continuously and with such a sense of frustration. He was used to working in accordance with an orderly pattern, but there was no chance for that here. Once a home, long lived in, begins to be pulled apart, the operation quickly assumes an explosive quality. There were moments when he felt like a disaster victim standing amid the wreckage of his old familiar world, not knowing what to lay hold of first or where to turn.

Through it all, the routine demands of living kept piling up relentlessly. Each morning, while they were still in the old apartment, the incoming mail would be left by the elevator man on the little marble-topped table in the foyer. Each day the ringing phone would bring its quota of small problems— problems which, despite their unimportance, must be met. Would he leave a two weeks' visitors' card at the Club for Joe Marcus from Milwaukee? Would he be willing to serve on a little special committee—no work, just a couple of meetings? A young Englishman was coming to New York—a charming fellow (all Englishmen always were). Would it be convenient —would they—could they?

Ordinarily he would have disposed of the mail by stuffing it in his brief case and dumping it on Miss Parkinson's desk the next morning. But there was no longer any Miss Parkinson to take down his replies, to make telephone calls for him, to arrange his life and smooth his way. His comfortable old ruts had disappeared overnight and he stood in the middle of a vast plain devoid of direction signs.

He had thought of retirement as something serene, tranquil, orderly, and during his last few months at the office he had frequently looked forward to his first day as a free man: the day when he could turn over and go to sleep again if he so desired, when he could do as he chose, dress as he chose, take a drink if he wanted to, not take one if he didn't want to, go to sleep when he felt tired, be himself, in short, for the first time in decades.

It had turned out so differently. Instead of sleeping luxuriously far into the morning he had begun the day by waking at six, tense as a pointer. There had been no question of going back to sleep. He had slipped out of bed and worked at his desk in the already half-dismantled library until breakfast was ready. There was something about the feel of a desk under his elbows that soothed him.

At breakfast he had placed the *New York Times* beside his plate with a feeling of anticipation. He had always been too hurried to read the *Times* thoroughly. Now he proposed to go through it at his leisure from front to back.

Mrs. Crombie glanced apprehensively at the pantry door. "Verma's served notice," she said. "She won't go to the country."

He looked up, unbelieving. "Verma?" he said. "Why she can't do that—she's been with us for twenty years."

"Well, she can and, what's more, she has. All this talk she's been hearing about retirement has proved contagious. She's going to retire herself—going out to live with her sister somewhere in Illinois."

"But what in the world . . ."

"Well, you know, dear, I've been thinking about it and I've come to the conclusion that maybe it's a good thing. In the first place, it saves us money and you say we have to economize."

Mr. Crombie nodded eagerly. "And in the second place, we'll be coming to New York once a week and you can't keep dragging Verma back and forth like a French poodle. Besides, there's no maid's room in the little apartment and she certainly wouldn't want to stay out in that lonely place all by herself."

"It *isn't* a lonely place," he said.

"It would be for Verma."

"But who's going to do the cooking?"

"I am, I suppose. I can't say I look forward to it."

"I can't say that I do, either. You haven't tried to cook since we were first married, but I can still remember it."

"I dread it and hate it, but maybe I won't when I get used to it. At any rate, that's the score and we might as well face it."

"I suppose so," he said, "but this is a fine time of life to start facing things. Oh, well—we'll get along somehow. Most of our friends seem to." He tried to make his voice sound cheerful as he resumed his attack on the *Times*, but he felt uneasy and disturbed, conscious that already something comfortable was moving out of his life—something he had always taken for granted. Wasn't it John Marquand who had said that we never appreciated anything until we lost it?

He finished the *Times* and discovered that it was almost ten o'clock. That was far too long a time to spend absorbing news, most of which he forgot before he turned the page. On the other hand, now that he was retired time didn't matter so much. Perhaps it was a good thing just to relax.

Then Jinny had pounced on him. Did he know that the morning was half gone and there were a thousand things to be done in connection with the country house and the new apartment and the impending sale of the one they were in? All that day he had answered phones and run errands. Just before lunch Jinny had given him a long list of things demanding immediate attention and disappeared. He never knew where. The apartment was unbearably still and lonely. Feeling put-upon and low in spirits, he went down to the Club for lunch. He ate at the long common table with a group of men he had never seen before and, after doing a few of Jinny's errands, returned to the apartment exhausted.

He felt sleepy. Well, he was free now. If he was sleepy why not sleep? He threw himself on his bed. After dozing for fifteen minutes, he sprang up. God, was he going to start

hitting the sack in the middle of the afternoon? He wandered
into the living room and picked up a magazine. He had always
complained that he never had any opportunity to read the
magazines to which he had been subscribing for years. He
started to read the first article, but either it was extremely dull
or there was something the matter with his brain, for at the
end of ten minutes he had no idea what the author was talking about and no great desire to find out.

The cleaning woman appeared. He hadn't known she was
in the apartment and he was startled. She wanted to know
when she could do the living room. He delivered it into her
hands and went back to his desk in the library with the feeling
that this was where he had come in.

3

THEY SOLD THE OLD APARTMENT
almost immediately. The purchasers, an unlovable couple who
went about peering into closets and exchanging sneers,
wanted occupancy as soon as possible—or sooner. Jinny said it
was better that way. A move as big and as complex as this
should be done quickly, not dragged out. They would select
what they needed for the little apartment, then send everything else to the country and weed it out after they moved in.
In that way the whole thing would be very simple indeed.

"We can save some money," said Mr. Crombie, co-oper-
atively, "by taking out as much as we can in the station
wagon—all the loose stuff and that sort of thing."

The day elevator man at the apartment began to dread calls from the tenth floor, knowing that when his door opened he would be faced by a hallful of dilapidated suitcases, loose clothes on hangers, open cartons from which things fell when you picked them up, floor lamps, framed pictures, most of them so old that the paper was hanging from their backs, books, radios, and a motley of small articles all of which, under the ground rules governing apartment houses, he must deliver to the doorman, armful by armful, while the other tenants of the building buzzed angrily for the elevator.

People living in high-grade apartments simply did not go in for this slaphappy, gypsy way of doing things. When they moved, the proper kind took themselves off to Antigua or Jamaica or the Arizona Biltmore while duly accredited members of the movers union transferred their goods from the old home to the new with such efficiency that when the master and his lady returned, their clothes were hanging in the new closets in their accustomed order.

Mr. Crombie became so uncomfortably aware of this that he tried to compensate for his behavior by tipping like a movie star. Fortunately he didn't have to repeat this costly process at the other end of the line. There he was on his own in the most literal sense. "I'll help you," Mrs. Crombie would assure him, seizing several hatboxes and a loose Thermos bottle as they drew up in front of the kitchen door at Sunset Hill. Then she would disappear permanently into the house while Mr. Crombie staggered back and forth with insecure armfuls until the station wagon was empty.

"Where do you want me to put this stuff," he would yell as he entered the kitchen door.

"I'll be right there," Mrs. Crombie would call, cheerily, from some remote part of the house.

After waiting a few minutes he could no longer stand the pain in his arms and would pile everything on the floor and go back for another load. They would work until sunset and drive back to town in the evening, stopping for dinner at some roadside tavern along the way.

Mr. Crombie was so used to eating in public places on an expense account that it pained him to see his pocket cash melt like butter on a stove. The day had been when the friendly greeting of a headwaiter was something to warm the heart. Now he began to regard all purveyors of food and drink as bandits, and as he looked about at the family groups stuffing themselves phlegmatically all around him, he could only conclude that everyone in New England was loaded except the Crombies, or else they didn't pay their income taxes.

And then came "M" Day, when a group of beefeaters invaded the apartment and in grim silence began transferring their belongings to the sidewalk below.

For years Mr. Crombie had been observing similar piles of other people's furniture standing at the curbside, waiting to be packed into vans. It had always interested him to note that, no matter how expensive the apartment house from which these lares and penates came, they always looked as if they belonged in a tenement and not a very good one at that.

Now, when he went down to inspect progress at the van level, he was shocked to discover that their fine old mahogany pieces and their interior-decorator upholstered chairs, when exposed to the glare of the noonday sun, had the same dilapidated, beaten-up look. It depressed him so that he considered the advisability of giving everything to some thrift shop and starting all over again, thus saving the hideous cost of vanning.

4

IT WAS SUNDAY MORNING. THEY were having breakfast in the sun-flecked dining room at Sunset Hill. Through the open door leading to the terrace a warm breeze entered from the valley and ruffled the pages of Mr. Crombie's paper. All about them the floor was strewn with half-emptied cartons and a miscellany of objects which had been laid there because the person carrying them didn't know what else to do with them.

"If we don't get this mess cleaned up pretty soon, I'm going crazy," said Mrs. Crombie.

"I know," he said, "but the thing to do is not to get excited about it. There's a lot to be done, but we have eternity to do it in. I'm retired. We must get used to that. Plenty of time for everything. That's the kind of philosophy we must cultivate. Then life will flow like a river."

"That's nice," she said. "But don't forget we go to New York tomorrow afternoon for your directors' meeting Tuesday morning and the river stops flowing for a couple of days."

There was a look of dismay on his face as he laid down the paper. "Oh, no," he said, "we can't go off and leave things like this."

"Do you want to miss your meeting?"

"No, of course not." They were silent, she waiting, he thinking. "I'll tell you what we might do. If we drive down to New York after lunch it somehow knocks the whole day out.

I don't know why, but it does. Couldn't we start at six o'clock and have dinner on the road? Then we'd have a full day here. It probably would be a good idea to do the same thing on the way back. I think it's nicer to drive in the cool of the evening, anyway."

"O.K.," she said. "I'll do anything to get this place straightened out so we can begin to live in it, and of course we've got the same problem with the place in town. What it amounts to is that, now you're retired, life is so hectic we have to run a night shift twice a week."

"Once we get settled . . ." he said, soothingly. "Will you make me a piece of toast?"

"Do you realize," said Mrs. Crombie, dropping two slices of bread into the toaster, "that we must buy another toaster for the apartment?"

The dreadful implications of this statement slowly permeated Mr. Crombie's consciousness.

"And do you realize," he said with dramatic slowness, "that that applies to almost everything we own?"

"Oh, sure, practically *everything*."

"I'll have to have another safety razor and another hairbrush. We must duplicate all the kitchen things. We'll need another ice bucket, another radio, another television, another set of dining-room furniture, china—we'll have to order writing paper for both places. Good God!"

"Of course," said Mrs. Crombie. "What did you think we'd do—tow a U-Haul-It after us everytime we went to town?"

"I didn't think," he moaned. "Why don't people ever think of the simple, obvious things? Why, it's terrible. It's worse than the Ark. At least the animals were for free, but this—this is going to cost a fortune."

"Oh, well. Take it easy. We'll just get the things we have to have and if we buy the rest gradually we won't even notice it."

"I don't know why it is," said Mr. Crombie, "that you seem to feel that if we can spend money in such a way that we don't notice it, it's the same as not spending it at all."

But Mrs. Crombie wasn't listening. As far as she was concerned the crisis was over. She was casting an appraising eye at the congestion around them.

"You know," she said, "when you have an apartment as big as ours was you never have to throw anything away—you just push it behind something and there it stays forever and ever. Now that it's finally been pulled out into the daylight, for heaven's sake don't let's shove it out of sight again without getting rid of the things we really don't want."

Mr. Crombie looked pained. "This thing is like an open-ended pipe," he said, "with the water running in one end and going out the other. Half our time has to be spent buying duplicates of practically everything we own and the other half throwing things away. Why is it that what was so precious a few years ago suddenly becomes so objectionable that we won't even give it house room?"

"Because, dear, things get worn out. Our habits change. We have no further use for things. There are lots of reasons. Now you take that beaten-up raccoon coat that you used to have in college. The fur is all worn off the back. You're never going to wear it again, but there the old moth sanctuary hangs, taking up room. Now that's just one item. . . ."

"You bet it is," interrupted Mr. Crombie. "It's one item that we're not going to toss out, either. That's the coat I wore all through Harvard. I sometimes think women are devoid of sentiment. Why, I wouldn't let that coat go for anything. Anyway, I'll get a lot of use out of it in the country."

"Doing what? Sleigh-riding?"

"No, not sleigh-riding," he said. "Listen. I don't go around throwing *your* clothes away. Why don't you leave mine alone."

"O.K., O.K.," she said. "I didn't know you were going to

get all worked up about it. I'm simply trying to tell you that I don't want to store away a vanload of things we know we're never going to use again. Now here's what I suggest. You sort out the rest of your books and papers and get them stowed away in your library. While you're doing that I'll go over the rest of this stuff. Whatever I think we should get rid of I'll put in one of the guest rooms and I'll swear not to throw anything away until you see it."

"All right," he said, "but I don't want anybody fooling with that coonskin coat."

Her face twitched slightly. "I'm going to work right now. We can do the breakfast dishes later." Mrs. Crombie hated "doing the dishes" almost as much as she despised cooking.

5

IN HIS PANELED LIBRARY, WITH the door shut against intrusion, Mr. Crombie emptied the cartons onto the old floor boards. Occasionally he opened the door and tossed an empty carton into the hall just to let the world know he wasn't browsing. Gradually, like a rising tide, their contents inundated the floor of the library, the fireplace, his desk, all available chairs, the empty bookshelves and the window sills.

As he hurled the last box out and picked his way back into the room, he felt like a man standing in the exact center of his past life. Surrounding him was the autobiography of Graham Crombie, his successes and failures, his hopes, celebrations and disappointments. All were recorded in this unorganized mass of papers, photographs and clippings. Was it wise to preserve these things? Who, other than himself, would ever care about them or even know their meaning? Wasn't it better to obliterate the trail as one went along?

He picked up a bundle of paper tubes held together with an ancient elastic band which immediately disintegrated. Selecting one, he unrolled it with difficulty. It was a panoramic picture of his Twenty-fifth Reunion. Taking it to the window he cleared a chair and sat down to examine it more closely. There he was in the second row with Jinny. Lordy, she had been beautiful in those days—still was, as a matter of fact; in a more autumnal way, of course. And there was Joe Sims. You'd never know him now, God knows. That must be Skip Binger right behind him, looking a bit potted. He probably had been. Poor old Skip had certainly messed up his life. Bottled up would be a better word. Well, that was something that wouldn't be thrown away. He released the edges of the picture, which immediately rolled itself back into a cylinder as if anxious to return to the oblivion from which it had been so briefly snatched. He picked up another tube. It was a picture of his World War I outfit taken "somewhere in France." He had known all of these men intimately, lived with them day and night for months, damn near died with them a couple of times. Now he couldn't even remember their names.

All through the morning he burrowed like a mole into the past, rereading old letters, diaries, speeches, looking over dozens of loose photographs, thrown into boxes to await the day—which would never come—when someone would paste them into albums. It was like swimming backward in time through waters in which he no longer belonged.

Heaven knew what he was going to do with all this stuff, but certainly *he* couldn't throw it away. It was his life and one doesn't throw his life into the scrap basket like so much

Christmas wrapping. No. That was what executors were for. They'd get one look at this verbal compost heap and give it the old heave-ho. He hoped he wouldn't be hovering around like those people in the Topper book. Carefully, almost tenderly, he piled everything in the cabinets under the bookcases. Step two would be to go through it all some rainy day, putting everything into chronological order. For what? For whom? For his executors to throw away, of course.

As the hours wore on he felt more like the curator of an ancient museum than a man embarking on a new life. Why did older people always prefer to look backward rather than forward? Probably it was because they had too little future left to completely occupy their attention. At any rate it was a habit which he intended to fight.

They belonged where they now were, *The Private Papers of Graham Crombie,* nesting undisturbed in the dark cabinets of an ancient house; near him, part of him, but the unseen part—the part that pertained to his roots and not to the Graham Crombie who lived in the open air above ground. It was almost three o'clock. He went in search of Jinny who, dirty and disheveled, had been equally engrossed, although along radically different lines.

"Well, did you weed out a lot of that rubbish?" she asked as they ate their luncheon sandwiches in the cluttered kitchen.

"Oh, yes," he said vaguely, "quite a lot."

"I'll bet you didn't get rid of one empty envelope," she said. "You're hopeless, but the library's your department, not mine. Now I *really* accomplished something. As soon as you've finished your lunch I want you to come up."

There was triumphant excitement in her voice. Men, thought Mr. Crombie, are basically collectors; women, disposers, whether it be money or goods. This was too nebulous an idea, however, to warrant starting an argument.

6

THE SPARE ROOM LOOKED LIKE AN overcrowded attic. Mrs. Crombie glanced anxiously at him as he entered. "I know it seems like a lot to throw away," she said defensively, "but this is all stuff that is broken or worn out. We just have no *use* for it. Now take this old rocker that used to be in the maid's room. It's all coming to pieces. We don't want that, certainly."

"But it can be fixed," said Mr. Crombie. "Surely you don't throw things away just because they need a little glue. That's just the kind of project I want for my workshop."

"But if you fix it—which I doubt if you ever will—what are you going to *do* with it? We haven't any maid's room either here or in the City—or any maid to rock in it."

"Listen dear, maids aren't the only people who like to rock."

"You're thinking of Whistler's *Mother*," she said. "She's dead."

"The trouble with you is you get a notion about something and that's the end of it. You say 'rocking chairs are no longer fashionable so let's take all the rockers down to the Salvation Army and get rid of them and then on the way home let's stop at that antique shop and look at that cobbler's bench and that darling little child's cradle that would be just the thing for firewood in your study.' You . . ."

"All right, all right," interrupted Mrs. Crombie. "Putter

with it if you want to, just as long as you get it down in the
cellar, or wherever you think you're going to do these things,
so I can get this house in shape."

"That's more like it," said Mr. Crombie. "I'm not set up
down there yet, but I'll put it somewhere in the meantime.
Don't tell me you're going to give that sewing table away.
Why, that was a wedding present."

"Darling, it's so scratched and battered that there's no
finish left on it. I wouldn't put it in a kennel."

"Why *would* you put a sewing table in a kennel? All it
needs is refinishing. I can scrape it and make it look like new."

"All right," she said with a sigh, "if you want to fill the
place with derelicts that you're never going to do anything
with, go ahead."

"What do you mean 'I'm never going to do anything with'?"

"Graham Crombie, you've never handled a tool in your life.
You've never been able to hang a picture without knocking
half the wall down. Now, God knows I want you to have
your hobbies, but you seem to think that just because you have
a big cellar to play around in you're automatically a cabinet-
maker. I don't know anything about these things, but my
common sense tells me there's more to it than you seem to
think. I have a feeling that if you don't start slowly you're
going to get so discouraged you won't be fit to live with. Why
don't you do the little necessary things first? For instance,
there's a broken sash cord on the spare-room window and
there are about a dozen panes of glass that need fixing. Those
are things that *have* to be done. If you want to save money,
start on them."

"Listen, Jinny, you don't understand. Today there are
power tools. Do you know what I mean by power tools? They
do all the hard work for you and a child can handle them. And
there are 'how to' books that make the whole thing easy.
You're thinking of the old-fashioned cabinetmakers. The

hand-finishers. Now, don't you worry, I'll take the sewing table, too."

Piece by piece Mr. Crombie transferred much of the wreckage of their past to the back porch preparatory to taking it out to the barn. The remainder he carried up to the big attic. "What do we have an attic for," he said. "Didn't you like to browse around old attics when you were a little girl? Where's the romance in a great big *empty* attic? And all these old curtains and things. Kids love to dress up. This will be a regular costume shop."

"Darling, the kids have their own places now and their own things."

"It's the grandchildren I mean—you have to make the place interesting for them if you want them to like it."

In the spacious front hall the movers had placed a big wooden settee with a high carved back embellished with a mirror and numerous hat pegs.

"Gosh," said Mr. Crombie. "I haven't seen that in thirty years. It used to be in the front hall of that house we had in Bronxville just after we were married. That really is a horror. Where's it been all these years?"

"Stored down in the basement of the apartment," she said.

"Well, we certainly can get rid of that—no argument on that one. And that about takes care of things, I guess."

She put her hand on the old dark wood. "I suppose it should go," she said, "but it makes me sort of sad to say good-by to it. It used to stand in our front hall in Cleveland when I was a little girl. I don't know whether you remember that dark, ugly old house. It was a palace to me."

"I know," he said firmly, "but the past is the past. Trying to hang onto it is one of the most dangerous things in the world, especially at our age. By the way, what did you do with my coonskin coat?"

"I hung it in the hall closet until I get a chance to spray it and put it in a new mothproof bag. Why? Do you want to wear it?"

He ignored this as unworthy. "Let's knock off," he said. "We've done enough for one day."

7

"LAST NIGHT I WORKED OUT A schedule for myself," said Mr. Crombie at breakfast. "If you don't have some kind of a systematic plan you never get anything accomplished."

"I thought you told me we had all of eternity to get things done."

"That won't be long enough if we don't get some order into our lives. It makes me nervous just to flop around like a codfish on a dock. First of all I'm going to get up at a regular time every morning. Seven is about right. I'll slip on an old T shirt and a pair of pants and take a fast walk down to the village for the paper. By the time I get back, shave and take a shower you'll have breakfast ready. Now I think breakfast is important. It should be a nice, quiet meal. . . ."

"You'd better get two papers," she said.

"After breakfast I'll take care of whatever letter-writing there may be. Then I want two uninterrupted hours for reading. I've never had two uninterrupted hours to read in my life and I'm going to begin right now. Then we'll have a cocktail—just one—and lunch. After lunch, a half hour's shut-eye—no more."

"Wait a minute," interrupted Mrs. Crombie. "When are you going to do all this?"

"I'm beginning today," he said.

"Like fun you are. Not with all there is to be done around this place. Yesterday you put all that broken furniture that you're going to fix out on the back porch. You said you were going to take it down to the barn or someplace. I don't care where you take it, but I want to get that porch cleaned up. I have a hunch that in a town like this more people come in by the kitchen than by the front door."

"Couldn't it wait until after lunch?" pleaded Mr. Crombie. "That's my chore time."

"It could *not*," she snapped. "There'll be plenty of 'chores' after lunch—and remember we're leaving for New York at six."

"All right, all right," he said resignedly, "but there should be a rule—there *must* be a rule—once I get started nothing is to interfere with my morning schedule."

"As soon as we get this house settled, I'll promise not to interrupt you even if I drop dead."

8

MR. CROMBIE LOADED THE BROKEN furniture into the station wagon and drove down to the old barn. Since their arrival he had been too busy to inspect the barn. In fact, he had had no time to leave the house at all except to go down to the village for newspapers and the mail. His life in New York had been nomadic in comparison.

The huge barn doors, built to admit a loaded hay wagon, were stuck at the top. He managed to pull one open at the bottom far enough to insert a piece of board. Using this as a lever he pried the door open still farther and inserted a second board above the first. This was a most inconvenient way to open a barn door, but he was in the country now, where men must learn to contend with all sorts of things.

As he pried the door open with the second board far enough to insert a third, he felt a glow of satisfaction that he, Graham Crombie, was able to meet a difficulty of this kind using the tools at hand. This was the way his ancestors had built America. As he put his weight on the third board there was a sound of splintering wood and what was left of the door swung open. Oh, well—it had to be fixed anyway. Just another project.

It took him some moments to get used to the half-light inside the barn. A few rays of sunshine entered through the cracks between the sideboards tracing parallel bars of light on the ancient floor. On the left was an empty hayloft. Beneath it there had probably been stalls for cows. These had long since been ripped out, however, and the entire barn was filled with a conglomeration of shapeless objects.

It was obviously an old structure; probably older than the house. The rough ax-hewn beams were fitted one into the other and secured with wooden pegs. The floor boards, hacked and splintered by thousands of horseshoes, were even wider than those in his library. The whole place smelled of rotting wood, musty burlap, mice and age.

A crude, homemade ladder led to the hayloft. Mr. Crombie climbed it cautiously. Near the edge lay an ancient Flexible Flyer with a crushed runner. Behind it was a picket gate, attached to a gatepost with long iron hinges. Gate to what? He

climbed into the loft and stumbled over a rusty bar bell and
an assortment of round weights. Why in the world would
anyone need exercise in a place like this? A number of posts
which, presumably, had supported the roof of a porch were
stacked in a corner. What porch?

Under a pile of boards the mildewed head of a rag doll
protruded like a hurricane victim. Beside it was what looked
like the top of a human skull. On closer inspection it turned
out to be a battered white croquet ball. He descended to the
floor of the barn without looking further.

The first thing was to make room somewhere for the furniture in the station wagon. He had to think for a moment why
it was he was storing it here anyway. An old rope swing which
hung from an almost invisible rafter stirred uneasily as a
sudden breeze blew in the open door. He started nervously,
then smiled as if someone had been watching him. Picking his
way to the nearest corner, he began to clear a space; a broken
doll carriage, a bicycle with the back wheel missing, an oar
from a racing shell, an old wooden hayrake with most of the
teeth missing. Leaning against the wall behind them was an
atrocious oil painting of the barn, which he set aside carefully.
It was so bad it might be valuable.

He reminded himself of an archaeologist uncovering layers
of civilizations. This was not his place at all. He was an inter-
loper, a trespasser on other people's property. He could almost
feel the presence of past generations staring at him angrily
from dark corners, chin-whiskered farmers, little girls in sun-
bonnets and pantalettes, bronzed young college athletes, little
boys with bubble gum . . . "What are you doing here, old
man? This is *our* barn. Get out and leave our stuff alone."

Quickly, almost apologetically, he unloaded the furniture
from the station wagon, piled it in the corner and hurried out
into the sunlight.

The brook ran close to the southern end of the barn and

between it and the barn he noticed a half-obliterated path. He
followed it, pushing aside the brambles with his legs. Behind
the barn, half-buried by weeds and young bushes, were the
foundations of what must have been a chicken house. Nearby
were the ruins of some dog kennels. The roofs of the little
houses had fallen in and the few remaining shingles were
green with moss. The runways were still marked by a few
rotting posts and shreds of sagging chicken wire.

He followed the path to a point where it crossed the
stream on flat rocks. On the other side it disappeared into the
woods through a tangle of briars. Ahead of him in the fork of
a big sycamore were the remains of a tree house. The climb-
ing-cleats, nailed to its shaggy sides, were already half-
absorbed by the bark. Scattered everywhere among the sumac
bushes were old boxes, broken camp chairs and rotting posts.

Under a blanket of brambles a battered sawbuck lay on its
side. He managed to pull it free. He would need this for
sawing up firewood. The sun was warm in the sheltered clearing, the gurgle of the brook pleasantly soporific. He crossed on
the flat stones and sat down with his back against the sycamore. All this mess would have to be cleared out. It was a
Gargantuan task, but there were enough posts and whatall
scattered around to supply firewood for the winter.

Once cleaned out, it occurred to him that it might be a
likely spot on which to build a shack; a place where he could
get off by himself and think, secure from interruption. At that
moment he saw Mrs. Crombie's head appear around the
corner of the barn. She was shielding her eyes with her hand
and apparently looking for something.

"Gray," she called, and there was a note of panic in her
voice.

He hesitated a moment. "Yes," he called back, rather
crossly.

"For heaven's sake, Gray, where have you been? You had

me scared half to death. The station wagon has been standing there for an hour with the doors open and you nowhere around."

"Do I have to be around when the station wagon doors are open?"

"Don't try to be funny, dear. I was really worried. There are so many things that could happen to a person in a wild place like this. What in the world are you doing back here?"

"Looking the estate over," he said, getting to his feet.

"Well, you'll have to look it over some other time. That damn little pump in the cellar has stopped working and we have no water."

9

"THE PUMP, EH?" SAID MR. BARN-hauser, the real-estate agent. "Well, it was about due to go. Them people never took no care of things. I'll tell Guernsey to come over and slip in a stand-by pump while he's ordering you a new one. Got to have some water pressure somehow."

"What do you mean 'while he's ordering a new one'? I thought you said the mechanical equipment was all O.K. and that the people who had owned the house always kept everything up."

"The pump's O.K.," said Mr. Barnhauser, "but O.K. don't mean things don't wear out. That's a *good* little pump. Best there is. But I guess maybe it's wore out."

"Who's Guernsey?" asked Mr. Crombie suspiciously.

"Guernsey Le Bleu?" said Mr. Barnhauser. "He's the plumber that's handled your house all his life. His pa and his granpa before him—only his granpa wasn't a plumber. He was a carpenter, if you know what I mean. Folks has changed things around so often on this place, shiftin' em here and shiftin' em there, that Guernsey's the only one knows where anything is."

"Is he any good?"

"Guernsey, you mean?" said Mr. Barnhauser as if they had been discussing a number of alternatives. "Oh, Guernsey's all right. He's a bit excitable sometimes. Apt to go off his rocker if he gets crossed up. But he's a good plumber all right. Whether he is or not, he's the only one what understands where anything is."

"Well, send him right up, will you?"

"No time at all," said Mr. Barnhauser. "I'll get him to drop whatever job he's on. Don't make no difference how important it is."

An hour later a battered Cadillac limousine tore into the driveway and came to a skidding halt. A little man, so smeared with oil and grease that it was difficult to distinguish his features, slid out from behind the wheel and approached the kitchen door, where Mr. Crombie was waiting for him.

"I'm Guernsey Le Bleu," he said in such a loud voice that Mr. Crombie instinctively took a step backward. "Bit deaf. Don't hear good. Bad ears. Barnhauser says old water pump's finally give out. Fell apart. Done in."

"When I bought this place they told me it was in first-class condition," shouted Mr. Crombie.

Mr. Le Bleu made a sound like a sheep that has bitten into some bad-tasting weeds. "Ain't been no good for years," he said. "Not much good when 'twas new. Pfui." He sat down on a box and pulled out a pipe which he proceeded to fill carefully from a dirty envelope.

"Got a nice place here," he said, "if you ever get it in shape. Last owners didn't care about nothin' but fishin' and huntin' and likkerin' up. Used to be good fishin' and huntin' around here. Not so good now. Too many people. Overpopulated. Was a time, though, when a man or a boy could go out . . ."

Half an hour later Mr. Le Bleu, having expounded at length on the past glories of the town of Highfield, was launched on a detailed description of the shortcomings of Sunset Hill's former owners. Mr. Crombie could find no suitable place to interrupt. Remembering what Mr. Barnhauser had said about Mr. Le Bleu's tendency to abandon his rocker if crossed up, he decided that the situation did not warrant taking any unnecessary chances. Finally sheer weariness, caused by leaning against the doorpost, made him desperate.

"What are you going to do about the pump?" he shouted. "We have no water."

Mr. Le Bleu frowned. He had obviously been crossed up. "Don't worry your head," he said. "Stop worryin'. Loosen up. Relax. I'll put in a stand-by for now. Take three-four weeks get a new one. Buncha drag-heels. Dopey. Dumb."

"Do you think we *have* to have a new pump?"

"Oh, sure. Three-four weeks. Then you get it. Good pump. A-1."

Mr. Le Bleu rose from the box reluctantly and removed a huge kit of tools from the rear seat of the Cadillac. "Tools," he said, stamping imaginary mud from his feet before entering the kitchen. "Morning, ma'am."

"Good morning," said Mrs. Crombie. "I do hope you're going to get us some water pretty soon."

"How much does a new pump cost?" shouted Mr. Crombie. But Mr. Le Bleu was already headed for the cellar stairs.

"Mighty pretty weather for June," he said, snapping on the stair light. "We'll have this bugger out in a jiffy. Right away. Quick."

Mr. Crombie followed him into the cellar. He watched Mr. Le Bleu for some time in silence.

"Can I get anything for this pump in trade?" he asked timidly.

Mr. Le Bleu, already furiously at work disconnecting pipes and unscrewing bolts, gave his sheep cry, which Mr. Crombie interpreted to mean that no one in his right mind would give him a nickel.

Mr. Crombie hoped there might be some mention of what the new pump was going to cost, but Mr. Le Bleu was so absorbed in ripping the old one apart and creating general chaos that it didn't seem to matter very much, so he went upstairs. Mr. Le Bleu made frequent trips to the Cadillac and each time he paused to shout a word of encouragement.

"Not long now. Pretty soon. Poco pronto. Lot of old junk down there."

He finally appeared wiping his hands on a bit of oily rag which he laid on the kitchen drainboard. "Think you got a leak in line to artesian," he said. "Can't tell. Don't know. Don't worry. Get it fixed quick. Ought to be pressure now in half-hour. If gauge don't go up to fifty pounds let me know. Somethin' wrong. Leak. Nice to meet you." He disappeared, leaving an oily smudge on the knob of the door.

"Well, I certainly hope that whatever it is goes up goes up," said Mrs. Crombie. "I never thought about water before. I always took it for granted. Turn on the tap and there it is waiting to leap out at you like that Moses affair. By the way, where *is* the artesian well?"

"I don't know," said Mr. Crombie miserably. "I just never thought to ask."

"Well, what does it *look* like? My idea of a well is a round place with a roof over it and a pulley—you know what I mean. Old-oaken-bucket stuff. There's certainly nothing like that around here."

"I think an artesian well is some kind of pipe," said Mr. Crombie, uncertainly. "We'll have to find out about that."

"Fine time to be finding out," snorted Mrs. Crombie. "Anyway, you tell that greaseball that we've got to have some water."

Mr. Crombie made frequent trips to the cellar. The wheel on the side of the little pump was whirling around at what seemed to him alarming speed, but there was no response from the pressure gauge. At the end of an hour he phoned Mr. Le Bleu. Mrs. Le Bleu didn't know where her husband was, but she'd tell him the minute he came in. No, she didn't know when he was coming home. She thought he was working on the school job.

Two hours later there was a smell of burning rubber from the cellar and shortly after that the little pump became silent. It was dark outside when Mr. Le Bleu finally appeared.

"Burned out my stand-by," he shouted. "Never mind. Old. No good. Leak somewhere." There was a hole high up in the cellar wall through which an assortment of pipes escaped into the darkness. Mr. Le Bleu produced a long flashlight, climbed up on a box and started to insert his body into the hole. It gave Mr. Crombie claustrophobia just to watch. "Where are you going?" he asked anxiously.

Mr. Le Bleu, already inside the hole, turned his head and looked under his arm. "Got to look at artesian well. Leak someplace. No compression. On the bum."

"Where *is* the well?"

Mr. Le Bleu slid back out of the hole. In the half-darkness of the cellar Mr. Crombie could only see the whites of his eyes shining like dim lamps in his blackened face.

"Used to be out behind house," he said. "When they built the new wing doggone architect built it right over well. It's right under one of them beds. Just dug a crawl space big enough for a snake. Too small. No good. Pfui."

He hoisted his body up to the hole once more and, like a lizard entering its cave, slowly disappeared. Mr. Crombie climbed up on the box and followed his progress by the reflected glow of the flashlight. The thought of Mr. Le Bleu entrapped under the floor of the downstairs spare room was disturbing. He would have to rip up the flooring to save him. How in the world did one rip up a floor? And if Mr. Le Bleu died in there . . .

"Are you all right?" he shouted.

There was no answer, but a distant metallic clanking indicated that at least the worst had not yet happened. Could it be that Mr. Le Bleu was signaling for help, the way trapped submarine crews hammered their S.O.S. messages on the side of the hull?

He almost shouted with pleasure when the light of Mr. Le Bleu's flashlight finally shone in his face, indicating that the return journey had commenced. In due course his dirt-smeared head appeared once more in the opening. "Take the flashlight," he said. "Got to turn 'round and come out way I went in. Backassward."

The man seemed to be made of rubber. As his feet touched the box, Mr. Crombie restrained an impulse to seize him by the hand and congratulate him on his escape.

"Foot valve's gone," said Mr. Le Bleu. "Rusted out. Rotted. Kefui."

"What's the foot valve?" shouted Mr. Crombie. He felt as if he might be going to throw up.

"Bottom o' the well. Pump sucks water through tube. Valve shuts. Else water runs right back into well. Understand? See? Nothin' to worry about."

"But what do we do now?"

"New valve," said Mr. Le Bleu. "Gotta pull old one out. Big job. Lotta work. Tough. Pipe's right under floor. Gotta dig a hole under foundation of house. Dig a little room under floor. See? Line it with concrete blocks so's we can git at it again if we hafta. Cut off pipe. Pull up foot valve. Not bad. Might be worse."

"But who's going to do all this?"

"Son-in-law," said Mr. Le Blue, promptly. "Mason. Plasterer. Good boy. Busy now on new school. Get him around soon's I can. Quick. Prompt."

"But what are we going to do for water?" There was a quaver in Mr. Crombie's voice.

Mr. Le Bleu pushed back his cap and scratched his head. "Well," he said, "neighbors'll be glad to lend you a few pails. Emergency. Everybody help. Got any place you could go?"

"We are going to New York tonight for a day or so," said Mr. Crombie, gloomily.

"That's it. New York. Have yourself a time. Gay white way. Relax. Enjoy it. Come back. All done. Finished. Complete. Good as new."

"But how much is all this going to *cost?*" asked Mr. Crombie.

Mr. Le Bleu was gathering up his tools. "Son-in-law's just had a baby," he said. "Boy. Son. Got three nice kids. One's a little backward. Be all right. O.K. Mother's not so hot herself. Well, don't worry. All fixed up when you get back."

"Perhaps instead of coming back on Wednesday night we ought to stay in town until that awful man is sure everything's running right," said Mrs. Crombie. She seemed to accept this alternative quite philosophically.

"We'll give him a ring Wednesday," said Mr. Crombie.

When they phoned Mr. Le Bleu he was in fine spirits. "O.K.," he said cheerily. "All done. Fixed. New foot valve. Fine job. Last a lifetime. No more trouble. Had a little accident, though. Nothin' much. Little thing. Must have jarred house, poundin'. Living-room ceiling let go. Came down. Nothin' hurt. Just a couple little china things. Made the place a mite dirty. Moved furniture into dining room. Son-in-law's comin' tomorrow. Good plasterer. O.K. Top grade. Come back any time. Everythin' workin'. Hunkeydory. That old ceiling's been due to fall for years. Lucky you wasn't sittin' under it. Good break."

"If we stay in New York any longer," said Mr. Crombie, "that man will have the whole house flat on the ground. We're going back."

10

FOR THE NEXT FEW DAYS THEY ATE in the kitchen. Mr. Le Bleu's son-in-law, an enormous, Samsonesque young man, who always stripped to the waist before he commenced work, had built a low platform on the living-room floor which enabled him to reach the ceiling without the use of a ladder. The furniture, grey with plaster dust, had been moved into the dining room, where it lay piled, one piece on top of another.

"These are the days," said Mrs. Crombie, "to get everything else in the house set. Then, when Muscles gets through admiring his torso in the mirror, we can fix up the living room and we're in."

Each day they worked like galley slaves from early morning until the sun began to sink across the valley. Then they also sank, exhausted, into the big wooden chairs on the terrace to watch the western sky put on its evening show behind the hills. The valley was filled with a smoky haze. The silence was unbroken save for the sound of the brook gurgling nervously to itself as it hurried across the lawn to seek refuge in the woods.

"I can hardly believe it," he said. "A month ago I was a businessman; an office slave. Now I'm free; free as the birds. And we own this beautiful place. All that business about the well and the living-room ceiling has been a little discouraging, of course, but we were foolish to think that you can buy an old place like this and not find *something* the matter with it."

He tossed the ice cubes out of the two slender-stemmed glasses and filled them from the pitcher. Sipping contentedly, he gazed across the valley. "Pretty nice," he murmured. "Pretty nice." Whether he meant the view or the cocktail didn't really matter.

"It *is* lovely," agreed Mrs. Crombie. "You know, if it wasn't for cooking dinner and washing up afterward it would even be wonderful not having a maid."

"I know what you mean," said Mr. Crombie. "Eat whenever you want to."

"Providing you can find something to eat. I'm so tired, the thought of getting supper makes me ill."

Mr. Crombie sipped his martini with the expression of a man weighing a heavy problem. "There must be some stuff in the icebox that doesn't need cooking," he said. "I'm so stiff from wrassling junk in that barn that all I want is a couple of these and a hot bath."

She sank back in her chair as if Mr. Crombie's remark had relieved her of further responsibility. They sat in silence watching the valley shadows grow deeper. She made a sudden slap at her forehead. "Don't tell me," she said. "If there are mosquitoes in this place I can't bear it."

"I haven't felt any," said Mr. Crombie. "Imagination, I guess. Psychosomatic. I asked Barnhauser about them when we bought the house and he said most of the natives up here didn't know what mosquitoes were." A moment later he slapped his ear violently and then his ankle. "Good gracious," he said, " the place is alive with them—all of a sudden."

"Where in the world did they *come* from? Hold still, there's one on your forehead." She fetched Mr. Crombie a slap that sent half the contents of his glass over the stones of the terrace.

"Sorry," she said. "We can't stay out here, that's certain. Let's finish our drinks in the kitchen."

They sat dejectedly on either side of the metal kitchen table.

"The one thing we bought this place for was that view," said Mr. Crombie, "and now we can only look at it through the window on account of the goddam mosquitoes."

She did not reply for several minutes. "Do you know what I'm afraid we'll have to do?" she said finally. "We'll have to build a screen porch on part of the terrace. Then we could sit there in any kind of weather, regardless of mosquitoes or tornadoes or what disasters have you."

"We could *eat* out there, too," he said, turning the idea over in his mind. "That might be pretty good."

"Yes, and if you give a cocktail party and it starts to rain you don't have to herd people into a hot, stuffy house like cattle."

"We could build a chimney at one end for cookouts," he said.

"And then *you* could do the cooking. Men *always* do the cooking outdoors. You could have a big apron with funny jokes written all over it and I'd never have to go near that damn stove again."

"I've always thought I'd like to be able to cook a few things well," he said. "Specialties. You know."

"I wonder who does that kind of work around here?" she said.

"What kind of work? Specialties?"

"Building screen porches."

"Mr. Le Bleu's son-in-law, I suppose. I'd like to get this out of the family, though, so we can be sure that while one relative is working he doesn't bust something up for the next relative to fix. I'll check up on it. I met an awfully nice fellow down in the village today. Name of Battle—Oswald Battle. Came here for his health about thirty years ago. Runs a little antique shop, but I guess it's mostly to give him a place to get away from his wife. He's a great talker. Knows everybody. I'll check with him tomorrow."

"Don't go hog wild," she said, picking up the pitcher and the glasses. "We seem to be running up quite a lot of expense. Well, I suppose if we're going to eat we'd better face it—unless you just want a hot bath, the way you said."

//

MR. BATTLE WAS ENTHUSIASTIC about the idea. He not only knew of a contractor who would be just the man for building a screened porch, but he also thought he might possibly be able to lay his hands on some porch furniture of distinction. He had in mind a chap by the name of Charlie Crumb to do the building. Quite an unusual fellow. Something of an architect. Another place he'd save money. (Mr. Crombie couldn't remember hearing about the first place.) Well-read fellow, too. Quite a philosopher. Mr. Battle would bring him around that afternoon.

The two of them arrived just about cocktail time. During

the day Mr. and Mrs. Crombie had moved the furniture back into the living room. "I guess we'll have to sit inside on account of the mosquitoes," she apologized.

"Looks like a good place to sit," said Mr. Crumb, sinking into Mr. Crombie's favorite chair. He was a frail, wispy little man with a bulbous forehead who looked more like a professor from a small-time college than a contractor. Mr. Crombie came in carrying a tray with four glasses.

"Nothing for me," said Mr. Crumb, holding up his hand like a traffic cop. "Hardly ever touch it and we're only going to stay a minute. I got to get home to supper."

"Same with me," said Mr. Battle. "My old lady'll be tearing her hair out wondering what's become of me. Great worrier, Mrs. Battle."

"Why don't you telephone your wives and tell them to come over?" suggested Mrs. Crombie.

"Oh, *no*," said Mr. Battle in alarm. "No, that wouldn't do at all. I'll just take a little one and hurry along."

"That's me, too," said Mr. Crumb. "Just a little one for sociability's sake."

Mr. Crombie gave them each a brimming glass and they settled back contentedly.

"It's very good of Mr. Battle to bring you over," said Mr. Crombie. "We've been thinking about adding a screen porch. . . ."

"Do you remember that screen porch of old Mrs. Meadows?" asked Mr. Crumb, addressing his question to no one in particular. "The screening got so old it rusted out, so her husband took it off entirely. But he didn't say nothing to the old lady. She didn't see so good and she set great store by that screen porch."

"Well, sir, she never noticed the screenin' was gone and she used to set out there every evenin' an' the funny thing was that the mosquitoes had become so used to the screenin' that they just assumed it was still there and never tried to come in."

Mrs. Crombie was too absorbed in her immediate problems to appreciate this bit of folklore. "Do you have mosquitoes here all summer?" she asked.

"Oh, lordy, yes," said Mr. Crumb. "But that Meadows outfit were a queer lot. They had a daughter. . . ."

By seven-thirty Mr. Crombie had taken the martini pitcher out to the kitchen twice. From time to time he tried to bring up the subject of the porch, but Mr. Crumb and Mr. Battle were too busy discussing their intimate friends and neighbors, most of whom appeared to be either fools or knaves.

The phone rang. "It's for you, Mr. Battle," said Mrs. Crombie.

"Oh, my, my," he said nervously, "it's probably Mrs. Battle. I know it is. Won't you tell her we've just left and I'll be home in about five minutes?"

"But we haven't talked about the porch," said Mr. Crombie.

Mr. Crumb gave him a puzzled look as if trying to recall something. "Oh, the porch," he said, his face relaxing. "I'll be up in the morning with my stone mason an' we'll take the measurements."

"But I've got to know what it's going to cost before we go ahead."

"Absolutely," said Mr. Crumb. "Sound business. We'll do it on a cost-plus basis. That's the best way on a job like this where you don't know just what you're runnin' into. Saves *you* money. Saves *me* money."

"I'll tell you one thing," said Mr. Battle. "I'll vouch for this fellow being the honestest guy in the valley."

"That ain't necessarily sayin' much," said Mr. Crumb. They both gave hearty exit laughs and prepared to leave.

"Come on," urged Mr. Battle. "I'm going to get hell."

"What you worryin' about," said Mr. Crumb. "You'd get hell anyways."

12

MR. CRUMB AND HIS ASSISTANT appeared the next morning while Mr. and Mrs. Crombie were having breakfast. Mr. Crumb introduced Mr. Salvatore, who shook hands all around.

"We don't want to disturb you folks," said Mr. Crumb. "Just tell us where you want the porch an' we'll go out and have a look around."

"We want to put it right off the end of the living room, where the terrace is," said Mrs. Crombie.

"Datsa good place," said Mr. Salvatore, beaming amiably. "Maka fine porch. All terrazzo."

"We don't *want* terrazzo. We want to use the same kind of flagstone that is on the terrace now."

Mr. Salvatore looked hurt. "No terrazzo?" he said.

"Those are details," interrupted Mr. Crumb. "We'll just go and measure things up."

The Crombies finished their breakfast hastily. "Let's get out there," said Mrs. Crombie, "before they begin building it out of concrete, encrusted with seashells."

Little stakes had been driven at each corner of the terrace. Mr. Salvatore was stretching a white string between them. "We're goin' to pull up all this old stone and give you something nice," said Mr. Crumb. "This stuff is no good. Old field stone, most of it."

"But we *like* it," said Mrs. Crombie, "and besides we don't want a porch as big as the terrace."

"We just want a small porch where we can sit and maybe eat, with a chimney at one end so we can cook out," added Mr. Crombie.

"Cozy porch?" said Mr. Salvatore, obviously puzzled. "Can't usa these stone anyway. Gotta build platform two-three inches high so'sa water can't run in. Maka nice floor. Different colored stones . . ."

"But we don't want different colored stones," said Mr. Crombie. "Just plain flagstones laid in concrete. Plain. Understand? Plain flagstones. The whole thing shouldn't be more than so big." He paced it off. "How much do you estimate for that?"

Mr. Crumb, obviously disgruntled to find the job diminishing to chicken-coop proportions, figured rapidly for several minutes on an old envelope. "About $3,000," he said, "maybe more, maybe less. We'll do it cost-plus, then you won't have to worry."

"*Three thousand dollars!*" cried Mr. Crombie, dismayed.

"What amount did you have in mind?" asked Mr. Crumb coldly.

Mr. Crombie looked despondent. "I guess I didn't have anything in mind," he admitted. "I just can't keep up with the world." Mr. Crumb relaxed. "Time was when you could build a little *cottage* for three thousand dollars."

Mr. Crumb and Mr. Salvatore, concluding that this must be some kind of a crazy city dweller's joke, laughed politely. "While you're at it," said Mr. Crumb, "you might as well have nylon screening. Latest thing. Practically invisible. Never rusts."

"That would be nice," said Mrs. Crombie. "Screen porches always make me feel as if I was in a cage."

"We'll use hand-split shingles on the roof like is on the

house and hand-hewn beams doctored up to look old like the rest of the house."

The Crombies agreed this would also be nice. "And we can cut an entrance right into your livin' room here. Look nice with a Dutch door. And then you'll need lightin'. Base plugs all round and some kind of a handsome fixture comin' down from the ridgepole. Old wagon wheel. You know. I think I can lay my hands on a beauty. And carriage lamps either side of the door goin' out to the terrace. Got a fine pair at the shop."

"Gotta put some drains on terrace," said Mr. Salvatore, "elsa water back up. Gotta dig a dry well."

"Won't all that cost an awful lot of money?" asked Mr. Crombie.

"Gracious no," said Mr. Crumb, reassuringly. "What I always say is, if you're goin' to have somethin' then have somethin' good, not somethin' you'll be ashamed of."

"Datsa right," nodded Mr. Salvatore. "We builda da fine porch. You no be 'shamed."

"How long will it take?" asked Mr. Crombie, feeling like a bug whirling helplessly toward a drainpipe.

Mr. Crumb scratched his head and looked appraisingly at Mr. Salvatore. "Well, let's see. I'm tied up a while on the school job, but I guess Sam here could go to work right away. You can't build the porch till you build the foundations."

When they had gone, Mrs. Crombie dropped into a chair on the terrace. Mr. Crombie paced nervously back and forth over the despised field stones. "Listen, dear," she said. "Don't get so upset. This isn't just a whim. We *have* to have a porch."

"Nobody's had to have a porch up to now and the house has been here for a hundred and seventy years," he said. "Why do *we* have to be the fall guys?"

"Well, the people before us must have had citronella for blood," she said. "I tell you a porch is a must, Gray. We've put a lot of money into this house and we certainly want to be able to sit outside without being eaten alive. What's a few thousand dollars after all you've poured into it?"

He looked at her incredulously and was about to say something, but changed his mind. "I'm going to clear out some more of that rubbish behind the barn," he said, finally. "If we're going broke, we might as well be tidy about it."

13

A WEEK LATER MR. LE BLEU appeared in his Cadillac. Mr. Salvatore and two assistants were busy making a mess of the formerly neat terrace.

"Addin' on?" asked Mr. Le Bleu, hopefully. "Buildin' somethin'? Expandin'?"

"No, no, just a little screened porch," said Mr. Crombie casually, hoping to dispel any notions that might be forming in Mr. Le Bleu's mind that the village had discovered a new Comstock lode.

Mr. Le Bleu nodded. "Come to check furnace," he said. "Clean out tubes. Boiler. Go over compressor. Ain't been done for years. Poor economy. Don't pay."

He disappeared into the cellar, emerging from time to time to fetch additional supplies from the Cadillac. It was late in the afternoon when he finally came up for the last time covered with black soot. "Judgin' by what I took out of the bugger," he shouted, "system ain't been cleaned since it was put in. All clear now. Drink out of it. Condenser's all shot, though. Get you a new one. Old condenser never was much good. New kind last you a lifetime. Lot of your couplin's wore out. Comin' back tomorrow."

He stood halfway through the kitchen door scratching his head while holding his greasy cap between his thumb and forefinger. Mr. Crombie had already learned that when Mr. Le Bleu hesitated something cataclysmic was apt to be in process of gestation. "Spose you know that furnace's too small," he said. "Been tellin' 'em that for years. Tryin' to save money. Economize. Pfui."

"What do you mean it's too small?" asked Mr. Crombie belligerently, but with a sinking heart.

"Don't get up enough steam. Like tryin' to heat the whole town with tea kettle. Heats old part O.K. Never goes round the corner into that bedroom in new wing. Might's well throw that room away, come cold weather. Seal it up. Raus mit it."

Mrs. Crombie moved into the conversation, dish towel in hand. "But they told us this whole house was warm as toast in the coldest weather. That room has three radiators in it."

"Pfui," said Mr. Le Bleu. "Ten radiators ain't no good, ain't no steam in 'em. Furnace's in wrong place. Oughta be over in other corner. Might help if I change all the valves. Old kind. Never was no good. Can't get at 'em anyway. All that panelin' around radiators. Gotta come tomorrow. Nice day. Too hot. Muggy."

"I wonder if it wouldn't be cheaper," said Mr. Crombie, when Mr. Le Bleu had departed in the Cadillac, "to get somebody from New York to pull this old wreck down and then build ourselves a split level."

"Darling, you always get so depressed when things don't

go just right. You know, I'm beginning to think that plumber has something the matter with his own valves."

"Anybody that hangs around this place long enough is bound to have," said Mr. Crombie.

14

HE WAS WEEDING THE FLOWER and bush beds outside the kitchen window. His neat mind had always looked forward to weeding a garden. One's business life was bound to be more or less overgrown with unfinished projects, loose ends, things which must be made to fit even though they didn't. And there was nothing you could do about it. By contrast, a garden offered something sharply defined, tangible, where through quiet concentration one might achieve at least a momentary perfection of clean brown earth and flowers. It was a perfection which did not last, of course, but its realization, if only for an instant, brought a sense of peace by restoring one's confidence in basic order.

If only they didn't have to go to New York every Monday evening. There was so much to be done around Sunset Hill that a man needed a ten-day week to do it all instead of the four or five days that they spent here. And even though they didn't start for the City until six o'clock in order to have a full working day, the preliminaries to starting seemed to carve out a large slice of the afternoon for some reason or other.

"Gray, if you're going off in the woods someplace be back here by four o'clock."

"Why four, dear, if we're not starting until six?"

"Because it takes you half an hour to let go what you are doing and the best part of an hour to scrub yourself and get into your store clothes and then you've got to pack your own overnight bag. I'm too busy."

"I don't see why you have to fuss so," he complained.

"Because I have to bring a lot of this food or it will spoil and I have to have some clothes in town and there's a mountain of stuff to go to the cleaners. Oh, don't try to understand. Just take my word for it and pack your own bag."

They had finally settled on an ancient tavern about half-way between Highfield and New York. The food was good, but the service was bad, as a result of which it was usually ten-thirty before they reached their destination at either end.

"It's like having a hundred and four evenings a year chopped off your life and thrown away," said Mrs. Crombie as she climbed wearily into bed at the end of the journey. "By the way, I found a note from Jane Marbury asking us to dinner on Thursday and to go to the theater afterward. Don't you think we could stay in Thursday and go back to the Hill Friday?"

"But that's what we did last week. We'll never get anything done——"

"Nonsense," she snorted, switching off her bed light, and in his heart he was inclined to agree with her. What it all added up to was that they lived in *two* places, each of which made full-time demands on them that must be met on a half-time basis.

15

THE CROMBIES HAD FRIENDS IN Litchfield, Connecticut, who were not only inveterate gardeners, but who also seemed to have solved the riddle of keeping perfection static. No weed was ever visible in their immaculate flower beds. For them grass grew like a lush carpet where grass was supposed to grow, but no blade had the temerity to encroach upon the areas where grass was taboo. The turf bordering the graveled walks was cut with ruler straightness and even the trees co-operated in the general discipline by failing to develop any dead branches.

These were the standards that Mr. Crombie had set for himself, but they were not easy to live up to. In fact, like everything else in this new life, simple things, like weeding, seemed to be full of technical problems which only experts could solve.

For instance, there was the matter of those little green shoots which were always popping out of the earth. If one pulled them up they proved to be flowers. If one let them continue popping, they popped as weeds. Grass also had an irritating way of sprouting right in the midst of things that properly belonged there, as a result of which it had to be plucked out blade by blade.

Then, again, it was quiet and peaceful to sit on the grass with outstretched legs and weed the *front* portion of a bed, but when one came to grips with the rear areas the situation was quite different. Sitting down was then obviously out of the question. You had to stand, legs apart, bent over like a grazing giraffe. Giraffes, however, were used to this sort of thing. They were brought up that way. But after fifteen minutes the effect on retired men was excruciatingly painful.

Bushes presented their own particular problems. They were a natural sanctuary, for instance, for last fall's dried leaves which, with the solicitude of a brooding hen, they cradled tenderly in the forks of their inner branches. The only way to get them out was to lie flat on one's face and reach under with clawing fingers. Each handful removed disclosed a new nest nearer the center and when you pulled yourself stiffly to your feet, it was usually to discover that you had been lying on a clump of iris.

It was the edging, however, which really defeated him. No matter how carefully he stretched his strings, his half-moon cutter would eventually tear out a clod of weeds, leaving a deep nick in the nice straight edge. Each time he was forced to cut back a little farther in order to straighten out former blemishes. It was quite apparent that even at this slow rate of attrition the entire property must ultimately be reduced to one great flower bed.

On this particular morning, as he grubbed for crumbling leaves between the back of a lilac bush and the foundations of the house, his pre-retirement philosophy about gardening began to undergo a subtle change. Instead of symbolizing basic order, it occurred to him that man was the only living creature which fought nature in this absurd way. The birds and the beasts accepted things as they were and utilized them in their daily lives. The little creatures of the forest and fields didn't run themselves ragged trying to remove dead leaves from under bushes or pulling up weeds from the meadows. All these things belonged where nature had placed them and man merely proved what a muttonhead he was by stubbornly refusing to acknowledge this obvious fact.

Thus bemused he heard a voice issuing through the screen of the kitchen window like a muted radio. "Gray, where are you? Gray. For heaven's sake. There's a woman coming up the driveway in a convertible. She's getting out. She's dressed up like Astor's pet horse. Come quick!"

Welcoming the excuse to stand upright, Mr. Crombie placed his garden tools in the basket and walked around the end of the house. His face was covered with grime through which rivulets of sweat had cut brown channels. His hands and clothes were smeared with damp earth and there were broken leaves in his hair. Mrs. Crombie in a torn sweater, her hair disheveled, was talking to a smartly dressed woman just outside the kitchen door. As she saw Mr. Crombie rounding the corner her face became so contorted by dismay that the stranger turned to ascertain the cause.

"Oh, Gray," she said accusingly, "this is Mrs. Partridge."

"*Miss* Partridge," corrected the lady.

"Of course. I'm so sorry. Miss Partridge is being kind enough to call on us. She lives right over the hill." She waved her hand vaguely. "I can't tell you how embarrassed I am, Miss Partridge, to have you find us in this condition. You see, we have no maid. . . ."

"I have no maid, either," said Miss Partridge in a tone which indicated that in spite of this she did not go around looking like a comedy tramp. One fleeting but nonetheless comprehensive appraisal of her trim tweeds had already told Mrs. Crombie what Miss Partridge's kitchen, house, garden and daily life were like. She belonged to the cool ones.

"We really aren't quite settled yet, but you must come in. The house is a mess—but we love the dear old place already," she added, hastily, sensing that when one lived in a town like Highfield one loved old houses. "I'll go around and open the front door for you."

"Not at all," said Miss Partridge, crisply. "I *always* come in through the kitchen. Everyone in Highfield comes in through the kitchen." She walked through the cluttered confusion and Mrs. Crombie was miserably aware that no detail escaped her guest's keen eyes.

"For heaven's sake go and wash," she hissed. "We'll be in the living room, dear," she said, more loudly.

Miss Partridge sat stiffly on the edge of the sofa and took a swift inventory of the room. "You have some nice things," she said graciously. "Is that table old?"

"I'm afraid not," said Mrs. Crombie. "It's a reproduction we bought just after we were married."

Miss Partridge lost interest. "What in the world is that platform affair you're building at the end of the house?" she asked.

"That's going to be a screened porch," said Mrs. Crombie, eagerly. "We're going to cut a doorway leading to it in that corner of the living room. We're thrilled about it."

"A screened *porch?*" Miss Partridge's disbelieving voice could not have been more incredulous if Mrs. Crombie had said they were building a "two holer." "This is a New England Historical Society marked house, you know."

"I know," said Mrs. Crombie, "we're very proud of that." Her face fell. "Isn't it all right to build a screened porch on a New England Historical Society marked house?"

"Well, if you want me to be frank," said Miss Partridge, "it doesn't quite belong."

"But the mosquitoes in the evening . . ." Mrs. Crombie's voice broke.

"There were mosquitoes here when all these old houses were built," said Miss Partridge, "but people didn't put on screened porches. It's your house, of course, to do with as you want and it's presumptuous of me to even mention it, but I'm afraid Highfield people all feel they have a kind of proprietary interest in these old places. You'll probably hear a few squawks, but just don't pay any attention to them. You've got to go ahead now, with the foundation half done. People know you're new here and they'll understand."

Mrs. Crombie was crushed. "I couldn't be sorrier," she said. "We never thought. We wanted a place where we could sit out in the evenings and maybe eat out occasionally. We just never thought about what it would do to the house."

"Don't bother your head about it," said Miss Partridge. "When people see it they'll probably all build screened porches on *their* houses. This is just a fussy, ingrown old town, that's all. You know there's a saying around here that in most communities a house is a home, but in Highfield it's a profession. Could we look around a bit? I know the place so well I'd like to see how you've fixed it up."

At the head of the stairs they could hear Mr. Crombie singing in the shower. "This is our bedroom," said Mrs. Crombie. "We love it. It's so big. And in the morning the sun just *floods* in."

Miss Partridge seated herself in a chair by the window. "This room hasn't changed one iota since Alice died in it. You didn't know Alice Clayton, did you? Of course not. She was my closest friend. This was her room. I used to come in every day during those last awful months. The Claytons were one of the oldest families in Highfield. Alice's great-grandfather . . ." She lost herself in the chronicles of the Clayton family. Mrs. Crombie sat uneasily on the edge of the bed, wishing Graham wouldn't bellow so in bathrooms just because they made his voice resonant.

". . . and then one day the end came while I was sitting just where I am now." Miss Partridge, overcome, began pawing through her handbag. Mrs. Crombie handed her a paper handkerchief from a box on the bedside table. At that moment the bathroom door opened and Mr. Crombie, still singing, strode into the room in the starko.

Miss Partridge gave out something between a sob and

a gasp. "Good God," said Mr. Crombie simply. Turning with dignity he re-entered the bathroom and shut the door softly.

"Don't worry about it another minute," said Miss Partridge as Mrs. Crombie followed her to her car. "I shouldn't have dropped in at this time of day without letting you know. Highfield is a great place for calling, though, especially on new neighbors. I'll give you a ring soon and put on a little dinner so you can get acquainted with some of the nice people who live around here. Say good-by to Mr. Crombie. I'm sorry I didn't see more of him."

16

MISS PARTRIDGE WAS RIGHT. Highfield was a great place for calling. Mr. Crombie learned to keep an eye out for strange, shiny automobiles. When he saw one turn in the drive he hid in the woods, if possible, like some shy creature of the forest. Finding a comfortable place under a tree and ignoring his wife's calls, he would lie drowsing and watching until the visitor went away, after which he would reappear casually around the corner of the barn, dragging some object to indicate that he had been busy in a remote part of the property.

Gradually the inhabitants of Highfield and its vicinity began to emerge as individuals. There were not too many of them and all were gregarious, with the result that life was settling rapidly into a pattern of dinner and bridge evenings.

"Good Lord," said Mrs. Crombie. "New York was a lonely wilderness compared to this place."

"What bothers me is how we're ever going to pay back all these people," said Mrs. Crombie. "I'm sure of one thing and that is I'm not going to put on a dinner party and cook it myself. We've ruined ourselves enough already by building this porch."

"There must be somebody that will come in and cook."

"I'm going to find out," she said, "and if there isn't we'd better put the house on the market."

Several days passed, then as they sat resting for a moment on Mr. Salvatore's stone platform, like actors in a tableau, Mrs. Crombie brought up the subject again. "There are *two* cooks," she said. "Two. In the *whole* village. One is Mrs. Frankenthal and the other is Mrs. Peabody. And don't think for one minute that you can pick first one and then the other. It's like two clubs. Mrs. Frankenthal heads one club and Mrs. Peabody the other, and if you choose one and she isn't available you don't go poaching in the other gang's territory."

"Sounds like the makings of a good rumble," said Mr. Crombie. "Which gang are you joining?"

"There's no question of that," she said. "Miss Partridge decided it for us. She called Mrs. Frankenthal to tell her that we were regular."

"Then we don't have to have letters of recommendation?"

"Not with Miss Partridge around. Now I think we ought to build a dinner around the Morris Clements. They're awfully nice and they've asked us for dinner twice. I'll try and work it for next week."

"Better nail down Mrs. Whosis first," he advised.

"Oh, I will. Don't worry."

17

. THE FOLLOWING DAY AFTER A
morning spent in the jungle behind the barn, he staggered
wearily back to the house for lunch. He had postponed his
regular morning schedule until this major chore was done.
The clearing out of this relatively unimportant area had
become an obsession with him. It was like a gladiatorial contest in which one or the other contestant must perish and it
sometimes seemed to him that the cards had been stacked
before the show started.

As he whacked away at the brambles, the sweat running
into his eyes, his muscles aching from the unaccustomed
demands being made upon them, his heart pounding, he
envisaged the day when his body would be discovered lying
face down in a clump of poison ivy. "Mr. Graham Crombie of
Sunset Hill, Highfield, who has been missing from his home
for several days, was found this morning in his wood lot (that
was better than 'behind the barn'), where he had been working when he was overcome. . . ." He swung his Sears
Roebuck machete savagely at the base of a clump of brambles.

"Mr. Crombie was a latecomer to Highfield, but he had
already won the affection and respect of the entire community. . . ." He heard the sound of organ music and a great
sadness welled up within him as he struck another blow with
the machete.

Now, as he approached the house, the vision of an ice-cold

martini drove all other thoughts from his mind. He realized
that it had been playing around in the back of his consciousness for the last half hour. He'd better watch out. When
retired men began to hit the stuff they were apt to act like
South Sea characters in a Conrad novel. What bunk! He
used to take a drink before lunch when he was in business
without all this flimflam. Ah, but then he was entertaining
some customer. All right. Now he was entertaining Jinny and
if it put him to sleep most of the afternoon he couldn't think
of a more delightful prospect. Wasn't he a free man? His step
quickened.

He went to the little portable bar that had been set up in
the corner of the dining room. "Gray, don't tell me you're
going to start making those things regularly in the middle of
the day!" That was one of the troubles with being retired. In
the old days he had been his own master from the time he left
the house in the morning until he came home at night.

"I'm exhausted," he said.

"You'll be more exhausted after a couple of those."

"Good," he said. "Then I take it you're not going to join
me."

"Oh, I don't care—I suppose if you're going to have one
. . ."

"Don't have one to please me," he said. "This stuff is white
gold." Why was it that so many women acted as if they were
doing you a favor by drinking sixty cents' worth of your
liquor?

They sat on either side of the kitchen table. "Wait till I
tell you about our dinner party," she said. "I called Mrs.
Frankenthal first. She only works out on Saturdays now because she's going to take some kind of a day job in one of
those little modernistic factories down in the valley. She was
booked up this Saturday and the next, but she'd be glad to
come the Saturday after *that,* if you please. So I nailed her
down and called Mary Clement.

"Now here's where the story begins to get good. Mary said —get this—Mary said she couldn't be sorrier, but she'd *just* engaged Mrs. Peabody to cook for her on that night on account of some people coming from New York for the weekend.

"So I got her to save the *next* Saturday. Then I called back Mrs. Frankenthal and believe it or not she was free. So I called Mary back and clinched the deal and then I got those attractive Bakers who have been so nice to us, and Miss Partridge, and that deaf old Mr. Fogarty. He likes to play bridge because when people sit around and talk he doesn't know what they're saying. So now we're giving a quiet little d᷉ ner for eight people *three weeks from Saturday.*"

Mr. Crombie looked distressed. "I thought things would be simpler in the country. You know—I thought we'd be able to call people around five in the afternoon and say 'Why don't you drop over and have a bite with us?' That's the way I'd like to live."

"Well, it isn't the way I want to," said Mrs. Crombie. "Not when I have to do the cooking."

18

THE INTERVENING WEEKS PASSED quickly. "Good Lord," exclaimed Mrs. Crombie. "I completely forgot we have that doggone dinner party coming up on Saturday."

"Who's coming?" asked Mr. Crombie.

"I'll have to look it up."

"Better phone them. They've probably forgotten by now."

"Or they might have the year wrong," she said.

On the Saturday morning of the dinner, the phone rang while they were at breakfast. It was Mary Clement. "I couldn't be sorrier, my dear, but Morris and I are both in bed with some kind of a flu virus. We're just able to crawl around enough to keep from starving, but we couldn't *possibly* go out tonight. No, dear, there isn't a chance. If you could see us you wouldn't want us."

There were tears in Mrs. Crombie's voice as she replaced the receiver. "There goes my party," she said. "We gave it for the Clements."

"Get somebody else," said Mr. Crombie reassuringly. "You can get somebody else."

She shook her head dubiously. "I'll try," she said, "but at this late hour . . ."

It was a rainy, raw day. He spent the morning in his library catching up on his mail. At eleven o'clock Mrs. Crombie appeared, in obvious distress. "Old Mr. Fogarty was going up the front steps of his house this morning and they came away from the porch and he landed on his back and sprained his ankle."

"How do you do a thing like that?" he asked. "He must be a retired acrobat."

"I couldn't care less. All I know is the old mummy can't come for dinner tonight. The only people I could get to fill in for the Clements were the Penlocks. They're terrible and we certainly owe them nothing, but if you're going to give a party you have to have guests."

"Never heard of them."

"Oh, yes you have—we've met them half a dozen times. Now we're only going to have *one* table of bridge and you can talk to the Penlocks. They play so badly you ought to be glad."

An hour later the Bakers fell out. The virus was spreading. But the accommodating Penlocks immediately came through with two unexpected house guests.

"It would be much easier," said Mr. Crombie that night after they had poured out the Penlocks and their house guests, speeded the obviously critical Miss Partridge on her way, paid Mrs. Frankenthal and locked the house for the night, "if, in the country, where the simplest things are complicated, we could send a check to people whom we owe for hospitality instead of paying them in kind."

"It would be even easier," said Mrs. Crombie, cryptically, "if the country was filled with country people and the city with city people and never the twain . . . never, never, never."

19

It sometimes seemed to Mr. Crombie that retirement was like getting married all over again. Both parties were forced to make as many adjustments as a bride and groom. Ever since their marriage, for example, Mr. Crombie had been leaving the house at eight-thirty each morning and returning some time before dinner. During the intervening nine or ten hours he and Jinny lived in separate worlds. Of course, they discussed happenings of mutual inter-

est when they came together in the evening, but their daylight
hours were nonetheless independent because of that.

This schedule was so usual in any New York businessman's
life that neither of them had ever thought much about it. It
was taken for granted that a businessman should spend approximately nine hours a day away from home. In addition to
that, both parties to the marriage contract normally devoted
another eight or nine hours to the business of sleeping, including going to bed and getting up. They were thus left
approximately six hours of each day for connubial bliss of
what might be called the more routine sort. When one looked
at it that way and realized that marriage only affected about
twenty-five per cent of one's life, it was hard to understand
why people had so much difficulty with it.

Both he and Jinny had welcomed the opportunity which
retirement afforded them to spend more time together, but
they were soon aware of the fact that just because of this,
each one had lost something that they had valued more highly
than they realized.

Jinny had never asked him to account for his time away
from home. If he didn't get back to the apartment until seven
she was glad to see him and that was that. He, in turn, never
asked her where she had been. It was a mutual, tacit agreement between them, a warranty of freedom, and it had worked
for forty-two years.

During his courting days she had been one of the most
popular girls in Cleveland. Even after he had won the long,
competitive race he had gone through agonies of doubt when
she was out of his sight. Try as he would, he could not help
questioning her anxiously as to where she had been and with
whom—above all, with whom—until one day she put her arms
around his neck and said, "Darling, you ought to know by
this time that I love you. If you don't, you're dumber than I
think. But don't ever try to build fences around me and I'll

never build them around you. If I have to hold someone with fences, I don't want them and I don't believe you do, either." They had never referred to the matter again.

It was one thing, however, to be away all day, engrossed in the scrambled activities of an active business life. Under those circumstances what one did in the late hours of the afternoon became no more important than what one did during the late hours of the morning. It would be an entirely different matter for a retired man to hang around the house all day and then suddenly disappear around five o'clock on an unexplained errand. There was no occasion for such eccentric actions in a town like Highfield, but it irked him to realize that had there been he would be obliged to account for it.

Although she never intimated it, Mrs. Crombie also missed the days when her dearly-beloved cleared out at eight-thirty each morning and she was free to chart her own course for the rest of the day without comment or criticism—days when she could go to the hairdresser without having to explain why it was necessary, why it took so long, or to listen to a satirical discourse on the amount of money which her hair had cost her since the unfortunate day when she took it out of pigtails.

"Why in the world you girls insist on calling them 'permanents' when they have to be done every few weeks is more than I can figure. And why can't women wash their own hair. I do. It's just a matter of standing under the shower and rubbing soap on it."

And when she came back from the supermarket and he helped her carry in the huge paper bags, he always looked for the cash-register slips. "Good God! Twenty dollars and eighty-five cents! What are we having, a banquet? I could take you to the top restaurant in New York for that."

"Darling, if you'd only let me run my department and you

run yours. This isn't tonight's dinner—these are staples that
we have to have in the house."

"Do we have to have frozen brownies?" He was unloading
the bags. "How do we know these people aren't overcharging
us? Do you ever go around to other stores and check their
prices?"

She made a despairing gesture with her hands. "No, I
don't go around to other stores checking prices. These people
are not cheating us. After buying food all these years I think
you might at least give me credit for knowing when I'm being
overcharged. And don't tell me again that if you ran your business this way it would have gone broke long ago."

There wasn't any question about it. She missed her old
freedoms; the ability to have lunch with a friend and talk
girl talk; the fast snack out of the refrigerator when lunch
was merely nourishment instead of a meal; the afternoons
spent wandering around Bergdorf's, Saks, Bloomingdale's and
the little side-street shops, just keeping in touch with things;
the silly hysterical afternoon bridge games at Susie Allen's,
the matinees, the casual five-o'clock drop-ins on friends where
you would always find amusing people. She missed these
things.

There was another side to the coin, however. Gradually,
Mr. Crombie began to get a new slant on what it takes to run
a house. As he watched Mrs. Crombie handle the countless
minute details involved in keeping two people alive under
modern conditions—the little daily stints of laundering, the
never-ending round of bed-making, room-straightening, food
preparation and the disposal of its messy aftermath, the tend-
ing of plants, the interminable letters—his admiration for her
ability mounted each day.

Jinny's life was devoted to keeping dozens of little things
going at the same time. He remembered an act that he had
seen once at Radio City Music Hall in which a young man

started two dozen dishes spinning on the tops of wobbly sticks lined up on a long table. As each dish slowed down and threatened to fall, he managed to reach it just in time to set it spinning again by rotating the sticks. That was Jinny's day —rushing from one plate to another, setting each in motion before it fell, then on to the next.

As a background to it all were the interruptions to which she seemed to be constantly subjected. He thought he knew all about interruptions, but the ones with which he was familiar at least had some slight relation to the business in which he was engaged. Jinny's interruptions were related to nothing. A young man from the Fuller Brush Company; a fresh-faced youth selling combined magazine subscriptions; a neighbor, choosing a moment when Jinny was up to her elbows in suds to pay a formal call; the amazing regularity with which her time-saving gadgets, the dishwasher, the vacuum cleaner, the washing machine, broke down and the hours she spent trying to persuade the repairman to come and set them in motion again.

Frequently he was pulled into these crises. "Gray, dear, the car is making the most horrible noise. It goes 'wheek, wheek' every time I let in the clutch and it almost stopped, coming up from the village. Won't you take it to Robbins Garage and find out what's the matter? We can't get stuck without *any* car. This is the night we're going over to Smithtown to have dinner with the Tuckers. We simply must buy a second car if we're going to live in the country."

Or, again, "I hate to keep interrupting you, but I haven't had a chance to do the marketing and now Mabel Harris is coming over to talk about the Community Chest and, knowing Mabel, the stores will all be closed before she gets through. Would you be a darling and slip down to the A & P and get the things on this list because we haven't anything to eat in the house."

"Dearest, the most terrible thing—I was letting the water out of the basin upstairs and all of a sudden a foul jet came jumping out of the drain hole and hit me right in the face. I called the plumber and he said it was the tile field which has been in for about fifty years. Only, the trouble is the man who put in the tile field is dead and nobody seems to know where it is, so won't you talk to the plumber, because the Curtises are coming for the weekend and we certainly don't want dirty water squirting in their faces."

As he lounged around Robbins Garage waiting for the car to be fixed, or stood patiently in line with his wire baby carriage waiting for a woman who had apparently bought food supplies for a polar expedition, or held long, technical discussions with the plumber, quite certain that neither one of them knew what he was talking about, but that it was sure to cost a lot—as he watched whole days get rubbed out standing around, waiting around, rushing around on futile errands, he occasionally wondered what would have happened if retirement hadn't occurred just when it did and released him for this kind of duty. Had he been obliged to go to the office, who would have done all these things? But he *didn't* have to go to the office so it was a rhetorical question. But what *did* men do who lived in the country and had to go to work each day?

20

I⊤ WAS SUNDAY NIGHT. THEY HAD just returned from playing bridge with the Bakers.

"What was the name of that odd creature with the beard?" asked Mrs. Crombie.

"Didn't you know? That was Professor Turner from the college. He teaches philosophy. Somebody told me he was quite a scholar. Written a lot of books and all that sort of thing. He asked us to drop in the next time we're over in Middleburg."

"Well, you can have him. I thought he was a terrible bore. All he talked to me about was what dreadful people his associates were."

Mr. Crombie looked disappointed. "It might be an opening into that college crowd," he said. "I've always thought it would be stimulating to get to know them."

"If Professor Turner's a sample . . . well, we're not going over tonight and I'm going to get some sleep. If we're driving to New York tomorrow I've got a bad day ahead of me. I wish to goodness we could stay put for a while so I could get something done around this place."

"So do I," he agreed. "Here we are at the end of three months and I haven't even started to set up my workshop in the cellar. Outside, the whole place still looks like an abandoned duck farm. I was going to do a lot of reading and I haven't cracked a book. I was going to do so *many* things. Where does the time go?" There was a trace of hysteria in his voice.

"I don't know, dear," she said soothingly, as to a small child who shows signs of a tantrum. "But you must remember that we've been through a whale of an adjustment. Four months ago you were living in a push-button world with a slave of a secretary and a highly organized office to back her up. Then you suddenly find yourself in a little country town where you have to do everything yourself. You're still groping for the push buttons and they just aren't there any more."

"I know all that," he said impatiently. "I *want* to do things myself. I also want to get my days under control."

"Why don't you then?" she asked impatiently. "It may make you happier."

"I intend to," he said. "From now on I'm going to spend the morning in my library. I don't want any interruptions. Just pretend I'm not here. If people phone, take the message. If they call, you attend to them. If the house catches fire, work it out with the Fire Department." He looked at her fiercely as if anticipating opposition, but she said nothing.

21

HE FINISHED HIS BREAKFAST quickly, scarcely bothering to look at the *Times*. "Good-by," he said, rising from the table. "See you at lunch."

The sun was shining through the windows of his little

library. From somewhere down in the valley came the distant whine of a power saw. A catbird called from the apple tree just outside. The world was alive. This was the way to start a day; everything in hand, incisive.

The first thing was to get the paper work out of the way. A pile of envelopes, most of them unopened, lay at the end of his table-desk. Probably bills. Those were bad enough, but not half as bad as the letters requiring answers. He hated writing longhand letters. It took him forever and nobody could read his handwriting. After dictating for thirty or forty years a man forgot how to write. How in the world did men like Benjamin Franklin and Thomas Jefferson carry on a massive correspondence with an old goose quill? And most of it just to exchange ideas!

He picked off the top envelope from the pile and ripped it open. It was from George Caulkins of the National Borum Company, enclosing a speech which he had made before some captive audience in Indianapolis. "The Death of Free Enterprise—a Murder, but No Mystery." George loved titles like that and he always thought the country was going to pieces.

"Dear Graham," George had written, "I am enclosing a copy of a little talk I gave to the Watrous Society in Indianapolis a few nights ago. I thought you might be interested. Unless we want the Democrats to eliminate free enterprise in this country, we must all put our shoulder to the wheel.

"Do let me know what you think of my little effort."

In the old days when George's company had been one of his best customers Mr. Crombie would have dropped the speech into the wastebasket and written a long, laudatory letter. Now he dropped the letter in the basket and placed the speech on a pile of similar documents to be read at some future time. Being retired, he supposed it was important to keep up with these things.

His eye wandered through the open window to the plat-

form of the unfinished porch. At the point where it joined the
house he noticed a pile of rubble obviously left there by Mr.
Salvatore. Did that wop think that he, Mr. Crombie, was going to clear up his, Mr. Salvatore's mess? He made an angry
note on his scratch pad: "Crumb re mess."

The next few envelopes contained bills which he piled together neatly for future attention. Then there was a letter
from Frank Babbitt. Frank had proposed somebody for the
Club by the name of Otto Jenkins or Jensen. Why didn't
people write so you could read their letters. Would Mr. Crombie write a letter in Jenkins'/Jensen's behalf? He couldn't
remember anyone by either of those names. Better let that one
simmer. He placed it on a third pile which represented "Matters Pending."

The next one was from Gleason. He hoped that everything
was going well and wanted Mr. Crombie to know how much
everyone missed him. When Mr. Crombie was settled in his
new house, which Mr. Gleason had heard was charming
(heard from whom?), they hoped to see him more often
around the office (damned lie).

In the meanwhile, there was a wild Irishman by the name
of O'Kelley who was giving everyone a great deal of trouble.
He had a small account—very small indeed—and he was always asking for special favors and hanging around bothering
people. They knew that he was a friend of Mr. Crombie's,
but he had become such a nuisance that everyone felt he
should be told to take his business elsewhere and they had
about decided to do this. Of course, if Mr. Crombie felt
otherwise . . .

He laid the letter on the table and looked out across the
valley. O'Kelley had been a legacy. During the war he had
done something for Joe Loomis' son—saved his life somehow
or other. When O'Kelley inherited a little money, Joe had
asked Mr. Crombie, as a special favor, to take on the job of

handling it for him. You were always getting things like that thrown at you in the investment-counsel business. The man had been a headache, just as Gleason said, but over the years he had grown to like the bouncy little Irishman. Once he was cast adrift he'd lose his money in a year, but if the boys had decided out, then that was that.

Deep in thought, he turned instinctively to dictate a reply to Miss Parkinson, but there was no Miss Parkinson waiting with her notebook on her knee. An oppressive feeling of not belonging swept over him. He seemed to be sitting in some-body else's paneled room looking out through somebody else's window on a strange and alien world.

He would be in town tomorrow. After his directors' meet-ing he would drop in and see Gleason. At the same time he could get Miss Parkinson to find out who this fellow Jenkins or Jensen was?

More bills. If they didn't stop spending money they were going broke. Here was a letter from Henry Lee inviting him for dinner at the Club to say good-by to Fletcher Sands. Fletcher was leaving soon to take up his new job as Ambas-sador to Spain. That would be a good dinner. He knew just who would be there. But it was on a Friday night. He'd have to write Henry immediately and explain to him that although they came to town each week they always returned to the country on either Wednesday or Thursday night. They might make an exception, of course. What was the difference, when you stopped to think of it, whether they were in the country or the city? He'd speak to Jinny. Certainly he couldn't answer this now. He placed it on top of "Matters Pending."

He was bored. His eye wandered to his bookcases and noted that *Europe since 1815* was upside down. He got up and set it on its feet. Some day he wanted to read it again. Next to it stood *The Journals of Lewis and Clark*. He had asked for it for Christmas several years ago and never read it. He wondered how many of these books, that he claimed to love so much, were still unread. He began making a test count on the left-hand section. The door opened and Mrs. Crombie stuck her head in, timidly.

"I hate to do this to you, darling, but I really don't know what to do. It's that old Admiral Peterborough. He's got some banker with him who thinks he knows you. They insist on seeing you just to say hello."

"Why didn't you tell them I was out?"

"I did and they laughed at me and said they saw you through the window as they turned in the drive."

Mr. Crombie groaned dramatically. "The Admiral is showing his friend around the outside of the place," she said. "Maybe if you can keep them outdoors you can get rid of them quicker."

Half an hour later, having pushed the Admiral and his friend into the latter's decrepit sedan, he resumed his seat in the library. There were only a few more envelopes, all containing bills, which he placed with the others. Well, that took care of the paper work. Now for an hour or so of reading; something worthwhile, something with meat on it. He got up and walked over to the bookshelves. How about the Lewis and Clark *Journals?* He didn't feel like Lewis and Clark this morning. Let's see what else . . .

From the cellar beneath his feet there came the sound of pounding. The ancient windows rattled with each blow. For heaven's sake what was going on now? One might just as well try to read in the Grand Central Station. He went in search of Mrs. Crombie, but she was nowhere around and her car was gone. In its place stood Mr. Le Bleu's Cadillac. Mr. Crombie descended the cellar stairs with a sinking heart.

Mr. Le Bleu had removed the metal casing of the furnace and clamped a huge Stillson wrench to some gadget near the top. He was pounding the handle of the wrench with a ham-

mer. "Break the son of a bitch if I have to," he cried as Mr.
Crombie appeared in the circle of light cast by the hanging
bulb. "Bust it. To hell with it."

"What's the matter now?" yelled Mr. Crombie.

"Condenser. Wanta take it off. Ain't goin' to get steam with
this bugger. Too small. No good to begin with. Rusted out.
Kaput." He renewed his attack on the handle of the Stillson.
There was a sharp crack and Mr. Le Bleu almost fell into
Mr. Crombie's arms.

"Broke off," he shouted, triumphantly, holding up a jagged
piece of metal for Mr. Crombie's inspection. "Flaw. Bum
metal. Pfui. Have to drill the rest out. Take time. No hot
water till I get her fixed. Don't need it this weather. Good
thing we got at it before it turned cold. Lucky."

Mr. Crombie followed him dispiritedly up the stairs. "But
I don't understand," he said, "the furnace is perfectly all right.
Then you come in and break it and walk out."

"Break nothing," shouted Mr. Le Bleu. "Rotten metal. Furnace's no good. Never was. Won't heat house. Tell you what
—instead of fooling with it I'll give you estimate on new
furnace. Modern. Baseboard heating. Copper pipes. Back tomorrow."

He was out of the house and into the Cadillac before Mr.
Crombie could collect himself. "Get the hell out of here,"
he yelled as Mr. Le Bleu swung the car onto the road. "I
never want to see you on the place again." Mr. Le Bleu
nodded through the open window and disappeared in the direction of the village.

He phoned Barnhauser. "I fired that damn plumber you
sent me. He's nuts."

"Nuts?" said Br. Barnhauser, thoughtfully, as if weighing
the matter. "Sorry to hear that."

"Not as sorry as I am. He comes in here, breaks my furnace
and walks out. *Now* what are we going to do?"

"Yes, what *are* we going to do?" agreed Mr. Barnhauser in a tone which placed the whole responsibility on Mr. Crombie. "You see, the only *good* man in town is Henry Hopkins and he's tied up on the school job. He don't know where anything is on that place of yours, neither."

"What good does it do me to have someone who knows where things are if all he does is break them?"

Mr. Barnhauser made a clucking noise. "I'll drop down to the school an' see if I can persuade Henry to come over an' take a look. He's a good man. Awful busy, though."

Mr. Crombie went back to his library and sat at his table, idly drumming his fingers on its surface and staring out the window. He heard Mrs. Crombie return. She mustn't find him doing nothing. Better get at some reading. His nerves were too frayed for anything heavy. The world's great books could come later. He picked out a murder mystery that he had bought to read on a plane and then had slept all the way instead. *The Case of the Unknown Blonde;* that might be just right for today. Turning on the standing light beside his leather armchair, he started to read.

"Lunch," said Mrs. Crombie, opening the door. His morning in the library was over.

"Get a lot accomplished?" she asked cheerily as they munched their sandwiches in the living room.

"I'm almost nuts," he said.

"What's the matter, dear?"

"I fired the plumber."

"Mr. Le Bleu?" she asked, incredulously. "But, Gray. What are we going to do? He's here all the time. He's sort of a plumber-in-residence."

"Not any more, he isn't. He came in this morning, broke off the top of the furnace so we couldn't get any hot water, then said he'd get me an estimate on a new furnace and I threw him out."

She looked at him admiringly. "Oh, Gray, why did you do it while I was away and couldn't see it? But what in the world are we going to do without any hot water?"

"Mr. Barnhauser's working on that," said Mr. Crombie vaguely.

"Well, we go to New York this afternoon, so it doesn't really matter," she said cheerfully.

22

THE FOLLOWING DAY HE MADE HIS first visit to the office since he had walked out of it, a retired man, three months before.

As he entered the familiar elevator he felt as apprehensive as a debutante. The elevator door closed itself behind him with the firm efficiency of a door that tolerates no nonsense. "Floors, please," said the operator.

"Twelve," said Mr. Crombie. He was under the impression that the other people in the elevator were looking at him curiously. The operator pushed a number of buttons, then, relaxing against the side of the cab, he began to hum while he examined his passengers coldly as if they had been a collection of window dummies.

The elevator came to a stop, adjusting itself nervously to the floor level. One had the feeling that it was irritated at something and would speak its mind before the day was over. "Washstep," said the operator, interrupting his humming. Mr. Crombie did not move. "Twelve out. Washstep," said the operator, sharply.

"Oh," said Mr. Crombie, as one awakening from a nap. He was in the hall, standing outside the double doors of Crombie, Hamilton and Gardiner. Through the glass he could see old Penrose, the receptionist, bending over his desk, sorting cards as usual. He pushed open one of the doors and entered.

Old Penrose looked up, then, recognizing Mr. Crombie, he sprang to his feet and hurried around the desk. "Mr. Crombie, sir." Seizing Mr. Crombie's hand in both of his he wrung it warmly. "This is a great pleasure, sir. We've all missed you terribly. I suppose you'll want to see Mr. Gleason. He has somebody with him, but I'll let him know. How have you been, sir? You're looking well."

"I'm fine," he said. "Couldn't be better. You're looking pretty fit yourself, Penrose. Don't interrupt Gleason if he's busy. Is Miss Parkinson tied up?"

"I'll see, sir. She was with Mr. Gleason a few minutes ago."

Mr. Crombie sat down in one of the overstuffed leather chairs which flanked the round oak table in the reception room. How many times had he come out from his office to rescue customers from the depths of these chairs? *Business Week* and *Fortune* were still in their accustomed places on the table but *The New Yorker* was missing. It would be just like Gleason to have had *The New Yorker* removed. In a few minutes he heard a delighted little cry behind him.

"Mr. Crombie. I'm *so* glad. . . ."

He thought Miss Parkinson looked somewhat older, but after a certain age everybody looked somewhat older every time you saw them. He wondered if he looked somewhat older to Miss Parkinson.

"Come," she said. "You can sit in my office and talk to me until Mr. Gleason's through with his caller. He knows you're here."

She led the way as though he were a stranger. He sat down beside her typewriter desk. The door to his old office was shut. It made him feel vaguely uncomfortable.

"Who's with him?"

"I don't think you'd know her. She's a new client and as rich as an Arab sheik. But now tell me about yourself. How have you been? How is Mrs. Crombie?"

Mr. Crombie told her.

"And you like the country?"

"Crazy about it," said Mr. Crombie. There was a momentary silence. "Any changes around the office?" he asked.

She made a face. "Oh, it's not the same place without you, Mr. Crombie. Everybody hates it. Everything is run by committees now. Nobody can get any work done. They're always at some committee meeting. Some say it's because Mr. Gleason can't decide anything for himself. He can make rules, though. You didn't believe very much in office rules, but he can dream up a new one every few hours."

"What kind of rules?"

"Well, do you know that secretaries can't smoke any more except in the washrooms? That almost caused a palace revolution. And then there are no more coffee breaks. No more *coffee* breaks, mind you! And Old Penrose keeps a time card showing when everyone gets in in the morning and when they go home at night and how long they take for lunch. For lunch! How do you like that?"

Mr. Crombie was careful not to indicate, by the twitch of a facial muscle, *how* he liked it.

"There've been a lot of changes in the departments, too. The chart group and the economists have been put together in a new department. Tom Potter is in charge of it."

"You mean they put Tom Potter over Myron Crawford?"

She nodded. "We all feel so sorry for Mr. Crawford. It's taken the starch out of him."

"But Tom Potter isn't an economist—he's an account executive and a damned good one."

She shrugged her shoulders. "I know," she said. "Then they put all new business under young Partridge. He's supposed to co-ordinate it, or something. That broke Mr. Applegate's heart. Oh, there's been plenty of blood spilt."

"Any changes on the staff?"

"No. Just the usual come and go. You know, of course, that Mr. Buckley is due to retire in December."

The news gave him an unexpected glow of pleasure. So they were going to jettison Buckley, who thought he was so invaluable. He *was* one of the best technical men in the shop. One by one they'd all be dropped over the side and he hoped they'd like it. "Buckley's a good man," he said. "He'll be hard to replace."

She fingered the keys of her typewriter. "When the old crowd go, I don't know what's going to happen. I go out myself next year."

"You do, don't you? I'd forgotten that."

"You insisted on having women retire at sixty. Why, I could never understand, but there it is and out I go."

There was an uncomfortable silence.

"They threw poor old O'Kelley out," she said.

"They wrote me that they were thinking about it." (So they had acted without waiting for his opinion.)

"I felt sorry for the old fellow. He was pathetic when he came out of Gleason's—Mr. Gleason's—office. This was sort of his home."

"How about you?" he asked. "Are you getting along all right?"

"Oh, I get along," she said. "I know how to handle that situation. You know me on office politics. Never open your mouth except to eat and drink."

The inner door opened. A large woman came out, followed by Gleason.

"Oh, Graham. I'm so glad that you're here. I want you to meet Mrs. Pauling. This is Mr. Crombie, Mrs. Pauling—the person I was just telling you about."

"Who?" asked Mrs. Pauling.

"Mr. Graham Crombie—the founder of Crombie, Hamilton and Gardiner."

"Oh?" said Mrs. Pauling.

Having thus taken care of the amenities, she turned back to Mr. Gleason. "I'll expect to hear from you, then, by the end of the week." Nodding vaguely in the direction of Mr. Crombie, she hurried out.

"Well, Graham," said Mr. Gleason heartily, "come in. Come into your own office." He put his arm around Mr. Crombie's shoulders. "Same office. Nothing changed. Same pictures on the walls. Same furniture. We want to keep things the way you left them, Graham."

Mr. Crombie sat down in the visitor's chair beside his old desk. Mr. Gleason rather self-consciously pulled an odd chair over from the corner and sat down beside him. They chatted about various members of the staff, about Mr. Crombie's new life, about the market. As Mr. Crombie recalled the conversation later, there was much talk, but they really didn't *say* anything. Quite evidently Gleason had no problems requiring any advice from Mr. Crombie. Nor was he going to open himself up to gratuitous suggestions. He glanced at his wrist watch.

"Graham, I couldn't be more apologetic, but I have a meeting at eleven-thirty and I'm late now. Look here. All the boys will want to see you. Why don't you sit here at my—*your* desk and Miss Parkinson will get them in as you want them. . . ."

"No, no, Joe. I wouldn't feel comfortable doing that. This is your desk now. No, you run along to your meeting. I'll just wander around and say 'hello' to the ones who aren't busy."

Gleason, after a few harassed instructions to Miss Parkinson, scuttled off in the direction of the elevators. Mr. Crombie started down the long corridor past the row of private offices, each with its secretary standing guard at the door;

everything was precisely aligned, sterile, not a displaced paper clip to mark the fact that this was where two hundred human beings spent a large part of their lives. Myron Crawford was in his office, but he had a visitor. He saw Mr. Crombie and, excusing himself, hurried out to greet him. "Graham, it's grand to see you. We've all missed you so. I'm awfully sorry I'm tied up. Are you going to be around long? I want to chat with you."

"No," he said, "I'm on my way, but I'll be popping in from time to time. How are things going?" Then he remembered what Miss Parkinson had told him and wished he had not asked the question.

"Fine," said Crawford. "Everything's just fine. But we miss *you*, Graham. Well, if you're not around when I finish with this gentleman, don't forget to stop in and see me the next time you're in the office." He lowered his voice, conspiratorially. "This man at my desk is from Texas and I don't like to keep these oil tycoons waiting." They both laughed as if this was very funny and Myron Crawford went back to his Texan.

The next office was empty. Then came Bill Buckley, who was on the phone as usual. He had a secretary that Mr. Crombie had never seen before. "Will Mr. Buckley be long?" he asked.

"I'm afraid so," she said. "He's been on that call for fifteen minutes already and he sounds as if he were going to go on for quite a while."

Mr. Crombie nodded. "I won't wait," he said.

"Who shall I say called, sir?"

"Oh, nobody—it's not important."

He moved on.

Tom Potter was out. Partridge was out. Tom Bingham was working in a confusion of pamphlets and statistical charts scattered all over his huge oak desk. While Mr. Crombie stood hesitating in the doorway, Tom looked up and his face split into a wide grin.

"Graham, you old walrus, where in the world have you been hiding all these weeks? We were going to send out the Saint Bernards. Come in. Sit down. I couldn't be more delighted."

He had always liked Tom Bingham. There was nothing complex about him, although he had one of the best brains in the office. His words carried no double meanings. For the first time that morning Mr. Crombie felt at home as he sat beside Bingham's desk and listened to his booming voice.

Tom didn't give a hang about office politics. He had no operational ambitions. He lived in a slide-rule world; a world of decimal points and book values and times earnings. Things like salary and status he left to take care of themselves.

"Well, what's been going on?" asked Mr. Crombie. He wished he could start a conversation on some other note than "How's business?" but it seemed to be the one common denominator, the sole rope that still bound him to these men with whom he had worked for so many years, but who would be strangers the moment the rope was cast off.

"Oh, nothing special," said Bingham. "What we lose on the bananas we make on the oranges. Let's see—you were still here when we brought in the Snowden business, weren't you?"

"Never heard of it," said Mr. Crombie.

"Really, Graham? I can't believe it. That was an interesting show. California group. One of the hardest nuts we ever had to crack—and the biggest. But we cracked it and it's in. It's made us God's gift to the transcontinental airlines, though, and I think a few of our wives are going to divorce us."

He gave Mr. Crombie a quick summary of the Snowden picture, but Mr. Crombie was an inattentive listener. For thirty-five years he had prided himself on knowing every detail of the business—on following every thread of its complex

texture. Now, a few weeks after his retirement, he had lost
touch so completely that he didn't even know about its peaks.
This was a good example of the value of retired men as consultants.

Bingham was cordial and relaxed as always. Anyone could
see, however, that he was up to his neck in work. Mr. Crombie suddenly remembered the retirement bums who used to
plant themselves in the chair beside his desk just when he was
working against a deadline. They were so sure you were glad
to see them that you couldn't bear to hurt them, but they
never seemed to sense when a man was busy. He rose quickly
as Bingham finished, and when the latter protested, he mum-
bled something about a luncheon engagement.

As he wandered aimlessly down the hall, peering into the
empty offices, a girl came out of Mr. Applegate's office carrying a sheaf of papers. She was an exceptionally attractive girl
—not a girl at all, really, but a woman in her early forties. For
a moment he could not place her. Then he remembered—she
was the one in Statistics; the one who had done such brilliant
work that she had been made head of the department just before he left. For the life of him he could not remember her
name, but that was nothing strange; he couldn't remember
anyone's name these days.

She saw him and hurried toward him. "Mr. *Crombie*," she
said, "how wonderful! We've missed you so. We really have."
Everyone had told him how they had missed him, but this
young woman, whose name he couldn't recall, was the only
one that carried conviction in her voice.

"You look so *well*," she was saying, "as if you'd been living
out of doors all your life. And you've lost weight."

What more responsive chord could she have touched in a
man of sixty-five? Mr. Crombie unconsciously sucked in his
stomach and drew up his chest. A most attractive, blonde-
haired girl with laughter lines in the corners of her eyes—

what *was* her name? She had a particularly lovely, deep voice; a voice as confident as her level blue eyes, which seemed to be probing you while she talked. How odd that he had never really noticed her before.

"... ten years younger I'd say, at the least. Why is it that when people retire they immediately start looking younger? That would make a nice statistical study someday when we have nothing to do. But tell me. Where do you live and what do you do, now that you're on your own?"

"Well," he said, "we live near a funny little village called Highfield in a nice old house that was built in 1790 and looks out across a valley to a range of mountains."

"No wonder you look like a man whose days are crowded with pleasant things," she said. "You can tell the empty-day ones the minute they come into the office."

She leaned casually against a table littered with SEC reports, as if inviting the conversation to continue. What in the world was a girl like this doing in Statistics?

"I've never been so busy in my life," he said. "But I don't exactly know what at. I seem to be so tangled up with *things* that I don't have *time* to really do anything."

She smiled. "Page Miss Parkinson," she said. "It must be awful to work with someone as efficient as Miss P. and then suddenly find yourself all alone in the boat and on a strange ocean at that." She straightened up and glanced at the papers in her hand. "Well, it certainly has been nice to see you and I'm sure that as you get more used to the country you'll find the time that you seem to have lost momentarily." She held out her hand.

He didn't want to break off the conversation. "What are you doing for lunch?" It was an impulsive and stupid question, and he regretted it before the words were out of his mouth.

She looked startled and drew away slightly. What did she

think he was going to do? Grab her? Then, noting his embarrassment, she grinned. "Why, nothing," she said, "I was going out for a sandwich."

Well, he was in for it and it was nobody's fault but his own. "Will you have lunch with me?"

"Why . . . why . . . I'd like to . . . very much."

Why in the world had he done it? Why had he put himself in such a ridiculous position? What would the people in the office say if they saw him walking out with . . . with . . . with whom? Wouldn't Gleason love it? He'd probably have to spend the next hour listening to her family problems. He didn't even know if she was married. He tried to get a glimpse of her left hand. She saw his eyes searching and held out the hand, smiling. "Yes," she said. "Once. It didn't take. I'm one of those dangerous divorcees. Still want to take me to lunch?"

"Naturally," he said. He was conscious of the pleasant sense of not too imminent danger that grass widows always gave him.

He took her to "21." No one ever bothered his head about the person you were with at "21" unless, of course, it happened to be a celebrity or you were one yourself. The only person who saw them leave the office was Old Penrose and after all there was nothing unusual about two people leaving a big office and going down in a public elevator at the same time.

The downstairs dining room at "21" was full. He was glad. It was crowded and noisy. On the second floor, Philip gave them a banquette table. "Why don't we have a pair of martinis?" he asked as an assistant maître d'hôtel came up, pencil poised over pad. "They're good here."

She raised a hand in protest. "In the middle of the day? Do you think so? Oh, well, here goes one brilliant career in Crombie, Hamilton and Gardiner. Make mine a Gibson. If I'm going to blow gin at them, I might as well lace it with onions."

"Two Gibsons," he said.

They sipped the drinks and made small talk. "Why did you ask me to do this?" she asked suddenly.

He studied his glass, turning its stem slowly between his thumb and forefinger. "I don't know," he said. "Quite frankly I don't know."

"Would you be relieved if I just tossed this off and reeled back to Statistics?"

"I think I asked you because you were the only person in the office who made me feel that you were truly glad to see me back. The only one that I wasn't interrupting."

"Nonsense," she said. "They were all glad to see you. Perhaps I was the only one who wasn't busy."

"That's what I mean. I don't suppose a retired man has any right to go prowling around an office where everything is moving in high. I remember how mad I used to get at the desk-parkers—the ones who 'just came in to say hello.' What is this American craving to say 'hello'? And why do retired people want to come back? Is it a 'revisit-the-scene-of-the-crime' complex, or what?"

"Could it be they're looking for something they've mislaid?"

"I don't know what you mean."

"I mean something they've left behind and they don't know what it is."

"The whole thing is beginning to sound like Peter Pan," he said.

"I think you know what I mean. I've been told you understand that sort of thing better than most of them."

"Who told you that?"

"Miss Parkinson."

"Do you know Miss Parkinson well?" That was a stupid lead.

She laughed. "Don't worry. I won't tell her you take girls to '21' whose names you don't even know."

To his chagrin he felt himself blushing. She threw back her head and rocked with laughter. He noticed that the light filtering through the window above the banquette gave her hair a reddish tinge. It was pretty hair.

"Wouldn't it be more romantic if I took on a stage name? I hate my real one and it's a good time to get rid of it. To you I am Tanya. I've always wanted to be Tanya and have a waxen complexion and jet-black hair and dangerous, almond-shaped eyes."

He looked so foolish and miserable that she let her hand rest on his for an instant. "Sorry," she said. "I didn't mean to tease you. You know how pleased and flattered I am to be here with you. I can't really believe it's true. Tell me more about yourself—your family and all that sort of thing. And more about your life in Highfield."

"It's all pretty tame," he said, still hurt.

"It's not tame to me," she said. "I don't know about the off-stage life of tycoons."

"First let's have the other half of these."

"Good God, what a man! Well, I suppose I might just as well be fired for a sheep as a lamb."

He ordered another round of drinks and lunch. Then he started to talk at random, haltingly. Her obvious interest dissipated his self-consciousness. With increasing eagerness, as his tension relaxed, he poured out to this unknown girl the story of his life; his early struggles to build Crombie, Hamilton and Gardiner; how close to the rocks they had come in the Thirties; and then the successful years when they knew they were over the hump.

He told her how he had felt about retirement; the shock of discovering that it was not just a meaningless clause in a pension plan, but something that applied to *him*, personally; the deep hurt when he realized that his company was not only going to get along without him, but was waiting with respectfully controlled impatience for him to pass through the door. He told her things that he had not fully realized himself until that moment and that he had certainly never told Jinny—his misgivings as to the new role that he was about to play, his desire to make a clean break with his past because he did not think he could face the future in any other way, his life in Highfield and his present, hitherto unexpressed perplexities about it.

"Well that's about it," he said finally, "the biography of nobody."

"The biography of a great guy," she said. "I wish we'd had a tape recorder. That story shouldn't be allowed to dissipate itself in the scented air of '21.' "

They were silent, pursuing their own thoughts. "And now," he said, "a word about my unknown friend."

She shook her head. "No," she said. "There is nothing worth telling. Only bad girls make good biographies."

"But what in the world is a girl like you doing in Statistics?"

"I used to ask myself that question. I guess I was always good at math. Girls aren't supposed to be, I know, but I was just queer. When Tom and I broke up, my world was so shattered that I had to do something to put it in order or go stark, raving nuts. Figures are orderly. They're the antithesis of confusion. They know nothing about half-truths. You add them up and there is the truth. Take it or leave it. I didn't have any training, of course, but it seemed to me that a company like yours must have some job humble enough even for me—adding up freight-car numbers or something. So I applied and to my dismay they hired me. And that's the biography of a washout."

"And now you're the head of the department," he said, "that's quite a washout. How many years have you been there? I ought to know but I don't."

"Five, come December seventeenth at precisely nine o'clock."

"Quite an achievement," he said. "Quite an achievement."

"No reflection on your management, but the competition wasn't very keen."

"Well, it's too late to start worrying about that now," he said. "I'm out from under. A free man."

"I wonder," she said.

"Wonder what?"

"How free you are. As you told me your story you sounded a little bit like a lost man and there's quite a difference."

He looked at her in surprise. "Why do you say that?"

"Oh, I shouldn't have. I don't really know why I said it. Skip it."

"But people don't say things without a reason."

"I truly couldn't put it into words. Forgive me. It just seems to me that anyone who has contributed so much to the world over so many years can't suddenly stop contributing. Men like you are creative just as much as if you were writers or composers or artists or what have you. Painters don't throw down their brushes when they're sixty-five and go around shouting 'I'm free.' Writers don't jump on their typewriters. Musicians don't drop their instruments in the river. A creative man never ceases to have a creative future as long as his arteries remain open."

He was irritated with her for the first time. "Listen," he said. "I've been working like a horse since I graduated from college. I deserve my day in the sun."

"Of course you do," she said soothingly. "I was being selfish. The world *needs* men like you so very badly. But you've earned your right to happiness, God knows. It was just your mention of freedom that got me started. I'm not quite sure what freedom is, but I have some rather unorthodox ideas about it." She looked at her wrist watch. "Good gracious. It's almost quarter of three. Just exactly what am I going to say when I stagger into the dignified offices of Crombie, Hamilton and Gardiner in the middle of the afternoon surrounded by a not-too-faint aroma of Eau de barroom? Shall I say, 'The Founder abducted me and got me tight'?"

"Look haughty and keep still. Remember you're an executive now and executives never explain."

He paid the check. They descended to the first floor, passed through the ceaseless swirl of customers and greeters just inside the entrance and were once more on 52nd Street. An empty cab swerved to the curb. "I'll say good-by to you here," she said. Standing on tiptoe she threw one arm around his neck and kissed him, hard. "That's for freedom and a wonderful lunch," she said. Then she was gone.

He didn't even know her name.

He walked east to Fifth Avenue. Walking would give him time to think. Someone had once said that New York was like ancient Baghdad; a place where anything could happen, however improbable. But to have it happen right in his own office was something else. When Crombie, Hamilton and Gardiner began to go Baghdad it was disturbing. Or had it been just Crombie? How would he ever dare enter the place again? As he walked, a strange feeling of emptiness took possession of him and increased until it became almost unbearable. Something had come into his life which had momentarily satisfied an unconscious hunger. Now it was gone and the realization caused the sunny world of Central Park to look suddenly grim and forbidding.

What the hell was the matter with him—was he getting senile?

He walked to their little apartment. Jinny was out, which was somehow a relief. He threw himself on the bed to think and in a few minutes was snoring gently. He was awakened some time later by the small noises of Jinny moving about the room.

"I can always tell when you've had lunch at the Club," she said. "Two or three of those lethal martinis and you're out like a lamp most of the afternoon."

"They should be prohibited by law," he said, yawning sleepily. It was the first time he had ever deceived her. But what alternative did he have? No woman since Eve had ever believed a story such as his.

23

TIME PASSED SO QUICKLY THAT they failed to see autumn shouldering summer off the stage, until one day the maples began to turn and the air was speckled with falling leaves.

Sunset Hill was finally rounding into shape. Mr. Crombie was face to face at last with the projects and plans he had dreamed about on that transcontinental jet almost a year and a half ago. There was no longer any excuse for procrastination. This realization made him vaguely uneasy. There was something wrong and he couldn't put his finger on it.

He tried hard to be conscientious about his morning schedule, but it just didn't seem to work out. The trouble was that the world refused to hold sacred the privacy of a man who was merely reading. People read in subway trains and in hamburger joints. Why should anyone have to shut himself up in a room to do it? As a matter of fact, why should anyone choose the busiest time of day to read at all? Even Mrs. Crombie could never quite understand his irritability when she interrupted him to say that someone wanted him on the phone, or to announce the arrival of the man to fix the dishwasher.

It was the same with his afternoon routine. He had planned to spend the last half of each day grooming what he hoped by that time would be an almost perfect garden, or producing little gems of handicraft in his workshop or just lying beside some meadow pond watching the drama of life unfold.

Up to date, however, his garden was still more or less of a mess, he hadn't even started his workshop and if there was a meadow pond in the neighborhood he hadn't found it.

It wasn't his fault that these things were so. The difficulty was that each day seemed to produce its quota of details which must be cleaned up immediately.

As a result, life had become a kind of continuous make-ready. Once he disposed of these items which screamed so harshly for attention, he could undertake the things which really counted. Then, at last, his day would fall into an ordered pattern and he would be free to read, or garden or just wander through the woods in the late afternoon, accompanied by his dogs.

His dogs? He had almost forgotten them, although they had played such an important part in his early dreams. Then they had always been romping around him on these walks, yelping with delight, dashing off into the bushes on fruitless hunting expeditions, returning to jump up on him triumphantly with muddy paws. Dogs did something to one's ego. They were constantly assuring you that you were one of the world's great guys. Regardless of how much of a slob you knew yourself to be, you could be certain they would never find out—and even if they did it would make no difference.

Now it became increasingly apparent that there were to be no dogs in the picture. What in the world were you going to do with a lot of dogs when you left for town on Monday afternoons? You certainly couldn't take them into the little apartment and if you tried to farm them out for two or three days every week they would become so confused that they would have nervous breakdowns. Why in the world couldn't he live in one place the way everyone else seemed to?

It worried him, this inability to get the simplest things done in the course of a day. He would wake up in the middle of the night and fret about it. How in the world had he formerly found time to build up a business, raise a family, be on half a dozen boards, work actively on committees and either go out in the evening or plow through the contents of a bulging brief case?

Was it possible that as people grow older the nature of time changed? Could it be that it speeded up for the aged in some mysterious way, as if a bored universe were skipping through the end of the chapter just to get it over with? Or was the answer less metaphysical? Did older people work more slowly? Did it take a man of sixty-five longer to write a letter, shave, clean out a barn, read a newspaper, than a man of thirty? Did men become perfectionists as they grew older, polishing, polishing, reluctant to let go?

It might be that certain people were born with a compulsion to complicate their lives, while others could live blissfully motionless almost indefinitely, like lizards in the sun, too indolent to blink their eyes. Perhaps it was his misfortune, or good fortune, whichever way one looked at it, to belong to the former group, and he was struggling unconsciously to build up pressure in a world which demanded none, which was positively antagonistic to it.

And then again perhaps the reason why he couldn't find time to do any of the things he had planned to do after retirement: reading, roaming, gardening, lying on his back and watching the clouds go by, was because he didn't want to do them. There was no compulsion behind them. They could be done or left undone and nobody really gave a damn. During all his busy life he had only done things which had to be done. This habit had become so fixed over the years that it seemed futile to do anything for which no one was waiting.

He looked at the luminous dial of his wrist watch. It was

five minutes after four. On some distant farm a rooster crowed and, far down the valley, an associate answered. He turned over impatiently and pulled the sheet over his head against the treacherous encroachment of the dawn.

24

AT LEAST HE COULD BUY THE equipment for his workshop. Thus committed, action might follow. He went down to Mills and Bradley's Hardware Store and bought a full set of carpenter's tools, including a rotary power saw and several other pieces of power machinery that Mr. Mills said were essential for babbiting and doweling, whatever *they* were. He also bought a huge square of pegboard for hanging up his tools, and lumber for his workbench, sandpaper and glue and assorted nails, levels and T squares and plumb lines and several gadgets that he had no idea how to use or what they were for.

"There," said Mr. Mills. "That'll get you started. Best not to get everything at once. Add things as you find you need 'em."

He didn't even ask the cost of this collection. After all, if you were going to set up a workshop you had to have the proper equipment and that was that. When he returned home, the station wagon loaded with tools, Jinny had gone with a friend to some meeting in the village, using the recently purchased second car. He was glad. It gave him a chance to unload the stuff and get it down to the cellar without a barrage of acid comments. He had made such a fuss about buying that second car that he knew he was vulnerable.

He piled everything neatly in a corner of the cellar and turned to stare at the blank stone wall. That was where the pegboard would go on which he would hang his hand tools. In front of it would be his workbench.

The old nightmare which had caused him so many wakeful hours came charging in on him once more, only this time he couldn't pacify it with a sleeping pill and send it away. How in the world did one attach a pegboard to a stone wall? How did one attach anything to a stone wall, for that matter? After the pegboard there would be the paneling. He sat down on an old box and focused on the problem. Perhaps one bored holes in the stone with some kind of an electric gadget. But then, when you stuck things into the holes, why didn't they come right out again? It all seemed rather hopeless.

He turned his attention to the workbench. Perhaps that was the first thing to do. A workbench had a heavy top and sturdy legs, but how did you attach sturdy legs to a heavy top so that the whole thing didn't wobble like a newborn calf and ultimately collapse when you leaned on it?

Mr. Mills had done some figuring on a scrap of paper and given him the various kinds of boards and two-by-fours which, properly handled, would, he had assured him, turn into a workbench. They lay on the cellar floor in a disorderly pile. Mr. Crombie poked at it gingerly with his foot. How could anyone know what to do with an assortment like that? Perhaps he had better have someone help him put up the pegboard and build the workbench—someone who knew what he was about. Then at least he would have a place to hang his tools and something to work on. After that everything should be simpler.

He went upstairs to phone Crumb. To his amazement he

reached him. Mr. Crumb was laid up with a bad cold. He didn't seem to think that attaching a pegboard to a stone wall was much of a problem and he tossed off the building of the worktable equally lightly. The only trouble was that he himself was tied up on the school job. That was why he hadn't been able to finish the porch. No, he didn't know of any handyman-carpenter. There wasn't any such thing any more. Carpenters all wanted steady work and at the moment every mother's son for twenty miles around that could hammer nails for twenty-five dollars a day was working on the school job.

There was a fellow named Blatz over Smithtown way. Nobody liked to hire him because you never could tell when he was going to be taken drunk. Mr. Crumb would probably see him at Lodge Meeting the next night. If he was sober, which was doubtful, he'd have him get in touch with Mr. Crombie.

Mr. Blatz had been at least sober enough to remember to telephone and he turned out to be the greatest boon that had come into Mr. Crombie's life since he moved to Highfield, in spite of the fact that he didn't work very fast or very long at a time, and he didn't like to work at all unless Mr. Crombie hung around and talked to him. He said he was the lonely type and working in a cellar you saw funny things coming out of the cracks in the wall if they wasn't nobody with you. So Mr. Crombie sat on a wooden box and talked in order to keep Mr. Blatz's mind from funny things. At the same time he watched carefully to see how one attached pegboards to stone walls, but Mr. Blatz was usually standing in his line of vision and it all seemed so simple that he didn't like to disclose his ignorance.

While Mr. Blatz was putting up the pegboards and starting the workbench, Mr. Crombie told him of his idea about paneling the whole end of the cellar. Mr. Blatz agreed that this would be pretty. Without further discussion he appeared

the next morning with a pile of boards sticking over the end
of his light truck and proceeded with the paneling, which he
then stained and waxed according to his taste.

"Now," he said, "we got to put in some outlets for them
power tools; then a couple of fluorescent lamps over the workbench an' I guess we're about through down here."

It all did look very efficient and shipshape. There was no
question of that. "By the way," said Mr. Blatz, packing his
tools into a battered carrier, "them power tools needs extra
voltage. I guess you know about that. Before you use 'em the
light company's got to run in a heavy line and you'll need a
new fuse box for the extra circuits. That ain't too bad 'ceptin'
the light company's so busy you can't ever get 'em to do
nothin'."

Instead of being depressed by this news, Mr. Crombie was
actually relieved. At least the moment was postponed when he
had to face the mystery of the power tools. He followed Mr.
Blatz up the cellar stairs. As usual, Mrs. Crombie was standing in the midst of a confusion of cooking utensils. Mr. Blatz
sat down in the only unoccupied kitchen chair.

"Well," he said, "got your man fixed up nice down there.
He oughta be able to build a new house with all them con-
traptions." Mr. Crombie watched his wife with an anxious expression. "I was just sayin' to him that I'm all ready now for
anything else you want done." Mr. Crombie couldn't remember his saying any such thing.

"Oh, that's wonderful," cried Mrs. Crombie. "I have a
thousand things for you to do. Doors that won't open, and
doors that won't close and shelves and broken . . ."

"But those are the things I built the *workshop* for," protested Mr. Crombie. "Those are the things *I* can do, now that
I'm set up."

"I've been waiting to get these things done for months," she
said. "We won't live long enough if I wait for you, besides

which you don't need to worry—there'll be plenty more." But the discussion was academic. Mr. Blatz was already taking measurements for a shelf above the kitchen sink.

Mr. Blatz had peculiar ideas about being paid. Up to this point he had only been willing to accept a small amount each week, paid on account. When he had finally finished the last item on Mrs. Crombie's list, he was paid in full with a sizable check. Grinning from ear to ear he rattled out of the driveway in his old pickup truck, waving gaily as he turned into the main road. They never saw him again.

Questioned about him, Mr. Crumb said he'd heard he'd been put in some institution for the D.T.'s, but that might be just loose talk. The little house where he lived was closed up and eventually a bulldozer removed it (with or without Mr. Blatz inside) to make room for a Thruway.

Whenever Mr. Crombie had occasion to go into the cellar, he always snapped on the fluorescent lights and looked at his workshop with pride. Everything was spotless. Each tool hung straight and true. The power tools were concealed beneath neat canvas covers. The lights were reflected by the waxed paneling. Some day he'd have to hang a few pictures down here.

Then he would return upstairs, happy in the knowledge that at least one project had been brought to a successful conclusion.

25

THERE WAS A FEELING OF SNOW
in the air. The sun was setting behind a lattice of bare
branches. A lonely chill crept up from the valley. The evening breeze, moving through the leafless trees, sang in an
alien tongue; one that Mr. Crombie felt he was not meant to
understand. Nature was taking over for the night.

He hurried to finish cutting up the pile of branches beside
the sawbuck, with the consciousness of intruding in a world
from which he was forever barred. It was dark in the big barn
when he stacked the last armload on the rapidly growing pile
of kindling. His woodpile, neatly separated into different
sizes, had become a measure of his daily accomplishment.
Picking out a big log for storage on the back porch, he started
for the house. Through the shaft of yellow light streaming
from the kitchen window passed the first snowflakes of the
season.

Mrs. Crombie was preparing dinner. He stood for a moment and watched her. There was a tense, worried look in her
face. How she hated cooking. And how patient and uncom-
plaining she had been about it. It made him feel guilty as he
realized that she was doing all this for him.

Her face lit up as she heard the kitchen door open. "Hi,"
she said. "I was afraid the trolls had taken you. You're not going to have a very good dinner tonight. I've been trying to

make veal *scaloppine* and it just doesn't *scaloppine*. I've done everything exactly the way the book says. I guess I'm just dumb."

"You're not dumb, you're just too bright to stand over a stove and stir things."

"Nuts," she said. "There are plenty of women a lot brighter than I am who can find their way around a kitchen. Go fix the martinis. I'll let this mess simmer."

He thought she looked particularly appealing in her smudged work apron, with her hair mussed and that frustrated look in her eyes. Women who were habitually poised were always more appealing when caught off balance. "I'm having a luncheon tomorrow for the Women's Committee of the Community Chest," she said. "Do you suppose you could shift for yourself, darling? I hate to put you out, but twelve women would drive you crazy. They do me." She was in balance again.

"Oh, sure," he said. "I'll beat it out of here early."

"But where will you go? You have no Club to hole up in around Highfield."

"Oh, I'll go over to Middleburg," he said, vaguely. "I'll have lunch with some of the college crowd."

"What college crowd?" she asked curiously. "We don't know any of them."

"Oh, I've met a few," he said noncommittally. "I might drop in on Professor Turner."

On the following day he took the car shortly after noon and started down the road without the slightest idea where he was going. He was filled with a sense of having failed somehow. When he had moved to Highfield he had thought that a person with his financial and business experience would be God's gift to a town of this size. Now at the end of six months he was beginning to realize that whatever financial assistance he might render to the businessmen of Highfield would be in the form of checks drawn in their favor.

He had conceived of this rural community as his new workshop—a place where he could continue to build as he had at Crombie, Hamilton and Gardiner. His first step would be to put the village on a sound financial basis. After that he would bolster up its civic pride. He would teach it to clean up the litter on the green and outside Gates Drug Store, to put some paint on the firehouse and to take better care of its beautiful old trees. He would get them doing square dances (about which he knew nothing) and introduce evening art classes (about which he knew less). He would develop a historic consciousness. A town as old as Highfield must have a history. He had even toyed with the idea of making a New England Williamsburg out of the place.

These had been mere formless dreams, but it had not taken him long to realize that the Village Fathers had other ideas. Here was no community of amiable yokels and picturesque characters waiting to be molded. The inhabitants of Highfield were quite as close to the modern world as Mr. Crombie and in many ways appeared better able to cope with it.

The only thing they retained from the past was a fierce independence. No one was going to tell them where to drop their chewing-gum wrappers and old newspapers. No one was going to make monkeys of them with crazy things like square dances, nor were they going to be costumed figures in a museum village. They were freemen and if one of them wanted to build an abattoir on his property next ot the Village Green it was his inalienable right to do so.

For some reason Jinny had fitted into the picture much better than he had. It was true that she had not been obliged to contend with the flinty group who controlled the political destinies of the village, but in many ways their wives were of even tougher fiber. In spite of this they had accepted Jinny almost immediately, placing her on their committees, seeking her advice, and before long following her leadership. He had never had an opportunity before to observe her in action.

Now he had nothing but admiration for her ability and tact; admiration that was seasoned with a dash of hurt pride.

He drove down the hill to the village. Oswald Battle was just leaving his antique shop with Mr. Crumb. Mr. Crombie pulled over to the curb. "You fellows want to have lunch with me?" he asked.

They looked puzzled. "We're both going home to lunch right now," said Mr. Battle. "Glad to have you come and take pot luck if you got nothing better to do."

"Me, too," said Mr. Crumb. They looked at him curiously, obviously wondering why he wasn't going home for lunch like everyone else. It had been stupid of him. The only place to eat in the village was Joe's Place, which was only suitable if one was starving and even that was subject to debate.

"No, thanks," he said embarrassed. "Thanks very much. My wife's having a committee meeting." He left them to ruminate over this statement.

"Odd fellow," said Mr. Crumb. "Nervous type. He called me up the other day and give me hell for not getting that porch of his started. You might think he was intendin' to sit out there all winter. Don't seem to realize there's a school job goin' on in this town."

"Might be he's tryin' to get away from his wife," said Mr. Battle, following a line of thought closer to his heart. "About the only way you can live with some women is to run away from 'em."

Mr. Crombie drove through the village and at the crossroads, a mile out, he turned left on the Middleburg road. There would be some place in a college town to get a decent lunch and then . . . What then? He might call on old Professor Turner. No, the old man would be busy and in any event he didn't want to listen to a discussion of the intolerable qualities of the professor's associates.

He'd go to the movies. Must be one in Middleburg.

He ate lunch in a students' cafeteria, reading a copy of the Middleburg *Reporter* which the last customer had left on the table. After lunch he found the movie theater. It was a small building, badly ventilated and filled with students of both sexes who had come there more for the purpose of expressing their mutual desire than to see the picture.

The film had to do with the adventures of two female impersonators who got into trouble with the police and concealed themselves among a group of WACs who were embarking for some Pacific outpost. The air in the little theater weighed on him like a German feather bed and after a while he fell asleep. The clatter of machine guns wakened him with a start. Where was he? For a moment it was his inclination to drop down between the seats. Then things swam into focus.

The faintly illuminated clock on the side wall indicated five minutes before four. The female impersonators were being chased by someone. Then they both fell into the arms of two blonde WACs, a general fell off a dock and the picture was over. Mr. Crombie sleepily joined the crowd of young men and women inching their way up the aisle hand in hand. He drove his car out of the parking lot and headed for Highfield through the anemic sunlight of a late winter day.

Of all the fatuous ways to spend an afternoon, this was it! What was the matter with him? He had always prided himself on being rich in resources. Now he began to wonder. He was a book lover who didn't read, a music lover who never went to hear any music, a student of nature who never bothered to look at it, a gardener who pulled up the flowers and left the weeds to grow.

He was a phony—that's what he was. A hapless dreamer of impractical dreams. The only thing he knew anything about was how to handle people, and run a business. But that was behind him; something belonging to the past. If he was going to have a future he must work on it just as hard as he had worked on his past. No more afternoons like this.

The Committee had left by the time he reached the house. Jinny was pushing the vacuum cleaner around the living room. "You poor lamb," she said, "shooting the breeze with a lot of old college professors all afternoon. I'm never going to let you do that again—throwing you out of your own house."

"Oh, I didn't mind it," he said. "It's a good thing to get out once in a while and see the world."

"God, those women were deadly," she said.

He felt better.

26

ON NIGHTS WHEN JANUARY WINDS tore across the valley, battering angrily at the old house and rattling its windows; on mornings when, numb with cold, he struggled to start the half-frozen car before the batteries were exhausted; on days when driving southeast rainstorms created a sea of mud around the house—at such times he found himself trying to remember just what it was that had caused him to decide that this was the setting best suited to what were cheerily referred to as the declining years.

By mid-January, winter really went to work on Highfield. The snow fell quietly, intermittently, but each fall added its quota to that which had already accumulated, until the earth was muted under a thick sparkling blanket and the big plows had transformed the roads into white-walled corridors.

The plow drivers were friendly people and they kept Mr. Crombie's driveway open as far as the kitchen door. There it ended in a mountain of snow. With backbreaking exertion he shoveled a path to the barn just wide enough for a wheelbarrow loaded with firewood. It was rather shocking to him to find how soft he was after almost eight months of country life. Fifteen minutes of digging made him lean panting on the shovel, listening to his heart thumping against his ribs like a trapped animal trying to break through and escape. He had never realized that being a successful country gentleman was so much a matter of muscles.

The weekly round-trip to New York had become a perilous and uncertain adventure. They would start out on a clear road and end up crawling over glare ice, fed by a half-frozen drizzle which coated the windshield with ice until the wiper was immobilized and he had to drive to the nearest gas station with his head out the window like an old-time locomotive engineer.

Their friends in New York could not understand why they persisted in struggling back to the wilderness each week at a time when New York was offering its most beguiling charms. But Mr. Crombie was adamant. "We are country people," he would say. "Highfield is our home, just the way New York is yours." Mrs. Crombie said nothing, and hours later, when they found the entrance to Sunset Hill blocked by drifted snow, he was inclined to agree with her silence.

Then came the January thaw. The winds subsided. The sun blazed fiercely down on the white world. From underneath the drifts and the man-made piles, little rivulets began to flow. The hard-pressed snow on the roads became slush, tossed and retossed by flying wheels. The surface of the earth turned from ice to water. With the change, the sounds of the living world were once more released, the gurgle of running brooks, the drip of eaves, the skittering of a squirrel along a wet tree branch.

In Mr. Crombie's immaculate cellar, water began to appear on the gleaming walls, moving slowly downward, drop by drop. It came from everywhere and nowhere and the merged drops finally turned the cellar floor into a shallow lake. Mr. Barnhauser, hastily summoned, came up to look the situation over. He didn't seem particularly disturbed. "What you expect, all this water drippin' off the eaves? Just lies there against your foundations. Gotta go somewhere. All these old houses got leaky cellars this time a'year."

"But can't you do anything *about* it?" Mr. Crombie was not used to situations which could not be controlled.

"No. It'll stop when the ground freezes again. Then it'll dry up in the spring. Oh, of course you can mop it up if you've a mind but I wouldn't bother. Just wear a pair of galoshes when you go down in the cellar. Feels to me like we're due for a cold spell."

He was right. That night the roads froze into coral-like ridges. The snow acquired a glittering crust. Down, down, down went the mercury. No heat found its way into the guest-room wing. On Monday night the water pipes in the guest bathroom broke and the water, long penned by a core of ice, rushed joyously through the breech over the bathroom floor, under the bathroom door and into the bedroom.

They didn't discover it until the following morning. "For pity's sake don't just stand there looking at it," said Mrs. Crombie. "Go down and shut something off."

He put on his galoshes and went down. In one corner a ganglia of pipes disappeared into the crawl space under the guest room. There were valves everywhere—most of them marked with red tags on which some former owner had written cabalistic notations like "2-B" and "D-4."

Mr. Crombie stared at them thoughtfully for a long while. Finally he turned all the valves off, and sloshed his way back to the cellar stairs. At the top he removed the galoshes and carried them in his hand to the guest room, where he put

them on again and entered the bathroom. Water continued to
pour through the plaster and under the baseboard. He could
hear it gurgling contentedly within the confines of the wall.
The place was getting like a marina.

Mrs. Crombie came to the door. "Something else has happened," she said. "There's no water running anywhere in the
house. I've been all around."

"It's all coming out here," he said.

"Why in the world doesn't this one stop when all the
others do?"

"I don't *know*. Don't ask me silly questions. Maybe the
place is bewitched. I just don't know." His face had the
dazed look of one suffering from shock. "I just don't know,"
he repeated.

"You'd better get that new plumber up here before we all
start floating down the road like a houseboat. A lot of good *he*
turned out to be."

Mr. Parsons, the new plumber, was not home. His wife
thought he was working on the school job. Mr. Crombie
eventually found him there, or at least he found his legs,
which were planted on the top of a stepladder and disappeared
through a hole in the ceiling from which a rhythmic clanking
sound emerged.

"Is this Mr. Parsons?" asked Mr. Crombie, addressing the
legs.

The clanking ceased. "Yes," came a voice, Jehovah-like.

"I'm Graham Crombie." The rhythmic clanking resumed.
"There's a pipe busted in my guest bathroom."

"They're poppin' like balloons all over town," said the voice.
"Always do, this kinda freeze. Did you turn off the water?"

"I can't find the spigot, or whatever you call it."

The feet began to descend the ladder and Mr. Parsons, covered with dirt, hove into view. "I don't know where it is, no
more'n you do," he said. "Have you looked for it?"

"I turned off everything I could find," said Mr. Crombie.

"And don't that do it?"

Mr. Crombie shook his head miserably. "Everything else is shut off but the leak."

Mr. Parsons shook his head, also, but in the manner of one who gives up trying to deal sensibly with a moron. "All right," he said. "I'll be up in two-three hours. Damage's done now. Little more water ain't gonna hurt none."

Mr. and Mrs. Crombie sat helplessly in front of the living-room fire and waited for him. The gurgle from the guest-room bath and the incessant tick, tick of the water pump running nonstop in the cellar formed a background for their gloomy thoughts.

"Let's go to New York," said Mr. Crombie.

Mrs. Crombie alerted like a setter aroused from its dreams by the sound of a welcome step outside the door. "Oh, Gray, could we? Wouldn't it be cheating?"

"It would only be until the first of April," he said, severely. "As a mater of fact, if we go down to visit the Carringtons in Delray in March we won't be in town more than six weeks."

"Oh, darling," she said, her lethargy gone. "Let's celebrate. I'll drive down and get a big juicy steak and one of Mrs. Peterson's pies and you can build a huge fire in the dining-room fireplace."

"I don't know why we have to celebrate because the house is sinking and we're abandoning ship."

She did not heed this. "And we'll put out the best china. A full-dress feast, complete with candlelight."

"To hell with the water pipe," said Mr. Crombie. "I'll see if there's any of that Chianti left."

27

THEY RETURNED TO HIGHFIELD ON
April first. Mr. Battle had become the self-appointed superin-
tendent of Sunset Hill. During their absence he had not only
seen to it that the broken pipe was repaired but, quite on his
own, had had the bathroom replastered and repainted and the
cellar walls waterproofed. He had even persuaded Mr. Crumb
to start work on the screened porch. The bills for these various
jobs, plus ten per cent for Mr. Battle, lay in a neat pile on
Mr. Crombie's writing table. "It's lucky we came back," he
said, "before that ass Battle redecorated the whole house."

Like a capricious woman, April changed its moods a dozen
times a day. At one moment the hot sun would bring out the
intangible, intoxicating smell of spring. Life was poised just
beneath the earth like an actor waiting in the wings for his
cue. Then suddenly a puff of cold wind would come sweeping
up the valley. The cloudless sky of a moment before would
become gray and dour and a chill rain would move like a cur-
tain across the fields and forests.

April, harbinger of spring and child of winter, was always
luring one with soft promises and then rushing off with a
mocking laugh. Mr. Crombie bought garden books, garden
tools, garden seeds. He was ready, whenever April would
make up its mind, to cover the black earth with flaming
beauty, although he wasn't very sure what the little seed
packets with the funny names contained.

And then, one morning, they saw the first green shimmering in the trees at the edge of the forest; a shade so delicate that it disappeared as one approached it. The grass had suddenly become greener and the song of birds rose from the bushes on the edges of the fields.

"Spring is going to be beautiful in Highfield," said Mr. Crombie. "We ought to plan our weekends—who we want and all that sort of thing. Otherwise we'll get jammed up with a whole lot of people we don't care a hoot about, and won't be able to have the kids."

"Who probably won't want to come anyway," she said. But nevertheless she brought a pad and they made out a schedule. The children took up most of it as they could have only one family at a time and they wanted them all frequently. Then there were people to whom they were indebted and people to whom they wanted to show Sunset Hill and people that they just plain wanted to see. It was a formidable list.

"Do you realize," she said, "that a crowd like this wouldn't leave us one single weekend to ourselves from now until Christmas?"

"That's nonsense," he said, "I want every other weekend free."

"Then you'll have to cut out everybody but the children, and you'll have to cut down on them."

They finally reached a compromise which left them with three free weekends, up to Labor Day.

"I'll get the children anchored first," she said. "Then we'll have to sign up Mrs. Frankenthal and a maid for the rest of their lives."

"This thing is going to be awfully expensive, isn't it?" said Mr. Crombie.

"Well, darling, if you're going to have a houseful almost every weekend you certainly can't expect me to entertain them and do all the work besides."

"Oh, of course not," he said hastily. "I think I'll do some

work in my library now. I won't have much time from here
in with guests and children and gardening and everything."

"You mean you'll read while I sit on the telephone and
call all these people," she said.

When he saw her at lunch she looked disturbed. "Did you
get the kids nailed down?" he asked.

"You're not going to like this, dear. I talked to them all.
Each family has agreed to come once during the spring, but
then I'm afraid that's more or less that for the time being.
They won't be pinned down too far ahead. You see, darling,
you have to look at this from their point of view."

"I know," he said. "I've heard it all before."

"Well, it's the truth, dear."

"Yes, and it's also the truth that if we offered to take their
children off their hands so that they could go somewhere,
they'd jump at it."

"Of course they would, dear. Don't you remember how we
used to try to pawn off the children on your family when they
were little? You must stop being hurt all the time and try to
get used to the fact that they've grown up. They're not *children* any more; they *have* children. They're *adults* leading
their own lives and wouldn't you hate them if they didn't.

"Do you remember how poor Mother used to plead with us
to come out to Cleveland for Christmas or Easter or to spend
our vacation with her at the camp? I suppose this kind of
thing has gone on since people lived in caves. If parents could
only realize that there comes a point where your children
don't really *need* you any more. They . . ."

"But they *do* need us," he broke in impatiently. "They
need us when they pile up a stack of doctors' bills, and when
it looked as if Pat's marriage was headed for the reefs, she
came running to us fast enough, and what would have happened when Dexter lost his job if we hadn't been ready to
help?"

"I know," she said, "and that's the way they ought to need

us—in the pinches, not all day long. We're there like a backstop. And they know it. And they'd feel adrift if we weren't, but they're *outside,* that's the point. They're no longer in the enclosure. And they unconsciously resent any attempt to drag them back."

"You always get so psychological," he said. "We buy this lovely place so we can see our grandchildren. It's as simple as that. And then, when we ask them to come, everybody gets Freudian."

She stood looking out the window for some time before replying. "I'll tell you what they want us to do," she said finally, "and we ought to be smart enough to want to do it. They want us to lead our own lives. We led our own lives before they came and now it's time to pick up where we left off. We didn't buy this place for them. We bought it for ourselves because it represented a way of life we wanted."

"I suppose you're right," he said. "I'm sure you're right. But I don't like it any better for that. It makes the whole thing seem rather empty . . . pointless."

"Listen, dear. The trouble is that when people get to this chapter we're talking about, they begin to look backward instead of forward. They don't see any future—just past. Now, darling, we have a future, you and I. You have one. I have one. And we have one together. That's three futures. I've been watching you get the backward look for over a year now. It worries me. You're a dynamic person. I hate that word; everything's 'dynamic' these days. But that's what you are. And dynamic means motion. At least I think it does. And as far as human beings are concerned, there's only one way for motion to go for my money and that's forward."

Her voice had become suddenly tense. He looked at her, trying to read in her troubled eyes the import of her words.

She resumed her seat, grinning sheepishly. "Gracious, what an outburst. Well, now, back to the weekend schedule. Let's see whether our friends feel the same about us as our children."

They sat long over the list. "The trouble is," she said, "we owe so many people. We've been lazy."

"It's not laziness," he said, "but there's so much to do around this place and when you have people here for the weekend . . ."

"I wish I could get that on a tape recorder," she said, "and send it to the kids. But we've got to pay these people back. Now look. You can't have the Applegates with the Browns. That's for sure. They'd kill each other at the end of twelve hours. I suppose we *must* have the Hendersons, but I dread it. She's stiff as a poker and he's one of those weekend drinkers with all the standard reactions. Before Saturday night is over I feel like slipping on a suit of armor. Yes, the Cranshaws, I suppose. God, they're bores."

"Why do we accept so much hospitality from people we don't seem to like?" he asked.

"I don't know," she said, "but I'm sure you can't tear them up and throw them away now. They're here, sitting in the middle of our lives, and my future for the next three days is going to be on the end of a telephone trying to get them to come to Sunset Hill."

"I think I'll plant some of those seeds," he said.

"Oh, darling, *please* wait until we can plan it out together. Don't you think . . ."

"I'm not a complete fool," he said indignantly. "All you do is poke them in the ground."

"Of course you're not. And I suppose if you're going to have a future you might start it in much worse ways than poking seeds in the ground. Remember not to put them in upside down."

The sun was hot in the angle of the house. Mr. Crombie sat on the warm flagstones and studied the little seed envelopes. What was in Jinny's mind? What was all this about new chapters and futures? Probably nothing. She was always dressing up simple ideas in costumes. He ought to put these tall jobs in the back. That was the way to go about planting a garden. Tall in the back, ground huggers in front.

As he carefully planted the seeds in neat rows he was suddenly seized with the same sense of futility that had come over him so frequently during recent weeks. What in the world was he, Graham Crombie, doing, kneeling on an alien terrace, poking seeds into the ground in the middle of a spring afternoon? The question irritated him. He was gardening, and gardening was a time-honored occupation, creative and healthful.

But who in hell cared whether he planted these seeds or not? What difference did it make? That was it. What difference did it make?

He sat for a long time staring at the little envelopes. The flowers depicted on them looked so gay and colorful that he felt somehow disloyal as he laid the envelopes carefully in the wicker basket and placed his gardening gloves on top of them. Something within him was struggling for expression. He needed to be alone, to be with himself without even the company of a packet of seeds.

He walked down to the barn and took the path over the brook and into the woods. During the past weeks he had cleared it roughly to a point where it ran into an old wagon track that led down to the valley. He turned into it now, walking as fast as the surface of the ground permitted.

He wanted to think, but he wasn't quite sure what he wanted to think about. Something was disturbing him profoundly, but he couldn't bring it into focus. "You have a future," she had said. But the trouble was that, to his business-trained mind, a future meant only one thing: new obstacles to be overcome, new heights to be scaled. That

meant business. There must be roads to achievement, however, which did not lead through the commercial jungle. At
the moment he could not think of any that he was capable of
following, or wanted to if he could.

But what was the matter with the road which he had
chosen? Wasn't he writing the new chapter that Jinny was
talking about right here and now? And under the most ideal
conditions? Wasn't this where his future lay; serene, peaceful,
contented?

The wagon track came out on a narrow hard-surfaced road.
Turning to the right he walked furiously, seeking the muscu-
lar fatigue that alone would cure the inexplicable turmoil
within him.

28

THEY SAT ON THE TERRACE WATCH-
ing the setting sun balance itself for an instant on the knife
edge of the purple hills.

"Whoever named this place Sunset Hill named it well,"
she said. "It's so beautiful at this time of day that sometimes
it makes me want to cry." The sun burrowed into the hill
like a hen settling herself on her eggs. "On second thought,"
she said, "I'll make *you* cry instead. That's more fun. I finished begging people to come for a weekend about an hour
ago and if you ever ask me to do a job like that again I'll
divorce you. I'd rather arrange a Summit Conference. Come

inside where you can read my lists and I'll break the bad news."

"Now," she said, settling herself beside the lamp and putting on her glasses. "The kids are coming on these four weekends. Generously, magnanimously and unselfishly they have agreed to that. I've kept three weekends free on the improbable chance that someone might ask *us* somewhere and every other weekend from now through August is tied up tighter than a drum. There it is, baby. You'd better start negotiating with your liquor dealer."

As he read the list his face registered consternation. "But my Lord, Jinny, most of these people aren't the ones we decided on."

"I know it," she said. "But every time I'd get one couple nailed down, nobody else could come on that particular weekend. There were very few of them that I wanted to sit staring at all by themselves for three days, so I had to shop around until I found a pair of lonely hearts to go with them. I'll admit it has resulted in some odd combinations, but it was the best I could do. We seem to know the most forward-planning group of people in America."

"But we hardly know the Thurstons. Why should we have *them*. And with the Andy Bruces, of all people. And the Carters. They're dreadful. Why the Carters, for heaven's sake?"

"Because you wanted to fill your weekends, and I couldn't find anyone else. I told you that. Maybe you could get some work out of them around the place."

"Wouldn't it be cheaper and pleasanter if we were to cancel the whole thing and go abroad?" he said. "You know— 'urgent and unexpected business—terribly sorry.' "

"No, dear," she said. "We've joined the weekend set at the hard end and we're going to enjoy it if it kills us. Maybe it will be more fun than it looks from here."

29

MR. CROMBIE HAD FOUND LITTLE
enough time for the daily chores when they lived a quiet
normal life. Now, with people coming on Friday evening and
staying (God forbid) until Monday morning, he had no time
for anything. His mail lay unopened on the writing table.
His books stood on the shelves as unread as ever.

He had turned over the grass-cutting to a pack of young
men who had reduced the operation to a kind of lawn ballet. Now, unable to cope any longer with the garden, he
handed it over to this same group. When he remembered the
hours he had spent on his knees picking out grass blades from
between tender petals of iris, he was filled with awe as he
watched these young men rush into the flower beds, leaving
them at the end of an hour as weedlessly sterile as the beds of
Rockefeller Plaza.

By these ruinously expensive means he had reduced his
outdoor responsibilities to wandering around with a wheelbarrow, picking up broken branches, Jinny's prunings and
odds and ends of paper which were forever being blown about
the lawn.

Late on Friday afternoon the week's assignment of guests
would arrive in a swirl of noisy vigor which everyone realized
was only temporary. They screamed with pleasure at the
view. They couldn't wait to see the house, and they delivered

their tithes of candy, books and liquor to the usual accompaniment of protests.

At first Mr. Crombie welcomed the donations of liquor as so many extra dividends. Later he came to regard these gifts with apprehension, particularly in the case of two-bottle donors who, having deposited them on the piano with a loud bang to assure their having been properly noted, would then cast off the role of guest and assume a kind of suzerainty over Mr. Crombie's entire supply of bottled goods, suggesting from time to time that it might be a good thing if everyone had a quick snort, after which, without more ado, they would pour unmeasured slugs of Mr. Crombie's best Scotch, or insist on refilling people's glasses long before they were empty. "That stuff won't do you any good. Let me chuck it out and get you a real one."

In the beginning Mr. Crombie had cherished the illusion that people coming to the country for a weekend would welcome the opportunity to tone up their flaccid muscles and to draw a little pure air into their carbon-coated lungs.

In anticipation of this he made up lists of odd jobs that he had been trying to get done for weeks. He would lead up to the subject with studied obliqueness. "How would you fellows like to take it easy this morning and fool around the place? Put on your old clothes. I'm going to dabble around a bit. I don't want you to do any work, of course, but if you're itching to get your hands dirty I've got a lot of tools in the barn." They would follow him with the sagging shoulders of condemned men who, with ropes around their necks, were being asked to dig their own graves.

"Here's a turf-cutter, Bill. If you want to cut back the grass along the walks it will be a great help. Not bad fun, either. And here's a pair of snippers, Harry. Those lilac bushes at the end of the terrace need thinning out."

They took the tools without enthusiasm and followed him

back to the terrace where he tried to instill a little élan into the occasion by keeping up a nonstop pep talk. "It sure is good to get out in the sun and do a little light bending and twisting. That's the trouble with us old fellows. Never get any exercise. We don't need *heavy* exercise. That's the last thing we want. It's just the twisting and turning stuff that's so good for what ails you. Do you remember Walter Camp's *Daily Dozen?* He went to the Zoo and studied tigers. . . ."

They listened apathetically and eventually laid down their tools in inconspicuous places, where he would find them rusting days later, if ever. Lowering themselves quietly into the big wooden terrace chairs they watched him work, chatting lazily of this and that and with one eye carefully noting the progress of the sun toward its juncture with the yardarm.

30

THE WEEKEND WITH THE BEAMS and the Buckleys had been quite different. Later he came to regard it as one of the turning points of his life. Joe Beam had roomed with him at Harvard, and had been associated with him in various business ventures ever since. Henry Buckley had been one of the wheel horses of Crombie, Hamilton and Gardiner. Both of them had retired shortly after Mr. Crombie.

Joe had been the head of a big electrochemical company with plants scattered across the country. He was a huge man, with enormous drive, which for years had kept him moving restlessly over the length and breadth of the United States, inspecting his various branches, attending conventions, making speeches, keeping himself posted on the activities of his competitors.

As a result he knew everyone worth knowing in the business hierarchy and in spite of his blatant masculinity he had a woman's sense for gossip. If a merger was in the offing, if a company was having difficulty with its bank credit, if a corporate head was about to fall, Joe Beam knew about it almost before those involved.

Henry Buckley was a different type. Joe Beam's world was filled with people, Henry Buckley's with figures. He read balance sheets and income statements as a musician reads a score. Figures told Henry Buckley immediately what was wrong with a company, what its stock was worth or the proper terms of a prospective merger. His uncanny ability along these lines had brought much valuable business to Crombie, Hamilton and Gardiner.

Joe had retired a few months after Mr. Crombie, declaring that he proposed to spend the rest of his life traveling. He wanted to settle down in each country he visited long enough to study its history and its folkways. Whatever he did, one could be sure he would do it thoroughly. At the end of eight months he and his wife had returned to New York scarcely on speaking terms after forty years of congenial married life. Now they were based in a little apartment in New York from which they made sudden impulsive darts to all parts of the world. It was a doubtful compromise.

Henry, on the other hand, had bought a secondhand cruiser on which he proposed to spend most of his time. Why he had suddenly taken to the sea nobody knew, unless it was that the compactness of shipboard life appealed to his tidy, mathematical mind. After a winter spent mildewing on the coasts of Florida he had changed his mind, or rather, Mrs. Buckley had changed it for him. The boat was about to be sold and they were also living in a small apartment hotel in New York trying to reorient themselves.

"Sure, traveling was a good life," said Joe Beam. "Nobody knew better than I did how lucky I was to have a wife who was enough of a tramp to enjoy that sort of existence. Everything looked fine, but just sitting around in Saint-Jean-de-Luz reading French history didn't add up to anything. That is, for me it didn't.

"Neither does the life we're living now, dashing around like a couple of nervous bird dogs. Sure it's fun to fly down to the Bang Bang Club for a weekend of bone fishing, or to go flying off to Karachi to take in some religious ringding, but so what? I'm so constituted that trips like that must be a reward for effort, not just a means of killing time."

"That's just the way I feel," said Henry Buckley. "I wake up in the morning all set to lead a life of high achievement and then I suddenly realize that nobody cares whether my achievement is high or low or whether I achieve at all. How in the world can you accomplish anything if nobody cares? Even the medieval monks who spent their lives in cells illuminating pages of the Bible must have known that eventually someone besides God would appreciate their work."

Joe nodded. "I agree with you. A fellow has to be working toward an end or he'll find himself weaving baskets. You can't live in a vacuum or as a dot surrounded by infinity. You have to have a goal, and a time limit for getting there, and competition. If you're not matching your brains against someone, how do you know they're any good?"

Mr. Crombie listened and said little, but he found this conversation disturbing. The very things that had been troubling him vaguely for over a year were troubling these men as well. "Why do you suppose it is," he said, finally, "that other men seem able to retire successfully? Why should we find ourselves misfits in a world that seems to suit others perfectly?"

There it was; the admission that he was a misfit in the world of Highfield and Sunset Hill. He had not been prepared to cross this line, but now that it had been done he felt an immense load lifted from his shoulders. He noticed Jinny watching him with an odd expression on her face.

Joe Beam answered it. "Because it's the way we're made— all three of us. We thrive on competition and we fall apart without it. Being what we are, we lived the kind of life we did and now we can't live any other. Luckily for the world, everybody isn't the same. I've known lots of men who've retired and never lifted a finger the rest of their lives. And they've been happy as clams. That's about what they were, in my opinion. When they retired it wasn't into a new life. They just kept on doing what they'd always done—nothing."

"That's pretty rough," said Henry Buckley, "but I agree with your premise. Men don't change their characteristics just because they're sixty-five, whether they want to or not. We just happen to have been thrown up on the beach by a clause in a pension plan and we haven't been able to find our way back to the water."

"You're so right," said Joe. "It's hard to find your way back to the water after you've been given the old heave ho into the seaweed. You know what? I wish the three of us could dream up something that would give us an excuse to have an office and go to it every day. A place . . ."

"I'm sorry but you lads have to break it up," said Mrs. Crombie, glancing at her wrist watch. "We're going to drive over to Sky Mountain for dinner and on the way we're stopping in to see Sam Baker's new house in Bradbury and have cocktails with them. After that we're taking them to dinner with us."

31

AUGUST ARRIVED, HOT AND STEAM-
ing. Mr. Crombie walked down to the post office rather enjoying the feeling of sweat trickling down his face and soaking
his shirt. Oswald Battle was sitting in front of his antique
shop fanning himself with an old newspaper.

"Why is it, do you suppose," asked Mr. Battle without preliminary greeting, "that city folk pay such enormous prices to
go to the country in the summer? If it was any hotter than
this in the city, folks'd be cooked."

Mr. Crombie nodded. He had been turning this very idea
over in his mind as he came down the hill. "Well, at least *we*
don't qualify as city folk any more," he said with some pride.
"We've been here over a year now. We moved in a year ago
June 20."

"You don't think that buys you citizenship in Highfield, I
hope," said Mr. Battle. "These people don't measure by years
—they measure by generations. If your family came here in
the 1600s you're automatically in. An' I suppose they'd recognize the 1700s, with qualifications. But after that they begin
to get picky and choosy. You know Henry Blossom that has
the farm about a mile up the road from you? Well, his family's been here since they took over the place from the Indians.
But he married a girl from Middleburg. He married her forty
years ago, but Highfield folk still speak of her as a foreigner."

The post office was deserted except by its usual smell of damp, decaying paper. There were only half a dozen letters in his box; three or four bills, a letter from the Airy Breeze Summer Camp, one from a real-estate agent in Middleburg that he'd never heard of and a letter from *Who's Who*. They probably wanted him to revise proof on his write-up.

He had planned to stop on his way back for a chat with Oswald Battle, but the latter had left his seat in front of the shop and the shop itself was closed. A little note had been stuck in the door saying that the proprietor would not be back. Disappointed, Mr. Crombie started the long climb back to Sunset Hill.

The old house was empty. Mrs. Crombie had gone to some committee meeting. He took the letters into his study and sat down at his writing table. Opening the bills first, he placed them in an already bulging folder. An enormous fly buzzed senselessly as it attempted to escape through the window screen. Mr. Crombie raised the screen and brushed it out. He opened the letter from the Airy Breeze Summer Camp. A half-starved little lad was sitting on a curbstone hugging his bare knees dejectedly. He couldn't go to camp because Mr. Crombie was a stinker and wouldn't cough up with a few dollars. All right. He was a stinker. He dropped the letter into the wastebasket and opened the envelope from *Who's Who*. It contained a printed notice informing him that, because he was now retired, his biography was being placed in file for eventual insertion in an edition entitled *Who Was Who* and if he was already dead would his executors please notify the publishers promptly.

It pointed up the fact as nothing else could have, at that particular moment, that there was something radically wrong with his life. If he was merely continuing to miss Crombie, Hamilton and Gardiner, that was absurd. His business life was over. That part of him was in the past tense. He was a retired man, free to enjoy the rewards of his years of toil. The trouble was he didn't seem to want to enjoy them.

Was it power that he missed? No, there was something else. Something more subtle than power. Perhaps it was the feel of the swiftly moving current of life all around him. Compulsion came into it somewhere. There had to be an "or else" element in life to give it seasoning; a "survival" motivation. Wasn't the sickness which seemed to be affecting the peoples of the world due to the efforts of the politicians, the labor leaders and the do-gooders to eliminate the "or else" element?

What was it Joe Beam had said? "Being the kind of men we are, we lived the way we did and now we can't live any other way." That was the truth. If only, as Joe had said, they could dream up something—some form of activity that would recreate at least a microcosm of their old life.

The idea which he had originally passed over as a conversational spark suddenly caught. His mind went back forty years to the day when he had discussed the formation of an investment-counsel firm with Hamilton and Gardiner. Both of them had been far more brilliant than he was in their respective fields, just as were Joe Beam and Henry Buckley. But apparently he had had something else to contribute, some ingredient that was necessary to combine their talents into merchandise that the public wanted to buy.

He put the unopened letter from the Middleburg real-estate agent into his shirt pocket. He wanted to think. It was too late and too hot to bother about lunch. Breaking out a tray of ice he made himself a Tom Collins and carried it out to the porch. A strange feeling of peace and contentment mixed with excitement seemed to flow through his veins. Perhaps he had put too much gin in his drink. He was sleeping when Mrs. Crombie arrived home shortly after five.

32

HE FOUND THE LETTER FROM THE real-estate agent as he was preparing for bed. His first reaction was to throw it away unopened. Then his old training reasserted itself. Always open everything. You could never tell.

"Dear Mr. Crombie: I have no idea, of course, whether Sunset Hill is for sale and I am aware of the fact that you bought it only a year or more ago. In the real-estate business, however, nothing ventured, nothing gained, so I am venturing to bring to your attention a situation that may or may not be of interest to you.

"A new Freshman Dean is taking office at Middleburg College in the fall. His name is Matthew Pratt. The Pratts do not want to live 'on top of the campus.' They are young and have definite ideas how they want to bring up their three little girls. They want to find a place about ten or fifteen miles away and that puts Sunset Hill right in their range.

"We passed your place yesterday while I was showing them the pathetically few things that are available. They fell in love with it and insisted that I write and ask whether, by any chance, you would be willing to sell. I told them what I thought you paid for the place and that you had put *a great deal of money* into it during the last year or so. That did not seem to faze them in the least and I judged from their conversation that if they can find exactly what they want they will pay a good price for it.

"Won't you give me a ring at your early convenience? I would have come to see you but I had to go to New York. I will be in my office early Friday morning."

Mr. Crombie handed the letter to Jinny without comment. She was in bed, reading.

"What's this?"

"A letter."

"I had already guessed that." She read the letter, then reread it very slowly. Then she gave it back to him silently. She watched his face as he read it again. He placed it on his dresser and crossing the room, sat on the edge of her bed. For a few moments neither spoke, each seeking to read the answer in the other's eyes.

"You know. . . ." he said, finally, and paused.

"What?"

He took her hand. "I don't want to upset you, darling," he said. "Moving to the country was my idea. I know that. You fell in with it because you thought that when I retired I was entitled to live the kind of life I wanted to live. You were a city girl. It took a lot of unselfishness to let the old apartment go and move into the wilderness and I appreciated it. I still do."

"Darling, I . . ."

"Let me finish. We both fell in love with Sunset Hill the moment we set eyes on it. We've both put a lot of effort into it and I've watched you accept this life and become a part of it. You've been much more successful at that than I have. You fit in better. Perhaps it's because a woman doesn't have the same pulls that a man does. I've lived in the midst of turmoil all my life and I'm beginning to think I miss it. I miss doing things that somebody's waiting for, if you know what I mean. I can't get used to doing things that nobody gives a damn whether they get done or not. I . . ."

"Darling," she interrupted, and there was a note of nicely

controlled hysteria in her voice, "what *are* you trying to say? Are you suggesting that we sell the house and move back to New York?"

"No," he said, "I don't go as far as that. But this seems like such an unusual opportunity that I thought we ought to discuss it. This time I want to do what *you* want. I want to live the kind of life that *you* want to live. I . . ."

Her eyes filled with tears. She reached up and pulled him close to her. "Darling," she said. "My very special darling. Do you think it's too late to call up that damn real-estate man tonight?"

PART IV   *Circuition*

Those last days at Sunset Hill taught Mr. Crombie how much longer—how very much longer—it takes to build than to destroy. He often thought of the months of seeking and of anxious negotiation which had passed before they actually bought the property and of the additional months of hard work that had been necessary to put it into shape. And then, with a few pen strokes at the end of a legal document, it was gone.

Why, after the expenditure of so much effort, had they agreed so eagerly to abandon it? What was it that was driving them back to the City which he, at least, had always asserted was only a place for work and not for living? What was this sense of inner excitement which was causing them both to approach the complicated reversal of all their plans with the enthusiasm of children?

And there was no question of its complexity. They were reverting to Scene One. To do so it was necessary to pick out the properties called for in that set and to dispose of those that were no longer necessary. The time had come when the two-of-everything formula must be liquidated. The voyage of the Ark was over.

They made a room-by-room inventory of their worldly
goods, from beds to bric-a-brac. From this they chose the
items that were to go to storage until a bigger apartment
had been found; and a bigger apartment was most certainly
called for. If only they hadn't sold the old one! What was
left over—well, it would have to be given to the children.

"It breaks my heart to see all these expensive things that we
bought only a few months ago being tossed out," he said.
"Isn't there any place . . . I mean, couldn't we fit them in?"

"The answer to that is 'no,' " she said firmly. "You don't
have to feel so badly about it. The kids need this stuff in the
worst way. The thing to do is to think how happy we're going
to make them."

"It puts me all in a glow," he said. "How are we ever going
to decide who gets what?"

"Very simply," said Mrs. Crombie. "We'll have them all
come for Sunday dinner and draw lots."

This seemed like a reasonable idea until it was discovered
that the children were so trammeled-up in the webs of their
frenzied lives that they couldn't possibly tell what Sunday
they might be able to come to Sunset Hill. The only thing
they were agreed upon was that in all probability they could
never agree on a common date.

Most of them saw no reason for going through so much red
tape about a simple thing. Let each one, they said, state what
he or she wanted. That was all there was to it. Which might
not have been so had they not all wanted the same things.
Each conceded everything else to the others, in a big, mag-
nanimous gesture.

"I've often wondered how people tear their hair," Mrs.
Crombie remarked. "This is obviously the place to find out
as far as I'm concerned."

"I'd much rather send the whole ball of wax to an auction
room and let them bid it in if they want it so much—or tear
their own hair."

They made typewritten lists of everything available and sent a copy to each child, asking that they mark their choices, bearing in mind that no one child could expect to receive *all* the important items. When the last schedule was in, the score remained unchanged.

There followed long evenings of expensive telephone conversations during which it sometimes seemed that the foundations on which the Crombie family rested were being irretrievably shattered.

"Listen, Dad. I'm only an in-law. If Pat wants those things so badly then Dexter and I are going to drop out—I mean drop out entirely. Let her have them, for all we care. She raised the same ruckus about that portrait of Dexter's grandfather and we're getting sick of it."

Or, "Dad, it's your furniture, of course. You've got a right to give it to anyone you choose, but do you realize that Linda and I have never had *anything* except those two worn-out old armchairs that nobody else wanted."

"I really do hope," said Mrs. Crombie after a long telephone conversation with Pat, "that we never have to give away anything again—ever—until we're both dead. They can pull each other to pieces then, for all I care."

"I'll tell you one thing they *won't* want," said Mr. Crombie, trying to cheer her with a constructive thought. "That enormous, hideous samovar your mother brought us from Sweden years ago. It's always been in the way, we've never had a place for it and we certainly aren't going to lug it back to town."

"It isn't hideous," she said. "It's a lovely antique samovar. It has quite a history. Mother wrote it down for me. I think her letter is still in the samovar. But it *is* bulky, I'll admit that. And I'll also grant you that I'm sick of polishing it. I wonder whom we might give it to."

"Some Swedish outfit, perhaps, if you know of any."

"Now that you speak of it, when I was in Middleburg

the other day I saw something called the Swedish-American Home. I remember it because Middleburg seemed such an unlikely place for homeless Swedes. Let me look in the phone book."

She returned in a few minutes. "I was right. It's the Swedish-American Home for the Aged. Why don't I call them tomorrow?"

"Writing might be better. They'll probably insist on half a dozen people approving everything they do. I'll drop them a line. Maybe we can work out some kind of an income-tax deduction."

He wrote the following morning; a long, persuasive letter describing the samovar as a rare antique and giving its history taken from his mother-in-law's letter with embellishments. After a week had passed without receiving a reply he drove over to Middleburg and obtained a copy of the annual report of the Home. From this he learned the name of the Chairman of the Board of Trustees, to whom he wrote an even longer letter, having thought of several interesting touches to add to the history.

This letter was scarcely in the mail when Sam phoned. "Linda," he said, "just remembered that wonderful old samovar that used to be in the linen closet in the old apartment. Linda's grandmother was Swedish, you know, and so now the one thing she wants is that samovar. She says we'll forgo all the rest of the giveaway if she could just have that." Besides which, he added, they were both sick and tired of this interfamily bickering. It was getting on Linda's nerves and interfering with her painting and the only thing that he and Linda had ever had . . .

". . . was an old armchair that nobody wanted," interrupted Mr. Crombie.

"How in the world did you remember that?" asked Sam. "Well, that's the story anyway and that's the way we feel."

Delighted by this unexpected break, Mr. Crombie wrote a long, apologetic note to the Chairman of the Board of the Swedish-American Home, explaining the situation and withdrawing his offer.

He telephoned Sam at his office to tell him what he had done. Sam said he couldn't be more pleased. He knew Linda would be equally delighted. Of course, in their tiny little house at Sneden's Landing they had no room at the moment for a thing as big as the samovar. They were seriously considering an addition, however, and if this happened they would provide a suitable place for it without question. In the meanwhile they would just leave it where it was.

"What's the matter, dear? You look depressed."

He slumped into the big wing chair. "It isn't a question of not *wanting* to dispose of things during your lifetime," he said. "You *can't* dispose of them."

2

THE LAST MOVING VAN HAD LEFT. Mrs. Crombie was not there. She had gone to New York the day before, claiming a cold, but Mr. Crombie had a hunch that she had not wanted to be in at the death.

The old house was as bare as the day he had first seen it, a little over a year before. Stripped of furniture it no longer seemed to belong to him. In some subtle way it had established an identity of its own. For a brief moment it belonged only to itself, remembering the generations that had occupied it during the past 175 years, waiting for the generations yet to come, quiet, poised and utterly oblivious of this semi-stranger who had rested there for a moment like a migrating bird and was now on his way again. He took one last tour through the empty rooms. They seemed to regard him reproachfully.

"Why did you fix us up with such loving (and expensive) care if you were going to walk out? Why did you have that crazy old carpenter put shelves in your bedroom and build a toy closet in the attic? Why did you spend a whole weekend trying to paper the walk-in closet? Why, why, why?" He hurried out the kitchen door and slammed it shut behind him.

The sun was moving down to the western hills. It was that lovely amber time of day when all objects appear to grow larger and the countryside assumes a special blue-green lushness. He started to get into his car, then on an impulse he shut the door again and walked down the drive to the barn, where he took the little path that skirted its south end.

From the back of the barn he had an unobstructed view of the dark tree masses that flanked the meadows in their descent to the valley. Far below he caught the glint of the river and on the farther side, already partly shadowed by the hills, the scattered buildings of a farm showed gray-white against the darkness of the trees.

What had brought him to this place which he was now leaving? Why had he sought it so persistently? Was it an unconscious reaching back for something in his childhood which the turning pages of the years had covered up? Spacious old houses standing under forking elms; the singing stillness of summer days; wagons moving slowly down sandy roads, their wheel spokes picking up small heaps of dust; the lazy intermittent whirr of hand-pushed lawn mowers, the importance of the seasons, of the winds, of the weather; the enormous length of days. Were those the things he had been unconsciously seeking?

It was a mistake to try to recapture the past. Thomas Wolfe wrote a whole book about that. The past existed only in one's memory. Of course, it was true that certain of its physical aspects would still remain, but it was important to bear in mind that the eyes which had seen them originally, and the ears that had heard them, were gone forever and today's eyes and ears would find them distressingly different. Far better to stick to the memory pictures.

He was standing in the middle of the area where he had toiled so arduously during the last twelve months. In order to counteract the sentimental mood which he felt creeping over him like a sticky tide, he tried to conjure up all the distasteful things connected with this spot, the poison ivy, the gasping weariness, the blistered hands, the hours spent staggering about with logs for hungry fireplaces, the hopeless, unending struggle with encroaching nature.

All these things were etched vividly in his mind and yet all he could see as he looked about him for the last time was beauty. Perhaps this was due to the fact that he was no longer responsible. Now that it was no longer his duty to eliminate them, the flaws had been absorbed into the whole and the whole was good.

He walked to the car, got in and drove away without a backward glance.

3

IT WAS AMAZING HOW QUICKLY they seemed to settle back into the life of the City. Mrs. Crombie had dropped effortlessly into her old routine of committees, lunches, shopping, bridge, telephones and people. It was rather a mystery to her what her husband did all day. She had anticipated difficulty when he was confronted for the first time, as a retired man, with the hyperthyroid life of New York. He had apparently found something to keep him busy, however, or she would have heard about it long before this. It puzzled her, but, following their established custom, she asked no questions. He seemed happy. Let that suffice. When he was ready he would talk.

"You look as if you'd swallowed a covey of canaries, or a bevy, or however canaries come," she said as they sat down to dinner one evening in late September. "Come clean, darling. Has some moppet told you she understands you?"

"I was saving it till I had plenty of time for all the gory details," he replied. "All right, this is as good a time as any. Let me begin at the end and work back to the beginning. Joe Beam and Henry Buckley and I are going into business together."

She placed her soupspoon overcarefully on the saucer and stared at him incredulously. "You're *what?*"

"We're going into business. We've formed a little company. At least we're going to form one if the lawyers ever get through fussing with it."

"But what *doing,* dear? What *doing?*"

Her expression was one of such genuine astonishment that his voice became almost apologetic. "It's nothing big. Don't worry. We're not going off the deep end. It just so happens, though, that between the three of us we know a lot of corporation executives in this country and we know quite a lot about their businesses and what makes them tick, or not tick, as the case may be.

"A few weeks ago Joe had an idea about bringing two companies together and when that fellow has an idea he usually starts working on it. Well, to his surprise the idea began to jell almost immediately and when he told me about it at Sunset Hill that gave *me* an idea: Here was a piece of business just begging for a company to take care of it. Here were Joe Beam and Henry Buckley and myself just begging for a company to take care of us. I got hold of both of them right after we moved back to town. It was a natural. Joe and Henry are both experts in their different fields and they complement each other beautifully—a wonderful team—and I, oh I guess they're just taking me along for the ride.

"At any rate, they leaped at the idea like a couple of trout. I think it had been rattling around in all of our minds since that weekend at Sunset Hill. It was this piece of business of Joe's, though, that brought it into focus—made it seem practical.

"And then, do you know what happened right on top of all that? Miss Parkinson came back from her cruise. You remember they retired her six months ago and she blew herself to a trip around the world. She called me up and asked me how I liked retirement. I told her I wasn't retired any more and neither was she—she was the senior, and at the moment the only, secretary of the about-to-be-born firm of Crombie, Beam and Buckley."

"What did she say? Is she really coming?"

"Why, naturally," he said, surprised.

"But why in the world didn't you tell me about all this? Why did you keep it a secret?"

"I didn't want to tell you until we were all set. I was afraid you might persuade me not to. Do you think we're crazy?" He looked at her anxiously, seeking her approval.

She rose from her chair and coming around the table, threw her arms around his neck. "I was never so happy in my life," she said. "That's how crazy I think you are. Now I've covered you with lipstick. Go get a paper handkerchief and then tell me all about it."

When he resumed his seat at the table he looked like a small boy who suddenly finds himself praised when he had expected a scolding. "Do you realize," he said, "that I will have a regular office again; a place where I can go every day, where my mail will be waiting for me every morning and where I can answer it *that day* instead of worrying about it for a week."

The eagerness in his voice would have told her the story even if she had not known it already; the yearning for some place where he belonged, some place where he would be surrounded by the old familiar atmosphere of controlled confusion, some place where he would sense again the feeling of pressure which would indicate that he was once more an integral part of a busy world.

He told her more of the details. Joe Beam's merger negotiation would be their first piece of business. After that—well, after that they would undoubtedly dig up other similar situations. They wanted to keep themselves free, however, to tackle anything that came along which appealed to them and which they thought they were capable of handling. They were sure that other things would turn up. In fact, their difficulty might be to keep the show small, if one could judge by the reception that had been given Joe Beam during the course of a quick tour through the Midwest for the purpose of spreading the news.

As he talked, her mind went back once again to the night when he had told her that he was leaving the Guaranty and forming the firm of Crombie, Hamilton and Gardiner. Now he was doing it all over again. The same pattern. The same judgment of men. The same sense of timing. Old leopards never changed.

4

As ONE MOVED THROUGH THE streets of mid-Manhattan, in whatever direction, the eye pierced the skeletons of giant buildings in process of construction. No matter where you went you remained within a colossal ring of mounting steel and concrete, a tiny dot in the center of a fantastic arena.

On Third Avenue, on Second Avenue, on the connecting side streets, on every important corner, huge top-heavy cranes hoisted steel beams on threadlike cables over the unheeding heads of passers-by. Mountains of brick and sand blocked the all but impassable streets as office buildings and apartments rose phoenix-like from the acrid dust of demolished brownstones.

The whole face of mid-Manhattan was being changed so rapidly that people in busses, unable to spot familiar landmarks, got off at the wrong corners and motorists from the suburbs held up the profane traffic trying to read the street numbers. Where did all these businesses come from which moved into these new glass temples almost before they were finished? Where did all the people come from who fought for living space in these huge air-conditioned pueblos?

Concealed somewhere in this maelstrom was the bigger apartment they were so desperately seeking. Each morning Mrs. Crombie set out on her rounds and each night she returned, weary and empty-handed.

"I'll go crazy," she said, "if I have to spend much longer tripping over things in this miserable little apartment, but I'm becoming completely discouraged. I'll bet I've looked at ten of these new apartments today and each one was more revolting than the last. I wish you could see some of them. No, I'm glad you can't. The ceilings are so low they'd give you claustrophobia. And the living rooms are so long and narrow they look like bowling alleys. I haven't seen a good, old-fashioned, square living room in a week. To make things worse, none of them has a fireplace. How do they expect you to arrange furniture without a fireplace?"

"I've always wondered what fireplaces were for," he said, in a feeble attempt to ward off hysteria. She ignored it.

"And the kitchens! There's so much stainless steel that you have to wear dark glasses while you cook. They squeeze in every expensive gadget they can dream up, but no maid's room—not even a place for a maid to sit down if you had one. Now anybody who can afford kitchens like those can certainly afford to hire someone to put them to better use than frying hamburgers.

"When you've seen the kitchen you've had it. The rest of the place is about as solid as a Japanese hotel. If you blew your nose everyone on the floor would know you had a cold. The whole setup gives me the creeps. And as for the prices! I don't see where people *get* all this money."

"They must cheat somewhere," said Mr. Crombie, consolingly. "God, how I wish we were back in our old apartment." It was as much a prayer as an expletive.

"Wish! I'd give my eyeteeth and a couple of false ones to walk in that dear old door and find nothing changed."

Another week went by with no results. Then one night she came home with excitement in her eyes. "Graham, it's incredible. It's a miracle! You could never guess in a thousand years. Those Clarkson people—the ones who bought our old apartment—are being moved to California by their company. It's on the market and I've got an option on it until tomorrow morning."

"You're fooling," he said incredulously.

"I'm not," she said. "I've been there and gazed on it with my own eyes. It nearly made me cry to see it all cluttered up with someone else's furniture, but it looked good even at that. And big—Lordy, I'd forgotten how big it is."

"What difference does it really make how big it is?" he said. "It fits our things and our things fit it. It fits us the way a shell fits a snail. Jinny, shall we buy it back?"

"Well, you know how I feel. But I think you're in for a shock."

"What do you mean—the price?"

She nodded. "About half again as much as we sold it for."

"To hell with it," he said. "Inflation will get us out whole. Let's do it."

She hugged him. "Oh, darling, that's just what you were supposed to say. I feel as if I were back home after a long, long journey."

5

IT WASN'T A BIG BUSINESS, AL-
though there were indications that it might grow faster than
they said they wanted it to. But perhaps that was something
they said to people as a hedge; just in case things became
sticky. They were used to growth as a yardstick of success
and in spite of what they might say, they probably would
have been mortified if they had failed to bring it about in
their new venture.

Growth or no growth, they were happy. The constant ringing of the phones was a trumpet call. It satisfied something
which had been an unconscious hunger to all of them since
they had retired. To be involved once more in the incessant
attempt to reach men who were perpetually in conference, to
find one's self interrupted a dozen times while dictating a
letter, to be hopelessly bogged down on the days' schedules,
to be rushing to meetings, making luncheon appointments,
taking business trips, attending dinners, moving again in that
ever-behindhand world in which they had lived for so many
years—all this was manna to their confusion-starved souls.

It was good to have Miss Parkinson sitting beside him, her
notebook on her knee. It made him feel once more complete,
as if a missing piece of him had been found and slipped into
place.

"Were you surprised?" he asked.

"Not a bit," she said. "I knew you'd be back at the old

stand in one form or another. In fact, I timed my trip to get back just about when I did, figuring you'd need me."

"Why were you so sure?"

"Oh, I don't know. I've lived so long with top brass that I guess I've learned to know it better than it knows itself."

"If you knew so much why didn't you tell me before I spent all my money finding out the hard way?"

"What good would it have done? You wouldn't have believed me. You were obsessed with the notion that you'd earned your place in the sun. Or at least that's what you said. I've often wondered if you weren't more or less unconsciously bluffing. But if I'd said to you 'Don't go to the country. It's not your dish. Work is your dish. If you try to pretend it isn't you'll starve to death'—if I'd said that, you wouldn't have paid any attention to me. You had to dig it out for yourself."

"But isn't there something wrong with the whole picture?" he asked. "Haven't I failed somewhere? Suppose I *have* been primarily interested in business all my life. Is that any excuse for not having developed some outside interests as I went along? And if I had, wouldn't I have been able to retire happily when the time came?"

"Nuts," she said. "I don't know why people always try to make it sound as if there's something wrong—something unworthy—in being completely absorbed in business. Why shouldn't a man be absorbed in his business just as much as a writer is absorbed in his writing or a research chemist in his laboratory?"

Mr. Crombie looked out the window in front of which two bedraggled pigeons were strutting back and forth as if on sentry duty. "In lots of ways I couldn't agree with you more," he said, "and yet I can't help having a sort of a guilty feeling about it. If I'd only developed some hobbies . . ."

She snorted and, rising from her chair, went to the bookcase behind his desk and pulled out a dictionary. "I've always meant to look up that word," she said. "Let's see . . . 'heard' . . . 'hobgoblin' . . . here it is . . . 'hobby: a favorite occupation, subject, topic or the like, pursued for the amusement or interest it affords.' That's just about what I expected and just about my idea of it. You worked all your life to build something. You didn't work for 'the amusement or interest it afforded'—you worked because the creative instinct in you kept driving you on to make Crombie, Hamilton and Gardiner a perfect organization. You didn't succeed. That kind of goal can never be reached. But what's wrong with the trying? Isn't that hobby enough for anyone?"

"But shouldn't there be an end somewhere? A place where you call it a day?"

"Why?" she asked impatiently. "Your interest is business. Why should you have to take up travel or golf or rug-hooking as your life work just because you're sixty-five? Why shouldn't people go right on doing what interests them?"

She stopped suddenly. "What do you suppose made me sound off like that? I'm sorry."

"Please don't stop," he begged. "All this is music to my ears." He wondered whether Miss Parkinson realized that she was following her own prescription.

"No," she said. "I've talked too much already. Just one sentence from Oliver Wendell Holmes, the Supreme Court boy, then I'm through. I ran across it years ago and I've never forgotten it. He said, 'To live is to function; to stop functioning is to stop living.'"

"O.K.," he said, noting the landing of a third pigeon on the window ledge. "And let me cap that with one fresh from the griddle of Graham Crombie, the Crombie, Beam and Buckley boy, quote you can't retire from life unquote."

She glanced at her wrist watch. "You're going to be late to your luncheon appointment," she said.

ABOUT THE AUTHOR

Edward Streeter was born in New York on August 1, 1891, and graduated from Harvard in 1914. He was a reporter for the Buffalo *Express* from 1914 to 1916, and a correspondent for that paper while he was with the New York National Guard on the Texas Border from June 1916 to March 1917. He says it was then that the first germs of *Dere Mable* came into being, and the book was written in a South Carolina training camp in the fall of 1917. Published early in 1918, *Dere Mable* became an immediate best-seller.

After the war, during which he served overseas as a first lieutenant, Edward Streeter did free-lance writing for a couple of years. He then joined the Bankers Trust Company, where he was a vice-president until 1929. During that period and in the twenty-five years that Mr. Streeter was a vice-president of the Bank of New York, he successfully combined writing and banking. Since his retirement in August of 1956, he has devoted his full time to writing.

Mr. Streeter and his wife live in New York City. They have four children, all married.

Besides *Dere Mable*, Mr. Streeter's other books include *Daily Except Sunday, Father of the Bride, Skoal Scandinavia, Mr. Hobbs' Vacation, Merry Christmas, Mr. Baxter,* and *Mr. Robbins Rides Again.*

1

THE GAME BEGINS

WHEN I WAS SIXTEEN YEARS OLD, my parents summoned me into the small den of our suburban home on Long Island. They sat me down opposite them and proceeded to outline a plan.

"Look, John, we all know that your sister is the smart one," my father began as my mother nodded in agreement, "so we've had to make a family decision about college. Your mother and I have agreed that we have to save our money so your sister can go to a well-known, prestigious school."

He then produced an envelope and withdrew five brochures. They were all from small, private men's colleges, each located in the middle of nowhere in Virginia, New England, or Pennsylvania and each with a bargain-priced tuition. It was up to me to select one.

Four years later, when I was twenty, my parents followed up that earlier confidence builder with a second sit-down in the same spot. My father's tone was pretty much the same as well.

"John, we need to be honest with each other here," he started out. "By almost any criteria you've pretty much underperformed in college. For openers, you went from being a National Honor Society student at a very competitive suburban high school to a C student in college."

My mother was not going to be left out this time. Fortified by a couple of martinis, she jumped in. "You screwed around too much. You're completely irresponsible with money. You're very immature."

While I'd like to say those accusations were unfounded, the truth is they were not formed in a vacuum. So I said nothing.

"Since this is your senior year in college," my father continued, "it's time to discuss the best plan for you after graduation."

My best bet, he said, was to find a large company that was willing to give me a chance. Once there, I needed to make sure that I did whatever they told me, showed up on time every day, and kept my mouth shut. "And don't be a wise guy," he added.

"Just follow that plan, and you'll have no problems," my mother urged. "Then you stay at that company for thirty or forty years. So when you're sixty-five, they'll take care of you until you die."

I remember considering their advice. For about five minutes. This book is about what I did instead.

I'll do us both a favor and bypass the early work experiences: the lemonade stand, the lawn mowing, the paper route. We've all done some variation of these tasks—designed to teach us the value of a dollar, project management, and other realities of working for or running an organization.

Moving forward, I need to clear up a couple of things. First, to the best of my knowledge and recollection, everything described

in this book really happened over the last thirty years in the world of SCRABBLE. That said, there are a couple of disclaimers. For example, in some cases I've changed names or completely left them out when legally necessary.

I've also changed the venue in a couple of places—from a boardroom to a restaurant, from Chicago to Los Angeles, that kind of thing. That's pretty much it. Oh yeah, I should also say that I suffer no illusions about my own role in all these stories. I have it on good authority from a disturbingly large and well-credentialed roster of people that the case could be made that at times I was overconfident, clueless, evasive, lazy, political, and dead wrong. And, of course, all the observations and opinions expressed in this book are mine only.

Mostly, though, I'm proud of what I've accomplished and experienced. I am humbled by the people I've met and worked with. They include famous authors and journalists, numerous celebrities, brilliant game players, legendary word nerds, corporate CEOs, television and movie executives, my own colleagues at the National SCRABBLE Association (NSA), kids in the National School SCRABBLE Program, and so many more. All of them had critical roles in our collective mission to first revive a sagging SCRABBLE brand and then craft a plan to ensure the future of this glorious game. And I'm thankful for all the remarkable people I've met and worked with and the wild, random adventures this job afforded me.

I'm thankful as well for the spectacular work atmosphere I enjoyed all those years. My office was in an old sea captain's house on the East End of Long Island, almost exactly a hundred miles from midtown Manhattan. At the height of the NSA's activities, there were ten of us working there, the women outnumbering

men two to one. Depending on the day, there were also as many as three dogs hanging around. We had a screened-in porch where we held our summer meetings and a kitchen where soup was invariably being made in the winter. The phone rang constantly; many days we fielded well over fifty calls. They ranged from people wanting us to settle a dispute over a rule or word to someone asking us to send a ninety-year-old lifelong SCRABBLE fan a birthday letter to a Hasbro executive asking for input on a new game idea.

Ironically, very little SCRABBLE was played on the premises during the workday. We were too damned busy. Among our core responsibilities:

- Overseeing the activities of more than two hundred official SCRABBLE clubs throughout North America
- Scheduling and sanctioning nearly three hundred SCRABBLE tournaments annually
- Publishing the *SCRABBLE News* eight times a year
- Maintaining the official tournament rating system
- Coordinating up to seventy-five literacy fund-raising events annually
- Working with publisher Merriam-Webster on updating the *Official SCRABBLE Players Dictionary*
- Reviewing SCRABBLE book manuscripts and new product ideas for Hasbro
- Searching the media and Internet for SCRABBLE knock-offs and trademark violations
- Overseeing the National School SCRABBLE Program and doing outreach to schools, parks and recreation

departments, educational conventions, libraries, and more

■ Organizing and promoting the National SCRABBLE Championship, the National School SCRABBLE Championship, and the World SCRABBLE Championship

■ Serving as technical advisers when SCRABBLE was used in a film, television show, or commercial

2

OPENING MOVES

I KNEW VIRTUALLY NOTHING ABOUT SCRABBLE WHEN I began this adventure. I did come from a family of word and game lovers, but my gaming pursuits at the time were poker, crossword puzzles, trivia, and backgammon.

When I say I come from a family of word lovers, I should confess that we came from the darker side of the word world: grammar. Yes, grammar, that purist pursuit that engenders, if not outright encourages, endearing personal qualities such as self-righteousness, pedantry, and a sense of superiority. In our household, should any family member misuse or mispronounce a word, he or she could pretty much count on the correct usage being shouted out instantaneously, often by more than one other person. Forty years after the incident, my family still chuckles smugly about the time my uncle Richard blurted out the word IRREGARDLESS when telling a story. Clearly, he had mistakenly blended REGARDLESS with IRRESPECTIVE. Still, he was hooted

out of the room, bolting in a flustered huff. Sadly, Uncle Richard did not live to see that IRREGARDLESS is now included in *Merriam-Webster's Collegiate Dictionary, Eleventh Edition.*

It's important for those of us in the Grammar Police to examine our motivation:

- Is it to make the world a better-communicating and more ear-pleasing place?
- Is it to help a friend or loved one avoid an embarrassing grammar situation in the future?
- Is it simply to satisfy our own need to be right?
- Is it a means to show someone up—a boss, an enemy— by making ourselves look smarter?

Only you and your conscience know your true motivation. However, the Grammar Police in my family defused any negative accusations by employing this mantra: it's not about being right, it's about being *accurate.*

Ultimately, this topic raises the question of what to do in daily conversation when confronted with an appalling misuse or mispronunciation of a word or phrase. The more tolerant of us will simply shrug it off—perhaps silently and complacently noting the transgression—and move on. Others, with a fervent commitment to pristine language and, perhaps, a dark personal need, have a number of options.

One is *correctly using the mangled word or phrase a bit later in the same conversation.* Let's say your neighbor uses the word BANAL while telling a story, mispronouncing it as "*bay*-nul" as opposed to the preferred "buh-*nal.*"

After wincing, you allow the story to continue. Then, after

the topic has moved on, you find a way to use the word yourself later on in the conversation, pronouncing it correctly. At that point, you've done all you can. The onus is on your neighbor to recognize the transgression.

Option two: *just flat-out call the offender on it*. As I said, my family would simply shout out the correct usage or pronunciation in the culprit's face, a gleeful Greek chorus of the self-righteous. There is, however, a tamer and arguably more practical and sensitive approach than that brutal tactic. I confess to employing it exactly once in my life.

A colleague of mine, well educated and highly successful in business, was telling a story about attending a very high-profile, black-tie charity affair. A modest guy, he remarked about his fascination and slight discomfort at "being there hobnobbing with all the HOI POLLOI."

I immediately knew his intended meaning: that he was among the upper class. Sadly, the actual meaning is the complete opposite, and I was dismayed—for him—by his unfortunate choice of phrase. Of course, we are all guilty of sprinkling our conversations with the occasional foreign phrase, right? It's an efficient and time-tested technique to subtly display our intellect and sophistication. Or so we'd like to think.

My sense was that he might have been thinking of "HOITY-TOITY," a similar-sounding phrase with a slightly foreign tinge. It has a secondary meaning of "highfalutin." Regardless, something possessed me to stop my friend dead in his tracks with this question.

"Excuse me, Max, but if you were misusing a word in conversation, would you want me to tell you?" When I told another word-loving friend about this later, he eloquently replied, "Dude,

how the fuck is he supposed to answer that question!" He maintained that my approach could be classified as nonviolent social aggression.

At any rate, Max allowed that of course he'd want to know if he was misusing a word. I was even certain I detected a sliver of gratitude in his reply. Before I corrected him, I explained that I myself am the kind of person who would definitely want to know as opposed to going through the rest of my life unwittingly offending language sticklers—and looking stupid. Later, I decided upon reflection that this approach was both impractical and socially dangerous. That left me with no choice but to consider the third option: *the anonymous letter.*

While this option may seem a bit of overkill and of dubious character, it is effective. I hasten to add that I've never actually employed this tactic. However, an example might be along these lines.

Dear Brenda:

You are one of the smartest and most wonderful people I know, and I treasure our relationship. However, I need to write to you about an important matter that's been going on for some time. There's no easy way to tell you this, but I've noticed a number of times that you've been misusing the words LIE, LAY, and LAIN and I feel compelled to call it to your attention. Please know that, according to experts, these are among the most misused words in the English language. So don't beat yourself up too much! I just thought you'd want to know.

Sincerely,
A friend

The benefit here is twofold. First, you've successfully removed one more instance of incorrect word usage from the atmosphere. Second, you've helped a friend—whether it was asked for or not.

In addition to my family's word and grammar vigilance, my early life was subject to an authority of an even higher order—the Roman Catholic Church. This dynamic operated on two levels. First, the traditional English curriculum—taught at my all-boys school by grim, presumably celibate monks—was disproportionately devoted to language, vocabulary, and reading. To this day, should a syntax emergency arise, I could effectively diagram a sentence to avert a disaster. At least I like to think so.

I remember one time, in fifth grade, being whipped with the knotted rope belt worn around a monk's waist for a reading mistake. I was standing in front of a class of fifty boys, reading aloud a passage about Monaco. I kept saying "prince-abil-ity" instead of "princ-*ipal*-ity." Six times I mispronounced the word, and six times the rope lashed the back of my thighs. Finally, I was sent to my seat in shame. The monk immediately called up another boy, who promptly read it correctly, punctuating it with a gloating smirk in my direction.

I got off easy. A year later, a teacher hung one of my classmates out a third-story window by his ankles for using the word "ain't."

But the church did contribute to my word nerdom in other ways. For example, I was an altar boy. This meant that as a ten-year-old I had to learn hundreds of words and phrases in Latin in order to serve Mass. Understandably, this contributed to a lifelong curiosity about words. Later, four years of Latin in high school helped me understand the value of Latin roots as well. It

also developed an ability to memorize hundreds of words that served no purpose whatsoever in the real world—a very useful skill for SCRABBLE players. The reality is that no one is going to go very far in the world of tournament SCRABBLE who isn't willing to commit to memory obscure but tile-valuable words.

Here's an example of such a word: UMIAQ. Every tournament SCRABBLE player knows UMIAQ. It means "an Eskimo canoe" and is also spelled with a K: UMIAK. It's of interest because it is one of just three words in the English language that has a Q and U that are not connected. The others are QIVIUT, which means "the wool of a musk-ox," and BURQA, an alternative spelling of BURKA. Pretty obscure stuff, huh? Yet one day, many summers ago, I received an excited telephone call from my friend and frequent SCRABBLE opponent Herb Scannell, who at the time was president of Nickelodeon. He had just returned from a vacation to Iceland. His excitement was palpable through the long-distance connection.

"You'll never guess what I just saw on my trip!" Herb gushed. "I was leaving the airport in Greenland. About a mile outside of the exit, I spotted a sign nailed to a tree. In big letters, it said 'Umiaq for Rent'!"

"No shit! You're kidding me!" I was excited as he. This was a word nerd's version of people seeing the image of the Virgin Mary on a piece of toast or a tree stump. Only after he hung up did I realize that I'd forgotten to ask whether it was the UMIAQ or UMIAK spelling. In the spirit of full disclosure—and to head off angry letters and calls—I should mention that UMIAQ has additional alternative spellings. Among them are OOMIAC and OOMIACK.

▪ ▪ ▪

It's probably the single question I've been asked the most over the last twenty-five years. "So how does one get to be the executive director of the National SCRABBLE Association?" Of course, the subtext to that question is often "Why you?"

I can't speak for anyone else, but here's how it happened for me. I *literally* can't speak for anyone else, because I'm the only one who's ever had the job. However, there was an official organization before the National SCRABBLE Association that went by the catchy name of SCRABBLE Brand Crossword Game Players, Inc.

The earlier organization was an in-house division of Selchow & Righter, then the SCRABBLE trademark holder and manufacturer. It was a relatively small, family-owned company, best known for SCRABBLE and Parcheesi. The SCRABBLE Brand Crossword Game, Inc., unit was comprised of a company executive with a couple of assistants. No one in the organization admitted to being an accomplished SCRABBLE player, nor were any tournament players actively involved in the running of the organization.

At the time, 1982, I was working out of our house in the country, trying to write a novel and doing advertising and public relations for a couple of clients both locally and in New York City. My brother-in-law worked at advertising giant J. Walter Thompson in Manhattan, where Selchow & Righter was a client. As often happens in that business, a colleague of his, John Nason, was leaving to move over to the "client side" to become the vice president of marketing for Selchow & Righter. As Nason's new

job would be on Long Island, about an hour from my home, it was suggested we meet.

John Nason and I hit it off immediately. He was a thoughtful, smart, elegant man, who had cowritten an excellent book on advertising entitled *Advertising: How to Write the Kind That Works.* He was looking to form alliances in his new job and suggested that I might be able to contribute to the fledgling *SCRABBLE Players Bulletin* published by his company.

That's how it all started. I then spent a couple of years working with Nason's colleague Jim Houle, a nice wacky-scientist kind of guy, who ran the SCRABBLE Brand Crossword Game Players Division. I wrote some stories for their newspaper; I visited some official SCRABBLE clubs and, at Houle's suggestion, entered a sanctioned SCRABBLE tournament in Connecticut.

It was the first time in my life—but far from the last—that a number of SCRABBLE tournament players greeted me with a blend of suspicion and contempt. I had not done myself any favors in my presentation. For openers, I was wearing a jacket and tie, whereas the players were dressed somewhere between casual and sloppy. Most seemed serious, studious, and humorless. Worse, I was woefully unprepared. I'd barely glanced at the rules, had no idea of the insider's list of key words, and did not give strategy a thought beyond finding a word on my rack and laying it on the board. Even though I'd been placed in the Novice Division, I was destroyed and humiliated in the first three games. My opponents didn't seem to be having much fun either, despite their lopsided victories. At the end of the third game, the pleasant woman in her fifties who had just vanquished me leaned across the table. "Don't take this the wrong way," she said, "but you're in way over your head."

I immediately went over to Jim Houle, who, though not play-ing, had accompanied me. We agreed that my time would be bet-ter spent roaming the playing floor to observe some games and moves. I'd also have lunch and dinner with the players to be bet-ter understand both them and SCRABBLE's appeal. In addition, I'd study some of the various written materials around the tour-nament, including newsletters, word lists, and flyers for upcom-ing tournaments and more.

By the end of my first tournament weekend, I'd reached three critical realizations. First, there was obviously a lot more to the SCRABBLE subculture than I'd ever realized. Secondly, there was a lot more subtlety to the tournament game than to the liv-ing room version. Third, for thousands of people throughout North America, SCRABBLE was far more than a game. It was both a consuming passion and a significant part of their identity.

So it became my job—a mission, ultimately—to recognize this curious passion and tell the story to the rest of the world.

3

HOW A WORD GETS INTO
THE DICTIONARY

PERHAPS THE MOST DOMINANT TOPIC OF conversation throughout my career has been the dictionary. This includes what words are admitted, what words are deleted, how often the dictionary is updated, and the difference between the "American" and the "British" dictionaries. How words get into your everyday desk dictionary is similar to how they find their way into SCRABBLE, so much of the discussion that follows applies to both.

The NSA routinely received calls from indignant SCRABBLE players, many in disbelief that an entry in the *Official SCRABBLE Players Dictionary* is, in fact, a real word. These were mostly living room players as opposed to tournament players. The latter are so used to seeing crazy stuff pop up on an opponent's board that nothing really surprises them, and many have a more-the-merrier attitude when it comes to admissible words.

The aggrieved tend to be longtime casual players, who will frequently cite "the King's English" as their guideline for what

words are real and what words are not. The phrase I've probably invoked most often with them over the years is "With all due respect, just because you never heard of it does not mean it's not a real word." I, like my colleagues at Merriam-Webster, believe that the language is a living, breathing entity and that words, meaning, and even grammatical usage are going to change over the course of time. As well they should. Otherwise, we'd all be walking around talking like characters from *Beowulf.*

Chief among the complaints are onomatopoetic words. Examples include MM, HM, HMM, WHOOSH, BRR, BRRR, and the like. These drive people crazy, despite the fact that they tend to be extremely playable and valuable words. I guess there are fewer Ogden Nash fans out there than I'd anticipated.

Another irksome category for word complaints is foreign words. The general rule of thumb is this: if there is no English equivalent, the word finds its way into our everyday language, then onto the pages of the dictionary. There are numerous examples, among them TACO, ADIOS, CIAO (and its alternative spelling JIAO), SI, AMIGO, and CROISSANT. When I explain this criterion, it tends to mollify most complaints. And let's face it. As the world gets smaller because of advances in technology and communication, this phenomenon is going to happen more, not less. This is especially relevant in regard to the Hispanification of the American culture and to the collision course the United States is on with the Middle East. Heck, twenty-five years ago most Americans had never even heard of Cinco de Mayo or a burka—let alone jihad.

Foreign currency tends to annoy people the most. XU, for example, is a monetary unit of South Vietnam and an extremely valuable SCRABBLE word. (For some reason, it does not take an s.)

A ZAIRE is a monetary unit of the former country of the same name. (No, I have no idea why there was such a lack of creativity in Zaire's Treasury Department.) A frustrated SCRABBLE player—a retired schoolteacher—had had enough when she called the NSA to complain about the word. "I dare you," she sputtered, "use the word in a sentence."

I thought for a moment. "How about a zaire for your thoughts?" I suggested. She hung up on me.

Later, I told my NSA friend top tournament veteran Robert Kahn about the encounter. He laughed and said, "Be thankful she didn't confront you about the word REI."

"How come?" I knew the word, of course, but never knew the meaning.

"It's probably the most indefensible word in the game," he said. "Look it up."

I did. REI is "an erroneous English form for a former Portuguese coin." Yeah, he has a point.

This episode brings up the question: How exactly does a word find its way into the dictionary, and where do the words come from? I'll answer the second part first. New words simply arise from the culture, as they have since the beginning of time, from many different corridors.

Some new entries are foreign words being assimilated into English. Technology, recently more than ever, has contributed numerous terms and will continue to do so. Examples include EMAIL, BYTE, WEBMAIL, SPAM, and BITMAP.

As hip-hop culture goes mainstream, it too will provide words and new meanings for existing words. PHAT has been acceptable for some time, and CHILLAX became acceptable in 2014. Other acceptable slang words include AWOL, MOOLAH, YO, and COZ.

Who finds these words, and how is it decided they are worthy of inclusion? The first round in the process is an activity called "reading and marking," and it involves all of the editors at Merriam-Webster.

Visit the desk of one of those editors on any given day and you'll find piles of publications, e-mails, and research covering every aspect of language and society. For example, a reading pile might include such diverse sources as *People* magazine, the *Congressional Record*, a scientific journal, the *National Enquirer*, *TV Guide*, *The New Yorker*, *Yankee* magazine, an educational quarterly, and the like. The task is simple: to read in search of good examples of words used in context. And what are the editors looking for? Most obviously, examples of new words, but also old words being used in new ways, variant spellings, capitalization, inflected forms, and evidence for where the words show up—whether it be in glossy weekly magazines, the *New York Times*, scholarly journals, or even a comic strip. When editors find good examples (also called "citations"), they mark them and send them to a data-entry group that enters them into the citation database. And when the editors have enough citations for a new word, it becomes eligible for admission into the next edition. This is a simplification of the process, believe me, but that is fundamentally how it works. For perspective, know that the Merriam-Webster citation file has citations dating back as far as the 1890s—more than sixteen million of them.

While this process has served us well, it is not immune to changing times—specifically technology and social media. So I asked my colleagues at Merriam-Webster if Facebook, Twitter, YouTube, and the like will streamline the inclusion process in terms of both speed of acceptance and volume of words. Is it

possible that new media staples such as LOL, WTF, and BTW will ultimately be viewed as actual "words" and find their way onto a SCRABBLE board?

John Morse, president of Merriam-Webster, was the first to weigh in on the subject. "My initial comment is that the term 'social media' takes in a lot of different kinds of communications. For example, in the physical world, all evidence of language use is noteworthy, but an example of a word taken from the front page of the *New York Times* is going to be more significant than an example taken from a family photograph album. And I think the same applies with social media." Hence the question becomes: How does a "new" word on someone's Facebook page rate in significance compared to one in a Twitter post from, say, the Associated Press? Only time—and future technology—will tell.

Morse agrees that the new-word inclusion process is speeding up. "I would say that the process has already speeded up significantly, and yes, that has happened because of the Web. My sense is that twenty years ago, the shortest lag (with a few notable exceptions) was around ten years, and a typical lag might be closer to twenty. And now, many words are getting in with a lag of five to ten, and sometimes faster than that." He goes on to say, "I do think the overall observation is correct: words establish themselves in the language faster, and we detect that sooner than before. And that happens because of the existence of the Web."

Stephen Perrault, Merriam-Webster's director of defining— now there's a great job title—says, "While we look to digital sources for evidence that we use as the basis for dictionary entries, we don't at this point gather a lot of citations directly from social media." So it appears that while social media will

be increasingly a factor in determining dictionary inclusion, evidence from mainstream professionally written and edited sources still prevails.

That said, Perrault reminds us, "I'll note 'the dictionary' itself is now increasingly thought of as an online database rather than (or in addition to) a printed book, and that plays a role in speeding up the process as well."

For some reason, this topic reminds me of the overused quote attributed to Andy Warhol, that in the future "everyone will be famous for fifteen minutes." While we should probably take the statement at face value, there are some who feel the late Pop artist was a media visionary. They make the argument that he meant that one day there would be so much media that there would not be enough celebrities to go around. So, over the years, we have had to elevate the likes of 1994's O. J. Simpson house-guest Kato Kaelin and today's Kim Kardashian to take the place of, perhaps, Walter Cronkite and Grace Kelly. Will the demands of social media become so immediate and deep that there will not be enough new words to go around? I guess we'll see.

As I write this, I am personally involved in this process, following a proposed new definition of the word CATFISH. Here's how it started.

In 2010, two friends and collaborators, Henry Joost and Ariel Schulman, directed a documentary film entitled *Catfish*. It made its debut at the Sundance Film Festival to both wild acclaim and controversy. *Catfish* is a true story that documents the Internet love story of Yaniv "Nev" Schulman, Ariel's brother, as he virtually meets, gets to know, and falls in love with a young woman he randomly met online. When Nev and the filmmakers decided to pay a surprise visit to the young woman, they found out she was

not who she pretended to be. To begin with, she was married and perhaps twenty years older than her online persona.

The woman's husband actually inspired the film's title. When told of his wife's deception, he shared an anecdote about a curious practice in the fishing industry. It seems that in the old days cod had a tendency to get sluggish and mushy when being shipped from Alaska to China in large vats. Someone had the idea of throwing catfish into the mix to keep things vibrant and inter- esting. Hence he depicts his wife similarly, saying with a shrug, "There are those people who are catfish in life."

Fueled by both the Internet and traditional media, CATFISH became a pop culture term in a matter of months. The very first examples of a new meaning for the word were showing up. As a noun, a CATFISH was now an individual who pretended to be someone he or she was not on the Internet. As a verb, one could now get CATFISHED or deceived by an individual with a bogus identity.

Below are a few sample excepts from the citation file at Merriam-Webster that traces the trail of its usage to the ultimate decision to admit CATFISH's new meaning into the dictionary:

After the film's debut, a new definition emerged: "someone who pretends to be someone they're not using Facebook or other social media to create false identities, particularly to pursue online romances."

BOSTON GLOBE, January 27, 2013

Criminal Minds star Thomas Gibson was duped two years ago by a stranger he met online, even sending her a steamy hot tub video. The 51-year-old actor . . . exchanged explicit

photos and videos with the North Dakota woman before he discovered he was being catfished and cut off all contact.

TMZ Australia, August 21, 2013

On their new MTV show *Catfish*, Nev Schulman and Max Joseph help people in online relationships discover if they're being duped. . . . After the Manti Te'o hoax . . . "catfish" became part of the national lexicon.

PEOPLE, February 11, 2013

So now you know how a word gets into the dictionary. It happens rarely, but over the years a handful of words have been *removed* from the *Official SCRABBLE Players Dictionary*, or *OSPD*. I'm not talking about the "word purge" of allegedly offensive entries mentioned earlier but about random words that, upon review, were deemed inadmissible by the editors at Merriam-Webster. One that tournament SCRABBLE players miss a lot is KEV, a noun meaning, according to the second edition of the *OSPD*, "a unit of energy." This was a handy word, allowing players to score well with the K and V while eliminating those cumbersome letters in favor of some more bingo-prone. ("Bingo" is an insider's term for a play using all seven tiles.) However, it was ultimately decided that KEV was not a word but rather an abbreviation. Bummer.

Another handy word removed from the *OSPD* in later editions was DA. It is an Italian preposition meaning "from," as in the name of the explorer Vasco da Gama. However, it was eventually decided that DA was *too* Italian, or perhaps *only* Italian. After further consideration, Merriam-Webster decided it was *ciao* for

DA. But DA was not DOA for long. It resurfaced in the fifth edition in 2014, now defined as a term of endearment.

One of my favorites is the word STETSON. It appeared in the original *OSPD*, defined as a "broad-brimmed hat." However, STETSON was gone by the second edition, published in 1990. It had been determined by Merriam-Webster—and perhaps by attorneys from the hat company—that STETSON was a trade-marked name, and hence properly capitalized and hence not play-able according to Rule 8 of the SCRABBLE game. Yet it appears again today in the list of acceptable words for tournament play. What happened?

STETSON was a case of diverging opinions from the two authorities who compile and select words for the *OSPD* and its companion volume, the *Official Tournament and Club Word List*, or *OWL*. The first group, of course, is the editorial staff at Merriam-Webster. The second is the official Dictionary Com-mittee of, until 2013, the National SCRABBLE Association and currently NASPA, the NSA's successor, the North American SCRABBLE Players Association. This is a group of hardcore word enthusiasts with strong opinions and the knowledge to back them up. As head of the NSA, I was automatically a mem-ber of the Dictionary Committee. I can say with certainty I did not make a single contribution to the Dictionary Committee in twenty-five years. I wouldn't have dared.

Just as civilians disagree about what words are good in SCRABBLE, the pros do as well. The NSA Dictionary Com-mittee argued that STETSON falls into the same category as ASPIRIN or MIMEOGRAPH—brand names that culturally are fre-quently used as generic words. "Some words meet our criteria,

but not Merriam-Webster's," notes former NASPA Dictionary Committee chairman Jim Pate. Remember, most tournament SCRABBLE players are looking for as many words to play as possible. Merriam-Webster, on the other hand, has to be mindful of the legal status of words. If a registered trademark is in effect, then the trademark status must be recognized and the word must be capitalized and hence falls prey to Rule 8.

However, with the creation and publishing of the *OWL* in 1998, a middle ground was reached. Merriam-Webster agreed, albeit reluctantly, to accommodate the NSA Dictionary Committee. Here are some *OWL* words:

AQUALUNG	LATINA
BENADRYL	LEVIS
BIRO	LUCITE
BRILLO	LYCRA
BUDDHA	MAILGRAM
CATHOLICS	MASONITE
CROCKPOT	NONGLARES
DACRON	ORLON
DUMPSTER	POPSICLE
EMMY	PYREX
ENUF	SORTA
FORMICA	TEFLON
FRISBEE	TOFUTTI
JACUZZI	TRES
JELLO	VASELINE
JETWAY	VELCRO
KEWPIE	WIMMIN
KLEENEX	ZLOTIES

Clearly, many of these are proper-noun product names. Yet the case can be made—and was—that they've become so integrated into everyday language that they belong on a SCRABBLE board.

The back-and-forth word forays in both general dictionaries and the *Official SCRABBLE Players Dictionary* serve to remind us that the English language is a growing, evolving, occasionally contracting entity in regard to both meanings and usage. Traditionalists who bemoan the deterioration of "the King's English" would be well advised to rethink their criteria.

4

WASH OUR MOUTHS
OUT WITH SOAP

N THE EARLY 1990S, TWO WOMEN were playing SCRABBLE in suburban Washington, DC. At one point in the game, a word was challenged. The players decided to settle the dispute by checking the *Official SCRABBLE Players Dictionary, Second Edition*. However, in skimming the pages, the women stumbled across the word KIKE. Understandably, they were appalled. And, in a you-can't-make-this-stuff-up scenario, one of the two women was a Holocaust survivor.

The pair proceeded to scour the book. To their horror and disappointment, they found not only every possible slur against Jews (JEW as a verb, KIKE, HEBE, YID) but those against blacks, Hispanics, Catholics, gays, and any other group one could name.

By the end of this exercise, the women were on a mission. They were going to have these words removed from SCRABBLE. Their first step was to get in touch with Hasbro, the game's maker.

I'm not sure whom they talked to that first time, but they were essentially rebuffed by the simple but correct explana-

tion that any word in the dictionary that is not a proper noun is acceptable in SCRABBLE play. After all, lexicographers cannot pretend a word doesn't exist just because someone doesn't like it. Also, however noble the intention, it's naïve to assume that if a word is removed from any dictionary, it's going to disappear from the language and conversation.

The dismissal from a Hasbro rep only inflamed the women further. So they took their case to the Anti-Defamation League (ADL), the powerful and effective organization dedicated to fighting anti-Semitism. As one might imagine, the group was all over the situation.

The ADL quickly fired off a letter to Alan Hassenfeld, chairman and CEO of Hasbro at the time, accusing the company of "playing games with hate." Hassenfeld, whose family was active in Jewish charities and causes, was in a tough spot, but he knew he had to act quickly. So he replied that Hasbro would remove all offensive words from the *OSPD* as soon as possible.

Because I was the person in the middle between Hasbro, the media, the dictionary publisher, and the players, the job fell to me and the NSA staff to both orchestrate this process and communicate progress to all those entities. The initial phone call went something like this.

"John, we need you to take all the offensive words out of the SCRABBLE dictionary."

"Which ones?" I asked, not joking.

"You know," the Hasbro exec continued, "all the usual curse words, body parts, racial and religious slurs, that kind of stuff."

He made it sound so simple. But I knew better. For openers, the mid-1990s was perhaps the zenith of the political correct-

ness movement, when, it could be argued, people sometimes went overboard in trying to do or say the correct thing.

My favorite example of this was the case in January 1999 of a Washington, DC, political aide, David Howard, who was quoted in the press as saying something about the need to be more "niggardly" in the management of certain city funds. NIGGARDLY, of course, is an old English word, admittedly obscure, defined as "grudgingly mean about spending."

However, there was a rush to judgment because the word *sounded* like what we refer to as "the N-word." In fact, it seemed the guy was having his resignation accepted before anyone could even open a dictionary. And when someone finally did, it was too late. Attempts to explain the real meaning were cumbersome and ineffective, as people were already too agitated. The rationale then seemed to me to waver to this: the guy should have lost his job for *bad judgment*—selecting a word that sounded too much like an offensive term. Finally, reason prevailed; he was rehired by the mayor's office.

So, accompanied by my NSA colleague Joe Edley, I began the dubious quest to find every despicable word in the English language to appease the Hasbro attorneys, the Anti-Defamation League, and anyone else who thought or hoped a word was going to disappear from use and the language simply by being removed from a game-related dictionary. We were aware as we began that this task was a bizarre blend of dangerous, silly, pointless, and futile. Worse, for me, was that it pitted my job requirements against my strong personal belief in free speech. Ah, the classic American dilemma, choosing between one's job and the Constitution.

Some of the considerations were complicated. For example, the words PANSY, CHICK, DICK, FAGGOT, BITCH, HOMO, and the like

are all hateful slurs, but they all have alternative, harmless meanings. So these words survived the cut with the offensive definition deleted.

The word MOTHERFUCKER was discussed, but was not part of
the assignment because the *Official SCRABBLE Players Dictionary* only goes up to eight-letter words. (Over 90 percent of all
SCRABBLE plays are eight letters or fewer.) But the conversation about the word reminded us of a famous story that came out
of a Tennessee SCRABBLE club back in the 1980s.

As the story went, a young man in his thirties was beginning
a game against woman in her eighties. His absolute best opening
play was the word SHITTY. He stared at the word on his rack, then
at the sweet face and carefully coiffed white hair of his opponent.
He agonized. He looked back at her face, back at his rack. He just
couldn't play the word. Instead, the young man made a much safer
play for far fewer points. But he had no doubt he'd done the right
thing. Across the board, the older woman studied his opening play
for a minute or so. Then she threw down the word FUCKERS for
80-something points, shrugged, and happily wrote down her score.

This story gets to one of the key points of this entire issue.
In SCRABBLE, words are simply game pieces. Expert players
often know thousands of words for which they do not know—nor
are they required to know—the meaning. As both *Word Freak*
author Stefan Fatsis and Will Shortz, *New York Times* crossword
puzzle editor, have stated to me: in SCRABBLE, meanings are
meaningless.

Obviously, this situation flies in the face of all cultural and lin-
guistic standards. We learn early in life that all words do in fact
have meaning and, at times, the attendant power. Words are—or
at least should be—chosen with care for reasons of emphasis,

sensitivity, clarity, and desired impact. So the concept of them being "meaningless" is both disconcerting and anti-intuitive, even just for the sake of playing a game.

But I digress. Our search continued. In addition to all the naughty words we could think of, we asked our colleagues at Merriam-Webster, the country's foremost lexicographers, to send us a list of every word that had a designation in their files as vulgar, profane, racist, a religious or ethnic slur, and the like. It goes without saying, the editors at Merriam-Webster were appalled that we were even doing this.

Some of their words were amusing. Did you know that PAPIST (a Roman Catholic) and JESUIT (a scheming person) are considered religious slurs? I can't say I've seen either used that way in my lifetime, perhaps scrawled somewhere on a church wall by a hate-filled graffiti artist. However, both words were used in a derogatory manner against Roman Catholics—depicting them as enemies of the Church of England—as far back as the early sixteenth century.

There were others, equally absurd or obscure. In all, we came up with about 175 allegedly offensive candidates. We submitted them to Hasbro for review. Our memo covered both our collective asses and two fundamental points: the list was by nature incomplete, and offensiveness is nothing if not subjective. It's like humor; one person's double entendre is another person's banana peel.

Later, a senior Hasbro Games division executive tried to grandstand at a meeting, proudly announcing we had overlooked the word TUP. When asked its meaning, he preened, "It means to have sex with a sheep."

I waited a minute for the room to absorb this information. I finally spoke. "Yes, I know the word. It means for a *ram* to have

sex with a ewe, not a couple of drunken farm boys. It's a veteri-
nary term."

The Offensive-Word story went viral, and within a week the
story broke nationally in the publishing column in the *New York
Daily News* written by veteran journalist Paul Colford. I was
just leaving an associate's office at MTV Networks, where I was
working on a writing project, when his assistant shoved a handful of those pink message slips at me. They read: John, call NBC
News; John, the *Wall Street Journal* is trying to make a deadline,
call ASAP; John, can you do an interview for *CNN* for the 6
o'clock news; John, the *Miami Herald* style section editor needs
a photo-call immediately; and whatever you do, John, please call
your office *FIRST*—they are swamped with more calls.

After a couple of conference calls, Merriam-Webster, Hasbro,
and I agreed that I would be the only official spokesperson on
the issue. It had also been decided—not by me—that I would
not be allowed to disclose any specific word that was going to be
eliminated from SCRABBLE. You can imagine how that went
over with journalists.

As a writer myself, I understood the idiocy and frustration
of it all for them. Here was an explosive story on any number
of levels, yet the press was not given access to the newly created offensive-word list. So they and I were reduced to a silly
dance along the lines of "Okay, Mr. Williams. How about I say a
word and you can tell me whether or not it will be banned from
SCRABBLE. Can you at least do that?"

So they wrote the stories anyway—scores of them—guessing at the banned words or suggesting readers simply use their
imaginations.

Personally, the worst part of this experience was that some-

how it became assumed that I was not only the individual who decided to remove "offensive" words from SCRABBLE play, but also the one in charge of selecting those words. That's when the fecal matter really hit the fan.

I began to receive letters and phone calls from all over the world.

- A man from Wales insisted that the word WELSH be removed because it had the same connotation as JEW used as a verb.
- In the same vein, I received an impassioned letter from a gentleman who identified himself as the official United Nations delegate representing the 1.1 million Romani (Gypsies) in North America. He asked that the word GYP (to swindle)—similar in meaning to JEW and WELSH—be removed as it was a slur against his constituents. His letter was accompanied by several pages of data, which theoretically proved Romani were the most maligned race in the world in regards to ethnic prejudice. Who knew?
- An Irishman lobbied for removal of the word PADDY-WAGON, as its origin was something like "a small truck filled with drunken Irishmen." Of course, PADDYWAGON wasn't even in the SCRABBLE dictionary because it was more than eight letters.
- An ardent feminist demanded that the word HISTORY be removed as it was blatantly sexist. Happily, the word HERSTORY was added to the SCRABBLE dictionary a few years later. OURSTORY perhaps waits in the wings for future admission.

■ A pacifist wrote, "I consider WAR and GUN to be the two most dangerous words in the English language and respectfully request they be considered for deletion." Being a pacifist, he did not demand, insist, or threaten.

■ Finally, in the mail came this. "I deplore what you are doing, Mr. Williams. I will find you and rectify this injustice." We called postal authorities and the FBI on that one. Remarkably, the sender had left a legitimate return address on the letter. Now that's commitment.

This entire exercise proved what I had said from the initial conversation, when I was charged with removing the offensive words from the SCRABBLE dictionary. Which ones?

When the dust finally settled on all this, a couple of things happened. The *Official SCRABBLE Players Dictionary* was revised as the Third Edition in 1995 with approximately 175 words removed. However, in a compromise enacted by the NSA, all words remained allowable in official club and tournament play in the United States and Canada. This was the genesis of the *OWL*, which had all the words but, as per the agreement with Hasbro, no definitions. It was available only to members of the National SCRABBLE Association. We, after all, were trained word professionals and would not let them fall into the wrong hands.

For educational purposes only, I've included the notorious word list in the appendix. I suspect you'll be turning there now.

At the end of it all, only one tournament player I know of resigned from the NSA. He returned about a decade later. He assured me, after one day back at the National SCRABBLE Championship, that it was "as gloriously crazy as ever." He was right. You can screw around with the words, but the people will prevail.

5

HOW I BECAME A PLAYER

T BECAME CLEAR TO ME THAT sooner or later I had to become a credible tournament player if I was to do my job well and effectively. However, I was a couple of years into being executive director of the NSA before I made a real commitment. I knew there would be a lot of time and study involved, not to mention the risk of looking stupid to a large number of people. Hence my reluctance.

Fortunately, I had Joe Edley as a teacher. Joe was, until 2011, the only person to win the National SCRABBLE Championship (NSC) three times. New Zealander Nigel Richards has since won the event a staggering five times, as well as the World SCRABBLE Championship (WSC) three times. He's now considered the greatest to have ever played the game—with no end in sight. Dave Wiegand, a resident of Portland, Oregon, has won the NSC twice and is always a threat to duplicate Joe's effort.

Remarkably, Joe accomplished this in three different decades: 1980, 1992, and 2000. One of the best tournament players in his-

tory, he is famous for his Zen-like mental approach to competition, which many opponents found both irritating and distracting. His tai chi exercises between rounds were legendary. One could often see Joe in the corner of a huge ballroom, silently morphing into meditative poses. Comical to many, it worked for him.

Joe is a masterful teacher. He has the patience of someone who has memorized 125,000 or so words and the passion of one who believes the world would be a better place if everyone played more SCRABBLE. A mathematician by education, Joe also has a very logical, systematic, and unemotional approach to any task. So the entire exercise was like being taught by Mr. Spock from *Star Trek*.

The cornerstone of our lessons was what is called an "open game," where we would see each other's racks and discuss the various options of each move. Among other skills learned in this technique is what players call "rack management," which means learning the thought process and steps in making a good SCRABBLE move. Among the considerations are these:

- Check out all the possible places on the board for a play. This is what we call "board vision." Start by checking all the bonus squares, or "hot spots."
- Look at those spots from both an offensive and defensive point of view. It's very often a balance. You want to score as many points as possible, but if it sets up your opponent for a big play it may not be worth it. And always check to see if there's already a dangerous opening for your opponent; it may make sense to block it with even a modest-scoring word.
- Remember, the best play is not always the most points

(this tends to be a huge flaw in many commercial SCRABBLE apps). Unless you're laying down a 7-letter play (bingo), a good SCRABBLE move is comprised of two parts: what you put on the board to score and what you leave yourself to work with on your rack. Think about it. If you make a high-scoring play but leave yourself with v, u, u, you've pretty much guaranteed your next three plays are not going to be favorable.

For a year Joe and I tried to play at least one open game almost every day. Early on, I would also have for reference the NSA's "secret word list." Compiled by expert player Mike Baron, this is a compendium of about 1,500 of the most valuable words every tournament player should know. It includes all two-letter words and three-letter words, common words using the power tiles j, q, x, and z, the vowel-dump list for a rack with too many vowels, and the q-without-u words. Using this sheet of words allowed me to both learn them and realize their strategic importance. In fact, learning these words was the first thing the NSA encouraged anyone wanting to become a better player to do.

It was twenty years ago, but I still have some random memories of those lessons. I'm sure Joe and I played at least three hundred games before I won a single match, and even then, I definitely had the better tiles. But I do remember the first time I defeated Joe. Obviously, I was overjoyed. Even better, Joe was extremely gracious. He was absolutely delighted for me. Of course, in my naïveté, I was sure this was a milestone and things would begin to even out between us, albeit incrementally. Joe, on the other hand, most certainly knew we could go another fifty or more games before I won again. He was right.

Two early plays I recall were seven-letter moves, both plurals. One was GUNITES. I'd seen the word around here and there and thought it was some sort of material used in the construction of swimming pools. That turned out to be true, but it also turned out that the word wasn't playable because it was a trademark and therefore capitalized; since then it's become acceptable. Another was FUNGOES, which I knew from baseball (a type of hit or a special bat used in practice). This word was good, and even better, Joe challenged it! I still lost.

So our practice games were enormously helpful, and I did in fact slowly progress. The games got incrementally closer. My strategy and board vision improved. And I was learning the words.

Everyone has his or her own way to memorize. Like Joe, I created my own flash cards. Remember, this was before all the numerous and refined studying techniques now available online or via customized software.

My methodology was a highly personal and random blend of mnemonics and word association. Here are some examples:

- I could never remember early on which was acceptable, PIA or MIA, so I did an index card that said PIA GOOD, MIA is *M*issing *I*n *A*ction. Hey, don't judge me; it worked.
- Another card was to learn the "back hooks" for the word ox—single letters that could be added to make a playable word. This one read: *OY!! OX TAKES AN O & Y (OXO, OXY)* Again, this worked for me.
- Other times, I'd just stack them visually:

TIKI
TIPI
TITI

In all, I probably created two hundred flash cards. Often, during a game, I was able to visualize myself actually writing the card out, which was enormously helpful.

Eventually, I decided to test the state of my fledgling tournament game. What better place than the belly of the beast—the notorious New York City SCRABBLE Club.

There were numerous stories about the club in regard to both the level of play and the atmosphere. The skill level was high, with numerous top-ranked experts. They regularly included Joel Sherman, Joe Edley, Ron Tiekert, Robert Felt, Ed Halper, Rita Norr, Rose Kreiswirth, Richie Lund, Lynne Cushman, and Paul Avrin. The atmosphere, depending on the night, ranged from hospitable to hostile. Hey, this was New York.

I had no illusions about this foray for my tune-up experience before my first tournament. I was achingly self-conscious about both my reception and my performance at the board. I knew many New York SCRABBLE players were contemptuous of the National SCRABBLE Association and authority in general, and this added unwanted pressure.

I played three games that night. I was completely destroyed in one by a low-rated intermediate player. I held my own in a close match with another player of the same caliber. However, the third game was something special.

Cruelly, I'd been matched up with one of the top players in the city. I'm not sure how this happened, but it did. It was clear from

the onset that he was not taking me—or our game—seriously. Who could blame him? This first clue was that he didn't even bother to track tiles. (Tournament players have a preprinted sheet of the 100 game tiles and can check them off as they're played, so as the game progresses they have a better sense of what letters are available.) The second clue was that he played the complete game upside down, not even bothering to turn the board to himself for a better look.

The good tiles were spilt fairly equally between us, and it ended up being a close game, with one bingo each. As the bag became emptier, I realized that the Q had not been played. I then scanned the board and realized that three of the four U's had been expended in earlier plays. Since my opponent was not tracking tiles, it occurred to me that he hadn't seen this situation developing.

As we reached the final turns, I had drawn the final U and he had drawn the Q. All of a sudden, he started to pay serious attention. But it was too late. The board had been shut down for a Q-play for him. I ended up winning the game by a couple of points because he had to "eat the Q" for a costly 20 points at the end. It's only fair to point out that this game took place well before QAT became acceptable, let alone QI. But I'll take it.

Buoyed by my practice games at the New York City club, I was ready for my first tournament, the Long Island Championship. It was held in Port Jefferson, New York, on St. Patrick's weekend in 1991. There were about fifty players in three divisions for a ten-game event. I was in the Novice Division.

As in many aspects of my life, my goal was not necessarily to excel but simply to not embarrass myself. Had I been able to enter this event in disguise with an alternative identity, that would have been fine with me.

I attended an opening reception and talked mostly about SCRABBLE and words. Of course, everyone knew who I was. Many wished me luck and welcomed me to the fold. Others peppered me with questions and complaints about the NSA—missing newsletters, high dues, low prize money, and the like. It helped give me perspective on Joe Edley's tournament experiences in the two-plus decades he was serving as NSA's director of clubs and tournaments.

Some people complained that Joe had some sort of advantage working at the NSA and being a competitive player at the same time. Chief among these was Bronx lawyer Ed Halper, a top player and club director. Every year when he renewed his NSA membership he'd write "FIRE EDLEY" on the check. But think about it. Not only was everyone gunning for Edley, but at every tournament his concentration would be broken between rounds with garden-variety questions about the SCRABBLE organization. No wonder Joe retreated into frequent tai chi trances!

In reality, without Joe Edley there is no way the National SCRABBLE Association could have achieved everything it did. Joe handled an enormous workload with ease and grace and helped the NSA forge its belief in the sanctity of the game. Among Joe's contributions:

- Edited and wrote much of the *SCRABBLE News*
- Scheduled two hundred SCRABBLE tournaments a year
- Administered and scored the NSA Club Director's Tests
- Handled player disputes
- Oversaw day-to-day participation in the *OSPD*
- Fielded numerous phone calls and correspondence

- Helped organize and direct National, World, and School SCRABBLE events
- Maintained the official NSA Ratings System
- Contributed heavily to the creation of NSA membership materials
- Created numerous puzzles and word quizzes
- Helped strategize NSA growth
- Interacted with SCRABBLE manufacturers on product development, testing, and marketing
- Gave numerous lectures and made other appearances

The SCRABBLE tournament scene and I personally owe Joe Edley an enormous amount of gratitude for his contributions to the game.

Now, back to my first official SCRABBLE tournament. It was around 8:00 p.m. on a Friday when I sat down across from my first opponent, a guy in his forties whom I'd never met. We wished each other luck, shook hands, and drew tiles to see who went first. He did, as he chose a tile closer to A. Inside, I sighed a bit. I'd learned that whoever goes first in a SCRABBLE match statistically has a 55 percent chance of winning.

Decades later, I couldn't tell you what my first rack was. But I remember my opponent's first play. He laid down COWY. Surprisingly, in both the course of my everyday life and in my studying obscure words for the game, I'd never seen that word. Ever. Not in a book. Not on the word lists I'd studied.

Complicating this was the fact that I'd promised myself that in this tournament, I was going to challenge any word I did not know. Yet here, in the very first play of my tournament career, I was second-guessing myself. My opponent had played COWY

with such nonchalance and confidence, it had me rattled. I asked myself which was worse: being duped by a phony in the first play of my first tournament or challenging a word that might have been routine even in the Novice Division.

Ultimately, I decided not to challenge. And it was a good thing. COWY was indeed acceptable. COWY means "suggestive of a cow." Happily, I went on to win that game. Twenty years later, however, I've still never heard or seen the word used even once outside of SCRABBLE.

The whole issue of playing phonies is both nuanced and controversial. Living room players—an arguably dismissive term tournament players use—generally disapprove of playing phony words. That quite possibly is the genesis of the needing-to-know-the-definition house rule many people believe to be official. It's not.

I played two more games that first night and ended up 3–0! That performance was beyond my expectations, and it propelled me into a blend of confidence and looseness I'd rarely experienced in any competition. Over the years, I'd heard athletes and SCRABBLE experts like talk about being "in the zone." I was definitely there. It was almost as if I were channeling someone else's ability and someone else's luck. I cannot remember many specifics of that evening, but it's a safe bet I was getting my share of valuable tiles. How else could I have done that?

I'd attended the tournament with my friend Rob Buchanan, a veteran journalist. A very good casual player himself, Rob had entered the competition thinking there might be a story there. He lived across the street from me, and we played many practice matches together. However, he hadn't really studied any word lists, so he was at a disadvantage even in the Novice Division.

The evening had not treated Rob as well. I recall he was 0–3 and not happy about it. A trip to the hotel bar seemed in order. After a couple of drinks, Rob and I decided to do what most tournament players do after a long day of competition: play more SCRABBLE. So we headed back to my room to break out the board.

At the bar, Rob and I had engaged in some spirited trash-talking. In reality, our SCRABBLE abilities were pretty close. So Rob chided me about being lucky, having inferior opponents to his, that sort of thing. Thus by the time we started play, our after-hours match had taken on the good-natured intensity of a showdown.

We poured an unnecessary third drink as we opened the board. A potential wager was discussed, then dismissed. Bragging rights would do. We drew to go first. In keeping with the evening's vibe, I selected an A.

Then I drew my seven tiles, arranged them on my rack, and stared in disbelief. There before me was the word ANCHOVY.

Talk about being in the zone. I stared at the word for another couple of seconds. Then I laid it down on the board. "Anchovy," I announced with poorly disguised glee, "94 points."

Rob stared silently at the board. He then turned his gaze to me as he stood and pushed his chair back. "Fuck you," he said, grinning and shaking his head. Rob went on to finish 5–5, a respectable performance for anyone's first tournament. We are still friends and neighbors, but we don't play SCRABBLE together anymore.

For the most part, the tournament continued the way it had started. I finally lost an afternoon game to a delightful woman named Stacia Camp, who showed me afterward how I could have—*should have*—won our match. By the end of the day, my

record was 6–1 with three games left to play on Sunday morning. I was leading my division.

At this point in the weekend, my performance was starting to attract some attention from everyone, experts included. Players in all divisions were very gracious and supportive. Some suggested I was really an Intermediate Division competitor "playing down" and was a Novice only because it was my first tournament. All I know is that I was damn relieved to have at least shown I knew the game. My instructor, Joe Edley, competing in the Expert Division, was thrilled.

The rest of the tournament was pretty much a blur. I remember finding—and nervously playing—the word IRONIST against a skeptical opponent. It was good. I won another. IRONIST, by the way, means "one who uses irony." Keep an eye out for it on future racks. The common letters make it appear quite often.

I was 8–1 going into the last round, matched against a young woman who was, I believe, 8–1 as well. She was very good and had played in several tournaments. With a victory, I'd win the whole thing. A loss on my part would tie us, and whoever had the bigger point spread in all the games would be the champion.

I remember the game was back and forth with several lead changes. Then we got to the very end. She was ahead by perhaps 40 points with about a dozen tiles left in the bag. I drew well on the next opportunity and ended up with the bingo ENTAILS.

Unfortunately, I scoured the board three times and realized there was no place to play it. SCRABBLE players know this is perhaps the most frustrating situation in the game—a bingo with no place to lay it down. Panicking, I frantically moved the tiles around on my rack looking for another word in this favorable group of tiles.

I'm sure any expert player watching would have immediately seen the other words: ELASTIN, NAILSET, SALIENT, SLAINTE, TENAILS. With the exception of SALIENT, I didn't yet know any of those words. The only one I could come up with was SALTINE.

So I sat and stared at my rack. I was pretty sure that SALTINE was a proper noun, a trademarked cracker name owned by Nabisco or the like. Yet a small part of me reasoned that it could be a generic word for a type of cracker.

The pressure was mounting as I rechecked the clock, rechecked the score, and scanned the placid face of my opponent. Finally, I accepted the fact that I had no choice. In a display of shaky confidence I laid down the word SALTINE.

Now it was her turn to think it over. She wrote the word down on a piece of paper and studied it. Then she looked back and forth at the board as if something might have changed. She had no choice either. If she did not challenge, I would win. Her best chance—a very good one—was that SALTINE was a phony.

It is not. According to the *Official SCRABBLE Players Dictionary*, SALTINE is defined as, duh, "a salted cracker." I won the challenge. I won the game. I won my tournament division with a 9–1 record. I was stunned, euphoric, in disbelief. Oh yeah, I also won $100, which I returned to the prize pool.

Little did I know it would be the highlight of my SCRABBLE tournament career. I should have listened to Mike Baron, who told me the day after the victory, "Consider retiring right now. You could go in the record books with one of the most impressive tournament debuts in history and lifetime winning percentage."

Instead, I made what was probably one of the stupidest moves in SCRABBLE tournament history. It occurred exactly one year later, again at the Long Island SCRABBLE Championship. By

virtue of my previous win, I now had a tournament rating of 1554. The NSA rating system was originally based on a variation of the one used in chess. Simply put, it essentially calculates how well you do against other rated players.

The ratings fall into three groups: Novice is 600–1199, Intermediate is 1200–1599, and Expert is 1600+. But as we grew, NSA rules allowed a player to "play up" a division in most tournaments. So in my cluelessness and arrogance, I thought, hey, I'm just 46 points from an official Expert rating. Why not play with the best? How cool, I thought. In just my second SCRABBLE tournament, I was already good enough to compete against the very top players.

This is a cautionary tale, so pay attention. For I was to learn a painful lesson: the difference between almost having an Expert rating and being an expert player.

When I arrived at the tournament, most of the experts treated me with at best a sense of bemusement. They already knew what I did not: I didn't belong in the same room with them. As a rule, experts also don't like lesser competitors "playing up." That's because should an expert by chance lose a game to the weaker opponent, the expert's rating will take a beating. If a 1366 player beats a 1941 player, his or her rating will rise appreciably, and the opposite will happen to the expert.

Well, it became clear they had nothing to worry about with me. I was in for a reality check of the highest order. Going into the final afternoon, my record was 0–10—almost the complete opposite of the previous year. Worse, I imagined myself being perceived by the other players as either a laughingstock or a pathetic figure. The only saving grace is that I come from the hit-over-the-head-with-a-shovel school of learning stuff. I was in

familiar territory. I simply sucked it up and went on. Fortunately, I drew good tiles in the last two games and won them both for a 2–10 record, finishing dead last in the Expert Division.

Though technically still eligible, I knew I'd never play in the Expert Division again. My rating had dropped to 1493, which theoretically made me a "high Intermediate." I say theoretically because my bumpy, ragged tournament experiences were far from over.

I was starting to learn a couple of key lessons about the tournament game and environment. For openers, it's important to remember that every time you sit down across from someone, chances are that person is as good as or better than you. That dynamic seldom exists when you compete at home, against friends. For the most part, I'd been a better player than most of the people I'd played. They were very smart people, excellent living room players who played SCRABBLE for, God forbid, fun.

I also learned that playing only periodically in official SCRABBLE tournaments was not the way to do it. There is a "rust factor" that can easily cost you a game or two. It could be the chess clock ticking off your twenty-five minutes, an intimidating opponent, playing six games in a day, sleeping in a strange bed, whatever. So I didn't do myself any favors by playing only one or two tournaments a year; I did a favor for the rest of the competition.

Probably the most resonant lesson from the experience is this: if you don't study, you are not going to get any better. Period. With the exception of my first tournament, I never took studying words very seriously. The reality is you can play twenty-five games a day, and have great strategic skills and board vision—

but if you don't know the words, you'll likely be saddled with the same rating forever.

In retrospect, I'd take that deal right now. As I write this, my rating is 1293, and my last full tournament was in August of 2007. Offering solace, Joe Edley assured me, "Your skills have not diminished. You're probably as good as or better than when you were rated 1554." What's changed, Joe explained, is that the ratings system has been altered slightly and that there are so many better players now in all divisions. My lifetime tournament record is 35–68, a winning percentage of .340. However, in my defense, my scores averaged a respectable 367 points a game. Mercifully, the statistic of the average score *against* me was unavailable.

I still toy with the idea of someday playing in a National SCRABBLE Championship. Despite thirty years of involvement with the game, I was never able to do it because of other obligations at these events. It's the Olympics of SCRABBLE, with the best players in the world in the same room as first-timers. In addition to the competition, it's also a celebration of the glorious game and those who've made it a significant part of their life. Look around the giant ballroom that houses a National SCRABBLE Championship and you'll see a veritable Noah's Ark of humanity. The game draws every single type of person imaginable.

And I have a plan for my return. First I'll play in a couple of local tournaments leading up to, say, the 2015 NSC. If my past performance is any indication, my rating should continue to systematically plummet. Ideally, I'd enter my first National SCRABBLE Championship with a rating between 1136 and 1171. That would put me squarely in the Novice Division. I think I

would do really well there, but could I last the thirty-plus rounds in four days?

I've been asked many times, both casually and in interviews, to reveal a few pointers for improving one's SCRABBLE play. I've assembled ten tips to keep in mind that will accomplish just that, and they are available in the appendix at the end of the book. These are taken from the book *Everything SCRABBLE*® by me and three-time National SCRABBLE Champion Joe Edley.

6

MEDIA TIME

A MONG THE MANY RESPONSIBILITIES OF MY SCRABBLE job was media relations. Previously, the task was called "public relations," but apparently that term fell out of favor because it was either too limiting or did not sound important enough. As one of my advertising friends used to tell me, "I can only charge about $1,200 for an idea, but I can get as much as $2,500 for a *concept!*"

One of my early goals was to convince Hasbro executives to make the story or event always about SCRABBLE and never about Hasbro. As a result we never had a single Hasbro banner or sign at any SCRABBLE Championship over two decades— heresy in marketing circles! Yet it paid off. Keeping the perception of SCRABBLE as a generic game made it more palatable to the media and corporate partners. When I called to pitch a SCRABBLE story to a newspaper or television show, I was not calling as a Hasbro exec or from a PR agency. I was calling from the independent National SCRABBLE Association.

And the event was never the "Hasbro" National SCRABBLE Championship.

Chief among our media-related tasks was booking a recently crowned SCRABBLE champion on one of the national morning shows: *Good Morning America*, *Today*, or *CBS This Morning*. Fortunately, we've been able to arrange numerous appearances over the years on these shows, as well as other outlets such as *Jimmy Kimmel Live!*, *The Martha Stewart Show*, and CNN, to name just a few.

A media favorite, one of the most colorful and beloved SCRABBLE Champions ever is "G.I. Joel" Sherman of the Bronx. His nickname was derived from his well-known gastrointestinal (GI, get it?) distress, which manifested itself in many forms. Oh, and he had to expectorate frequently.

No one in the SCRABBLE world ever thought twice about these quirks, which would have been questionably tolerated in the outside world. Joel is a great guy, a wonderful ambassador for the game. Hell, some would argue that having personality quirks is almost a prerequisite for a top SCRABBLE expert.

One particular memory resonates. We were backstage at *Today*, and I was prepping Joel for his appearance. We discussed the talking points we wanted to cover. We reviewed highlights and interesting words played. We outlined ways to prevent him from burping during his four minutes with Katie Couric. Just as Joel was about to go onstage, he turned to me and thrust a Styrofoam cup in my direction.

"Here," he said to me, "hold my mucus cup, okay?" I reluctantly grabbed the dubious vessel. A young NBC production assistant looked over to me. "Dude," he said, grinning, "they don't pay you enough."

I'm happy to say that Joel's interview with Katie Couric was flawless, funny, informative, and unassuming. He walked off the set and headed my way. I quickly pushed the mucus cup back in his direction.

The National SCRABBLE Championship was always the most important media outreach the NSA conducted. Started in 1978 by Selchow & Righter, it was held annually or semiannually in major cities all over the country. Over the years, participation ranged from just thirty-two players in 1983 in Chicago (an invitational format) to over eight hundred contestants in New Orleans in 2004.

The National SCRABBLE Association officially took over organizing and promoting the NSC in 1988. Over the years, this involved putting together a complex blueprint for an event. The process always began with selecting a host city in a major market. There were specific criteria for selection:

▪ Tourism appeal for the players' families and contestants themselves in off-hours
▪ Reasonably easy to get to from anywhere
▪ A selection of hotels with good rates and many nearby affordable dining options
▪ A good media town, i.e., strong daily newspaper, AP office, NPR station, local talk radio, network-affiliate television stations

There were all kinds of logistics as well. We had to hire word judges, a team of computer programmers and data-entry personnel to handle the thousands of rating calculations, division leaders and assistants to handle rulings and player questions, a

photographer, an online reporter, and a video team for in-house or Internet telecasts. (Typically, we would get up to six million hits with people watching the play-by-play commentary on our website.) In total, we often assembled a staff of up to thirty-five people to help us run an NSC.

While the National SCRABBLE Championship was seen by its participants as an annual or semiannual celebration of their culture and the ultimate competitive experience, we, of course, also had to tend to the business end. That meant getting national publicity to raise awareness of both the SCRABBLE brand and the glories of the tournament scene. Given some of the players' reluctance to be on television or in the media at all—and their resentment of corporate interference with their beloved game— we often had to do a delicate dance to make that happen. It made for some interesting challenges.

One year, both the sponsor and its New York media relations agency were concerned as we were heading toward the finals because the favorite to win the championship was deemed by them to be "not telegenic." A wonderful young genius, he was painfully shy and, to their thinking, somewhat unkempt. It had also been established by the player himself that—unlike most people—he couldn't have cared less whether he was on television or not.

The stakes were high, as we were already booked for an appearance on *Today* three days after the finals. This kind of "PR hit" could be considered worth over a million dollars—way more than the entire cost of putting on an event like this.

About thirty-six hours before the finals, the media exec took me aside. "Is there a way we can manipulate the scoring or pairings to minimize his chances?" he asked in all seriousness.

Having spent several days with this guy, I was not completely appalled at this request. "I'm afraid not. This isn't professional wrestling," I told him. "It doesn't exactly work that way."

Barely deterred, he thought for a second. "How about I send a couple of girls up to his room around midnight." He winked conspiratorially. "I'm sure we can find money in the budget for that."

I could only laugh. "Sorry."

"Then how about we media-train him?" he persisted.

I sighed. "Okay, if the player is cool with it."

So we set up a camera in a room, and the media maven spent an hour or two trying to transform this sweet, brilliant, shy SCRABBLE genius into a gregarious, charismatic spokesman. It didn't work.

It turned out to be a moot point. Our scheduled appearance was bumped two days later in the wake of a terrible airline disaster.

Probably the most challenging and complicated television experience was with the 1990 National SCRABBLE Champion, the late Robert Felt. When he won that year's event in Washington, DC, he was a veteran tournament player who had been favored to win "the big one" for a long time. Robert Felt was also one of the more interesting characters on the tournament scene.

Felt had a distinct look: a large head to hold his large brain, a doughy physique, a mass of coarse dark hair, and heavy, thick-lensed glasses. But what distinguished him the most was his ability—and tendency—to talk SCRABBLE plays and theory for hours at a time. A typical story of his might start something like this:

"I remember back in 1984 at a local tournament in Atlantic City. I was playing Tommy Tile, who I had a 17–9 lifetime record against.

Midway during the game, with the score 203–186 my favor, I draw a rack of MBTOASW. *I see the word* WOMBATS *and a spot in the lower left quadrant . . ."*

The guy seemed to remember every game, every opponent, every rack, every move of his entire SCRABBLE tournament career. And he would habitually walk up to anyone and just start talking—and not stop. Most people listened patiently for a few minutes, then excused themselves. Some lasted not as long and waited to hand Felt off to an unprepared passerby. Others spotted him coming and took off.

The most famous Robert Felt anecdote took place in England, where he had gone to test his skills against the Brits. As the story goes, a few of them were in a car as Felt was regaling the passengers with one of these endless narratives. He was in the midst of describing a past play when the car was sideswiped and forced off the road, and it either spun out or actually rolled over.

But this did not deter Felt. According to the other passengers, he never stopped telling the story, even as his fellow passengers were screaming in fear, as the car screeched to an emergency stop, and as the relieved passengers crawled out of the wreck. As they dusted themselves off, they heard Felt, uninterrupted: "So then, he draws the final S to join the blank I've tracked to be on his rack. So I know I've got two viable options. One is a piece of esoterica that won't play. The other is . . ."

My Robert Felt story is a little different. Let's start with his wardrobe and overall appearance a few days before the scheduled *Good Morning America* (*GMA*) appearance. Felt had arrived for the 1990 National SCRABBLE Championship with one outfit. It was a tattered blue oxford, faded jeans, and a pair of grubby

white sneakers. He'd also let his thick hair grow into a formless shrub, accentuating the look with a pair of enormous mutton-chop sideburns. It was a distinct look, even among a crowd of SCRABBLE experts, a number of whom couldn't have cared less about conventional style and grooming.

Felt went on to win the National SCRABBLE Championship that year, along with a $10,000 check. This was a nice payday for a man who went in and out of computer-related jobs. After the awards ceremony, we'd have approximately three hours before we had to get on a plane to New York, with a 6:30 a.m. call for *GMA*. As the clock ticked, I knew I'd have to do an emergency makeover.

To Felt's credit, he was a good sport as I rushed him to a barber for a trim and shave, then to a men's clothing store for some pants, a dress shirt, and a sports jacket. He'd use one of my ties and a pair of my shoes for the show.

That night, we made it to the hotel in New York, exhausted, but excited for the television appearance. Then, around 11:00 p.m., disaster struck.

To once again familiarize myself with the tournament story, I casually looked over the actual winning board I'd brought along. Our staff routinely took the winning board and superglued all the tiles in place. It served as a great prop for any interview, and there was always something cool about having the winning board itself in the studio.

But not this time. That's because in reviewing all the words, I noticed that DARKIE had been played in the bottom right-hand quadrant of the board. The word, of course, was an antiquated ethnic slur. To make matters worse, I'd heard from the produc-

ers that the interview was going to be conducted by Spencer Christian, an affable, beloved *GMA* weatherman, who did occasional feature pieces on the show. Spencer Christian is an African American.

By now it was nearing midnight, and I had a full-fledged dilemma on my hands. A dilemma, as once described to me, is a situation where you have two choices, neither of them great.

Fortunately, I'd learned early on to always travel with both an *Official SCRABBLE Players Dictionary* and an extra set of tiles. This discovery came the hard way early in my career—prompted by a reporter's question about a definition that had me floundering and a photographer's request for nonexistent tiles for a prop.

I found an all-night drugstore, bought some glue, and raced back to my room. Over the next hour, I carefully reconfigured part of the board. I began by changing DARKIE to DARKER. As you might expect, that involved changing some surrounding words as well. I finally finished, already dreading the next step in the process: convincing Robert Felt to go along with this. Felt, who I should mention died very young a few years later, was a SCRABBLE perfectionist. And, like a lot of top experts, he was also a purist who to some extent resented the fact that SCRABBLE was owned by a corporation, unlike games such as chess, poker, and backgammon. Many NSA members had an understandable sense of ownership of the game. They devoted their lives to it. Hasbro executives, while appreciative of SCRABBLE's legacy and genius, have scores of other games and toys to think about.

So at 6:30 a.m., I presented my case to Felt in the back of the network's limo. I mentioned that we found ourselves in an unfortunate, unanticipated, and untenable situation, but the impending

interview was not the forum to address the always volatile topic of offensive words being allowed in tournament play. I closed by reminding him he'd just earned $10,000 for playing a few days of SCRABBLE, which he'd have done for free.

Robert Felt could not have been more accommodating. He totally understood the situation and accepted the reconstructed winning board as his own. The interview was wonderful. The newly groomed Felt was fabulous. I breathed a huge sigh of relief, reminding myself again that you can't always believe everything you see on television.

The story had an afterlife. I learned in later years that the word had spread among top players to never bring any suits, ties, or dress shirts to a National SCRABBLE Championship because the sponsor and the National SCRABBLE Association would add a free new wardrobe to your winnings!

7

THE WORLD JOINS IN

O VER THE YEARS, MAJOR SCRABBLE CHAMPIONSHIPS fell into one of three categories: the World SCRABBLE Championship, the National SCRABBLE Championship, and the National School SCRABBLE Championship.

All three events share much in common. Most SCRABBLE championships are held in a huge hotel ballroom or convention center event space. For the most part, all participants pay their own way to these competitions, often thousands of miles away. Every contestant knows far more words than the average English speaker—and more than likely has been learning hundreds more in the months before a big contest. Many enter knowing they have a chance to win their division; others will be thrilled to win half of their games.

The first World SCRABBLE Championship, a smaller invitational event, took place in a private club in London in 1991. There were probably fewer than 100 people in the room. By contrast, the 2004 National SCRABBLE Championship in New Orleans

had nearly 850 players, plus staff, media, and onlookers for a total of nearly 1,000 people every day.

The WSC had its beginnings in Reno, Nevada—which bills itself as "the Biggest Little City in the World." Although the event itself was never held in Reno, it was the site of a historic meeting that was the genesis of this amazing tournament.

We were there the summer of 1988 for the National SCRABBLE Championship at the Sands Hotel. It was a precarious time for the culture of SCRABBLE tournament play. Selchow & Righter had sold SCRABBLE two years earlier to Coleco, a Connecticut-based company most famous for its line of Cabbage Patch Kids dolls. It turned out that by the time of the 1988 NSC, Coleco was already experiencing serious financial problems, coupled with its failed attempt to get into the personal computer business, and the company could only contribute $5,000 to the event.

As proven many times over the years, the players were undaunted by the woes, lack of interest, or financial whims of the game's manufacturer. So in the after-hours of the tournament a small group of us met to discuss our collective dream of a World SCRABBLE Championship.

On the "management" side of the table, the group consisted of the relatively new executive director of the NSA (me) and an executive at J. W. Spear & Sons, the UK-based owner of the game's worldwide rights outside of North America. Stodgy and not really a player himself, the Spear executive seemed tolerated at best by his English constituents. It was also clear that he considered me a brash Yank, poised to shake up the competitive SCRABBLE world.

Among the players from the UK—most there to play in a

US event for the first time—were Brian Sugar, Phil Appleby, Allan Simmons, and future World SCRABBLE Champion Mark Nyman. Australia was represented by John Holgate. Among the American players were, if memory serves, Mike Baron and Joe Edley.

Our agenda was short and simple with just two items. How would we resolve the dictionary differences, and who was going to host the first WSC?

The dictionary issue was which dictionary or word authority would be used to adjudicate the event: the "American," the "British," or some hybrid of both. At that time there were an estimated twenty-five thousand more words in *Chambers*, then the British word authority, than in the *Official SCRABBLE Players Dictionary* used in North America as well as selected countries such as Thailand and Australia. Think about it; the British had had the language far longer than North Americans, so it stood to reason the word source would contain a lot more words. Then, of course, there were the variants such as COLOUR for COLOR and MOULT for MOLT (to cast off an outward covering), many of which were also acceptable in North American SCRABBLE competition. It was eventually agreed that for WSC play a word had to be acceptable in either dictionary to be playable. If a word was successfully challenged, it came off the board and the player lost a turn. In order to be truly competitive for the WSC, players had to learn all or most words from both dictionaries—for North Americans an additional twenty-five thousand—and then *unlearn* them when they returned to their home country. This was a massive and cumbersome prospect, but the players did it.

In our discussion, Spear & Sons demanded that Thailand

should be banned from participating in any international event because of grievous illegal SCRABBLE manufacturing practices in that country. It was especially unfortunate that the Thai players became pawns in a commercial dispute, as SCRABBLE is arguably at least as popular in Thailand as in any other country in the world. No one knows quite how this came about, but word had it that it began when Thai leaders mandated that SCRABBLE was an official "sport" in the country and hundreds of school children were required to play in a national competition. Thai players, later admitted to compete, would go on to win the World SCRABBLE Championship—in English, their second language—in 2003 and 2009.

The process of choosing the venue for the first WSC was every bit as murky. Spear's executives were conservative by nature, and change was not something they innately embraced or pursued. Spear was a relatively lean, small family business and even though it held international trademark, remained unconvinced as to the game's true international potential.

So between Spear's cautious approach and Coleco's tenuous ownership situation, our initial meeting was inconclusive. That said, dialogue had begun, and a movement was under way.

1991 WSC, LONDON, ENGLAND

The first World SCRABBLE Championship, in London, was a landmark event for all organizers and participants. Many of us there were pinching ourselves in disbelief that the day had finally arrived.

Personally, I have an assortment of random memories. For

openers, the competition had pretty much been organized and formatted without any real input or consultation with the players themselves. As a result, there was an early elimination format that was so poorly designed that it eliminated perhaps the UK's best international player, Mark Nyman, before serious play even began.

This was a mind-boggling development to the American and Canadian players, whose sense of fair play overrode their relief at having a chief competitor eliminated. Unlike the organizers, they knew that a compromised early elimination round de-emphasized the skill factor in SCRABBLE and heightened the luck factor. Should a player get bad tiles—for example, no blanks or no s's—in a couple of consecutive games, he or she was essentially screwed. This poor planning is one of the reasons why major tournaments are well over twenty rounds, as calculations show that's when the luck factor has been mostly eliminated or brought under control.

So there we were in London when several members of the North American team decided they were going to protest the WSC format and not play at all. The most vocal was Robert Felt, who angrily maintained the tournament was now a travesty. It was 1776 all over again. The Colonies did not like the way Mother England was running things, and they were going to change it.

As I would do a few times over the years, I called an emergency meeting of the North American team, which totaled eleven players—eight Americans and three Canadians. There were also executives in attendance from the Milton Bradley Division of Hasbro, which was sponsoring and underwriting the entire trip for all of us. It goes without saying the executives were not par-

ticularly thrilled with this development. Their basic message to me was "Take care of this. And don't embarrass us."

I found an empty meeting room in the hotel and assembled the players. I began by assuring them that I completely agreed with them about the tournament's ill-conceived format. However, I reminded them of a few things.

First, we were guests in another country. It was myopic and unrealistic to assume every other culture was going to do things the same way we do. Second, our trip was underwritten by Hasbro. We owed it to them to complete the "mission." Third, carrying through with a protest would severely damage the fledgling international SCRABBLE scene before it even got started. I said the best thing we could do was play and win the first World SCRABBLE Championship.

Still several players grumbled around me. I felt like Walter Matthau in *The Bad News Bears*, managing the colorful collection of talented but nonconformist individuals. I closed the discussion by reminding them that the next such event would most certainly be hosted by us in North America, and we could format it however we chose.

And that's exactly what we did. The brilliant, modest, and sweet Peter Morris, from Lansing, Michigan, emerged victorious, becoming the first person to win both a National SCRABBLE Championship—in 1989—and a World title.

The Brits were characteristically polite, but not exactly happy with us. For openers, many thought our players were typical, pushy, talkative Americans—both in general behavior and in complaining about the format. They were also not thrilled about losing on their home turf. Hey, after all, it was *their* language. They would have their opportunity for revenge soon enough.

1993 WSC, NEW YORK, NEW YORK

We hosted the next World SCRABBLE Championship two years later, in 1993, at the world-famous Plaza Hotel in New York. The city was chosen because it was the media capital of the United States—if not the world—and all of us involved wanted to raise the profile of the event to the next level.

The opening reception began with a surprise visit from the gregarious Regis Philbin, who showed up along with his producer Michael Gelman. They'd been down the hall at an ABC function and were intrigued by the SCRABBLE signage around the hotel.

"Who knew there was such a thing as the World SCRABBLE Championship?" Regis quipped.

"Not as many people as we'd like," I told him. "That's kind of why we're here." I went on to essentially pitch Regis and Gelman the idea of someday having a SCRABBLE segment on their morning show. They said they'd think about it, as Gelman and I exchanged business cards. It took a while, but several years later we had a great piece on the *Live with Regis and Kathie Lee* show, with School SCRABBLE expert Daniel Goldman playing a match against both hosts. Daniel won handily.

Later, at the reception, I was astonished when two players from Kenya presented me with a beautiful carved ebony elephant with miniature real ivory tusks. It was about eight inches high, heavy and highly polished. It goes without saying that I was flattered. Fortunately, I found a way to repay their thoughtfulness. As we spoke, I learned that they would be staying with an African friend who was a graduate student at Rutgers in New Brunswick, New Jersey, and commuting back and

forth to the event each day. They did not realize that this would probably be well over an hour's trip each way in commuter traffic! But they had no choice as they were on a bare-bones budget. In fact, one of them told me that he had sold his car in order to attend the event.

As I looked around the opulent hotel reception, it all seemed terribly unfair. The Americans, Canadians, English, and others were completely subsidized by either sponsors or their own national SCRABBLE organizations. The Kenyans had little more than the clothes on their backs and perhaps a battered dictionary stuffed into a small, worn suitcase.

However, the SCRABBLE gods were smiling on all of us. Dave Wilson, president of Hasbro Games, was in attendance hosting the event. An avuncular guy, gregarious yet tough, Dave was a veteran of decades in the game business, extremely respected throughout both the company and the industry at large.

He and I had formed a great bond over the years. Early in our relationship, he called me into his large, homey, masculine office in East Longmeadow, Massachusetts, and sat me down.

"I have just two words for you, John," he began. *"Think SCRABBLE."*

"Think SCRABBLE," I repeated mechanically.

"That's what I need you to do. Every day. See, we have scores of games here, and everyone has to juggle multiple brands and responsibilities." I knew this to be true. These guys worked their asses off.

Dave went on to explain that he wanted to know that there was always one person out there always thinking about SCRABBLE— whether it was improving the game, marketing, publicity, events,

partnerships, whatever. No one at Hasbro Games had that luxury of time and focus. So tag, I was it! Until his retirement in 2005, whenever I saw Dave he'd come up to me, wink or slap me on the back and say, "Are you *thinking* SCRABBLE, John?"

My reply was always the same. "Every day, Dave. Every day."

Dave and I also agreed on a very fundamental marketing strategy for the game. It was simple: when telling the SCRABBLE story and building the brand, we should think more like chess and less like Monopoly. It was clear to us that the core properties of SCRABBLE and the perception of the game would play better from that perspective.

Back at the Plaza, I brought the two Kenyans over and introduced them to Gail Rubenstein, then Hasbro director of corporate travel, and Dave. After the players wandered off, I explained their situation. It did not take long before Dave turned to Gail.

"Do you think we can find them a room here?" he asked.

Gail smiled. "I think we can make that happen."

"And let's make sure they have room service," he added.

"Not a problem," Gail said.

We were all silent for a second, looking around the room. I spotted SCRABBLE players in turbans, saris, dashikis, yarmulkes, and more. It was Dave Wilson who spoke what we'd been thinking. He waved his arm across the room. "This is what games are really about. Not just business, not just profit and units sold. It's about people—connecting with each other through games."

So the two SCRABBLE players from Kenya spent the week at the Plaza Hotel in New York, enjoying the luxury and their room service dinners. They did not perform particularly well, but the experience was not about that.

This event at the Plaza had a few other highlights. It was, for

example, the first time I personally saw a seven-letter play made right on top of another one. It was played by an Israeli competitor— distinguished by his SCRABBLE yarmulke. His play, the talk of the early rounds, was something like the plays below:

ADAPTOR

RELEASE

TWOSOME

OEDIPAL

If one ever needed an example of why learning the two-letter words is so valuable, these plays pretty much provide it. Each play has one new seven-letter word and seven acceptable two-letter words.

An entirely different memory at the WSC 1993 is a practical joke at my expense. We'd been lucky enough to have been given a ridiculously large suite at the Plaza overlooking Fifth Avenue. To take advantage of this treat, my wife and business partner, Jane, and I decided to host a small cocktail party one evening during the tournament. There were perhaps twenty-five people there, including players, Hasbro execs, and international SCRABBLE association officials. Also in attendance were our longtime friends Troy and Joan Gustavson.

Troy and Joan owned and published our hometown newspaper, the *Suffolk Times*, and he was at the WSC to write a long piece about our involvement. His daughter, Sarah, and our eldest daughter, Kristen, both college students, were working as interns for the championship. The party was in full swing when I was approached by a rather reserved SCRABBLE official from Asia.

The guest bathroom was in use, he said, and he quietly, almost urgently asked me if there was another bathroom he could use. I assured him that he was welcome to use our personal bathroom in the master suite and pointed to the correct door.

He disappeared for a few minutes, then emerged from our bedroom with a strange look on his face. I waved, but he avoided my gaze. When I went over to investigate, he sort of shuffled away, proceeded to the door, and left. Perplexed, I went to the bedroom to see if there was anything wrong. As soon as I walked in, I could see the situation. It seems that my dear friend Troy had raided my closet. He'd taken four neckties from a hanger and tied one each on the four bedposts, so they basically looked like some kind of restraints used in a recent sexual escapade.

While this would have been hilarious had it been played on someone else, I was mortified. I rushed to the bed, undid the four ties from their respective posts, and stuffed them in a drawer. I had two thoughts. First, I was glad the gentleman had been the only person who'd seen this—especially considering there were newspaper reporters and Hasbro executives at the party. Second, I was wondering how I'd explain this prank to someone whose English was marginal at best. I never had the chance.

But the real story of the 1993 WSC was Mark Nyman, the newly crowned champion. Mark had established himself as a top player at a young age. He had come to New York several years earlier at age nineteen and amazingly finished second in our 1989 National SCRABBLE Championship. At just nineteen! And remember, Mark was playing with the "American" dictionary, which put him at a distinct disadvantage. It was truly one of the most astonishing tournament SCRABBLE performances in history.

Mark was everything you'd want in a SCRABBLE cham-

pion. He was young, handsome, polite, humble, and brilliant and liked to enjoy himself. We had become fast friends and socialized whenever our paths crossed in Europe or North America. He played a remarkable tournament and came from two games behind to defeat a former North American champion, Canadian Joel Wapnick, in a best-of-five finals.

The finals were being televised closed-circuit to a ballroom audience of perhaps two hundred people, including all eliminated players, officials, invited guests, media, Hasbro execs, and hotel staff who'd become fascinated during the event. The intensity was palpable as we watched the two players in perhaps the highest-stakes match of their lives. At one point, with the outcome still in question, Nyman leaned back in his chair, then forward again. Without breaking his serious expression, Mark picked up a pencil and scribbled something on his notepad.

The entire audience leaned forward in their chairs, straining to see what he'd written. As the camera went in for a close-up, we finally saw Nyman's note. It read: "I'D FANCY A PINT." The entire room went crazy with laughter.

Minutes later, Mark Nyman went on to win the game and the tournament. He and Wapnick entered the ballroom to a standing ovation and climbed up to the podium for the award ceremony. A weary and happy Mark strode up to the microphone as the applause slowly died down. At last, he looked around the room, leaned into the mike, and said, "I seem to be at a loss for words." The crowd again erupted in laughter.

As one might expect, the Brits were ready to celebrate after capturing their first World SCRABBLE Championship. Not only had they avenged their previous defeat in London, they'd done so in dramatic, elegant fashion. That evening, a group of us—

Americans, Canadians, and Brits—had a glorious Indian dinner together. Afterward, most of us were exhausted and headed to our rooms. But not Mark. He and a couple of his best mates were going to keep the party going. As they headed out into the night, I reminded Mark that we had a 6:45 a.m. pickup for *Good Morning America.* "Not to worry, John," he shouted happily as he crawled into the back of a waiting taxicab.

And I didn't worry—until about 6:00 a.m. Mark Nyman was missing. I called his room at the hotel—no answer. I called the head of the UK SCRABBLE team—no idea. Then the calls started coming to me. First it was the limo driver waiting outside the Plaza for us. Then it was a producer from *Good Morning America.* Then it was the limo driver again.

By 7:00 a.m. I was starting to get frantic. Obviously, I was worried about my young English friend, out for a night on the town in New York, a city he and his companions did not know particularly well. I resisted thinking about all the grim fates that might have befallen Mark in an unforgiving Manhattan night.

Of course, the professional side of me was worried as well. As always, it was understood that I would deliver the latest SCRABBLE champion to one of the "morning shows." As mentioned earlier, this exposure was worth millions of dollars in publicity for SCRABBLE, more than justifying the expense of the entire tournament. As we approached 7:15 a.m., I knew I was in jeopardy of losing our segment.

And then there were my all-important sartorial concerns— for Mark Nyman had borrowed my favorite suit and tie for the television appearance! Fortunately, there was a happy ending. Mark showed up around 7:30 a.m., cheerful, apologetic, and a tad

weary. Yet he absolutely aced the interview before heading back to the Plaza for a much-needed and well-deserved nap.

1995 WSC, LONDON, ENGLAND

In 1995, the World SCRABBLE Championship returned to London. It was held at the beautiful Park Lane Hotel near Hyde Park, and the Brits went all out in regard to amenities and hospitality. There was even the first—and last—semiformal dinner dance in the history of tournament SCRABBLE! The word SURREAL came to mind as I rocked out on the dance floor with my thirteen-year-old daughter, Alex, an array of SCRABBLE experts from two dozen countries flailing around us.

One of the more curious aspects of this event was the presence of rock star Robert Palmer, who had signed on as official greeter/ambassador. Palmer, a handsome, smooth, and affable guy, was best known to most of us as the star of the "Simply Irresistible" video. First aired in 1988, it was one of the most seminal rock videos in history. It featured Palmer, in a handsome suit and silver tie, backed up by half a dozen or so identical, gorgeous dark-haired models who stared blankly into the camera while allegedly playing various musical instruments.

My wife and I spent a fair amount of time with Palmer and his girlfriend at lunch and during the off-hours. It became clear that the rocker had a tangential relationship with SCRABBLE at best and was there to have some fun and pick up some extra cash because some PR or marketing exec decided the event needed a celebrity to offset the staid image of SCRABBLE. It was refreshing to see Palmer be a good sport about it all and a real gentleman.

The 1995 London World SCRABBLE Championship was ultimately won by Canadian David Boys. He defeated American Joel Sherman in the finals to collect the trophy and the seemingly random $11,000 first prize. The field had now grown from the initial nineteen countries to thirty-one. I liked the fact that the WSC had been won by American Peter Morris, Englishman Mark Nyman, and now Canadian David Boys. Only later did someone point out that Peter Morris was born in Manchester, England, and had Canadian citizenship as well.

1997 WSC, WASHINGTON, DC

We selected Washington, DC, for the 1997 World SCRABBLE Championships for all the obvious reasons. It is another great media town. It's easy to get to. And we could rely on the diplomatic corps to add an even more prominent international theme to the competition.

The Mayflower Hotel in the heart of the city was our chosen site. Like the Plaza Hotel before it, the Mayflower was gorgeous, historical, and prestigious. On our first visit to inspect the hotel, the Secret Service was all over the place in preparation for an event a few nights later that President Bill Clinton would be attending. I knew it was just a matter of time before someone asked me if we could arrange for the president to drop by the tournament. It had been reported numerous times in the press that the Clintons were big SCRABBLE fans.

It was warm in Washington when the NSA staff arrived the day before the competition began. From the moment we landed we were consumed with the ballroom setting up, fielding press

calls, assembling contestant materials and gifts, tracking down packages, tracing missing players, and more. Later, I went to bed early after dinner but was wide awake at 1:30 a.m. and had trouble going back to sleep. Restless, I decided to get dressed and go down to the lobby and out for a walk.

The lobby was understandably empty, with the exception of one man who was in the process of checking in. He caught my attention both by his mere presence at that hour and by his appearance. He was tall and lean with deep tan skin and pale blue eyes, framed by a shock of silver hair. He wore a rumpled suit and had a large distressed-leather suitcase at his feet. It was held together by a piece of rope.

Eavesdropping, I learned he had just arrived from the Middle East to compete in the World SCRABBLE Championship. I decided not to introduce myself quite yet and proceeded outside for a walk around the block. My head was spinning with gratitude for being so deeply and personally involved with SCRABBLE. That a simple game could have that kind of appeal for people all over the world was profound.

The competition, as always, was intense and dazzling. The final, for the first time in the history of the event, would be an all-American affair. It featured "G.I. Joel" Sherman against fellow New Yorker Matt Graham.

This was a matchup with built-in drama and personalities worthy of professional wrestling or a comic-book superhero showdown. Sherman is a sweet, self-effacing homebody. Graham, a stand-up comic, is brash, athletic, and intense. I liked both of them very much and considered them friends. Joel was a longtime expert, one of the few who'd ultimately win both a National and World SCRABBLE Championship. Matt was a well-known SCRABBLE

gambler, looking for validation among the SCRABBLE elite by winning his first major title.

It was an exciting final, with Joel prevailing. But for me, the interesting part came after it was all over. I learned that Matt—always the gambler—had approached Joel before the final and suggested a deal. The proposal was that they combine the first-prize money of $25,000 and the second-prize money of $10,000 and split the total right down the middle. I'm not sure what Matt's motivation was—a sure thing? In some ways, it made sense for both of them. Matt had left his job writing for *Saturday Night Live* and lived simply in perhaps New York's smallest apartment. He supported himself on a meager income from comedy gigs, writing, and help from friends.

Joel's financial situation was humble as well. He lived with his brother and father in the same house in the Bronx where he grew up. Various conditions kept him from being regularly employed, and he subsisted on a small inheritance and SCRABBLE winnings. Joel recalled later that he'd anticipated Matt's scheme—but he rejected it. Matt could not have been completely surprised.

1999 WSC, MELBOURNE, AUSTRALIA

For the 1999 World SCRABBLE Championship, we took things Down Under—to Melbourne, Australia. This was significant in several ways. For openers, it signaled that the sponsors, Hasbro and Mattel, were committed to making the event even more global. (Mattel had purchased Spear & Sons and the new international rights to SCRABBLE outside of North America.) Sure,

London, New York, and Washington were great and necessary to get things started. But choosing Melbourne brought the international aspect to an entirely new level. It allowed all of us in the SCRABBLE community to dream of future competitions in India, Canada, Bermuda, Hong Kong—all former British colonies and emblematic of the vast reach of the English language.

Clearly, the international scene was growing, albeit incrementally. As we saw it, our success was also reflective of the world's increasing desire to assimilate English. I'd like to think that was true. But let's face it; there are easier and more practical ways to learn English than by becoming an international SCRABBLE tournament player. Hell, half the words you learn would never even appear in everyday conversation. After all, when was the last time you heard a pal casually mention QAID (a Muslim leader, also spelled CAID), CWM (a deep-walled basin), or HAPKIDO (a Korean martial art)?

I'd never been to Australia and was thrilled for the opportunity, as was my wife. She was photographing the event and sending constant updates to NSA webmaster John Chew in Toronto, who posted them. Thanks to John's programming, we got over six million hits on the NSA website during the event.

After a couple of days exploring Sydney, we made our way to Melbourne for the championship. Mattel's Philip Nelkon, my international counterpart, had arranged a beautiful suite for us in the gorgeous Carlton Crest Hotel.

Here we were, thousands of miles from New York, and the first thing we saw—and heard—when we arrived at the hotel was "G.I. Joel" Sherman playing the piano in the lobby. Nearby, several SCRABBLE games were under way; players from all over the world had reconnected, exchanged pleasantries, and

then jumped right into playing. There was a good chance some of them had not even unpacked yet.

As in previous years, the opening reception was a wondrous whirl of diverse accents, national dress, and SCRABBLE ability. Again, I was astonished that fully three-quarters of the field of '98 didn't have a chance in hell of winning the tournament and most would be thrilled to win just half their games. I thought, too, how the World SCRABBLE Championship was a mirror of the world at large. Once again the Western nationals were well financed, while the Africans had made extraordinary sacrifices just to be there.

For example, one of Nigeria's most prominent players would finish every tournament and pretty much beg fellow players and organizers for spare boards, tiles, and other equipment. Nigerians were rabid about SCRABBLE, but games were hard to come by, even for those who could afford them. Blessed with good fortune, both our players and the NSA gladly gave him all we could.

One of the African champions once asked me if the National SCRABBLE Association could help him seek and obtain political asylum. While I'd become accustomed to pretty much anything crossing my desk over the years, this was a new one for me. A brief conversation with the State Department put a quick end to that endeavor.

At the 1999 WSC, I received two more unusual gifts, from the two players from Romania. One is a small triangular silk pennant emblazoned with three multicolored SCRABBLE tiles—F, S, and R. Above the graphic is the proud copy FEDERATIA DE ROMANA DE SCRABBLE. It has hung in my office for nearly fifteen years. It was explained to me that the Romanian English SCRABBLE Association had approximately fourteen members.

The other was a very good bottle of wine from, of all places, the Transylvanian region. Its label was rich scarlet, deep green, and bold gray and featured a leering portrait of Count Dracula. It was, of course, a dark, full-bodied red wine.

The 1999 World SCRABBLE Championship was won by longtime SCRABBLE expert Joel Wapnick, a music professor at McGill University in Montreal. With this well-earned victory, Joel joined the list of players to win both the National SCRABBLE Championship (1983) and the World SCRABBLE Championship. It was a long time coming for Joel, legendary for his word knowledge, and a group of us celebrated that evening miles away from home with a beachside sunset dinner at one of Melbourne's better restaurants.

2001 WSC, LAS VEGAS, NEVADA

The 2001 World SCRABBLE Championship, held at the lavish Venetian Hotel in Las Vegas, would be my most memorable for a number of reasons. For openers, unbeknownst to me, it would be the last WSC we at the National SCRABBLE Association would ever organize, attend, and publicize. And in many ways, it will remain the most dramatic WSC in history, chiefly because of the timing. Over a year in advance, it had been scheduled for November 13, 2001—which ended up being just two months and two days after the 9/11 attacks that pretty much changed the world as we knew it.

As one might expect, initially it was widely assumed that the tournament would be canceled after the attacks. The world was still cloaked in mourning, uncertainty, and fear. No one wanted

to fly. No one—from everyday people to large corporations—wanted to spend money frivolously. And the idea of simply having fun or celebrating *anything* seemed impossible and almost heretical. For Americans of a certain age, it was evocative of Pearl Harbor or the Kennedy assassination, a watershed "End of the Innocence" event that sent us reeling into a collective emotional dark hole.

Despite all the reservations about holding the World SCRABBLE Championship, it was decided we would proceed as planned. The opportunity to host a positive international event at this time was just too powerful to ignore. Sure, it was only a SCRABBLE tournament—we got that—but it was a start.

Before 9/11, we had representatives from over thirty-five countries registered to play. When we contacted them all after 9/11, every single one renewed the commitment to attend! Also of sudden significance was the fact that we'd have players from Iraq, Israel, Pakistan, Qatar, and Saudi Arabia.

However, we had made one critical error in our planning. As with any big event, we had checked the calendar for conflicts with Thanksgiving, Christmas, the Jewish holidays, the Olympics, elections, and everything else we could think of—except for Ramadan, the most holy of Muslim holidays. The way our schedule stood, we'd be forcing the Muslim players to compete on a day when they should be fasting and praying.

This oversight was brought to my attention in a registered letter from the president of the Pakistan SCRABBLE Association. Obviously, the timing could not have been worse. I had no excuse other than that I was—like most other Americans—embarrassingly ignorant about both the Arab world and Muslims. About all

I knew was that not all Muslims were Arabs and vice versa. The Pakistani SCRABBLE executive was very gracious in excusing my oversight. I assured him it would never happen again.

It goes without saying that security was a huge consideration. We'd had some experience with security issues over the years. As I mentioned, I received a death threat from a zealous word lover who was disappointed that words were removed from the SCRABBLE dictionary. A woman player had secured an order of protection against a SCRABBLE-playing male stalker. Then there were the random temper tantrums when players had to be escorted off the playing floor to calm down.

But the 2001 WSC security concerns were a little different. For one thing, we were in Las Vegas. While the city is a fun place for most of us, religious fanatics of all persuasions consider Vegas pretty much Satan's hometown. What better place to make some big politico-religious statement? Also, the fact that people from nearly three dozen countries were being "forced" to play the game in English—viewed by some as the language of Oppressors—might rub certain fringe thinkers the wrong way. Looking back, I realize the craziness of the time made us look at things in a way we'd never imagined. We still do.

Our fears were put to rest at pre-event meetings, when we were reminded that a top Las Vegas hotel probably has security as good as the White House. So by the time we arrived at the Venetian we were very comfortable, and it was our job to make our guests feel the same.

Another surprise awaited us as we checked in to the hotel. It was cowboys—hundreds and hundreds of cowboys. While scheduling the 2001 WSC, we'd somehow failed to discover that Las Vegas has a gigantic annual rodeo. The extravaganza is attended

by tens of thousands of people—almost every one of them staying at the Venetian Hotel, apparently.

The entire championship, one couldn't walk anywhere around the hotel without being surrounded by scores of guys wearing cowboy hats. This was especially amusing to the foreign SCRABBLE competitors. For many of them, this was their first trip to America—so seeing everyone walking around in cowboy hats confirmed their preconceived image of Americans. All that was missing was guns.

We opened the tournament with a welcoming reception with a total of eighty-eight players from thirty-five countries participating. Some of the players, most playing in their second or even third language, impressively came from these exotic destinations: Bahrain, Cameroon, Gibraltar, Guyana, India, Israel, Kenya, Kurdistan-Iraq, Malaysia, Malta, Oman, Philippines, Qatar, Saudi Arabia, Singapore, South Africa, Sri Lanka, Tanzania, Trinidad and Tobago, and Zambia.

The mood was a mix of cautious excitement, anticipation, and reflection. As players and guests arrived, the NSA staff formed a reception line at the entrance to the room. There were series of heartfelt hugs from strangers and a lot of teary-eyed conversations and reunions. It goes without saying that 9/11 was on everyone's mind, and I knew I had to address the topic in my opening remarks.

I'd learned early in my SCRABBLE career that I should always keep my remarks brief, but they were even shorter than anticipated. That's because the sound system wasn't working, despite every effort to fix it. Yet I needed to be heard by three hundred people, many of whom were still talking among themselves. Finally, I pulled a chair up to the center of the room and

stood on it. My wife, Jane, who has one of the strongest, most shrill New York "taxi" whistles around, silenced the room with one piercing screech.

The large room fell silent. On behalf of the NSA and Hasbro, I thanked all the players for their sacrifice and commitment, especially given the turbulence of the times. I reminded them that although our group was small in number, we represented the diversity and good in the world and what can happen when peoples work together. That was it. I jumped off the chair and faded into the crowd. The first person to approach me was my seventy-eight-year-old father, who was attending his first—and, sadly, last— SCRABBLE tournament. A former Nazi prisoner of war for three and a half years in World War II—at the notorious Stalag 17 POW camp—he was no stranger to international tension. "Nice job," he said. My father was a guy who dispensed compliments at about five per lifetime, so it meant a lot to me.

The 2001 WSC was arguably one of the most amazing in the history of the event. Fittingly, since it was to be the last ever held on North American soil, the Americans and Canadians more than made their presence felt. They ended up taking seven of the top ten places, including the final, which pitted defending champ Joel Wapnick, a Canadian, against Chicago's Brian Cappelletto.

A little background on Brian. As I write this, he has permanently retired from tournament play, which is a huge loss for the game. Brian is a brilliant player, a really good sport, and a genuinely nice guy. He was the first of just a handful of tournament SCRABBLE "prodigies."

Cap—as he's called—first got everyone's attention at sixteen years old, when he began to beat established SCRABBLE masters on a regular basis. One of the very first experts to realize Brian's

potential was the legendary SCRABBLE player, promoter, and author Mike Baron, from New Mexico. Mike is well-known for authoring *The SCRABBLE Wordbook*, the first comprehensive must-have volume for all tournament SCRABBLE players. It essentially presents all two- to eight-letter words in various lists and categories that make them easier to study and memorize.

Asked to recall the early days when Brian Cappelletto first came on the scene, Mike had this to say: "I had the pleasure of meeting Brian in his first tournament, in October 1985. He had just turned sixteen, and it was my thirty-sixth birthday. I thought I'd have an easy win. But Brian played aggressively, in a brash style the likes of which I'd never seen before, playing into the triple-word columns, exposing multiple hook spots, playing words no newcomer to the game had a right to know. Only by a lure and a challenged word (HEPS) was I able to eke out a 414–407 victory in our first match."

Always putting the good of the game ahead of his personal goals, Baron promptly sent the young Cappelletto some of his valuable word lists for study. "It was," noted Baron wryly, "ammunition he would soon use against me time and again."

Like many prodigies in various endeavors, Brian became a victim of his own potential. Many players assumed that he'd win a national championship sooner rather than later—possibly in his teens. Well, that didn't happen. It wasn't because Brian didn't have the talent, skill, and will to win. It was, many observers felt, because he hadn't reached the requisite level of maturity yet.

After thirty years of observing the best SCRABBLE players in the world, I've come to believe that the spiritual/emotional component is an absolute key to being a champion. There are many players who have all or most of the SCRABBLE dictionary

memorized. An equal number can anagram a ten-letter word in a nanosecond. Then there are others whose strategic thinking is almost flawless. Yet none of them will ever become a World or National Champion, because they can't quite achieve the level of calmness and maturity a champion needs.

Most SCRABBLE champions do not get overly excited when they win a game, nor do they punch holes in a wall when they lose. They do not fret about their current standing in a tournament or masochistically replay bad moves from an earlier game. They do not look ahead to upcoming games. Instead, they keep their focus in the game they are playing. Sure, anyone can draw bad tiles, but having the wrong mental approach—or none at all—is one of the few ways a player can beat him or herself. Besides carrying a bad loss into the next game, this might include being too cavalier about the time clock, trying too hard to psych out your opponent, or worrying about how your rivals are doing in the standings.

Brian Cappelletto finally got the proverbial monkey off his back when he won the 1998 National Championship in Chicago at age twenty-nine. Even better, he *lived* in Chicago, which was both convenient and media-worthy.

In Las Vegas, Brian had the opportunity to laminate his legacy with a win at the 2001 World SCRABBLE Championship. There was just one obstacle in his way, and he went by the name of Joel Wapnick. It goes without saying all of us were beyond excited that the finals would pit two of the greatest players in history against each other.

They did not disappoint. The first game was a nail-biter, with Wapnick winning at the very end by 3 points, 482–479. Consider it: a game of almost 1,000 total points decided by 3 points!

Word lovers were not disappointed either, as each player dredged up some spectacular plays from his arsenal of esoterica. Wapnick played WHEEP (to give forth a prolonged whistle) and BAJU (a short jacket worn in Malaysia)—a word not even acceptable in North America! (Wapnick knew it from international play.) Brian, for his part, played INDUSIA (an enveloping layer or membrane). I can state with certainty that I had never seen that word before and have not seen it since.

Though Joel won that first game, Brian went on to win the next three in a row to capture the title and take home the $25,000 first prize. He joined Peter Morris, Joel Sherman, and Wapnick as the only players at that point in history to have won both Worlds and Nationals. (Nigel Richards would achieve this later.) Like Peter Morris, Brian would retire early from the game, in his case to pursue a business career. Yet his place in SCRABBLE lore is intact. In fact, over the years I asked many experts this question: If you had to name one player who is just a bit better than everyone else, who would it be? Their answer would almost always be "Brian." What exactly earned Brian this distinction? Basically, he brought the whole skill set when he sat down at the board. For openers, he'd been playing at the expert level since he was a teenager—so he'd seen it all and was not intimidated by any opponent or situation. He knew almost the entire dictionary. His board vision and strategic skills were as good as anyone's. And he was calm and calculating in every game.

Brian Cappelletto's place in SCRABBLE tournament history would be eclipsed with the emergence of Nigel Richards. A quiet New Zealander who works in Malaysia as a security consultant, Nigel has dominated the World and National SCRABBLE

Championships in recent years. He's won the NSC five times as of this writing and the WSC three times. And Nigel is far from finished.

I remember Joe Edley telling me many years ago, "There's this new player named Nigel Richards who will definitely win a World Championships someday and may have more potential than anyone I've ever seen."

Nigel brings an impressive arsenal to every game and no apparent weaknesses. He's alleged to have a true photographic memory, knowing every word in both the "American" and international dictionaries. Don't try a phony word on this guy! He may also be the most placid competitor I've ever seen. It's impossible to tell by looking at him whether he is ahead or behind, or, for that matter, whether he's just won or lost a game. Nigel has said more than once that he really doesn't care that much about winning or losing; he simply loves to play.

Nigel also epitomizes the mind/body connection espoused by champions in many pursuits. I remember a National SCRABBLE Championship in Dallas where he had booked a hotel room over twenty miles away from the event. Each day for almost a week, he rode his bike to the tournament, played SCRABBLE for six or eight hours, went out to dinner, and then pedaled back to his hotel. Oh yeah, it was during a heat wave when the Dallas temperatures hit triple digits a number of times. And yes, Nigel won that championship as well.

▪ ▪ ▪

After the 2001 WSC both Hasbro and Mattel decided to either scale back or eliminate their financial support for an interna-

tional event. In mid-2013, it was announced that a third-party company called Mind Sports International would take over organizing and promoting the World SCRABBLE Championship. As described in the UK SCRABBLE newsletter, the company is "the driving force behind the internationally recognized Mind Sports Festival, which takes place in fantastic locations around the world, whilst working to promote all of the positive aspects behind intellectual sports in a bid to help increase popularity of these games with both new and established players."

It was also announced that the World SCRABBLE Championship would be renamed the SCRABBLE Champions Tournament, presumably for legal reasons. The first event, with a guaranteed first prize of $10,000, took place in Prague in late 2013. That the WSC would go through this metamorphosis and end up in the adopted home of Franz Kafka is priceless. As they say, you can't make this stuff up. The 2013 SCRABBLE Champions was won by Nigel Richards. Brit Craig Beevers won in 2014.

8

MAN VS. MACHINE

O NE OF THE BEST THINGS TO come out of World SCRABBLE Championships was a challenge match in May 1998 that teamed the top two finishers of the 1997 WSC, Joel Sherman and Matt Graham, together in a best-of-nine showdown against something called "Maven," at that time the state-of-the-art SCRABBLE software program. It was inspired by two highly publicized chess matches between IBM's program "Deep Blue" and international chess master Garry Kasparov, who won the first match, in 1996, and lost the rematch a year later.

The SCRABBLE Man vs. Machine match was first proposed to me by my friend John Tierney, an author and veteran *New York Times* columnist. An excellent SCRABBLE player himself, John wanted to stage the match for a long piece in a *New York Times* Sunday magazine. It would be titled "Humankind Battles for Scrabble Supremacy." (A wonderful in-depth article, it appeared on May 24, 1998, and is available online.)

The event would be sponsored by the *Times* as part of

SCRABBLE's ongoing Fiftieth Anniversary celebration. Obviously, all of us involved jumped at the chance.

As preparations began for the match, we had numerous considerations. Chief among these were our expectations. In theory, the human race would have a better chance with SCRABBLE than with chess because of the luck factor. Chess is all skill; the better man or machine should win. SCRABBLE is, by most accounts, 15 percent luck. Backgammon has been estimated at around the same as SCRABBLE. Based on my admittedly scant research, no one seems to agree on the luck factor in poker.

So if the human team of Matt and Joel drew reasonable tiles, it would be a competitive match. On the other side, the computer would have the entire dictionary completely at its disposal, mistake-free with no wrong guesses. Maven would also have a bit of a psychological advantage—if that's even possible for artificial intelligence. The advantage? Speed. It was more than likely that teammates Matt and Joel would have to carefully evaluate every move, discuss it, and then agree. It was also entirely possible they might disagree on the best move, with one guy ultimately caving in and conceivably pouting. Perhaps I'm exaggerating here, but the point is real. Never underestimate the subtle, corrosive damage a bad SCRABBLE move can do to the human ego and psyche.

So that was our reality. Maven, being soulless, did not have this potential liability. To perform well, Matt and Joel would need to find and agree on their best play. Maven could and would counter every move of its human opponents within two seconds. That could be disheartening at best.

So a group of us gathered in the penthouse of the old New York Times Building on West Forty-third Street in Manhattan.

It was a cavernous space, with high ceilings, windows overlooking the city, and scores of artifacts and artworks that chronicled the paper's history. There was a bar and kitchen area, beautiful rugs, and antique furniture as well. Looking around, I tried to imagine all the various functions that had been held here, populated with authors, presidents, tycoons, celebrities, and the like. And now it was SCRABBLE players. Us.

Our group included, of course, Joel Sherman, Matt Graham, and John Tierney. Also invited was NSA staff member and three-time National SCRABBLE Champion Joe Edley, who would serve as the official and word judge. This was curious, as Edley would be watching closely, doubtlessly second-guessing some of the plays of his colleagues. Hey, bring on the drama!

We'd also invited Brian Sheppard, the genius MIT computer programmer who invented Maven. We'd flown him down from Cambridge for the historic event. A polite, unassuming guy, Brian had not been a serious SCRABBLE player when he began to invent the world's best nonhuman SCRABBLE player. Yet through the experience of the project Brian—almost through osmosis—became a top-rated expert. He played his first tournament game in October of 1987 and his last in December of 1990. He achieved a rating of 1840 after just two events, placing him comfortably in the Top 100 ranking among all North American competitors. Also in attendance was Eric Chaikin, who a few years later would go on to codirect and produce the documentary *Word Wars*. It premiered at the Sundance Film Festival in 2004 and was later nominated for an Emmy. Eric's film featured both Joel Sherman and Matt Graham as central characters.

Rounding out the spectators was my friend Beth Balsam, an executive at Fleishman-Hilliard, Hasbro's PR agency for games

and other activities. A serious SCRABBLE lover, Beth made what may have been the play of the day. We were all hanging out at lunch playing anagrams. The topic was common words that anagrammed into names of celebrities. For example, one was PRESBYTERIAN, which amusingly rearranges to BRITNEY SPEARS.

We were all staring at the word NARCOLEPTIC when Beth blurted out "ERIC CLAPTON." A collective gasp nearly sucked the air out of the room. As Beth herself told me, "It was great. No one could believe that the friggin' PR woman came up with the answer first!"

"Yeah," I replied, "that one's definitely going on your lifetime highlight reel along with your wedding day and the birth of your first child."

The match itself was fascinating. Just before we began, I told Matt and Joel, "Not to add any pressure, but the entire human race is counting on you guys." In reality, no one could put more pressure on these guys than themselves. Confidence was another matter. Matt was convinced they had both the ability and experience to beat Maven. Joel thought they were evenly matched at best.

For me, there were a couple of vivid recollections. One was perhaps among the most amazing plays I'd ever seen. It was close to midway during the best-of-eleven match. Matt and Joel were trailing and had worked hard to come up with a good play in a crucial game. Maven, true to form, took a second and then threw down the word TIRAMISU for a gazillion points. Matt and Joel exchanged shocked, wounded looks and slumped in their chairs. Personally, I felt it was the deciding play of the entire day; there was no way these guys were going to win. I mean, really, think of the construction of that word. An eight-letter bad boy ending in

U? Is there any other eight-letter word ending in U in the entire language? If so, Maven could tell us in 1.5 seconds.

Then there was the inevitable shouting match between Matt and Joel as they started to fall behind. They essentially disagreed about the choice of a particular play, each convinced his move was the best. It became so contentious that I had to stop play for several minutes so the human beings could cool off. Maven, for his part, remained predictably nonplussed. It was quite a contrast: two agitated humans arguing in front of and gesturing toward their opponent—a computer and screen on top of a table. The match lasted nine games, with Maven winning 6–3. Matt and Joel had played as well as possible considering they were matched against an opponent with total, perfect word knowledge. Indeed, the guys made some brilliant, subtle plays that Maven could never have "seen" as they had not been programmed into its strategic DNA—yet. Most importantly, everyone in the room, including Maven inventor Brian Sheppard, agreed that Maven had clearly benefited by better tiles during the course of the day. So far, there has been no rematch.

■   ■   ■

However, humankind did get revenge a few years later when 2006 National SCRABBLE Champion Jim Kramer defeated the "Genius" SCRABBLE program from Real Networks in a best-of-three match in Seattle in an outdoor setting. "Gentleman Jim" is the former proofreader of the *SCRABBLE News*. He took home $10,000 for the win.

9

THE SCHOOL
SCRABBLE PROGRAM

YOU HAVEN'T LIVED UNTIL YOU'VE SEEN a group of twelve-year-old boys fighting over a dictionary. Nearly twenty years ago I witnessed this, along with a group of astonished teachers and parents in Springfield, Massachusetts.

The boys—in jeans, sports jerseys, and backward baseball caps—were taking part in a SCRABBLE tournament for local middle schools from all over the region. A disputed play had emerged during their match, and four boys ran over to the nearest dictionary and began a playful tug-of-war to see who could find the word first. "If I wasn't watching this myself," a nearby teacher whispered, "I never would have believed it."

That incident pretty much epitomized the mission and spirit of the National School SCRABBLE Program. It is probably the single most meaningful accomplishment in my twenty-five-plus years at the National SCRABBLE Association. Here's how it began.

By 1990, it was clear to us at the NSA that we were going to

have to devise a plan and course of action to create the next generation of SCRABBLE consumers and players. The America that spawned the initial SCRABBLE craze back in the early 1950s barely existed anymore. The days of Mom, Dad, Grandma, and the kids sitting around the kitchen table playing board games seemed doomed. The norm had switched to single-parent households, working mothers, MTV, and powerful new distractions such as the Internet and cell phones.

Since we could no longer safely assume kids would be introduced to board games in the family setting, we had to find fun, effective alternative ways to expose them to SCRABBLE. We knew the best way would be through schools.

This was easier said than done. Justifiably, American educators are extremely dubious about letting any commercial interest infiltrate the sanctity of the classroom. It was one thing—already controversial—to have vending machines in school cafeterias selling soft drinks, chips, and candy. Bringing a commercial product into a classroom and having students sample it was a far more challenging prospect. The only large-scale precedent and successful venture of the kind we knew of was when Apple donated computers to schools back in 1975.

Still, there were at least two factors that I knew could work in our favor. First, for better or worse, SCRABBLE was often perceived as a generic "brand" like chess, bingo, backgammon, and cards. The idea that it was a product owned and zealously guarded by a large corporation never even entered people's minds. To them, SCRABBLE was just another piece of the American culture—like baseball. Most everybody owned a board. Most everybody had played it at least once or twice. SCRABBLE had just always been there.

I calculated that this de-commercialized image of the game would help us counter any resistance from educators. I also knew that between word-loving teachers and parents, and thousands of NSA members throughout the country, we would have a motivated force of individuals to serve as our foot soldiers in this initiative. But the overwhelming selling point for the fledgling School SCRABBLE Program was the innate and obvious educational value of the game itself.

The learning aspects of SCRABBLE were twofold: the obvious and the subtle. The obvious included spelling and vocabulary. The less obvious were math, spatial relationships, decision-making, and "cooperative learning." The latter is a term for teamwork: students work in pairs or small groups on a specific learning task or project in an effort to organize classroom activities into social and learning experiences.

SCRABBLE is in many ways about math. In School SCRABBLE, kids have to keep a running score, which includes basic addition. They have to apply multiplication in calculating a specific move. And they quickly learn the core skill of figuring probability by knowing how many of a certain letter have been played and how many remain in the bag or on an opponent's rack.

Spatial relationships and decision-making are learned by developing board vision—seeing every possible play in every place on the board. At any given time, a player has numerous options all over the board for making a play, and the best play is not always about the most points. So we knew kids would learn critical thinking by having to both identify and evaluate their options. We introduced this concept in a very simple way. In classroom testing, we had each student find the tiles for his or her name and place it on the board, then move it around to cover

various bonus squares. They quickly understood it was worth different values in different places. Bingo!

The cooperative learning aspect was extremely interesting, and underestimated in the School SCRABBLE Program. If one accepts the premise that competition and life at large are not always about winning, it makes sense. Our overriding belief was this: if the School SCRABBLE Program was not fun above all else, it would fail. That's why we decided early on to have the kids play in pairs. For one thing, it would substantially limit the intimidation factor. No one likes to look stupid, especially middle school students; teaming kids up, we gave them a built-in sense of comfort by partnership. For another, some kids were better at spelling, others at the math side of the game, so teamwork maximized the chances for success.

Teachers soon learned to pair up kids in experimental ways: a shy kid with an extrovert, the class bully with a nerd, a black kid with a white kid, and so on. We collected a huge amount of anecdotal research. A long-term goal was to hire a team of educational experts to track two different classes for an entire school year. One group would participate heavily in SCRABBLE, both after school and in the classroom. The other would conduct their studies as always. After a year, testing would be devised to see how the former group matched up with the latter in spelling, vocabulary, dictionary use, math, and other more abstract skills such as collaborative ability and even attention span. (I should emphasize that this is a simplification of what the study would have been, had it progressed beyond the talking stage.)

A wonderful example of the collaborative aspect of cooperative learning emerged from a middle school in Pennsylvania during our early testing phases before the program launch. It

featured a twelve-year-old boy who had been deemed a "distraction" to other students because of erratic behavior. As a result, he was routinely marginalized from the general student population. He spent his days in an empty classroom with a tutor who also served as a monitor.

However, his School SCRABBLE Program teacher had the idea to have him participate in a session. After he was paired with a compatible partner, the experiment began. It could not have turned out any better. The boy immediately took to SCRABBLE and was thoroughly engaged. Better yet, he was a calm, focused partner. Encouraged by the initial progress, the teachers continued the experiment. His behavior continued to improve. Ultimately, they decided to take things further. The boy was introduced into an art class, where he was given a partner on a simple project. It worked! He was comfortable, engaged, productive, and increasingly social. I'm not saying he went on to be the valedictorian or president of the student body—I have no idea—but these were critical baby steps. And no path to wholeness or self-improvement starts without them.

Before the national launch of the program, our NSA-Hasbro team took our idea on the road to various schools for nearly two years to see what we could learn. Geographically, we chose three regions: the Springfield, Massachusetts area, Long Island, and Manhattan. Hasbro Games was located in East Longmeadow, a few miles away from Springfield. In many ways, it could be Anywhere, USA, which was exactly what we wanted. Long Island, where the NSA was headquartered, served as the testing ground for suburban and rural schools, and Manhattan would provide the urban experience. To be thorough, we agreed we had to visit classrooms from grades 1–12 in both public and private schools.

We had decided we needed three trips to every school. The initial trip was to introduce ourselves and the fundamentals of the game. The second was to give some advanced tips and begin competition. The third was to have an informal class championship. Bear in mind we were teaching the teacher as well.

It was clear on the first visit to grades 1–3 that they were not the ideal participants. Though sweet and cute, the kids were predictably distracted and fidgety. Despite being up for the new experience, they soon became bored. Also, their vocabularies and maturity were simply too undeveloped for them to find plays easily and quickly. I should add there were numerous incidents of flying tiles, missing letters, and dropped SCRABBLE boards.

We learned two key things going forward. Generally, kids under ten years old were simply too young. And for School SCRABBLE, we should replace the standard SCRABBLE board with the deluxe model, where the tiles are secured in grids.

Numerous trips to middle schools confirmed our thoughts that ages ten to thirteen would be the best participants in School SCRABBLE. That has been the traditional age range for the National Spelling Bee and many school chess programs. Also, kids that age are reasonably socialized but not too jaded.

One of our first field trips was to a middle school in Springfield. The kids took to the game almost immediately—well over half of them saying they'd played it at home. There were a lot of high fives, word challenges, and light trash talk. The teacher could not believe how engaged her students were. She uttered the phrase I'd hear numerous times in ensuing years: "They're learning and they don't even know it!" Exactly. She later wrote us and said she was using SCRABBLE as an incentive. "I told them if

they finished the lesson plan early, they could play SCRABBLE. I never saw them so motivated."

Trips to other middle schools yielded identical results, regardless of the location or composition of the class. Inspired by the experience, we developed materials geared specifically for the kids. "Cool Words to Know" was the two- and three-letter words, Q-without-U words, common JQXZ words, and more. Another piece, understandably popular, was "How to Beat Your Parents at SCRABBLE."

We developed materials for teachers as well. Our NSA School SCRABBLE Program director, Yvonne Lieblein, worked with NSA players Ben Greenwood and Christine Economos, who were teachers and educational consultants, to this end. First, they created key vocabulary exercises using the SCRABBLE board and tiles. Then they created lesson plans based directly on state and nationally mandated vocabulary guidelines, as well as a series of SCRABBLE-based activity books to be sold at retail.

Another key contributor was Dr. Paul Folkemer of the Benjamin Franklin Middle School in Ridgewood, New Jersey. Dr. Folkemer was a past National Middle School Principal of the Year and a true SCRABBLE fanatic. In fact, he'd created a daily SCRABBLE challenge that was telecast on his school's classroom network. The daily feature was picked up by a local cable access channel, and soon the whole town was playing along with the kids!

On an early visit to Benjamin Franklin Middle School, it had been arranged for me to play five games at once against five teams of two students each. At least one of those teams beat me as I scurried back and forth trying to make my best plays. In one key game, I was about to lose when I saw the seven-letter play POOPERS on my rack.

I was so focused that my only thought was "party poopers." Swear to God. So I laid the tiles down against my opponents, a pair of eleven-year-old boys. You can imagine their reaction to seeing the word POOPERS—and then the reaction of the boys next to them, then the rest of the class, then the dismayed teacher. Muffled by giggles and hoots of laughter, I tried in vain to explain the word, but the damage had been done. Only later did I learn that the word POOPERS was not a legal word in SCRABBLE, regardless of its meaning.

Our research visits to high schools proved less fruitful. In fact, we cut these short because it was apparent early on that SCRABBLE in the classroom or as an extracurricular activity just wasn't optimal for this demographic. The reasons were numerous. High school students are already overbooked, and even the most enticing SCRABBLE scenarios were no match for raging hormones. Almost every game we tried at the high school level became an opportunity for flirting, teasing, and goofing around. I remember vainly trying to explain the joy of playing an obscure word to a noisy, distracted group of Long Island teenagers. As I trudged back from the front of the classroom to join my colleagues, a sullen fifteen-year-old boy glared at me. "Dork," he muttered.

▪ ▪ ▪

When our field work was completed in 1992, it was time to both announce and launch the National School SCRABBLE Program. It was clear that we had two key needs: a partner to help us get into schools, and materials.

For the partner, we chose Scholastic, the venerable and highly respected educational publisher, which had a divi-

sion specifically charged with this kind of mission—to help companies responsibly and realistically introduce viable new products to schools. Scholastic had the experience, credibility, and database we needed. As a team, we all began work on a direct-mail piece introducing School SCRABBLE and its educational benefits. As we'd done so often before, the NSA recommended that the Hasbro name be minimized in the endeavor; make it about the game.

For the second element, the NSA created a School SCRABBLE Kit. The idea was to have everything necessary for a classroom of twenty-four students contained in one box. We recommended the following materials be included: six SCRABBLE games with the raised grid surface, racks, tiles, an *Official SCRABBLE Players Dictionary*, the "Cool Words to Know" word list to be photocopied, a curriculum guide for the teacher, and a five-minute video showing a classroom full of cool middle school kids having the time of their lives playing SCRABBLE.

I'll skip over the year-by-year growth of the program and simply say that it was a huge success by any standard. After a successful launch, we went on to sell more than thirty thousand kits in the next decade with over a million students participating.

We learned so much. One of the significant findings was that, at the end of the day, any endeavor is only as good as its local operatives. This holds true whether it's a Scout troop, 4-H club, chess club, or gymnastics club. We came to appreciate how much pressure is on teachers from so many sources: parents, the administration, the state educational offices, and the students themselves. We also learned that many teachers bought School SCRABBLE Kits with their own money or from a small class-

room budget rather than send the request through a labyrinth of financial approvals.

This launch also gave me a personal reality check in regard to dealing with a couple of large organizations. The National PTA, which I assumed would be a natural partner, was a complete dead end. A trip to their annual convention indicated to me that they were more about fund-raising than about curriculum. This led us to create a brochure on how to use SCRABBLE as a fund-raiser; one of the chief ways was to have people pledge money for points scored during a tournament. While the PTA never embraced this, we did have more luck with the Literacy Volunteers of America and its successor, ProLiteracy Worldwide. These groups stage up to seventy-five SCRABBLE-themed fund-raisers a year throughout North America and by late 2013 had raised nearly $2 million doing this.

My most disappointing institutional encounter was with the Department of Education (DOE) in Washington. I had called the office of my congressman in the House of Representatives. They gave me a contact name at the DOE, whom I called six times without a return phone call. On the first call, I simply left my name and a fifteen-word message. On the third phone call, I left a longer message. I emphasized that we were not looking for funding, an endorsement, or even a meeting. All we wanted was to know if in their myriad platforms for communicating with the nation's schools, there might be a place to mention this innovative new teaching idea. On the sixth call, I left a brief message: that I was no longer interested in the DOE's help, but was curious as to the magic number of phone calls needed before someone called me back. That went unanswered as well.

Another huge School SCRABBLE disappointment was my

dealings with Electronic Arts (EA), who held the license from Hasbro for the SCRABBLE Internet and Digital rights in North America. The NSA worked with them when they first acquired the rights, consulting on marketing and development of the online game. The executives I dealt with were fun, delightful people, but I concluded they were mostly interested in having "Endorsed by the National SCRABBLE Association" on their products.

Early on, I had urged both Hasbro and EA to take ownership of kids' SCRABBLE play on the Internet. In 2004, we suggested a plan to form online School SCRABBLE Clubs with proctored interclub play and individual play between members. I felt this was critical to the health—hell, survival—of the brand for the future. Imagine a middle school in Florida challenging a middle school in Illinois to a match!

EA agreed this was a great idea and authorized me to go on national television to announce it. So during an ESPN telecast of the National School SCRABBLE Championship—more on that later—I appeared, gushing about the development of this idea. Embarrassingly, it never happened. Unfortunately, as I write this, there is still no designated place for kids to play SCRABBLE with other kids or schools on the Internet. Most serious School SCRABBLE players have found their way either to Words with Friends or to an illegal site run out of Romania.

From the very beginning of School SCRABBLE, we had talked about eventually having a National School SCRABBLE Championship (NSSC). This was inspired by the National Spelling Bee as well as our own National SCRABBLE Championship for adults. Competitions of this kind were beginning to flourish. In addition to the spelling bee, there were national vocabulary,

geography, and math "bees" as well. Of course, the leader in all this was chess. School chess programs and competition have been thriving forever. This is pretty astonishing, given chess's learning curve and intellectually intimidating reputation.

Despite the lack of an official Internet school and kids' platform to help drive our efforts, the School SCRABBLE Program continued to grow—especially in terms of competition. So as we contemplated our first national event, we began with a couple of tournaments in Massachusetts, then a New England–wide tournament in Boston in 2001.

We learned a lot along the way. For openers, less is more. So rather than go with the adult tournament time limit of twenty-five total minutes, we kept the kids at twenty-two minutes per team. We also learned that kids bring a lot of playground behavior indoors for this sort of thing. There was a lot of teasing and trash-talking—to the point we had to establish a Sportsmanship Award to deter this.

Of course, there was a wide range of types of kids, skill levels, and hijinks. At one tournament, we had a pair of seventh-grade girls who realized their fifth-grade boy opponents were complete novices. Midway into the game, they decided to start laying random, absurd combinations of letters on the board. Their plays might have included nonwords such as GRUNK, MARP, and BANBAY. The boys were too intimidated to challenge and deferred on every play, so the girls won by hundreds of points. Needless to say, this particular girls' team did not win the Sportsmanship Award. In fact, because of this, we changed the rules to put a ceiling on the margin of victory a team could achieve.

One classic tournament sight was a game between two

eighth-grade girls and, again, a pair of fifth-grade boys. This time, the boys were from an all-male Catholic school. They sat stick straight, side by side, in starched white shirts, school ties, and blazers with the school crest.

The girls were another story. We all know the differences in physical maturity between a thirteen-year-old girl and a ten-year-old boy. So suffice it to say these two girls were light-years ahead of these two boys in the puberty sweepstakes. And their fashion sense had a touch more flair than that found at a typical Catholic school. Inspired by, perhaps, Britney Spears, each girl was fully made up, bejeweled, and confident.

Each time I walked by their table, the boys were doing one of two things. They either stared straight ahead, silently watching as the girls frolicked across from them, or they kept their heads down, eyes averted, as these apprentice sirens cast their spell over the board. I never did find out who won that game.

Another thing we learned was that every year the level of play became better and better. Sure, there were always newbies in the back of the room—and we embraced them—but the kids at the leading tables were becoming as good as some adult tournament players. There were numerous reasons for that. Sometimes parents, recognizing a new interest, brought the kids to a local adult SCRABBLE club for competition and pointers. Books such as *Word Freak* and *Everything SCRABBLE*® told about the joy of the game and offered tips and exercises. And there were now schools that'd been using School SCRABBLE for a number of years, so the second and third round of students were more advanced.

We went on to have our first National School SCRABBLE

Championship in Boston in 2003, spearheaded locally by SCRABBLE promoter Sherrie Saint John and her husband, Gregg Foster. From there, we held them in Providence, Orlando, and Washington, DC. Although the event was still held on the East Coast, we were starting to go national for competitors. From the early New England–only players, we now had kids from California, Texas, Indiana, North Carolina, Utah, Oregon, Canada, and more. Hasbro continued to support the NSA with a beautiful hotel site, thousand of dollars in prize money, an opening reception, breakfast and lunch, trophies, and welcome packages with games, T-shirts, and other goodies for students and coaches. Our friends at Merriam-Webster donated free SCRABBLE dictionaries and created an annual word-based contest with a substantial prize such as an iPad.

Below is an example of the contest for the kids for the 2012 NSSC. Let's see how well you can do against the young word wizards who entered.

Use Your Merriam-Webster
Official SCRABBLE Players Dictionary, Fourth Edition
to Score High
Spell it out for a chance to win a Kindle Touch
3G e-reader from Merriam-Webster!

A blue color (*adjective*) 10 points _ _ _ _ _ _ _ _
To gossip (*verb*) 24 points _ _ _ _ _ _ _ _
Standard keyboard (*noun*) 21 points _ _ _ _ _ _
Extremely idealistic (*adjective*) 26 points _ _ _ _ _ _ _ _

To seize a vehicle while in transit (*verb*) 22 points _ _ _ _
_ _

A cell formed by the union of two gametes (*noun*) 19
points _ _ _ _ _ _

To cover with a thin varnish (*verb*) 12 points _ _ _ _ _ _ _

The science that deals with animals (*noun*) 20 points _ _
_ _ _ _ _

A question (*noun*) 19 points _ _ _ _ _ _ _ _

A marketplace (*noun*) 17 points _ _ _ _ _ _

Answers on page 203.

Although the events were fully funded, it's important to note that every team paid its own way to the National School SCRABBLE Championship. The typical contingent from a school would be two kids, a coach, two parents, and a handful of siblings, so there was a fair amount of money involved. Sometimes teams were underwritten by a PTA or school activities budget. Often the school would hold bake sales or a car wash to raise the necessary funds.

It was inspirational to see schools, classmates, and the community getting behind this mission. In many areas, the NSSC competitors were considered as important as any athletic team headed off to a big tournament. One of the coolest scenarios was when a winning school returned home to a rally in which the National School SCRABBLE Championship silver cup was placed in the school's trophy case along with those of the football, baseball, and gymnastic teams!

This played to our core message to the kids: that you could

get recognition, travel, win money, and take part in serious competition even if you could not run fast, jump high, or throw a ball with accuracy. Hey, if I can convince one kid that Smart Is Cool, I will have justified my time on earth.

So by 2009, the National School SCRABBLE Championship had grown to the point that first prize was $10,000 for the winning team. Even better, we were about to make both the kids and adult experts TV stars!

10

SCHOOL SCRABBLE
MAKES THE GRADE

I T TOOK A COUPLE OF YEARS, but we were able to grow the National School SCRABBLE Championship into a truly spectacular event. The best part is that it grew in every way. More kids participated. The student competitors continued to catch up with adults in their abilities, and the world was starting to pay more attention to our core messages: it's cool to be smart, and competition can take many forms. As a bonus, it was proven that the world's favorite word game could enrich lives and help teach in unanticipated ways.

Our efforts reached their high point around 2010. The glint of an idea a decade or so earlier had gone from a small ballroom at the Marriott in Springfield, Massachusetts, Royal Pacific Resort in family-friendly Orlando.

By now, the event had become a family affair. It was routine to see a young competitor accompanied by as many as a half-dozen relatives—most of whom would sit patiently on the sidelines during play, even though they really couldn't see any

"action." Team uniforms had also become standard. Scores of col-
orfully decorated T-shirts, baseball caps, and hoodies bore the
name—or nickname—of each team. Examples might include the
Word Wizards, the Tile Masters, or the clever You Can't Spell
Awesome Without Me!

The NSA's Jane Ratsey Williams and staff also organized a
wondrous evening social to build camaraderie and relax the competitors a bit. It was always a themed party, once a luau with leis
for each guest, another time a Cinco de Mayo party complete with
a mariachi band. We'd serve up plenty of treats for the students
and their families, with ice cream sundaes, fruit parfaits for kids
with allergies, and a fun take-home memento. Another highlight
of the party would be games. It was fun to see these kids—after
a day of intense matches of SCRABBLE—playing other classics
such as Jenga, Scattergories, Perfection, Twister, and Boggle. To
add to the excitement we also made sure to have on hand a couple
of adult National SCRABBLE Champions—who are heroes to
kids—to play fun matches against groups of youngsters. These
events emphasized and reinforced the beauty of board games.
Children from North Carolina would be playing Monopoly with
kids from Toronto. Thirteen-year-old girls would be competing,
and practicing flirting, against two brothers from Texas.

As you might imagine, Hasbro executives almost wept with
appreciation as they witnessed this swirl of two hundred kids
and their families captivated by their products. After all, this
was not a Saturday morning commercial on Nickelodeon with
child actors; this was the real deal. It was important for all of us
involved to make this event the experience of a lifetime for everyone who attended—whether it was the team who won $10,000
or the fifth-grade first-timers who lost almost every game. As

in sports, the life lessons learned from games are invaluable and incalculable.

Then there was the actual competition. The skill level of some middle school students had become so refined and lethal that they now routinely played and defeated grown-ups in official play.

This evolution was hammered home in dramatic fashion at the 2008 National SCRABBLE Championship in Orlando. Remember, this is arguably the largest and toughest SCRABBLE tournament in the world, and that year it featured $100,000 in cash prizes. It included twenty-eight intense games over five days. Players competed in six divisions, depending on their skill level and rating. Astonishingly, four of the six divisions were won by kids coming out of the School SCRABBLE Program, the oldest being just twenty years old. If we'd ever had any doubts about the ability of the program to feed the tournament scene, they were eradicated by those performances.

The National School SCRABBLE Championship remains one of the most meaningful, exhausting, and fun experiences of my life—on both a professional and personal level. I'll never forget getting to know these young champions and their families. All of us at the NSA and the people from Hasbro Games also gleaned enormous satisfaction from watching the kids go through this experience.

While the championship is the high-profile centerpiece of the National School SCRABBLE Program, it's important to pay tribute to what is happening on the local level throughout the country. In Washington, DC, for example, we went from no presence whatsoever to having a School SCRABBLE club in every single middle school in the city—127 in all. Spearheaded

by DC resident Stefan Fatsis and, on the NSA side, Jane Ratsey Williams and Katie Schulz Hukill, the Washington initiative became a true template of what we were trying to do all over the country. It typically began with a visit to a school, or a conference with teachers or administrators from many schools. Most meetings began with us showing a fun, energetic video of kids playing SCRABBLE. Next came explanations about the School SCRABBLE Kit, educational benefits, program guidelines, and game rules, and random questions.

As with anything of this nature, the growth was organic. That said, once SCRABBLE was introduced properly into a classroom or as an after-school activity, the rest took care of itself. After all, SCRABBLE is nothing if not approachable for kids. The rules are simple, and there is plenty of scoring. Time and again, we witnessed the sense of discovery when students "got it." Just like generations before them who'd learned about the game around the kitchen table, these kids couldn't get enough of it.

Philadelphia became another hotspot for kids and SCRABBLE. The driving force there was Marciene Mattleman, a dynamo who seemed to know everyone in the City of Brotherly Love. Marciene is a longtime media personality and social activist, the kind of individual who is unwilling to take no for an answer. She and her organization, the Philadelphia After School Activities Partnerships (ASAP), had earlier success with a vigorous after-school program featuring chess. Now it was SCRABBLE's turn, and Marciene took it city-wide. Marciene, who coincidentally knew Stefan Fatsis from his days at Penn and as a young reporter, soon brought impressive participation to Philadelphia's School SCRABBLE effort as well. By 2012, Philadelphia had annual school championships, more than a hundred clubs, and thousands

of kids involved. Marciene also cajoled numerous mayors, politicians, and business leaders to both attend and contribute to the effort. Throughout this, Marciene was fortunate enough to work with NSA member Matt Hopkins, a local SCRABBLE organizer and one of the most respected people in the NSA community.

Chicago was a different story. As noted, outreach is only as good as one's local contact and operatives. In the Windy City, that turned out to be not an educational institution but the Chicago-based American Library Association via our main contact, Jenny Levine. Jenny's another hardworking, smart, caring person who believes in the greater good and has chosen the not-for-profit career to the benefit of all of us. She also introduced us to having a presence at both the American Library Association National Conferences and the Public Library Association. Working closely together, we were able to establish nearly eight hundred library SCRABBLE clubs across the United States for kids and families.

As clubs started sprouting up outside of traditional schools and libraries, we noticed that SCRABBLE clubs were also starting to sprout up in other unanticipated venues such as Scouts and 4-H clubs. To expand this outreach, NSA staff members started to attend various annual conventions to spread the word: middle school teachers, gifted and talented programs, the Girl Scouts of America, the National Reading Association, Newspapers in Education, the National PTA, and others.

Each conference taught us something new. We learned that education was a multilayered entity and a big business. It was also no place for idealists. Though we bore the warm and fuzzy banner of America's beloved word game—along with an innovative teaching approach—we were subjected to the same gauntlet of

skepticism, testing, waiting, and approval as anyone else. Every-one wants to do business with schools because it's an important and feel-good enterprise, but there is also a lot of money to be made. And, understandably, everyone has a voice: federal and state government, school boards, parents, and teachers. So we had to become realists with a lot of patience

Having grown up just thirty miles from New York City, I was especially excited about taking on Gotham on behalf of School SCRABBLE. We went at this a couple of ways. First, we have a mutual friend with Caroline Kennedy Schlossberg, who had become very active as a volunteer to Mayor Michael Bloomberg in an effort to improve the public school system. So we reached out to her, but our timing was bad. Ms. Schlossberg was consid-ering her first attempt at elected politics, possibly running for the US Senate from New York. She later was appointed ambas-sador to Japan.

Our next plan was to reconnect with legendary New York restaurateur Danny Meyer. One of the nation's most admired businessmen, Danny made his mark with such New York estab-lishments as the Union Square Café, the Gramercy Tavern, the Modern, Blue Smoke, and the Shake Shack franchises, among other ventures. A true SCRABBLE fan, Danny participated in our 1998 SCRABBLE 50th Anniversary SPELL-A-BRATION tournament at Madison Square Garden to benefit literacy. Other guests included Al Franken, Walt "Clyde" Frazier, literacy activ-ist and actress Tina Louise, Miss America, *New York Post* colum-nist Richard Johnson, and film critic Jeffrey Lyons.

Danny Meyer is known as a caring member of the commu-nity and has been involved in numerous charitable causes over the years. So the NSA staff met with Danny and his people and

created a project model we felt would work well for New York City and could then be applied to other major markets as well.

The plan was simple. Through Danny Meyer's Union Square Hospitality Group, we would reach out to various restaurants throughout the city. We would then encourage restaurants to purchase one or more School SCRABBLE Kits and donate them to middle schools in their neighborhoods. It would be as little as $49.95 to participate and a great public relations move by participating restaurants.

In addition to this involvement, Danny offered other support. For openers, he would host an event at one of his establishments where we would announce the initiative to the media. Danny also owned one of the city's most desirable Rolodexes, and he offered to invite numerous power brokers, celebrities and others to the event. Understandably, we were thrilled with Danny Meyer's graciousness and potential involvement.

Unfortunately, this is as far as it ever went. The timing was horrible in regard to Hasbro's participation. The NSA was in the throes of dealing with, in my opinion, the least imaginative and least cooperative team of Hasbro Games marketing executives in our twenty-five-year relationship. It got so bad that, despite our efforts, we went *an entire year* without a single face-to-face meeting with anyone at Hasbro! Meanwhile, the Danny Meyer ship had sailed. I suspect he was understandably astonished—and possibly insulted—by our inability to step up and pull the trigger on a project of this scope and importance. I sure was.

Fortunately, we eventually found our way to the New York City Parks and Recreation Department. Even by municipal standards, the Parks and Recreation Department was a vast and deep

operation. Among their responsibilities was the organization and supervision of various youth programs in the city's five boroughs.

The Parks people loved the idea of SCRABBLE. They had more than enough of the standard indoor and outdoor activities, and we represented a fresh idea. Plus, the prospect of Hasbro donating School SCRABBLE Kits had great appeal for the schools' cash-strapped budgets.

After our initial meetings with the coordinator, we began a plan to set up SCRABBLE activities at selected locations throughout the city. First the NSA held training sessions with the Parks personnel, just as we had with schoolteachers in Washington, DC, and Philadelphia. Many were unfamiliar with the game and initially intimidated by the prospect. We understood. One of the chief elements of resistance to SCRABBLE—regardless of the venue or group—is that people are afraid that playing will reveal them to be stupid, a terrible speller, or both.

Happily, our effort expanded and even culminated in several local Parks and Recreation tournaments, culminating in a city-wide tournament at the Castle, the headquarters in Central Park. I attended the event and watched the competition with Commissioner Adrian Benepe and his staff. Our goal was to have the winners represent New York City at the next National School SCRABBLE Championship. Unfortunately, as sometimes happens, our initiative lost steam when our main contact left her position, followed by Benepe himself not long thereafter. It's my understanding that this initiative is no longer active.

And then there's Los Angeles. Contrary to what some cynical East Coast intellectuals might assume, LA is one of the most active and successful SCRABBLE cultures in North America. Among its SCRABBLE stars is Roger "Trey" Wright, the 2004

National SCRABBLE Champion and a world-class touring classical pianist. There's also Mark Landsberg, whose record of 770 points scored in an official SCRABBLE match stood for nearly thirteen years. Also in LA were tournament expert and documentary filmmaker Eric Chaikin (*Word Wars*) and Scott Petersen, whose acclaimed *Scrabylon* garnered awards at numerous festivals around the country.

Unfortunately, we never really made any inroads with the LA public school systems or other conventional channels.

11

SCRABBLE HITS TV

O NE OF MY GOALS RUNNING THE NSA was to have an actual SCRABBLE match on television. Chess and poker had been on periodically over the years, and I felt that, done properly, a high-level SCRABBLE match would make for an interesting show. There had been a SCRABBLE game show in the mid-1980s, hosted by the ubiquitous Chuck Woolery. It was actually more like Hangman than SCRABBLE, so, as one might have expected, it was dismissed, if not reviled, by most serious NSA players. The production company even sent two casting people to the 1985 National SCRABBLE Championship to interview "real SCRABBLE experts" to appear on the show. A handful actually made it onto the air, where most got their butts kicked by your average experienced game show contestants.

While we'd had various champions interviewed over the years on television, a broadcast match had remained elusive for us until 2003. We had identified ESPN as our most likely platform for a number of reasons. First, we loved the idea of SCRABBLE being

positioned—if not perceived—as a legitimate, serious competitive event. Second, we knew that ESPN was expanding into multiple channels as well as quirky programming such as competitive
eating. We saw ourselves fitting right into that niche. After all,
it was ESPN that brought the successful National Spelling Bee
coverage to national television. It had become such a ratings success that ESPN's broadcast cousin ABC eventually took over the
program to expand the audience. Who better to fill in the programming void than SCRABBLE!

Third, we knew that—at the time—one could still essentially
buy one's way onto ESPN by buying an hour of time at a nego-
tiated price. After that, the buyer would own the commercials
within. In theory, the buyer could then sell off the spots to a third
party to offset production and time costs, or use them for itself.

But we were able to go one better. We ultimately convinced
ESPN to allot the time at their cost and pay for the production of
America's first televised SCRABBLE match.

As it turned out, the NSA was pitching the network from two
fronts. My talented colleague and School SCRABBLE Program
director, Yvonne Lieblein, had been talking to ESPN executives
at their Bristol, Connecticut, headquarters about telecasting the
first National School SCRABBLE Championship. I, on the other
hand, had been in conversation with veteran ESPN producer and
director Jonathan Hock. I met Jon through his best friend, Stefan Fatsis, and we connected over our love of sports, video, and
film. Jon is a gifted person, responsible for several programs in
ESPN's remarkable *30 for 30* series as well as wonderful documentary work. Jon loved SCRABBLE and was interested in pursuing the project through his own contacts at the network.

I had learned early in my career that very often a particular

media outlet might have more than one person chasing down a story. For example, a *New York Times* reporter might be talking to us about a SCRABBLE story while a *Times* columnist might also be thinking of doing a piece. It had happened with NBC, NPR, CNN, and others. I also learned early to simply let the chips fall where they may. It was up to these guys, not me, to decide who was going to do a SCRABBLE piece. They would find out eventually through the editorial process about each other's interest.

At any rate, Yvonne got the call first, and we headed up to ESPN to talk about the project. Jon Hock eventually dropped out. He felt he needed ninety minutes to do the show properly and a larger budget than ESPN was willing to provide.

Our ESPN contacts were friendly, smart, and enthusiastic. However, as we discussed the possibility of the National School SCRABBLE Championship show, I became concerned. The chief reason was that this was going to be the first year of a real *national* school competition—all the others had been regional. There was a plethora of variables and unknowns. How many teams would we have? How good was the level of play? How would the kids—and their parents—behave? As excited as I was to be in the meeting, my gut was telling me that to hold the first-ever NSSC and have it on television at the same time was not a good idea.

So I introduced the idea of having a SCRABBLE All*Stars tournament instead, postponing the NSSC broadcast until at least the following year. It was a concept similar to our 1995 SCRABBLE Superstars Showdown spectacular in Las Vegas. That event generated serious publicity—including a seven-page article in *Sports Illustrated*—and featured the fifty best players in the world vying for $100,000 in cash.

ESPN liked this idea a lot. For openers, it had the built-in all-star sports element. Even better, Hasbro would soon agree to both put up the prize money and underwrite the entire event. ESPN would provide the time and assign an approved producer to the project. They also assigned a designated ESPN person—dynamo Ashley O'Connor Mintz—to be our day-to-day contact.

The ESPN All*Stars event was an astonishing experience for all involved. The NSA staff and Advisory Board worked hard to come up with an eligibility format that was fair. In the end, we decided to invite all former world and national champions, with the rest of the field being eligible by tournament rating. Interestingly, former champions Peter Morris and Brian Cappelletto both emerged from self-imposed retirement for a crack at the $50,000 first prize. While NSA experts often and understandably bemoaned the lack of big prize money compared to chess or poker, this did represent serious progress. After all, not long before, first prize in the National SCRABBLE Championship had been just $5,000.

As expected, the event lived up to its billing in regard to the intensity of the competitors and the level of play. Technically, it was a challenge for the ESPN crew and announcers. These were guys used to filming and talking about nonstop action, and this venue was the opposite. Instead, the play-by-play consisted of words that could have been played, biographical backgrounds of the competitors, and fundamental SCRABBLE tips. For once, I half-wished a few of our more volatile players would start a fistfight or fling a board against the wall. We wanted to deliver viewers bang for their entertainment buck.

Because of time constraints—forty-eight minutes—we knew we were not going to be able to show a SCRABBLE match in

The SCRABBLE 50th Anniversary Celebrity SCRABBLE Tournament at Madison Square Garden in New York, March 1998. Former *Saturday Night Live* star and current U.S. senator Al Franken and his partner, NBA Hall of Fame player Walt "Clyde" Frazier, plot their next move. *(Marty Heitner photo/Alfred Butts Estate)*

One of the early prototypes of SCRABBLE from the 1930s. Note the architect's paper used by the game's inventor, Alfred Mosher Butts. Also note on the left that the game was still called Criss Cross Words at the time. *(Marty Heitner photo/Alfred Butts Estate)*

SCRABBLE inventor Alfred Mosher Butts in a publicity shot circa 1980. A brilliant, creative, and humble man, he admitted he was astonished by the worldwide success of his idea. It's estimated over 100 million SCRABBLE sets have been sold. *(Selchow & Righter photo)*

The late Rita Norr with John D. Williams Jr. in 1987, moments after she became the only woman in history to win the National SCRABBLE Championship. This photograph was taken at the Sahara Hotel in Las Vegas. It turned out that Rita and John owned houses barely a mile apart on eastern Long Island, more than two thousand miles away, where they played a match three days later. *(AP photo)*

MULLIGATAWNY—one of the most famous SCRABBLE moves of all time. It was played by the late Joe Simpson against his friend Fred Smedley at the legendary Washington Square Park SCRABBLE scene in New York. Fred opened with TAWNY. Joe studied his rack and found MULLIGA. Fred challenged, and they had to walk to Joe's nearby apartment for a dictionary that contained the word! Mulligatawny is a rich soup seasoned with curry. *(Patty Hocker photo)*

MILTON BRADLEY CO.

GAMES

Card and Paper Trimmers
School and Kindergarten Material

Cable -
MILTBRADCO

Springfield, Mass.

November 15, 1933

Mr. Alfred M. Butts
101 Park Avenue
New York City

Dear Sir:

After giving your game our very careful review and
consideration, we do not feel we would be interested in adding
this item to our line.

We are returning the model under separate cover.

Very truly yours,

MILTON BRADLEY COMPANY

George A. Fox

Manager Game Department

:S

Thanks, but no thanks. Here's a 1933 letter from game manufacturer Milton Bradley to Alfred Mosher Butts rejecting his submission of an early version of SCRABBLE. *(Marty Heitner photo/Alfred Butts Estate)*

The largest National SCRABBLE Championship in history, with over 840 contestants playing for the $25,000 top prize. Trey Wright defeated SCRABBLE National, ALL*STARS, and Superstars Showdown champion David Gibson for the 2004 title in New Orleans. *(Patty Hocker photo)*

Highest game score ever! Mike Cresta defeated Wayne Yorra 830–490 in the highest-scoring official game in history at the Lexington, Massachusetts, club on October 12, 2006. Cresta's 830 points eradicated the previous record of 770 points held by California's Mark Landsberg, and the combined 1,320 points shattered the previous mark by almost 200 points. Among the high-scoring plays: JOUSTED, LADYLIKE, FLATFISH, UNDERDOG, SCAMSTER, and QUIXOTRY. Astonishingly, neither player is a tournament expert. *(Patty Hocker photo)*

Games

Salem, Mass., U.S.A.

GRAND PRIZE AND GOLD MEDAL
WORLD'S FAIR
SAINT LOUIS, 1904
HIGHEST AWARD
WORLD'S COLUMBIAN EXPOSITION
CHICAGO 1893

NEW YORK
FLATIRON BUILDING
LONDON: 12 WHITELEY ROAD
CABLE ADDRESS
"PARKER SALEM"
WESTERN UNION CODE

October 17, 1934

Mr. Alfred M. Butts,
101 Park Ave.,
New York City

Dear Sir:

Our New Games Committee has carefully considered
the game which you so kindly sent in to us for examination.
While the game no doubt contains considerable merit, we do
not feel that it is adaptable to our line.

The games we have planned and developed far in
advance, make a very attractive addition to our line, and
are quite sufficient under present conditions. Therefore,
we are returning your material to you, under separate cover.

We thank you sincerely for your kindness and courtesy
in writing to us, and hope that you will remember us when
you think of games.

Very truly yours,

PARKER BROTHERS (INC.)

Development Manager

LRH;FGT

P.S. Of course, you know, you are invited to send
in any other ideas for games that may occur to you. All
games submitted will be for 1935 consideration.

Thanks, but no thanks (part 2). Here's a 1934 letter from game manufacturer Parker Brothers to Alfred Mosher Butts rejecting his submission of an early version of SCRABBLE. Somebody goofed. *(Marty Heitner photo/Alfred Butts Estate)*

SCRABBLE inventor Alfred Mosher Butts, pictured here fifty years after inventing the classic word game. Previous game owner Selchow & Righter uncovered a second game he'd constructed and named it Alfred's Other Game. Positioned as a solitaire version of SCRABBLE, it was launched in the mid-1980s but never really took off. Someone at the company's advertising agency thought it would be a good idea to do a James Bond–inspired photograph for the marketing campaign.

its entirety, move by move. The average tournament game takes about forty-five minutes, but we needed time for "up close and personal" player profiles, interviews and commentary, statistics and analysis, etc. So we ended up doing what colleagues everywhere do in the situation. We resolved to shoot as much footage as we could of everything and then figure it all out in postproduction!

The ESPN SCRABBLE All*Stars special featured my most humbling career experience, when I received a standing ovation when I delivered my opening remarks. I knew well that this was a diverse group, many of them ambivalent about me at best. I learned over the years to try not to take it personally. I came to realize that it was not me per se but what I represented. Essentially, I was the person between the business/corporate side of the game and the purist point of view.

As I've mentioned, many players—usually top experts—saw both me and Hasbro as necessary evils who came attached to the game they loved. Worse, the NSA and Hasbro pretty much called the shots as to how the competitive SCRABBLE world was run. We had money, power, and the law on our side. In addition, the players' world was occasionally chaotic, a free-form society with many smart, individualistic, offbeat people wary of authority over *their* game.

Although I'd tried hard to prove myself as a player, I was still an outsider. One of the reasons was that I did not compete regularly in local tournaments or at local SCRABBLE clubs. Part of this was practical. I lived forty-five minutes from the nearest SCRABBLE club. Also, I liked to have weekends for myself. And, although I knew nothing about leadership, I felt it was a good idea not to get too mixed up in the personal lives of NSA members. It would make the job that much more difficult. This is not

to say I didn't develop close friends among NSA members. I did, but carefully.

Perhaps the perception of me among players is best summed up in a couple of scenarios. One involves a friend of my family who happened to run across a well-known woman SCRABBLE player at a social event. He's a brilliant young guy, who had defeated me in the very first game we ever played. I remember it well, not only for the personal humiliation but because he had thrown down the word ROADEO against me. I knew damn well it was a guess on his part and challenged.

You know the rest. ROADEO turned out to be an acceptable word, meaning, basically, a rodeo for cars. Who knew! Anyway, he happened to mention the victory to the woman during the conversation, looking for some appreciation or validation. Instead, she immediately scoffed, "So what. John Williams is the *marketing guy.*" He might as well have told her he'd beaten a kindergarten student or a moron.

There was another conversation that epitomized the cluelessness and scorn some top players had for both me and Hasbro. It was a phone call with Floridian Bob Lipton, one of the very top American players for many years.

Lipton and I had enjoyed an ongoing dialogue for a long time, primarily about how I ran the organization and about the NSA policy on new allowable words. He was one of the early proponents of an expanded dictionary for North American play. It was referred to as the SOWPODS list, and it was essentially all the international, or "English," words combined with the existing "American" words. SOWPODS was an anagram of the abbreviated titles of the *Official SCRABBLE Players Dictionary* and England's *Official SCRABBLE Words.*

Lipton was of the more-words-the-merrier faction of tournament players. Not surprisingly, most in this group were top experts and avid studiers of word lists. Words such as ZA and QI—later acceptable here—were just more ammo in their arsenal. But there was one problem. This was a minority vision among NSA members at large.

It was my opinion at the time that most NSA players—and casual players at home—felt there were *too many words* already. Hell, there are four thousand four-letter words alone—many unknown by even midrated tournament SCRABBLE players. Now the SOWPODS group wanted to add another forty thousand more!

Lipton and another proponent, the late veteran expert Stu Goldman, insisted that the NSA mandate that the "international" word list be made official. Not so fast, I countered. I explained that the NSA was going to grow from the bottom up, not from the top down. Thus we really needed to take into account the opinions and wishes of lower-ranked players.

Lipton then asked me a question that left me stunned. It went something like, "Does Hasbro realize that SCRABBLE could disappear and go out of business if these new words are not adopted?"

In my opinion this was a question so mired in myopia and naïveté, I had no immediate answer. But I did have an ultimate answer: democracy. We decided to have the first organization-wide referendum in the history of the NSA in 2000. I felt this was too volatile a topic for the NSA to mandate one set of words over another. Let the players speak.

So we sent out ballots to all members in good standing and asked one question. Did members want the expanded diction-

ary, or were they happy with things just as they were? When the results were tallied, approximately 67 percent of the NSA membership wanted to stick with things as they were—no international words.

It's important to realize that I had no real opinion in this matter. For me personally, it would just be adding another batch of words I'd never know to the sixty or seventy thousand I already didn't know. But I felt that any change this substantial had to happen organically, and that's what I told Lipton and other SOWPODS adherents. To me, it was no different from the three-point shot becoming acceptable in basketball or the instant-replay review being used for official calls in pro football. It would, I explained, happen over time when, and if, it was meant to happen.

And that is exactly what occurred. In time, interest in the "international game" started to gain momentum, despite the fact that Hasbro had stopped sponsoring the World SCRABBLE Championship in 2001 and Mattel had systematically reduced its funding as well. However, as happened so often in the past, the SCRABBLE subculture rose to the occasion to provide missing elements for the hardcore player.

Previous examples of this include customized boards with superior turntables and personalized graphics or monograms. There were also customized tile bags, customized chess clocks, elongated racks, unlicensed books and study materials, limited-edition T-shirts, and more.

Anyway, interest in international play—and its accompanying dictionary—slowly began to build as the twenty-first century dawned. This was despite both manufacturers losing interest in funding the World SCRABBLE Championship. There were

myriad reasons for this. First, as with everything else in our lives, the Internet made a huge difference. Though mostly on illegal sites, you could now find a SCRABBLE opponent any time of day, anywhere in the world, of matching skill and preference in word authority. It was no longer necessary to tour Europe or be among the handful of competitors in a World SCRABBLE Championship to play the international game.

The landscape in learning new words had changed greatly, too, also due to technology. Gone were the days when players used to covet secret word lists, painstakingly researched and compiled the old-fashioned way—word by word. Now you could almost customize your study habits with a push of a keyboard button. For example, let's say I recognize that I have a weakness in five-letter words ending in CH. Don't laugh; it gets this precise and then some. I can find that list somewhere on the Internet, or create it myself, in a format that has been proven easy to memorize. Hence, the prospect of learning thousands of new words is not as daunting as it once was.

Ultimately, all this led to growth in the international game. By 2012, it had reached the point where many local tournaments and the National SCRABBLE Championship itself had a separate "Collins Division"—*Collins SCRABBLE Dictionary* being the name of the dictionary published in England by HarperCollins that includes both the American and English acceptable words.

All this is a way of saying the standing ovation from these experts at the SCRABBLE All*Stars event was meaningful. Even one of my biggest critics, perpetually disgruntled expert Marlon Hill, joined in. He had once said something like "John Williams represents everything that is wrong with SCRABBLE."

He also remarked that the game should be on a big-time circuit with players paid to wear Nike footwear and the like. Sadly, that doesn't appear to be happening anytime soon.

Another touching highlight of the event featured two of my favorite experts—Chris Cree from Texas and David Gibson from South Carolina. Chris is a larger-than-life, well-dressed, successful businessman, a Texan in every way. He has been one of the nation's top players for over thirty years and to some extent is my successor, as he—along with John Chew—is copresident of the North American SCRABBLE Players Association, the new governing body of the game in the wake of the 2013 closing of the NSA. More on that later.

Despite Chris Cree's proven skill, he has never been able to win "the big one," that is, a World, National, or All*Stars SCRABBLE Championship. But it appeared he finally might do it at the 2003 SCRABBLE All*Stars. As we approached the finals, Chris and David were paired in a do-or-die game. The winner would go on to the finals of the richest SCRABBLE tournament in history against arguably the strongest field in history. The loser, through the nuances of the pairing system, would automatically drop as low as sixth place.

It should be noted that David Gibson is one of the most unassuming and beloved players in the game. He also belongs in any discussion about the best players in history, having won the 1994 Nationals and the 1995 Superstars in Las Vegas. At the latter tournament, David took his $50,000 first prize, kept less than half for himself, and distributed all the rest among the other competitors! It was a display of sportsmanship and graciousness never seen in the SCRABBLE world before.

So these two longtime friends sat down for the crucial game

at ESPN SCRABBLE All*Stars. The room was thick with anticipation, the stakes astronomical. What happened next is best told by Chris Cree himself.

"So I'm ready to start, but first I look over at David," Chris recalled years later, "and he's crying." Chris knew exactly why. These guys had so much respect and love for each other that they were seriously conflicted about winning.

Chris continued, "So then I start to cry too. We look at each other in silence, then stand up and hug."

I'd noticed what was happening from across the room. By the time I reached the table, they'd progressed from crying to damn near weeping. Each knew one of them was poised for a painful loss at the hands of a close friend.

The three of us made small talk for a minute or two, and then they both jumped up again for another hug and a few more tears. Finally, Chris and David composed themselves and the game began. I too was on the verge of tears from the experience. It spoke so deeply not only about both men but about the complex relationship—in all sports and competition—between friendship and rivalry.

Sadly, the game itself was an anticlimax. David won decisively and went on to win the ESPN SCRABBLE All*Stars Championship, defeating 1985 NSC champion Ron Tiekert. Though admired and well liked by the SCRABBLE community, Ron was clearly not the favorite among the other competitors. For them, a David Gibson victory might mean divvying up the pot once again. And that's exactly what happened.

We spent a couple of months in postproduction cobbling all the footage into a forty-eight-minute telecast. It wasn't easy. Originally, we'd pushed ESPN for a ninety-minute time slot, but

the network rarely, if ever, had a ninety-minute show, and they weren't going to do it for SCRABBLE. Our wish to show a complete high-level SCRABBLE game with commentary, as well as some "up close and personal" profiles of various players, was seriously compromised.

Another concern was exposure and promotion for the eventual telecast. It was explained to us early in the project that ESPN does not do a lot of heavy promotion. This was especially true for niche programming, which we were. So while were we able to alert the entire SCRABBLE world about the All*Stars telecast, it was not exactly top-of-mind for either sports fans or television viewers.

That was reflected in the ratings. They were tepid at best, with perhaps a half million people watching at peak viewership. Televised poker had up to five times more viewers. Even the National Spelling Bee had had more than twice our numbers, although they'd had over twenty years to build the franchise. So both the network and we were understandably disappointed, but we had a five-year deal and plenty of time to do it better. And there was a lot of triumph as well. No network in history had ever broadcast a match featuring a branded board game. Dampened expectations aside, we'd achieved our goal of having a SCRABBLE match on national television.

Reviews of the show itself were scarce and mixed at best. The first airing was largely ignored by the press. Opinions among NSA members, however, were plentiful and predictably all over the place. Some wanted more strategy and less glitz. Others felt it played more like a highlight reel given the absence of a true complete game.

Suggestions for improving the next telecast were equally

diverse. One person insisted we should mike the players, even though most SCRABBLE experts rarely mumble more than a few words during a game. A friend said we should take a cue from professional wrestling—give the players theatrical entrances, stage names, and jerseys festooned with numerous sponsor logos.

Perhaps the best suggestion—one we'd come up with ourselves—was to develop some colorful and meaningful graphics to help tell the story and underscore the wondrous subtleties of the game. For example, if a player's rack featured the letters ISPDOTE, we could immediately flash on the screen all the anagrams of the word: DEPOSIT, DOPIEST, PODITES, POSITED, SOPITED, TOPSIDE. This would be a cool feature for a number of reasons.

First, it would reward the casual SCRABBLE player with words that were familiar. For the more advanced, it would feature some esoteric words. And chances are both parties would learn a new word or two. Another graphic, using the available artificial intelligence, was to illustrate the best play options from a statistical viewpoint. Then we could take those specific words and move them to various spots on the board to illustrate strategy and options.

In our postmortem with both ESPN and Hasbro, we agreed on one thing. Given the growing popularity and ratings of the National Spelling Bee and our positive experience at our first National School SCRABBLE Championship, it was definitely time to put the kids on television.

12

GOING HOLLYWOOD

A MONG THE LESSONS I'VE LEARNED IN dealing with Hollywood is that you are as good as anyone needs you at any given time. After that, no guarantees. This was absolutely hammered home to me during an experience I had back in 2000. I received a call from an LA-based production executive regarding the use of SCRABBLE in a proposed Jennifer Lopez movie, *The Wedding Planner.*

I should start off by saying that the movie was a big hit despite tepid reviews that saw it as another paint-by-numbers romantic comedy. The project, which also starred Matthew McConaughey, was a classic example of why major studios will always invest in a big star with a mediocre script as opposed to a great script with an unknown actor. It's a business decision: go with a sure thing.

I received this call a few weeks before shooting was about to begin. I'd already known about the project because a year earlier I'd read the screenplay for Hasbro to make sure that SCRABBLE was portrayed accurately and that there was no prurient content

or violence involving a SCRABBLE board, tiles, or other icons of the game.

Arguably playing against type, Jennifer Lopez had been cast as a SCRABBLE tournament player and devoted attendee at a SCRABBLE club in San Francisco. The script contained a few scenes involving the game. One was at the SCRABBLE club and another at an important championship, where JLo was poised to win both the competition and Matthew McConaughey's heart.

During the conversation with the production person, I had to explain that I found a few erroneous assumptions made by the screenwriters. First, no NSA tournament ever had four people playing the same game. It was always one-on-one. Second, other than Jennifer Lopez, every SCRABBLE player in the script seemed to be depicted as either a white-haired senior citizen or a crazed geek just this side of the Unabomber. Third, no tournament final ever took place on a stage with an audience of hundreds just twenty-five feet away, as written.

The executive listened patiently to my comments. Authenticity, he assured me, was "the key to the movie's soul." Taking this cue, I then explained such NSA tournament staples as chess clocks, tracking sheets, customized tile bags and racks, and more. As the conversation wound down, he asked me if I would be available to serve as the SCRABBLE technical adviser on the film.

It goes without saying I agreed. In fact, I spent the ensuing weeks extrapolating that upcoming gig in my imagination. It included the first-class flight to LA and a hotel suite down the road from the studio. Then there were the SCRABBLE lessons with JLo between takes and drinks with my soon-to-be main man Matt McConaughey, in which I'd impart some fresh perspective on the script's characters. And, though my participation

was already underwritten by Hasbro as part of my job, I'd most likely get a hefty check from grateful producers after my work was done.

So after we hung up, I wrote a long memo outlining my suggestions as discussed. The NSA also sent along boxes of supplies, signage, games, tiles, and dictionaries. Then I sat back and waited for the phone calls about arrangements or questions from JLo and other actors about their character's motivation and the like. Before long, some Hasbro execs and NSA members started referring to "the Jennifer Lopez SCRABBLE movie."

Weeks passed. Months passed. The phone calls never came. Eventually, the movie opened. I happened to catch an interview between JLo and Rosie O'Donnell in which they both gushed about their passion for SCRABBLE. I ended up seeing *The Wedding Planner* a couple of weeks after it had been mostly trashed by critics and NSA members. Still, I walked into a Manhattan movie theater with a relatively open mind.

That didn't last long. I knew we were in trouble when the first scene at the San Francisco SCRABBLE club portrayed the average member's age as between eighty and death. Then there was the scene where JLo reluctantly tells her new love interest that she's a member of the local SCRABBLE group and plays in tournaments. Her character searches his face as he absorbs this revelation.

"Pretty pathetic, huh?" she adds, hoping she hasn't permanently alienated him with this disclosure.

Overall, I'd guess the world's favorite word game was featured for perhaps ten minutes in the two-hour movie. Still, as the credits rolled, I optimistically stayed until the very end. At least I'd see my name mentioned as technical adviser. When that never

materialized, I waited to see my name nestled in the general thank-yous at the very end along with the caterers, the mayor's office, and the pet handlers.

Nope. You can bet when they come to me for help with the sequel, I'm really going to give them a piece of my mind.

MARTHA STEWART

For a number of years in the American culture, nothing surpassed an endorsement from Martha Stewart as—to use her famous phrase—"a good thing." So you can imagine my excitement when we arranged for an entire episode of her hit show to be devoted to SCRABBLE. I'd known for a couple of years from media accounts that Martha was a huge fan and very competitive, with a SCRABBLE board in each of her homes.

So an NSA contingent and I headed up to Westport, Connecticut, for the appearance. We'd also arranged for National and World SCRABBLE Champion Brian Cappelletto to fly in from Chicago. Between us, Brian and I would review SCRABBLE fundamentals with Martha in two separate segments. The producers told us that Martha was especially excited about our visit, as were NSA members and Hasbro.

The afternoon before we taped, I was backstage assembling all our props when Martha wandered through and stopped. "You must be the SCRABBLE man," she said. I allowed that I was.

The first thing that struck me was Martha's appearance. She is taller than I expected and has an athlete's build. Not surprisingly, she exudes confidence, an understandable guardedness, and a heard-it-all-before weariness. As it turned out, I was standing

in front of a large blown-up photograph of one of her beloved Chow Chow dogs. Trying to find common ground, I mentioned that I had a black half Chow Chow that looked very much like hers. The conversation ground to a halt when she told me that particular dog had recently died.

We were working in a part of the Martha Stewart empire that was a beautiful old house in a residential neighborhood in exclusive Westport. Attached to the house was a sleek state-of-the-art television studio that was completely hidden from the road. The entire staff and production team seemed to be young, hip, and well dressed. They were also very efficient. Most of them commuted from Manhattan, seventy-five miles away, and ate meals prepared in the studio's vast and gleaming kitchen. No surprise there. It was clear that Martha ran a tight ship.

Apparently, however, Martha was much less structured on the air. Right before the segment, the director called me aside.

"We need your help here," he began. "Martha is so smart and has so many ideas—her mind never stops. Because of this, she has a tendency to drift from our script or outline."

I was starting to get concerned as he continued. "So you and I have to review it now, and we need you to drive the spot."

"How exactly am I going to do that?"

"If she starts to go off message, reel her back in. Make her stick to the plan."

Now I was getting nervous.

As it turned out, Martha was great. She's so damned smart, and her SCRABBLE questions were original and incisive. Though we've never played a game, it's clear she understands SCRABBLE strategy very well. The piece came out even better than we anticipated. It's still on YouTube today!

With the exception of a couple of Christmas cards, that was the last interaction I had with Martha Stewart until years later. We reconnected along with some others on a conference call for a proposed project. At one point in the conversation, Martha interrupted and said, "John, you'd be very proud of me. Since I last saw you, I've had time to play a lot of SCRABBLE lately and have learned many new words and gotten a lot better." She was laughing at herself, referring to her recently completed time in prison. We all laughed as well.

JACK BLACK

I've had the good fortune to meet many famous and accomplished people because of my job as NSA executive director. Perhaps my most rewarding encounter was a brief one with the extraordinary actor and musician Jack Black. Like other celebrities, Jack had mentioned his SCRABBLE passion in numerous media stories over the years.

Meeting Jack was a completely serendipitous experience. I was staying in Manhattan at the apartment of film critic Jeffrey Lyons and his wife, Judy, our close family friends. Jeffrey casually mentioned he was going to interview Jack Black the next morning during his regular slot on WNBC. Explaining that the actor was a huge SCRABBLE enthusiast, I asked if I could tag along. Jeffrey said sure.

When we arrived at the studio, Jeffrey sent me to wait in the greenroom, where I encountered a producer who was not happy that I was there. She was understandably protective of the show's

guests and indicated it was not a venue for "fans" to meet celebrities. I apologized and said nothing else.

Just as we finished our awkward exchange, Jack Black walked down the hallway with his agent, publicist, and assistant and Jeffrey Lyons. The production woman shot me a quick scowl and quickly positioned herself between me and Jack.

Then Jeffrey spoke. "Jack, I'd like you to meet my good friend John Williams from the National SCRABBLE Assoc—"

Jack Black's usual animated face became ever more animated. "John Williams! Oh, my God. Your book *Everything SCRABBLE®* is like my *Bible!*" Jack turned to the group. "He not only runs the SCRABBLE Association, he's a great player in his own right."

It goes without saying I was feeling pretty good about this. I turned to the production woman, whose facial expression was somewhere between mortified and livid. I didn't have to say a word. Instead, Jack Black looked directly at her and spoke. "Is it okay if John comes out on the set with us? I'd like to talk SCRABBLE with him while we wait to go on the air."

She avoided my gaze completely. "Of course," she said with newfound enthusiasm.

13

JIMMY KIMMEL SPELLS IT OUT

WITHOUT QUESTION, OUR MOST MEANINGFUL HOLLYWOOD rela-tionship was with *Jimmy Kimmel Live!* The exposure would hugely benefit our School SCRABBLE Program and the National School SCRABBLE Championship. The catalyst in all this was Jimmy's brilliant producer Jill Leiderman. She had left a similar position at *Late Night with David Letterman* to take over Jimmy's show when it was still struggling in ratings after the launch.

Through talent, perseverance, and patience, Jimmy and Jill went on to build the show into the highly successful entity it is today. So we were understandably thrilled when it was proposed in 2007 that Jimmy challenge the newly crowned National School SCRABBLE champions to a SCRABBLE match on the show.

As it turned out, that championship team, Aune Mitchell and Matthew Silver, was historical. She was the only female ever to play on a winning NSSC team, and Matthew was the first to win two NSSCs—each with a different partner.

Jimmy Kimmel is a serious SCRABBLE player. That had been made apparent to me previously in LA at a St. Jude's Children's Hospital celebrity SCRABBLE tournament, where he was the winner and damn proud of it. So I knew he had no intention of taking it easy on the kids. Plus, the kids would be in for some good-natured trash-talking from Jimmy, as that's what the show is all about. No problem.

However, we did have one concern. Jimmy and the kids would be playing a "lightning round" version of SCRABBLE: the first side to reach 150 points would win. While I had little doubt the kids were much better players—sorry, Jimmy—this format would overemphasize the luck factor should someone get great tiles early.

And that's exactly what happened. Jimmy and his partner, Joe Rogan of *Fear Factor* fame, got the tiles to play the word SPAC-ERS for 76 points for an early, ultimately insurmountable, lead. Graciously, Jimmy acknowledged this.

To the show's credit, the format was changed going forward to reduce the luck factor, and the contests immediately became closer. There were other changes as well. One was the over-sized, customized SCRABBLE board the show's prop depart-ment designed and built for play. I've seen scores of custom-made boards over the years, and this was one of the most impressive in regard to both size and craftsmanship.

Another change was adding me to the segment as the offi-cial judge and word authority in case there were any challenges. While I'd been on television many times, I knew this would be more demanding for a couple of reasons. First, I would be responsible for verifying the score after each turn, which could be a heady prospect in a fast-paced game in front of a live studio audience. Second, I would be another person onstage to be a tar-

get for Jimmy's barbs. In other words, there was the potential for me to look stupid in any number of ways!

I didn't disappoint. It turned out that my vantage point to see the plays—behind an elevated podium a few feet away—was less than perfect. I also couldn't calculate the score quickly, or always accurately, because all the bonus squares were covered immediately by the play. So I was struggling to remember where, say, the double-letter square was while doing math in my head at the same time. On national television.

This scenario was compounded by the fact that the players knew their scores—and announced them aloud—the moment they made the play. So I was playing catch-up, which made for awkward dead-air time. At one point, as I struggled to verify the play, Jimmy looked over to me and said, "John, you're pretty much useless up here, aren't you?" The audience howled.

▪ ▪ ▪

Our trips to LA and the *Kimmel* show were always highlighted by the time the kid champs and I spent hanging out poolside at the Hollywood Roosevelt Hotel, surely one of the most surreal and decadent spots in the country.

The pool area at the Hollywood Roosevelt is right out of a movie—literally. You've seen it dozens of times on television shows such as *Entourage* and in numerous films. The hotel is usually utilized to make a statement about, or at least establish an atmosphere of, Hollywood hedonism. There are dozens of beautiful young women in scant swimsuits and an equal number of toned young men. There are also the obligatory band members and their groupies. The musicians are invariably the pale, gaunt,

bearded guys off in the corner—working-class English accents optional.

Two demographics not represented at the Hollywood Roosevelt pool scene are preteen SCRABBLE experts and sixty-year-old white guys. In other words, us. So one of my favorite things to do every year was to head down to the pool with the kids and set up a game of SCRABBLE right in the middle of all this. I should add the pool is packed pretty much every day, all day long. I'm not sure what all these people do for work. In fact, hardly anyone even swims. They are there to be seen.

With the exception of that first year, the team of young SCRABBLE champions was always boys, around twelve or thirteen years old. It goes without saying that none of them have ever seen anything quite like this scene. While I hoped the distraction of all these young women would give me an advantage in our poolside match, it rarely happened. It takes more than a string bikini or wet T-shirt to break the focus of these young word wizards.

Invariably people would drift over, mostly wondering who we were and why the hell we are there. As soon as they spotted the SCRABBLE board, the questions and comments started.

"Oh, SCRABBLE, I used to play with my grandmother. Then she died, so we stopped playing."

"Is this like Words with Friends?"

"Are these kids, like, good at this?"

"I see a word!"

When I told them who the kids were and that we were going to appear on *Jimmy Kimmel Live!*, their interest went up a few degrees. Among the comments after this revelation:

"Do you know Jimmy?"

"Can I get tickets?"

"Who else is on the show tonight?"

"My cousin is in a band. Can you give Jimmy their CD for me?"

■ ■ ■

Rehearsals were always fun. The kids and their parents would go over to the studio for a tour, and then we'd sit down and work out the segment. Jimmy wasn't around for this, of course, but his producer Josh Weintraub stood in for him as we rehearsed. Josh is damn funny in his own right and put the kids—and their parents—at ease.

The entire staff at the *Kimmel* show was the best I ever worked with in twenty-five years of doing both media appearances and television production. Their attention to detail, their consideration, their attitude, and their professionalism were exceptional, from the security guard at the door to Jimmy himself. They had two goals: make it a great experience for the kids and make good television. Oh yeah, having Jimmy emerge victorious might be a third priority.

Josh would tell the kids up front that Jimmy was going to tease them and give them a lot of good-natured ribbing. After the first year or two, the kids pretty much knew this from seeing previous shows, and they were cool with it.

Josh actually encouraged the kids to give it back to Jimmy, and sometimes they did. One year, Jimmy asked two-time winners Andy Hoang and Erik Salgado if their victory had been a big news story in their home state of North Carolina. "Yeah," Andy piped up, "we were right there on the front page of the

newspaper along with war, death, and all that stuff." Both the audience and Jimmy cracked up.

Perhaps the most dramatic exchanges came from the 2010 champ, Bradley Robbins from New Hampshire. Bradley was one of the better young NSSC players of all time. He was also pain- fully shy, quiet, and not especially animated. But we all witnessed a metamorphosis of Jekyll-and-Hyde proportions when it was show time.

I'm not sure whether it was Josh Weintraub's enthusiastic coaching, but it was a very different young Bradley Robbins who sat across the SCRABBLE board from Jimmy Kimmel that night. Bradley fired back at every quip Jimmy made with a pretty good comeback of his own. His partner, Evan McCarthy, almost did a double take on the third exchange. I can't remember exactly what it was, but basically Jimmy had made a scoring mistake and Brad- ley suggested the talk show host brush up on his basic math in addition to his spelling skills. It was spontaneous and fun to watch.

Some people in the SCRABBLE community thought Bradley had crossed the line in being too sassy. But he was only doing what he'd been coached to do. He'd also reached deep into him- self and found something neither he nor us knew was there. Jimmy took it all in stride. However, I did have one parent of a potential School Champion express reluctance to have her child on the show. "I don't want him to do what Bradley Robbins was encouraged to do," she told me.

Several years later, Bradley Robbins plays tournament SCRABBLE on the adult circuit, but he's moved on to other things as well. He goes by the name of Brad and is an aspiring rapper.

As I write this, I know my career as a *Jimmy Kimmel Live!*

guest is over. But I'll be forever thankful to Jimmy and the show for giving us a chance to showcase both our national School SCRABBLE Program and the remarkable student champions.

▪ ▪ ▪

All this reminds me of my one television appearance that did not happen. That would be in 2004 when I was asked about being on *The Daily Show with Jon Stewart.* The circumstances were less than ideal. It was the offensive-words topic all over again.

It began at the 2004 National SCRABBLE Championship in New Orleans. It was, in fact, the only time we ever had an NSC on ESPN. During our preproduction meetings the issue of having potentially offensive words on television came up. After discussions, it was agreed with veteran ESPN producer David Stern that we would handle it in the following manner: during the twenty-eight games leading up to the televised finals, the players could play any words they wanted, but for the finals, ESPN—and the NSA—would have to impose a ban on certain words.

These were the same words disallowed for the kids' championship, most of which coincided with a list of words the network had banned on its own. Predictably, most everyone thought this was absurd, but that was the reality if we were going to have SCRABBLE on television.

Of particular interest and amusement was the word RED-SKINS. An ethnic slur, it had been a no-no on the SCRABBLE offensive-words list since day one. But ESPN used the word routinely when reporting about the pro football team of the same name. So the dilemma arose as to the acceptability of REDSKINS for the telecast. As the old saying goes, you can't make this stuff

up. As I write this, ten years later, the Washington team is under increased pressure to change its name. Most feel it's only a matter of time.

So we get to the finals of Trey Wright versus David Gibson, both great guys and friends of mine. At one point in the game, Trey laid down the word LEZ. Both players nodded and wrote the score down, and Trey fished in the bag for three new tiles. Only then did we all realize the word could not be played on television. Chaos ensued in both the viewing room and the production booth.

We had to stop play immediately. Then we had to explain to both players and the crowd of three hundred spectators in an adjoining screening room what had happened. No one was happy. Trey was understandably upset. Gibson, being Gibson, was totally sympathetic. And the audience, most of whom were tournament SCRABBLE players, was jeering.

Worse, I had no idea what to do. Time stood still as I tried to figure out a solution. This exact situation had never happened in the twenty-five-plus years of tournament SCRABBLE, so I had no precedent for reference. Meanwhile, the players were twitching, the audience was squirming, and the cameras were idle. The one thing I *did* know was that I was not going to make this ruling by myself.

I announced that we were going to take a break. I then asked all the members of the NSA Advisory Board to gather for an emergency meeting. Once assembled, we reviewed all the various options we had. Ultimately, it was decided that Trey would withdraw the play without penalty, put his new tiles back in the bag, and make another play. Graciously, Trey did as we asked. He made a lesser play but still won the game and the championship.

However, that was far from the end of it. Among the spectators who witnessed this debacle was SCRABBLE tournament player Whitney Gould. I knew Whitney, and knew her to be a smart and very cool person. She's also a journalist. And she's based in San Francisco. As you might imagine, the LEZ controversy would be of interest to any reporter, especially one from a San Francisco newspaper.

So as this was all happening, Whitney approached me and said she was going to file a story with, I believe, the *San Francisco Chronicle*. She was almost apologetic, but I told her that as a writer myself I completely understood.

Over the years there have been basically two flash points where I knew the media would be all over us: the offensive words and cheating. Try as we might to generate stories about SCRABBLE's legacy, educational benefits, interesting people, big-money tournaments, and the rest, nothing appealed to the media as much as the sensationalism of dirty words and dirty play. In other words, Whitney's story went viral.

This led to the usual and demanding routine of explaining what happened, our position, and all the rest. As was always the case, I got to be the point man in the debacle.

At the height of all this, I received a call from a producer at *The Daily Show* who said the LEZ story had caught their eye. The show was looking for someone to come on to "explain" what had happened. That would be me. A fan of the show, I was at first excited about the prospect. Then I realized that "explain what happened" actually meant "defend your ridiculous position."

I'd failed to consider one fatal flaw. I could be as funny and articulate as I wanted, but it's the job of *The Daily Show* to make me look foolish, stupid, or both. At the end of the day, I'd be no

different to them from an arrogant NRA spokesman, Tea Party zealot, or corporate shill. And as soon as I was off camera, they could use charts, graphs, stock footage, commentary, and Jon Stewart himself to make me look like a clown. Sadly, that probably happens enough on its own; I don't have to go looking for it.

I declined the appearance.

14

WORDPLAY

NY SERIOUS SCRABBLE COMPETITOR CAN TELL you two
things in a nanosecond: his or her best play of all time
and the anagram of his or her name. It comes with
the turf. My best play was CONQUEST for 221 points. It was a
"triple-triple" extending from one triple word square to the next
for nine times the value, plus a 50-point bonus for using all my
tiles. The Q was already on the board.

If you are lucky enough to have a nice blend of vowels and
consonants in your name, chances are as many as a half-dozen
curious and fun phrases can be made from the letters. When I
first started being serious about SCRABBLE years ago, all of us
had to painstakingly shuffle the letters on our rack to try to find
the words within. As with so many other things, technology has
now made it possible to achieve in forty-five seconds what used
to take forty-five minutes. Just Google the word ANAGRAM and
you'll find numerous sites that will anagram any word or phrase,

including your name. Don't forget to use your middle or maiden name for variety or flexibility.

The first time my name was anagrammed was by my NSA colleague Joe Edley. We worked with John Dunbar Williams, leaving out the JR or JUNIOR. The first one Joe configured was ADMAN JOB WILL RUSH IN. This one was particularly apt, as before I started my SCRABBLE career, I was a partner and creative director of a small advertising agency. That said, anagrams of people's names are even more fun to me when they are beyond random with no context whatsoever. For example, the second anagram Edley came up with for my name was I HURL WILDMAN'S BANJO. Huh?

Joe Edley loves to anagram. He's convinced that, designed and marketed properly, an anagramming-based game could someday become as popular as SCRABBLE, Monopoly, or Trivial Pursuit. Call me skeptical—or even cynical—but I just don't see that happening in an increasingly dumbed-down America. Well, maybe if the anagrams were limited to three or four letters.

My family and I were once having dinner with Joe near Philadelphia after a SCRABBLE tournament at, of all places, the Franklin Mint. (The Mint had just launched a super-duper SCRABBLE set with 24K gold-plated tiles, and the tournament was a promotional event we set up with them.) After we had finished our meal, the waitress approached the table and asked if we'd like to hear about the desserts. We agreed.

"Well," she began, "tonight our specialty is peach melba."

Without missing a beat, Edley shouted out, "Cheap Blame!"— an anagram for the dessert name.

As the waitress stood there stunned and confused, my teenage daughter and her friend dove under the table in embarrass-

ment. Grinning, my wife faked a cough into her napkin while I tried to explain, which was almost more embarrassing.

This kind of thing happens all the time when you hang out with SCRABBLE players. During the 1998 National Championship in Chicago, one of our event interns, Ben Lyons, who went on to become an entertainment reporter and ESPN radio host, decided to attend a Cubs game with a group of tournament competitors. I asked him later how the game was; he shrugged and said it was okay. When pressed, he said it was tough to watch because some of his companions seemed more excited about anagramming the names on the back of the players' jerseys than about the action in the game.

As a matter of fact, baseball is the overwhelming favorite among sports for the SCRABBLE crowd. For openers, it is very strategic, and the pace is decidedly slow. (A major-league baseball game lasts, on average, three hours. The average SCRABBLE tournament game is forty-five to fifty minutes. The average living room game can last twice as long, depending on the number of players and disagreements.) Then there's the massive amount of statistics and mountains of esoteric knowledge to discover, memorize, and have ready should you ever need it. Just like obscure words. Most sports fans agree that baseball is the "geeks' sport." Not only do you have all that crazy stuff to know, it's only marginally athletic. Don't get me wrong. I love baseball, but it is the only sport where at any given time, sixteen of the eighteen participants are either standing still or sitting down. After the recently formed NASPA—more on that later—the two organizations most tournament players belong to are probably Mensa and SABR, the six-thousand-member Society for American Baseball Research.

The latter is a group devoted to the compilation and analysis

of baseball statistics. At their annual conventions, new evidence might be presented that could change a long-held record. For example, someone might have uncovered an obscure newspaper article or letter that casts doubt on a home run hit by Babe Ruth in 1931—thus changing his lifetime total from 714 home runs to a mere 713. While insignificant to most Americans, this is as exciting to this group as the admission of QI to North American SCRABBLE was to me. I get it. (Note: my example of Babe Ruth's bogus home run was purely hypothetical. Please, no calls or letters!)

■　■　■

A wonderful anagram moment took place in Los Angeles during the 1994 National SCRABBLE Championship. I was having dinner with a group that included World SCRABBLE Champion Mark Nyman, who's English, and veteran American expert Robert Kahn. After dinner the group stood outside the restaurant and chatted. I happened to look across the street and spot a large red neon sign that said SHERATON.

I studied the letters, convinced there must have been—given the favorable letters—several good anagrams. Yet after a few minutes I'd come up empty. Frustrated, I tapped Nyman and pointed to the sign.

"Mark, there's got to be a couple of good anagrams in there, right?"

Nyman stared at it for no more than two seconds. "No, sorry. But with an I, you'd have ANTIHEROS." The word is acceptable in the Collins international SCRABBLE dictionary but not in North America—although ANTIHEROES is.

I remember thinking that I could study anagramming flash cards ten hours a day for the rest of my life and I could never do that. Later, I wished I'd asked Robert Kahn, a superb anagrammer, the same question. Robert once played the word UNREALIZED from a SCRABBLE rack of AEILNRU, adding it to the ZED that was already on the board. He also once scored 801 points in a match, the second-highest total in history. The record is 830 by Michael Cresta in an official Boston club game in Lexington, Massachusetts, on October 12, 2006.

Probably the funniest anagram story was told to me by the writer and talk show host Dick Cavett a number of years ago. We were both presenters at the annual Wonderful World of Words Weekend at the Mohonk Mountain House resort in New Paltz, New York. The event was created by word lover and game expert Gloria Rosenthal and her husband, Larry, and now run by Will Shortz. If you're reading this book and finding it at all engaging, then you owe yourself a visit to this amazing venue. It's a weekend packed with mind-boggling puzzles, serious game playing, and programs and lectures by people like Ira Glass, Cavett, and Stephen Sondheim. I've been honored to present twice.

Anyway, Cavett and I got to talking anagrams. He told me that he was essentially an "anagramming savant" and that anagrams just popped into his head on a regular and random basis. Cavett's best story concerned an appearance on Johnny Carson's *Tonight Show*. During Dick's conversation with Johnny they were talking about—among other things—former vice president Spiro Agnew. The conversation went on to other topics; then other guests came on, and Dick moved down the guest couch.

As Cavett told it, later in the show Carson was interviewing an actress about her new movie when Cavett suddenly and loudly

blurted out, "Grow a penis!" The conversation screeched to a halt. The entire studio went silent as a thousand eyes bored in on Cavett. Flustered, he hurriedly went into an explanation about how Spiro Agnew's name anagrammed into GROW A PENIS. Laughter ensued. This anecdote is now part of the Anagramming Awards Hall of Fame at Anagrammy.com.

Obviously, anagrams are a critical part of the SCRABBLE skill set. If you've got AEIMNRS on your rack, you'd better be able to find MARINES, REMAINS, or SEMINAR or you're in for a long game. It's important to know that these skills can absolutely be developed and improved. There are numerous Internet study aids for practice. Those most favored by tournament players include Zyzzyva, Quackle, and Zarf.

The typical exercise below is at a level for most good casual players. Find an anagram for the each word. Answers are in the appendix.

1. PYRIC
2. CHURL
3. TRADED
4. SADDLE
5. RACOON
6. NASTILY
7. PAYOUTS
8. BEEFIER
9. DROOLED
10. EXCLAIMS
11. SPAWNING
12. INDULGED

No discourse on anagrams would be complete without examples of some of the better ones floating out there in the world of word lovers:

DORMITORY	Dirty room
EVANGELIST	Evil's agent
DESPERATION	A rope ends it
THE MORSE CODE	Here come the dots
MOTHER-IN-LAW	Woman Hitler
SNOOZE ALARMS	Alas! No more Z's
ELEVEN PLUS TWO	Twelve plus one
CLINT EASTWOOD	Old West action
SLOT MACHINES	Cash lost in 'em
CONVERSATION	Voices rant on
NORWEGIANS	Swen or Inga?
THE PIANO BENCH	Beneath Chopin
SOUTHERN CALIFORNIA	Hot sun or life in a car

PALINDROMES

And, of course, no conversation about anagrams would be complete without at least mentioning their complicated, confounding cousin—palindromes. A palindrome is a phrase, name or sentence that reads the same backward and forward. Common examples include:

STEP ON NO PETS

A MAN, A PLAN, A CANAL: PANAMA

If anagrams have at least one useful purpose—improving your SCRABBLE game—palindromes' one purpose is mind-boggling amusement. I'd never even think of attempting to create a palindrome, let along completing one!

One of the more interesting people in the word world is a fellow named Jon Agee. A gifted illustrator and gamer, Jon is considered one of the country's foremost palindromists as well. He is the author of such books as *ELVIS LIVES! and Other Anagrams; SIT ON A POTATO PAN, OTIS! More Palindromes*; and *PALINDROMANIA!* Jon is one of the most creative and original people I've ever met.

Astoundingly, Jon once told me that he could not really understand anagrams and why anyone would do them. This coming from a guy who does *palindromes!* Jon and I were doing a mutual book signing many years ago when a woman asked him to inscribe her copy.

"To whom shall I sign it?" Jon asked.

The woman replied, "Naomi."

"I moan!" Jon blurted out immediately.

Here's another fun story involving Jon Agee. Many years ago, a bunch of us had assembled at the home of Gloria and Larry Rosenthal, the Wonderful World of Words creators, for one of their periodic, heavy-duty game-play sessions. Gloria is a writer and former word-game editor for *Games* magazine and Larry a retired veteran of Madison Avenue.

An evening at the Rosenthals' always featured serious, high-level gamers who got together to play obscure, intense games and often test out new games from inventors. Guests that night included Will Shortz, Jon, David Feldman, a tournament bridge player, author, and game master, and me. I should add

that, while respectable at most games, I was in way over my head in this crowd.

After a couple of hours of games, we decided to head down to a local restaurant for dinner. It was a beautiful summer evening, and I wanted to show off my new convertible. So Jon and Will jumped in with me, while David Feldman went with the Rosenthals.

About halfway to the restaurant, we stopped at a red light. Almost immediately, a car with three women in it pulled up next to us. All of us were in our thirties and forties and, I'd like to think, checked each other out for perhaps a second or two. Then the light changed and everyone zoomed off. I remember thinking later: Man, if those women only knew! Those three guys in the convertible? The crossword editor of the *New York Times*, the country's foremost palindromist, and the executive director of the National SCRABBLE Association! Talk about chick magnets!

15

ARE MEN REALLY BETTER
THAN WOMEN?

T HE CONCEPT OF ONE GENDER BEING superior to the other at SCRABBLE has been—with the possible exception of the offensive-words controversy—the most discussed and volatile topic among players for years. At face value, it seems groundless, sexist, mean-spirited, and irrelevant. Yet it remains a topic that just won't go away. Having participated in hundreds of interviews over my years on the job, I'd have to say this is one of the questions most often thrown at me by the press.

Let's start with some assumptions. First, it's widely accepted by both academics and social scientists that women test better than men in regard to language skills. So, theoretically, women should be better at SCRABBLE, right? Wrong. Or at least not necessarily.

As author Stefan Fatsis so beautifully nailed it in *Word Freak*, SCRABBLE's "dirty little secret" is that it is about math. Also widely accepted is that men test better at math than women. At the very top level of the game, for example, it's pretty much

assumed that most of the top fifty or so players have committed all or most of the *Official SCRABBLE Players Dictionary* to memory. So that covers the word and language part of one's arsenal. That leaves the math-based skill set to determine superiority, which means having the ability to assess probability of tile possibilities. For example, there are twelve E's in the game; if seven have been played and there are only twenty-two tiles left, what are the odds your opponent has a vital E, or even two of them?

Another component in this skill set is what we call "board vision," the ability to look for—and find—every possibility on the board given your rack and position in the game. At the same time, you're performing multiple calculations and assessing spatial relationships. Of course, the deeper you are in the match, the more tiles have been played, so the more complicated the calculations are—and you're performing them for both yourself on offense and for your opponent as part of your defense.

On the day I wrote this, I went to the marvelous website Cross-tables.com. Created by players Keith Smith and Seth Lipkin, it is by far the most comprehensive collection of data from decades of official SCRABBLE tournaments. It features player rankings, ratings, tournament results, best plays, standings, highlights, and pretty much any other data one might want to know about themselves and other tournament players. (*Please bear in mind that the ratings and rankings discussed here were researched well before the publication date and certainly have changed, but the analysis is still valid.*)

I decided to review the statistics on Cross-tables.com to check the number of women listed in the Top 25 players in North America. There was one: Canadian Robin Pollock Daniel in twenty-fifth place. Maybe more disheartening for women is that

a thirteen-year-old boy, Mack Meller of New York, was ranked eighth. Granted, Mack is the current prodigy in a game culture that has only seen a handful in forty years, but still. What's the deal?

If we look deeper down the list, through the Top 50, we find two more women. Expand it to the Top 100 and the number of females rises to seven. Equally as inexplicable is the fact that only one woman has won a National SCRABBLE Championship in the history of the event. That was Rita Norr in 1987.

An unassuming role model, Rita, who died in 2010 at just sixty-six years old, was smart and gracious. She told me a number of times that she felt extremely fortunate to have won and was mystified why twenty-five years later her accomplishment was never duplicated.

So let's agree that, despite disturbing conclusions, we'll throw out the statistical evidence regarding male supremacy across the SCRABBLE board. How else could one explain it?

One theory is that men as a group still have more of a cultural imperative to be competitive and dominant, whether the venue is business, sports, board games, charades, whatever. Personally, I believe this will change over time as a couple of generations of young girls compete equally with and against boys in soccer, Little League baseball, and the like.

Perhaps the best theory was put forth by veteran *Sports Illustrated* writer S. L. (Scott) Price, who wrote a brilliant piece on tournament SCRABBLE back in 1995. After Scott spent some time with top-level tournament SCRABBLE players, he issued this simple explanation. "Forget about all your fancy theories," he told me. "Men are better at SCRABBLE than women because . . . *women aren't that nuts!*"

Men do have an affinity for trivia, collecting, and focusing on one thing to the exclusion of others. In my experience, women, not so much. Scott and I talked about how it's boys and men who early on memorize baseball statistics, car features, and other arguably useless facts. It's an easy transition from that dubious pastime to studying and learning thousands of esoteric words that no one else knows or uses. A cynical friend once suggested that a guy's knowledge of sports trivia is in indirect proportion to his actual athletic ability. More than one high school basketball team statistician has said to the team captain, "Sure, you can dunk a basketball. But do you know the name of Ty Cobb's parakeet?"

■   ■   ■

I decided to go right to the source and talk to three top female SCRABBLE players about their thoughts on the issue. The first was Robin Pollock Daniel, universally recognized for years as the top woman player in North America. While this is an enviable distinction, it's as if Robin walks around with an asterisk tattooed on her forehead. Why not just refer to her as one of the best players in the world?

Robin is distinctive for a number of reasons. She's scary smart, she's funny, and she's generous of spirit. The mother of two boys, Robin has worked professionally as a copywriter, a researcher, and a psychologist, among other things. While she is feared and respected by top players internationally, a major championship win has eluded her.

It certainly isn't for the lack of trying. Robin is one of the most dedicated students of the game ever. She spends three or four hours a day whenever possible studying words, playing online, or

conducting tireless replays of previous matches—both hers and others. There's a word-study program at Zyzzyva.net created by the brilliant Michael Thelen, where players can second-guess their peers' moves and analyze "best play" in various situations. The artificial intelligence will tell them how often they find the best play, the second-best play, and so on. Robin routinely finds the best play 90 percent of the time!

Even when she first started out as a tournament player almost thirty years ago, it was clear where Robin was headed. She won a Best Newcomer Award and in her second year of play jumped from a 1544 rating to a 1750 rating in one tournament! The Expert rating starts at 1600. Most people get there incrementally—often over a span of several years. Robin Pollock Daniel did it in one giant leap, and she never looked back.

Robin has been ranked as high as third overall—for both genders—and says the overriding thing to remember is that "tournament SCRABBLE is a meritocracy at the end of the day. It's really that simple." As a result, she says, men always accept her as an equal. Her record speaks for itself. "If anyone felt I was a bit fraudulent playing among the big boys, it was me—not them," she adds.

I asked her about being referred to as "the best *woman* SCRABBLE player in the world." Robin chooses not to see it as dismissive or qualifying. "It doesn't bother me in the least," she asserts. "I like it because at the end of the day I think of myself as a teacher, a mentor. It gives me credibility that I can leverage to help other women." When I kidded Robin about her fierce, word-nerdish study habits, more associated with men than with women, she laughed. "Yeah, well, as Woody Allen says, men cite statistics to delay orgasm."

Like the other women experts I interviewed, Robin is not hopeful that the situation will improve anytime soon for women tournament players. For whatever reason—biological, cultural, etc.—the statistics say it all. "It's the same now as it's always been," Robin laments. Despite the changes in the last twenty years—the introduction of the National School SCRABBLE Program, more tournaments, Internet play, new study techniques, and more—the rankings tell the same story. "We're very lucky if there are three women in the Top 50 at any given time."

A quick look at the results of the National School SCRABBLE Championship bears this out. That event is now over a dozen years old. Competitors are grouped in teams of two, which means there have been forty-eight finalists in all those years. Only one has been female: Aune Mitchell, daughter of well-known SCRABBLE organizer and coach Cornelia Guest. Aune was on the winning team in 2007 with Matthew Silver; she no longer competes regularly in tournaments.

Out of curiosity, I decided to check out the male/female ratio for the National Spelling Bee. More established and better known than the National School SCRABBLE Championship, the bee arguably targets the same type of kid and the same ages, fifth to eighth grade. In theory, School SCRABBLE, if properly managed, has the potential to overtake the spelling bee in the future. Let's face it, for most of us, SCRABBLE is a lot more fun than standing up in front of a bunch of people, trembling as you try to visualize, then correctly spell a twelve-letter word that even a World SCRABBLE Champion would not know. And when was the last time any of us participated in a spelling bee? A person can play SCRABBLE for his or her entire life.

In reviewing the results of the National Spelling Bee over

the last dozen years, we find that girls have won forty-six times through 2013. While not dominant, it is certainly statistically superior to their performance at SCRABBLE and better than boys, who've won the National Spelling Bee forty-one times.

Now let's look at crossword puzzle competition. Will Shortz, organizer of the annual American Crossword Puzzle Tournament, confirms that women have won that event three times in thirty-six years and finished second a dozen times. Will attributes women's better showing at crossword puzzles to the following reason: "SCRABBLE is almost purely a math game at its essence, which favors males, whereas crosswords blend some math acuity along with word skills and knowledge of various facts."

■   ■   ■

I next posed the gender question to Lisa Odom of St. Louis Park, Minnesota, another perennial top female competitor. Lisa started playing tournaments in 1989, having become hooked on the game in what was at the time the semiunderground New York club scene. This was the SCRABBLE world before *Word Freak* or SCRABBLE on ESPN. A time when tournament players still toiled in obscurity and sometimes only as few as a dozen players would show up at a handful of locations – a friendly restaurant, a church basement, or a YMCA. Everyone pretty much knew everyone else, and strangers entered at their own risk. Newbies and curious living room players were often treated with a blend of bemusement and contempt, and only the hard core would return.

Lisa Odom not only joined this scene, she thrived. Lisa's credentials are impressive. She has been the only female member

of the American team in the World SCRABBLE Championship three times, in 1993, 1999, and 2005. She was also one of a handful of women who competed in the $100,000 SCRABBLE Superstars Showdown in Las Vegas in 1995. In addition, Lisa is one of the few women in history to be a member of the 2000 Club, the most elite rating designation among tournament players—those who have been rated over 2000 in the official rankings. As of June 2014, only thirteen tournament players were rated 2000 or above. In addition, Lisa has also been ranked as high as sixth overall among the thousands of players who maintain ratings.

When asked to rate her competitive nature on a scale of 1 to 10, Lisa hesitated, then replied, laughing, "If I'm honest, probably an 8 or 9. But I wasn't always that way. It evolved over time." It must make for interesting games at home, as Lisa's husband, Steve Pellinen, is also a veteran top SCRABBLE expert and tournament organizer.

Lisa's approach to competition and SCRABBLE has evolved as well. During our conversation, she shared a personal mantra she has developed. It is the acronym LOVE: Look, Overlook, Verify, Evaluate.

Look simply means look over the complete board for all opportunities for both yourself and your opponent. *Overlook* means repeat that exact same exercise. It's amazing how many times players are certain they've found the best play—only to find a better one after one more pass over the board. *Verify* means make sure the play is good, the word acceptable. *Evaluate* means carefully assess that the play you are about to make is the best move. This, of course, means the best *strategic* move, not necessarily the most points. They are not always the same. Just ask anyone who's played some of the weaker SCRABBLE apps out there. For

them, it's always about points only! Why? Because very often no SCRABBLE experts were consulted when the manufacturers and marketers designed these apps.

As we discussed, a good SCRABBLE move is comprised of what you put on the board to score with and what you leave on your rack to work with. For example, let's say you score 37 points but leave yourself the tiles U, U, V, C. Sure, you scored some points, but you are going to have terrible racks for the next several turns because of your terrible tile "leave." A better play—strategically—would be to play off a couple of those tough tiles or exchange them for new ones.

Predictably, Lisa is a keen student of the game. She studies about five hours a week, she says, and once recorded and analyzed every game she played for an entire year using Quackle, the genius SCRABBLE analysis software developed by Jason Katz-Brown while he was still an undergraduate at MIT. "I took a year off between jobs," explains Lisa, who works in health care, "and, believe me, nothing helps your SCRABBLE career more than being unemployed!"

Like her peers, Lisa is at a loss to explain the lack of female presence among the SCRABBLE competitive elite. "This is not rocket science," she insists. "Women should definitely be able to do this." That said, she agrees that the immediate future does not look good and that women have not yet caught up with men in SCRABBLE competitiveness. "I really hope one of us wins a World or National Championship again in my lifetime," Lisa said.

That led to a brief story about Rita Norr, a friend and mentor to Lisa. Rita was known for her sweetness but could also be tough. Lisa described a situation decades ago when Rita had researched and compiled a "3 to make 8 letters" word list on her

own. Examples might be adding SEA to QUAKE to make SEAQUAKE or COT to QUEAN to make COTQUEAN. I know, I know. You're asking yourself, "Who would know this stuff?" I was flattered that Lisa assumed that I did.

Lisa kept asking Rita to share this secret list, but her friend refused for years. Remember, this was before computer-generated word lists existed. Many expert players hoarded their lists, not only for a competitive edge but because each represented perhaps a hundred hours of thankless, tedious research. In the end, though, Lisa's persistence and Rita's good nature prevailed and the list was shared.

As we ended our conversation, I asked Lisa to randomly tell me one of her favorite plays. She barely hesitated. "It was the word GOLGOTHA, played through an existing H on the board." It means "a burial ground." Like many people, I've seen the word over the years—but never on a SCRABBLE board!

▪ ▪ ▪

Debbie Stegman is the sassy, smart girl you knew in high school. She has an MBA from Columbia University and spent nearly two decades pushing the proverbial glass ceiling to become a vice president of Warner Bros. In 2013, she decided to take a break from the corporate world to spend more time "being happy" and, of course, playing more SCRABBLE. Debbie is newer to the scene than both Lisa and Robin but no less tenacious with the tiles. She played in her first tournament in 2000 and has been on a fierce streak ever since. After just her second tournament, she was approached by a couple of top female experts who'd been

watching the newcomer. "Some day, you are going to be one of us," they told her. That was all the motivation she needed.

The day we spoke, Debbie was ranked second among U.S. women and fifty-first overall. Debbie has a number of observations about the gender gap in tournament performance. She agrees with the other women I talked to that it all comes down to one's sense of competition. "I think women are more competitive within themselves as individuals, but not with other women," she suggests.

Debbie also says she's noticed an interesting gender-based dynamic at tournaments. "When a guy breaks away from the pack to take a decent lead in the field, everyone silently roots against him. Not on a personal level—at least most of the time— but because if he falters, their own chances improve. It's logical and natural." But on the rare occasion when a woman breaks away from the pack, she can almost feel all the other females bonding in support. "Women don't root against each other," Debbie says.

Like Lisa and Robin, Debbie does not feel as if her male opponents are ever holding back or deferring to her in any way. She's just another expert. I ask her if she ever feels it's an advantage being a woman in a division full of men. She pauses. "Not really," she muses, "although I'm not above putting on some fresh lipstick if I think it might distract my opponent."

Asked for one of her memorable plays, Debbie goes back to a match at the notoriously tough Manhattan SCRABBLE Club in midtown. One night, in a casual team game, Debbie was partnered with champions Robert Felt and Joel Sherman. In this situation, it's understood in the SCRABBLE culture that the lesser player pretty much sits in silence—just observe and learn.

But at one point in the game, Debbie just couldn't help herself. As Felt and Sherman intensely studied their rack and the board for the best play, Debbie impulsively grabbed the tiles and, in one swift move, laid down the word SCIENTISTS.

The table was stunned. The weakest player—a woman no less—had thrown down a *ten-letter word*! Even more astonishing is that the play was through disconnected letters already on the board. In other words, it's not as if TIS was there and Debbie simply built around it. No, she wove her way through. This is classic board vision, and it doesn't get any better than that.

When I ask Debbie about the future fate of female players, she says she is not encouraged by what she sees: "It doesn't look good for us." She notes that while participation in the National School SCRABBLE Program is roughly even gender-wise, for the most part only the boys seem to go on past the eighth grade and enter the world of adult play. The same with prodigies. There has never been a female SCRABBLE prodigy of the caliber of Brian Cappelletto, Adam Logan, or the current young star Mack Meller.

As the father of two daughters, and as a male who grew up in a house filled with sisters, a mother, and a live-in aunt, I remain as discouraged as Robin, Lisa, and Debbie for the prospect of another female World or National SCRABBLE Champion. In fact, it appears the odds are much better that we'll have a female president first. And I'm okay with that.

16

THE END GAME

FEW MAJOR THINGS IN LIFE END when or how we presume they will. That marriage was over long before that first, raw, stilted visit to the couples counselor. Your favorite team's championship hopes were exhausted long before they were mathematically eliminated. Sometimes the ending is a protracted, abstract, corrosive process that seemingly happened while you were asleep. Other times it can be an abrupt, unexpected bombshell, a veritable Dear John letter that arrives with a benumbing thud.

I knew my SCRABBLE career would end someday. I just didn't know when, how, or why.

I had specifically addressed "the end" a dozen years ago with Stefan Fatsis in *Word Freak*. Interviewed at the NSA's height of activity, I cautioned that it was unrealistic to assume this streak would last indefinitely. Over the course of my career, I'd worked for and with some fairly heady companies. They included not just Hasbro but Nickelodeon, Simon & Schuster, IBM, ESPN, MTV

Networks, Merriam-Webster, CNN, Paramount, and numerous others. I'd been around the block. I'd learned firsthand the truth of the old adage that the only thing in business that remains the same is change—so be ready for it.

Working with Hasbro—and previous SCRABBLE owners Selchow & Righter and Coleco—I'd probably collaborated with two hundred executives over the years. Some became friends and colleagues for decades. Others were simply bit players in the process. More than once, at all three companies that owned the game, my team and I had been told we would be working with a new executive who would be our point person for all SCRABBLE activities—only to find that person had been reassigned, had left, or had been fired before we'd even had a single meeting.

Navigating through the phalanx of executives was, of course, the most difficult part of the job. Nearly a dozen times, I had to journey up to Hasbro Games headquarters in East Longmeadow, Massachusetts, and tell the SCRABBLE story to a new corporate team or key executive who'd transferred from another part of the company—or who'd never been in the game industry until a few weeks beforehand. My task included explaining the evolution of the game and its marketing strategies, the tournament scene as a marketing and public relations tool, opportunities their predecessors had missed, potential pitfalls, and more.

I learned my ultimate approach to all this from an old friend and colleague, Fred Seibert, one of the smartest people I know. Among other things, Fred, along with partner Alan Goodman, was on the founding staff for MTV and an architect of both Nickelodeon and Spike TV. Fred went on to become president of Hanna-Barbera, president of MTV Online, an Emmy Award–winning producer, and all kinds of other stuff. Fred is always

around the action. As I write this, he was just acknowledged in the *Los Angeles Times* as the primary guru to the young man who launched the Internet sensation Tumblr.

One day at lunch, Fred told me this: "I was free when I totally accepted that some people in business are going to see me as a genius and others were going to think I'm a complete jerk." The key, of course, is to keep the latter group to a minimum—and to be aware of who is in which camp.

The second part is tricky. For understandable reasons, people don't often show their hand in business dealings. Hey, we're humans. That means, depending on the scenario, we're going to be defensive, territorial, paranoid, ambitious, confident, vindictive, or any of a host of other mindsets. Being an experienced game player—whether it's SCRABBLE or poker—can be helpful in the business world. We learn to size up situations and other participants quickly. We learn to recognize "tells" from people across the table. We understand when to be aggressive and when to lay back. We think strategically.

In working with SCRABBLE executives over the years, I bore this in mind. I also employed several other approaches in my M.O. First, I tried to get to know everyone—and understand them—as well as I could, both as people and as business partners. I worked hard to cultivate relationships at all levels—assistants, middle management, senior management. I worked hard for inclusion, always leaving a paper trail whenever I could to both cover my ass and get everyone involved.

I tried never to go over anyone's head unless it was absolutely necessary. Even then, I'd try to make sure the aggrieved party knew it was happening. No one was ever sucker-punched. Still, I know I pissed off some people along the way. But I don't regret

it. My motivation was never to flex my influence or steamroll my agenda. Instead, I clung to my mantra. At the end of the day, my decisions and actions were never about what was best for me, the game's manufacturers, or the thousands of hardcore enthusiasts. It was "Always what's best for SCRABBLE, the game."

When Stefan and I discussed my future and that of the NSA, I said that neither I nor the NSA members should ever take anything for granted. The routine changing of the corporate guard, the economy, and budgets made us all vulnerable to both whimsy and legitimate new marketing philosophies. It's well understood in the business world that when a new senior executive arrives, there's a coattail loaded with his or her people waiting for their chance. This can be former ad and PR agencies, former right-hand men and women, and relatives.

So I knew well that it might happen—no, *would* happen—at some point. It would be when the people who "got" me and my approach were outnumbered by those who did not.

After two decades, the process of serious change began around 2007. At the time, the Hasbro marketing team we worked with in East Longmeadow, Massachusetts, was a thoughtful group who understood games and game culture. In a series of meetings, we all agreed that it was time to reprioritize the NSA's efforts. The consensus was that the NSA's time and talents would be better spent identifying and recruiting new players and game purchasers and less time on the day-to-day administration of the SCRABBLE tournament scene.

To achieve these new priorities, the NSA would first turn over many of our responsibilities to the players themselves. This would include, but not be limited to, the sanctioning and organization of both local tournaments and the National SCRABBLE

Championship, the management of three hundred or so official SCRABBLE Clubs in North America, all rules activities, development of word lists and materials, and revisions of the *Official SCRABBLE Players Dictionary*. The new group would also be responsible for maintaining a list of tournament ratings for up to 10,000 past and present tournament players and for selecting the team to represent the United States and Canada at the World SCRABBLE Championships. All these had been responsibilities of the NSA for decades. But not for much longer.

I both accepted and understood Hasbro's thinking on this. It was hard to argue with the logic when viewed through the lens of a contemplative, experienced business executive. Which is not to say it wasn't personally disappointing. Remember, part of me was a passionate player as well, with a perhaps unrealistic perspective of the game as sacred, not to be messed with by bottom-line-driven game marketers who "didn't understand" its magic and power.

When asked the best way to go about this transition, we proposed the following to Hasbro.

- That we organize a two-day SCRABBLE summit at Hasbro Games headquarters in East Longmeadow.
- The NSA would compile a list of fifteen NSA players to form a Steering Committee for the transition of selected responsibilities and invite them to the summit. The group would be diverse. It would include players, activists, and organizers from all over North America. Some would be top SCRABBLE experts. Others would be successful businesspeople. Still others would be average tournament players. There would be attorneys,

computer experts, parents with children in the School
SCRABBLE Program, and more.
■ At the summit, the NSA staff, Hasbro Games executives, and the fifteen players would address the change
and work out the next steps.

Part of me felt like a guy who was planning his own funeral.
One of my survival skills has always been seeing change—or
trouble—a mile away. This dynamic was honed at home, where
both my parents were alcoholics. I could tell by the way the car
door slammed when my father got home from work what the
next several hours were going to be like. It was also developed at
an all-boys Catholic school, where I basically tried to stay under
the radar of the embittered monks who taught us and the tough
kids freshly arrived to the suburbs from Brooklyn, Queens, and
the Bronx. I realize this sounds very Dickensian, but that was
what it felt like to me.

We began with an invitation to selected players. It was pur-
posely vague, saying only that Hasbro wanted their input for a
discussion on the future of organized SCRABBLE. They were
thrilled. We explained that there would be some social aspects
with numerous meals, a tour of the factory where they could
actually see SCRABBLE being made right before their eyes, a
gift package, and the like. And, of course, Hasbro paid all travel
and hotel expenses.

So we convened, about twenty people altogether. The NSA
was represented by Jane Ratsey Williams, Joe Edley, Katie
Schulz Hukill, Patricia Hocker, and me. Our other key staff member, Theresa Bubb, held down the fort at NSA headquarters.

We started things off with a great cocktail party and din-

ner and kept things light. Hasbro execs mingled amiably with the players. We NSA staffers enjoyed ourselves as well, but the evening was compromised because of the hidden agenda we harbored.

Our meeting began the next day with introductions and some generalized overviews. Hasbro and I took turns explaining the upcoming changes and, to a lesser degree, the rationale behind it all. The group listened patiently. No one was particularly demonstrative in his or her reactions. Later, I surmised it was for a couple of reasons. For openers, there was plenty of vagueness about the transition. However, I believe that one fact stood out from the rest of the presentation and was the focus of the players: *after thirty years, they were finally going to have their own, solely player-run SCRABBLE association.*

This was a huge deal for them, and I knew it. This had been a dream for many of them for decades. And, despite the advances of player involvement in running the association under my tenure, there was always the perception—and I suppose the reality, too—that their fate was always in the hands of the Hasbro-supported NSA and the corporation itself.

This collective sentiment was made extremely clear as we opened the floor for discussion. I began with a proposal that we consider restructuring the NSA into two divisions. The first would be the Club and Tournament Division; this would be run completely by the players, with its own agenda and officers. The second would be the School SCRABBLE and Outreach Division. This would be run by the existing NSA staff. The two divisions would operate under the NSA umbrella.

It seemed like a reasonable and practical first step from my point of view. It would make the transition smoother; the new

players group could benefit from our experience and relationship with Hasbro, and over time they could evolve to complete
autonomy.

When I finished presenting this proposal, I looked first at the
Hasbro execs, a few of whom were nodding in, if not agreement,
consideration. I then turned to the players.

"Any comments on this?" I asked as I scanned the table.

I was greeted by blank faces and total silence. In retrospect,
it reminds me of the vaudeville comedian peering out at a mute,
unresponsive crowd and asking, "Is this an audience or an oil
painting?"

A few more seconds passed. Then we moved on. To me, it had
just been completely confirmed by the players that they wanted
to do it on their own. Even now, five years later, I'm sure my motivation was mixed at best. Undoubtedly, part of me was making
a last-minute attempt to keep my organization intact after more
than twenty-five years. Hey, I'm only human. Another part of
me sincerely felt an interim step would be good for all involved.
Having been the person squarely in the middle between Hasbro
and the players for so long, I knew there was going to be a lot
of nuance, unanswered questions, unexplored mutual territory,
and financial considerations. Some navigational experience could
help. But it was not meant to be.

The rest of the meeting was a blend of questions and observations, both the theoretical and the practical. It was agreed that
the players would take over all aspects of SCRABBLE clubs and
tournaments. This would be itemized and signed off on in the
coming months. The NSA would devote itself to getting as many
new people playing as much SCRABBLE as often as possible. Oh
yeah—and buying more games. Ultimately, it was agreed that

the new players' organization—soon officially named the North American SCRABBLE Players Association—would take over all club and tournament activities on July 1, 2009.

As early as that evening, I'd processed and accepted the new structure. I had to admit that there were plenty of upsides to the change as well. For one thing, I'd no longer have to deal with some of the peskier, tedious, and unsettling aspects of the job.

The complaints from NSA members were at the top of the list. Believe me, I understood where they came from: a passion for the game and a naïveté about the business end of the NSA—not the least of which were legal, practical, and financial constraints under which we operated. The NSA also received thousands of letters, e-mails, and phone calls over the years, which would soon no longer be our responsibility. Perennial favorites included lost game pieces, new ideas for improving SCRABBLE, looking to license the SCRABBLE name, complaints about words, complaints about rude behavior on illegal Internet SCRABBLE sites, looking for donations, looking for NSA endorsements, needing information and/or permission to publish a SCRABBLE book, incarcerated people wanting to connect, foreign SCRABBLE associations seeking materials . . . the list goes on.

I cannot let this topic pass without sharing a bit about the number of people in prisons who passionately play SCRABBLE. For years, not a week passed when the NSA did not receive letters from the incarcerated asking for merchandise, rulings on a play or word, or the feasibility of starting a SCRABBLE club at the writer's penal institution.

I had, in fact, once been challenged to visit a prison to play its champion in a match. I thought it would be a cool experience, but

Hasbro felt otherwise. They must have felt that in its own way, it would have been as least as dangerous for me as appearing on *The Daily Show with Jon Stewart.*

The NSA once received a remarkable letter from an inmate recounting a fierce SCRABBLE game against another inmate. It detailed an argument that had ensued over the admissibility of a certain word in SCRABBLE. Things became so heated that the sender of the letter ended up stabbing his opponent in the eye with the pencil they'd been using to keep score.

The inmate even included a photocopy of the warden's official report for proof, which also revealed the prisoner had spent fifteen days in solitary confinement for the attack. The prisoner concluded the letter to us by insisting that if he'd had an *Official SCRABBLE Players Dictionary* none of this would have happened. Everybody's a victim, right? If we'd send him one, he said, this type of violence would be eliminated. But these guys got off easy. In 1983, according to the *Houston Chronicle,* thirty-one-year-old Anthony Dutton was stabbed to death by a fellow inmate at the El Paso county jail during an argument over SCRABBLE rules.

This kind of stuff would ultimately be the province of the North American SCRABBLE Players Association and Hasbro personnel. The NSA would now devote itself exclusively to outreach for the National School SCRABBLE Program, to initiatives with libraries, literacy groups, Scouts, parks and recreations departments, and the like, and to public relations and media.

We performed those duties from July 2009 until July 1, 2013. But while our change was happening, so were several things at Hasbro. Chief among these, as reported in various newspapers, was Hasbro's decision to consolidate most of its U.S. executives

in one location: Rhode Island. So while the East Longmeadow, Massachusetts, Games Group would still manufacture the game, everything would be run out of Rhode Island. As these things often go in corporate America, this resulted in many resignations, firings, and transfers. Before long hardly anyone from the team of executives we'd been working with for twenty years at Hasbro Games was left at the company.

Going forward, the NSA and I would now be working with an entirely new group of corporate executives from Rhode Island. Early on, a few team members assigned to SCRABBLE left or were reassigned before we even met them or could get any traction. When we finally settled into our new team, there was one glaring thing that struck me: titles.

For most of my SCRABBLE career with Hasbro, our regular marketing meetings included Hasbro Games directors, vice presidents, senior vice presidents, and, often, the president of Hasbro Games. At our new meetings in Rhode Island, Hasbro was represented by a senior product manager, a director, and an assistant manager. In military terms, I'd gone from working with the generals and colonels to the lieutenants and captains. Don't get me wrong: they were smart and eager, and I liked them personally, but I'd gone from working closely with the power base and decision makers to, in many cases, never even meeting them. Instinct and experience told me that this did not bode well for the NSA, SCRABBLE, or me.

In the fall of 2012 the NSA staff and I did the dance with the new Hasbro regime. We mutually agreed that the National School SCRABBLE Program and attendant outreach would continue to be our focus, as the future of the game heavily relied on its success. As I'd done about every six months for the previous

decade, I also urged Hasbro to ratchet up its SCRABBLE Internet presence and commitment in the following ways: create a safe School SCRABBLE site where kids could play as both individuals and as part of a school team. Consider online tournaments for both adults and kids. And, dammit, please fix the only official existing SCRABBLE app on Facebook.

That particular flaw had been bothering me since the day it was introduced. The flaw? You can play a fake word on the official Facebook SCRABBLE app and *not be penalized!* The phony word simply comes off the board, and you can keep trying until a word is good. This bugged me and other players for a number of reasons. First, it violates the most fundamental rule in SCRABBLE: a word has to be in the dictionary to be good in the game. Otherwise, it comes off the board and the player is penalized by missing a turn. This flaw also favors the weaker player. Think about it. People spend years improving their SCRABBLE arsenal of words, yet some newbie can walk in off the digital street and keep throwing letters out there until he or she gets a bingo. (I went to the SCRABBLE Facebook site the day I wrote this in 2014. Over decade later, this has not been corrected.)

But I really should not have been surprised. I remember going to Electronic Arts in Northern California a decade earlier to see the SCRABBLE Facebook app in its final stage of development before launch. Hasbro had granted EA the SCRABBLE license earlier, and everyone was under pressure to make the deadline.

After a demonstration from an enthusiastic team of young electronic gamers, I saw this and other aspects that seriously needed to be addressed. No one argued with my points; they were too obvious and valid. In frustration, I asked the team what

SCRABBLE experts had been involved in the research, design, and development of this new version. Everyone was quiet for a second; then someone muttered something along the lines of "One of our designers, Jeff, and his girlfriend are SCRABBLE *fanatics*. They play, like, almost every night."

I said nothing. I'd seen this movie before in my business experience. It's about, at the end of it all, the deal being more important than the execution. It often seemed more important to meet the contractual deadline—show me the money—than doing it right. God forbid you get the product the best it can be, then you launch it.

It was this kind of episode that made me incrementally realize I'd become a dinosaur in a game business and game world that was changing. I got the distinct impression that the new regime of Hasbro executives saw me as a pesky hybrid: SCRABBLE purist and, quite possibly, obstructionist. And I understood that. I'd once been an impatient young executive before my SCRABBLE career, fidgeting during meetings while some sixty-year-old fossil explained, "This is the way we've always done things."

In January of 2013, I knew it was time to go. We all did. After weeks of discussions, it became clear that my vision for the game's future and that of Hasbro were no longer the same. If I had any doubts, the reality of Hasbro's new vision was made clear in a conversation with a former digital games colleague who shared some interesting information.

We were talking about word games, and I was informed that Hasbro had bought the rights to make a Words with Friends board game based on the Internet sensation that many have written was actually ripped off from Hasbro's SCRABBLE itself.

My first thought was ego-driven. Geez, I used to be the first

guy you called when the company was even considering anything about word games. Now I'm hearing about it as a fait accompli. Finally, I asked what was the thinking behind this move.

"Well," he told me, "we really wanted a SCRABBLE-type board game for the future, the next generation."

I remember thinking: You already have one, man. You already have one.

17

AFTER WORDS: AFTERWARDS

ULTIMATELY WE AGREED THAT THE National SCRABBLE Association after twenty-five years would be dissolved and we would turn our remaining activities over to NASPA and Hasbro marketing executives. July 1, 2013, would be our final day.

From the players' point of view, things were in good hands. Based in Dallas, NASPA is run by copresidents Christopher Cree and John Chew. This is an exceptional pair of individuals, whose personalities, skills, and experience are both impressive and complimentary.

Chris is a Texan, first and foremost. He's got a big personality, a small fortune, and a boundless heart. He's one of the most evolved men I know. Chris has been an extremely successful businessman in several areas and is widely respected both as a top player and as a person.

Years earlier, I'd named Chris as the NSA's first ombudsman, or player representative, at a time when many members were still

dissatisfied with the communication between them and the NSA. It was a successful move on all sides, and Chris's contribution to the NSA and the game at large is inestimable. He's also served as an NSA Advisory Board member and was an NSA Person of the Year, a SCRABBLE All*Star, and a tireless organizer.

John Chew is an academic, with specialties in mathematics and computer programming. John is as self-effacing as Chris Cree is gregarious. He has pretty much overseen all official SCRABBLE activities in Canada for the past fifteen or more years, including running North America's oldest official SCRABBLE club and the Canadian National Championship, among other things. Like Chris, John is a top player who has played in the World SCRABBLE Championship, served on the NSA Advisory Board, and been an NSA Person of the Year. John also travels all over the world as a tournament consultant for other countries.

Together, these guys along with key volunteer staffers have done an amazing job carrying on many of the former NSA activities—especially considering we had substantial corporate funding and a paid staff. They've already proven that with successful and well-attended National SCRABBLE Championships and other initiatives.

As for the Hasbro side of things, it's hard for me to say. Figuratively, it's hard to say because I haven't spoken to a Hasbro person since late June 2013, and I don't really know the company's current and future plans for the game.

Fortunately—yet again—we have Stefan Fatsis. As he's done so often and so masterfully, Stefan has addressed this chapter in SCRABBLE history with both passion and perspective. Here, for the final word, is his article from the July 14, 2013, edition of the *New York Times*.

SCRABBLING OVER SCRABBLE

By Stefan Fatsis

After more than 25 years managing, marketing and ref-
ereeing the competitive side of America's most venerated
word game, the National Scrabble Association has packed
up its tiles and gone out of business.

Its demise doesn't reflect a lack of interest in Scrabble,
which turns 65 this year. The game has never been more
popular. More than a million people, from kids to hipsters
to nonagenarians, play daily on Facebook. In May, nearly
200 students in fourth through eighth grades competed
in the National School Scrabble Championship. On Saturday, more than 500 die-hards, myself included, will gather
in Las Vegas for the National Scrabble Championship, a
five-day, 31-game anagrammatic marathon.

Instead, the death of Scrabble's organizing body—which
closed on July 1 following years of declining financial support from Hasbro, the game's owner—reflects a broader conflict between corporate and intellectual forces in American
cultural life.

Guess which one is winning. Played at its highest level,
Scrabble is a strategic sibling of chess, backgammon and the
Chinese game go. Top tournament players must master as
many of the 178,000 acceptable 2- through 15-letter words
as possible, "see" them among a jumble of letters, determine
which maximize the chances of winning and consider an
opponent's possible countermoves, all while a timer ticks
from 25 minutes to zero for each player to make all plays.

Like those old games, competitive Scrabble is a math-
brain exercise, one combining spatial relations, board geom-

etry and language maximization. Unlike them, it is owned by a company, whose goal is to generate revenue through the sale of sets and spinoffs and downloads.

"You have to understand that we are in the games-making business. We are not in the altruism business," a marketing executive for Selchow & Righter, Scrabble's first corporate parent, said during a meeting with tournament players lobbying for support in 1985. But those words could just as easily have been spoken last week by an executive of Hasbro, which has owned the rights to Scrabble in the United States and Canada since 1989.

During the past quarter-century, Hasbro has spent millions of dollars financing the independent National Scrabble Association. The association organized national, world and school championships; booked the winners on the "Today" show and "Jimmy Kimmel Live"; sanctioned more than 200 local tournaments a year; maintained a database of several thousand dues-paying players and calculated their tournament ratings; placed the game on ESPN for six straight years; published a newsletter; worked with Merriam-Webster on the official Scrabble dictionary (a fifth edition is in the works; get ready for "gi," "cuz," "ixnay" and more); and fielded inquiries ranging from disputatious living-room players seeking rules adjudications to a 1990s media blowup over the inclusion of the word "jew" in the lexicon.

Was that corporate money well spent? The publicity that the Scrabble association helped generate no doubt sold more than a few boards. But the group's performance could not and should not have been measured in such a reductive way.

Scrabble isn't a marketing or earnings-report star. It can't be hyped with an online vote resulting in a cat's replacing an iron, which Hasbro employed to juice sales of Monopoly. It doesn't rely on new cards that players need to buy to keep playing, like the Hasbro game Magic: The Gathering.

But as a game, Scrabble is remarkable. It carefully balances skill and luck and risk and reward. It exploits the breadth and beauty of the English language. It fosters mind-blowing creativity, heart-stopping tension and computer-stretching quantitative analysis.

Most people playing online or at the kitchen table aren't aware of Scrabble's complexity, let alone its tournament culture. Hasbro, obviously, is. The corporate question is whether it has a responsibility to both worlds, casual and competitive—and whether that responsibility extends to times like these, when Hasbro has been laying off workers and focusing on top-selling products.

Corporations from Coca-Cola to the N.F.L. are caretakers of some slice of history. Usually that history is central to the business. To Hasbro, Scrabble isn't. But it is an enduring piece of Americana, developed in a garden apartment in Jackson Heights, Queens, by an unemployed architect named Alfred Butts who spent years perfecting his game before it swept the country in the 1950s. I have yet to find a parallel for it—that is, a proprietary game with a subculture whose passion and sophistication transcend its ownership.

What's the value of that to a $4 billion corporation? Is it more or less than the $700,000 or $800,000 a year Hasbro spent on the National Scrabble Association at its peak—before it stopped paying for club and tournament Scrabble in

198 ■ WORD NERD

2008 and slashed the budget for school and casual Scrabble to the point that the association decided to cease operations.

But forget about money. What's the value of something like Scrabble to the culture at large? Does its owner have an obligation to nurture each side of the game, whether or not it jibes with the prosaic nature of the toy industry or boosts profits? Do history and intellect matter?

I spoke recently with Hasbro's chief marketing officer, John Frascotti. He said the right things about Scrabble's past and its competitive side. Hasbro is "committed to spending marketing dollars to promote the Scrabble brand and to promote Scrabble play," Mr. Frascotti said. He told me he believed the company could do what the Scrabble association did, at least for schools and casual players. "Judge us as we act, not as we say," he said.

I promised to keep an open mind. But since I started playing competitively and reporting on Scrabble 15 years ago, I've shaken hands with a moving walkway of Hasbro executives, all of whom have pledged love for and commitment to the game. And then the cuts came. Hasbro recently withdrew its last, token contribution to the national championship: $15,000 in prize money.

The winner of the tournament in Las Vegas will still be paid $10,000. After the company pulled the plug on them in 2008, competitive players formed their own governing body, the North American Scrabble Players Association, and, thanks to higher dues and participation fees, the tournament circuit has kept humming. If Hasbro does the same with School Scrabble—Mr. Frascotti said it wouldn't—I'll help find a way for my 11-year-old daughter and other young

devotees to compete for a title in an educational game that they adore.

Hasbro knows that we players will volunteer to do what it had paid others to do for it: support a culture that doesn't necessarily fit in an earnings-driven world of fad toys and movie tie-ins. Maybe that's smart business. But with ownership comes responsibility, and sometimes even a little altruism.

Well said, Stefan.

It is now August 1, 2014. I recognize, accept, and occasionally savor my ongoing irrelevance in the world of SCRABBLE. I still play every day online against a dozen or so opponents. They range from some of the top players to casual players I've encountered along the way. The former NSA headquarters—an old sea captain's house in historic Greenport, New York—has had the sign removed and its files emptied. I still hear about the club and tournament scene, only now it's second- or thirdhand and often weeks later.

Remnants remain. This winter I started a wood-stove fire using a handful of old wooden racks as kindling. Mostly, though, it's tiles. For years, random letters have turned up everywhere— in pockets, in drawers, under furniture, on the floor of my car, in the yard. One day shortly after I resigned, I found two tiles in a corner in my attic. They were a z and an e. I knelt down and switched around them on the floor. E z. Yeah, I thought. E z. Yeah, EASY!

I knew everything was going to be okay.

APPENDIX

TOP TEN PLAYERS IN NORTH AMERICA AS OF JANUARY 1, 2015

Please see www.cross-tables.com for most current stats

1. Nigel Richards	2141
2. Adam Logan	2097
3. David Gibson	2090
4. Will Anderson	2061
5. Mack Meller	2039
5. Jesse Day	2039
7. Ian Weinstein	2024
8. Conrad Bassett-Bouchard	2023
9. David Wiegand	2022
10. Joel Sherman	2010

ANSWERS TO NSSC CONTEST ON PAGE 112

CERULEAN, SCHMOOZE, QWERTY, QUIXOTIC, HIJACK, ZYGOTE, SHEL-
LAC, ZOOLOGY, INQUIRY, BAZAAR

ANSWERS TO ANAGRAMS ON PAGE 162

1. PYRIC = PRICY
2. CHURL = LURCH
3. TRADED = DARTED
4. SADDLE = ADDLES
5. RACOON = CORONA
6. NASTILY = SAINTLY
7. PAYOUTS = AUTOPSY
8. BEEFIER = FREEBIE
9. DROOLED = DOODLER
10. EXCLAIMS = CLIMAXES
11. SPAWNING = WINGSPAN
12. INDULGED = DELUDING

"OFFENSIVE" WORD LIST
REFERRED TO IN CHAPER 4

Words removed from the *Official SCRABBLE Players Dictionary*
in the mid-1990s because they were deemed offensive:

ABO	BADASS	BALLSY
ABOS	BADASSED	BAZOOMS
ARSE	BADASSES	BLOWJOB
ASSHOLE	BALLSIER	BLOWJOBS
ASSHOLES	BALLSIEST	BOCHE

BOCHES	CUNTS	FEMINAZIS
BOFFED	DAGO	FRIG
BOFFING	DAGOES	FRIGGED
BOINK	DAGOS	FRIGGING
BOINKED	DARKEY	FRIGS
BOINKING	DARKEYS	FUBAR
BOINKS	DARKIE	FUCK
BOLLOCKS	DARKIES	FUCKED
BOOBIE	DARKY	FUCKER
BOODIES	DICKED	FUCKERS
BOODY	DICKHEAD	FUCKING
BUBBA	DICKHEADS	FUCKOFF
BUBBAS	DICKING	FUCKOFFS
BUBBIES	DIKEY	FUCKS
BUBBY	DIPSHIT	FUCKUP
BUCKRA	DIPSHITS	FUCKUPS
BUCKRAS	DYKEY	GADJE
BULLDYKE	FAGGIER	GADJO
BULLDYKES	FAGGIEST	GANGBANG
BULLSHAT	FAGGOTRIES	GANGBANGS
BULLSHIT	FAGGOTRY	GAZOO
BULLSHITS	FAGGOTY	GAZOOS
BULLSHITTED	FAGGY	GINZO
BULLSHITTING	FART	GINZOES
COJONES	FARTED	GIRLIES
COLOREDS	FARTING	GOY
COMSYMP	FARTS	GOYIM
COMSYMPS	FATSO	GOYISH
CRAPPER	FATSOES	GOYS
CRAPPERS	FATSOS	GRINGA
CUNT	FEMINAZI	GRINGAS

GRINGO
GRINGOS
HAOLE
HAOLES
HARDASS
HARDASSES
HEBE
HEBES
HONKEY
HONKEYS
HONKIE
HONKIES
HONKY
HOS
HUNKEY
HUNKEYS
HUNKIE
HUNKIES
JESUIT
JESUITIC
JESUITRIES
JESUITRY
JESUITS
JEW
JEWED
JEWING
JEWS
JIGABOO
JIGABOOS
JISM
JISMS

JOHNSON
JOHNSONS
KANAKA
KANAKAS
KIKE
KIKES
LES
LESBO
LESBOS
LESES
LEZ
LEZZES
LEZZIE
LEZZIES
LEZZY
LIBBER
LIBBERS
MERDE
MERDES
MICK
MICKS
NANCE
NANCES
NANCIES
NANCY
NIGGER
NIGGERS
NITCHIE
NITCHIES
NOOKIE
NOOKIES

NOOKY
OFAY
OFAYS
PAPISM
PAPISMS
PAPIST
PAPISTIC
PAPISTRIES
PAPISTRY
PAPISTS
PEED
PEEING
PISS
PISSANT
PISSANTS
PISSED
PISSER
PISSERS
PISSES
PISSING
POM
POMMIE
POMMIES
POMMY
POMS
POO
POOED
POOFS
POOFTAH
POOFTAHS
POOFTER

POOFTERS	SHITHEAD	TOMMED
POOFY	SHITHEADS	TOMMING
POOING	SHITLESS	TURD
POONTANG	SHITLIST	TURDS
POONTANGS	SHITLISTS	TWAT
POOS	SHITLOAD	TWATS
POOVE	SHITLOADS	WANK
POOVES	SHITS	WANKED
POPERIES	SHITTED	WANKER
POPERY	SHITTIER	WANKERS
POPISH	SHITTIEST	WANKING
POPISHLY	SHITTING	WANKS
REDNECK	SHITTY	WAZOO
REDNECKS	SHKOTZIM	WAZOOS
REDSKIN	SHVARTZE	WETBACK
REDSKINS	SHVARTZES	WETBACKS
SHAT	SKIMO	WHITEYS
SHEENEY	SKIMOS	WHITIES
SHEENEYS	SPAZ	WILLIE
SHEENIE	SPAZZ	WOG
SHEENIES	SPAZZES	WOGGISH
SHEGETZ	SPIC	WOGS
SHICKSA	SPICK	WOP
SHICKSAS	SPICKS	WOPS
SHIKSA	SPICS	YID
SHIKSAS	SPIK	YIDS
SHIKSE	SPIKS	
SHIKSEH	SQUAW	
SHIKSEHS	SQUAWS	
SHIKSES	STIFFIE	
SHIT	STIFFIES	

IMPORTANT SHORT Q WORDS

QI	SUQ	QATS	QUAI	QUIN	QUOD
QAT	AQUA	QOPH	QUAY	QUIP	SUQS
QIS	QADI	QUAD	QUEY	QUIT	
QUA	QAID	QUAG	QUID	QUIZ	

2-LETTER WORDS FROM *OSPD5*

AA	AT	ED	GI	JO	MY	OP	SH	UT
AB	AW	EF	GO	KA	NA	OR	SI	WE
AD	AX	EH	HA	KI	NE	OS	SO	WO
AE	AY	EL	HE	LA	NO	OW	TA	XI
AG	BA	EM	HI	LI	NU	OX	TE	XU
AH	BE	EN	HM	LO	OD	OY	TI	YA
AI	BI	ER	HO	MA	OE	PA	TO	YE
AL	BO	ES	ID	ME	OF	PE	UH	YO
AM	BY	ET	IF	MI	OH	PI	UM	ZA
AN	DA	EX	IN	MM	OI	PO	UN	
AR	DE	FA	IS	MO	OM	QI	UP	
AS	DO	FE	IT	MU	ON	RE	US	

SHORT J WORDS FROM *OSPD5*

JO	JAR	JIB	JOT	JUT	DJIN
AJI	JAW	JIG	JOW	RAJ	DOJO
HAJ	JAY	JIN	JOY	TAJ	FUJI
JAB	JEE	JOB	JUG	AJAR	GOJI
JAG	JET	JOE	JUN	AJEE	HADJ
JAM	JEU	JOG	JUS	AJIS	HAJI

HAJJ	JAVA	JETE	JIVE	JOTS	JUPE
JABS	JAWS	JETS	JIVY	JOUK	JURA
JACK	JAYS	JEUX	JOBS	JOWL	JURY
JADE	JAZZ	JIAO	JOCK	JOWS	JUST
JAGG	JEAN	JIBB	JOES	JOYS	JUTE
JAGS	JEED	JIBE	JOEY	JUBA	JUTS
JAIL	JEEP	JIBS	JOGS	JUBE	KOJI
JAKE	JEER	JIFF	JOHN	JUCO	MOJO
JAMB	JEES	JIGS	JOIN	JUDO	PUJA
JAMS	JEEZ	JILL	JOKE	JUDY	RAJA
JANE	JEFE	JILT	JOKY	JUGA	SOJA
JAPE	JEHU	JIMP	JOLE	JUGS	SOJU
JARL	JELL	JINK	JOLT	JUJU	
JARS	JEON	JINN	JOOK	JUKE	
JATO	JERK	JINS	JOSH	JUKU	
JAUK	JESS	JINX	JOSS	JUMP	
JAUP	JEST	JIRD	JOTA	JUNK	

SHORT X WORDS FROM *OSPD5*

AX	FIX	MIX	REX	WAX	AXLE
EX	FOX	MUX	SAX	XIS	AXON
OX	GOX	NIX	SEX	ZAX	BOXY
XI	HEX	OXO	SIX	APEX	BRUX
XU	KEX	OXY	SOX	AXAL	CALX
AXE	LAX	PAX	TAX	AXED	COAX
BOX	LEX	PIX	TIX	AXEL	COXA
COX	LOX	POX	TUX	AXES	CRUX
DEX	LUX	PYX	VEX	AXIL	DEXY
FAX	MAX	RAX	VOX	AXIS	DOUX

DOXY	FALX	ILEX	MOXA	OXIC	SEXY
EAUX	FAUX	IXIA	NEXT	OXID	TAXA
EXAM	FIXT	JEUX	NIXE	OXIM	TAXI
EXEC	FLAX	JINX	NIXY	PIXY	TEXT
EXED	FLEX	LUXE	ONYX	PLEX	VEXT
EXES	FLUX	LYNX	ORYX	POXY	WAXY
EXIT	FOXY	MAXI	OXEN	PREX	XYST
EXON	HOAX	MINX	OXER	ROUX	
EXPO	IBEX	MIXT	OXES	SEXT	

SHORT Z WORDS FROM *OSPD5*

ADZ	ZIG	CZAR	JAZZ	QUIZ	ZEDS
AZO	ZIN	DAZE	JEEZ	RAZE	ZEES
BIZ	ZIP	DITZ	LAZE	RAZZ	ZEIN
COZ	ZIT	DOZE	LAZY	RITZ	ZEKS
CUZ	ZOA	DOZY	LUTZ	SIZE	ZEPS
FEZ	ZOO	FAZE	MAZE	SIZY	ZERK
FIZ	ZUZ	FIZZ	MAZY	TIZZ	ZERO
TIZ	ZZZ	FOZY	MEZE	TZAR	ZEST
WIZ	ADZE	FRIZ	MOZO	WHIZ	ZETA
ZA	AZAN	FUTZ	NAZI	YUTZ	ZIGS
ZAG	AZON	FUZE	OOZE	YUZU	ZILL
ZAP	BAZX	FUZZ	OOZY	ZAGS	ZINC
ZAS	BIZE	GAZE	ORZO	ZANY	ZINE
ZAX	BOZO	GEEZ	OUZO	ZAPS	ZING
ZED	BUZZ	GRIZ	OYEZ	ZARF	ZINS
ZEE	CAZH	HAZE	PHIZ	ZEAL	ZIPS
ZEK	CHEZ	HAZY	PREZ	ZEBU	ZITI
ZEP	COZY	IZAR	PUTZ	ZEDA	ZIZZ

ZITS	ZOIC	ZONE	ZOOM	ZOOS	ZOUK
ZOEA	ZONA	ZONK	ZOON	ZORI	ZYME

IMPORTANT VOWEL DUMPS

AA	ALEE	EAUX	LUAU	RAIA	AUDIO
AE	ALOE	EAVE	MEOU	ROUE	AURAE
AI	AMIA	EIDE	MOUE	TOEA	AUREI
OE	AMIE	EMEU	NAOI	UNAI	COOEE
OI	ANOA	EPEE	OBIA	UNAU	EERIE
EAU	AQUA	ETUI	OBOE	UREA	LOOIE
AEON	AREA	EURO	ODEA	UVEA	LOUIE
AERO	ARIA	IDEA	OGEE	ZOEA	MIAOU
AGEE	ASEA	ILEA	OHIA	AALII	OIDIA
AGIO	AURA	ILIA	OLEA	ADIEU	OORIE
AGUE	AUTO	INIA	OLEO	AECIA	OURIE
AIDE	AWEE	IOTA	OLIO	AERIE	QUEUE
AJEE	BEAU	IXIA	OOZE	AIOLI	URAEI
AKEE	CIAO	JIAO	OUZO	AQUAE	ZOEAE
ALAE	EASE	LIEU	QUAI	AREAE	

Q WITHOUT U WORDS FROM *OSPD5*

QI	QOPH	QANAT
QAT	CINQS	QIBLA
QIS	FAQIR	QOPHS
CINQ	NIQAB	TRANQ
QADI	QADIS	FAQIRS
QAID	QAIDS	NIQAAB
QATS	QAJAQ	NIQABS

QABALA	TRANQS	QWERTYS
QAJAQS	KAMOTIQ	SHEQELS
QANATS	NIQAABS	KAMOTIQS
QIBLAS	QABALAH	MBAQANGA
QIGONG	QABALAS	QABALAHS
QINDAR	QWWALI	QAWWALIS
QINTAR	QIGONGS	QINDARKA
QWERTY	QINDARS	SHEQALIM
SHEQEL	QINTARS	MBAQANGAS

IMPORTANT I DUMPS

BIDI	IMPI	IWIS	MINI	PILI
HILI	INIA	IXIA	MIRI	TIKI
IBIS	INTI	KIWI	NIDI	TIPI
ILIA	IRID	LIRI	NISI	TITI
IMID	IRIS	MIDI	PIKI	ZITI

USE THOSE U'S FROM *OSPD5*

ULU	GURU	KUDU	LULU	SULU	ULUS
BUBU	JUJU	KURU	MUMU	TUTU	UNAU
FUGU	JUKU	LUAU	PUPU	YUZU	URUS

TEN TIPS TO INSTANTLY
GET BETTER AT SCRABBLE

1. **Two- and Three-Letter Words.** Learn the 101 acceptable two- and three-letter words. They are the building
   blocks toward expert play and can boost your average
   score by as many as 50 points a game. They also create
   the opportunity for making multiple words on one move
   and finding additional places to play words by hooking
   onto or overlapping words already on the board.

2. **Secret of the s.** Use the s to pluralize an existing word
   to make two words at once. But use that s wisely. Don't
   use it on a move unless it gives you another 10-12 points.
   This doesn't apply if you have more than one s. Hint:
   should you have an extra s look for the suffixes NESS and
   LESS for a big-time play.

3. **Shuffle Tiles on Your Rack.** Shuffle the tiles on your
   rack frequently to find common letter combinations such
   as ING, ERS, PRE, RE, GHT, IES, EST, FUL, and more. As you
   do this, you'll be surprised how words will appear on
   your rack.

4. **Bonus Squares.** Always look for way to make plays
   using the bonus squares. Check especially for premium
   squares next to vowels.

5. **Consider Your Next Play.** A good SCRABBLE move
   is composed of what you put on the board to score and

what you leave yourself to work with on your rack. If you make a decent play for 28 points but leave a rack with vuuw, chances are your next several racks will be terrible. Go for a balance of vowels and consonants.

6. **"Bingos."** This is what tournament players call it when you use all seven tiles for a 50-point bonus. Again, look for common letter combinations. Over time, you should learn how to manipulate your rack to a bingo, especially if you have bingo-prone tiles such as the blank, s, e, r, a, t.

7. **q-without-u Words.** Words such as qi, qat, qaid, and others are invaluable for both scoring and getting rid of the q, as it's not a bingo-prone or particularly workable tile. A full list of these words is on pages 211–212.

8. **Look for Hooks.** "Hooks" are single letters that can be added to existing words to form other words. While the s is the most obvious, don't forget the y, d, r, or e. Examples: hand(y), plan(e), carve(d), and make(r).

9. **Choice of Plays.** Even if you have a great play, look for a better one. You'll be amazed at how often a second look around the board for options will yield an even better move than you'd planned. And, remember, the best SCRABBLE move is not always about the most points. You need to consider your "rack leave" as well as what opportunity your move might leave for your opponent.

10. **Attitude.** Remember that everyone draws bad tiles from time to time; it comes with the turf. Also remember that luck is a factor for both you and your opponent. SCRABBLE is supposed to be fun. Don't dwell on your mistakes.

CONTACT INFORMATION FOR NORTH AMERICAN SCRABBLE PLAYERS ASSOCIATION (NASPA)

For more information on tournaments and clubs, email NASPA —North American SCRABBLE Players Association—at info@ scrabbleplayers.org, visit www.scrabbleplayers.org, or mail PO Box 12115, Dallas, TX, 75225-0115.

CONTACT INFORMATION FOR SCRABBLE WORDBOOK OR AUTHOR MIKE BARON

Mike Baron, PO Box 2448, Corrales, NM 87048

ACKNOWLEDGMENTS

First and foremost, I'd like to thank all my colleagues and friends who worked over the years at and with the National SCRABBLE Association. It was always a team effort and could not have been accomplished without you. I'd especially like to thank the final team of Jane Ratsey Williams, Theresa Bubb, Katie Schulz Hukill, and Patty Hocker. Your energy and dedication to the game took us all over the world as one of the best NSA teams ever.

Many thanks to Will Menaker, my editor at Liveright/ W. W. Norton, for your insight, hard work, and patience in bringing *Word Nerd* to reality. And much gratitude to editor Bob Weill for his help and early appreciation of the project, as well as to copy editor India Cooper for making order out of chaos. Also much appreciation to Ken Weinrib and Neil Rosini for their legal expertise and guidance, as well as Norton counsel Laura Goldin. And so much appreciation to and admiration for my agent, Regula Noetzli, for her experience, vision, and energy over the years. *Word Nerd* could not have happened without you.

Special thanks to SCRABBLE players and friends Stefan Fatsis, Joe Edley, Mike Baron, and Robert Kahn for their suggestions and contributions to the manuscript. Special thanks also to Merriam-Webster's John Morse for his friendship, encouragement, and contributions. Much appreciation as well to my colleagues at Merriam-Webster—Peter Sokolowski, Meghan Lungi, Jim Lowe, and Jane Mairs.

Of course, this book—and more importantly my SCRABBLE experience—could not have happened without my many colleagues at the Hasbro Games division in East Longmeadow, Massachusetts. Your confidence in our work and willingness to try new ideas over the decades helped introduce millions of new players to the world's greatest game.

ABOUT THE AUTHOR

John D. Williams Jr. was the executive director of the National SCRABBLE Association (NSA) and national spokesperson for the game for twenty-five years. He has been a tournament SCRABBLE player and publisher of the *SCRABBLE News* and is coauthor of the game's best-selling strategy book *Everything SCRABBLE®*. Among other achievements, Williams was a cofounder of the World SCRABBLE Championship, an architect of the acclaimed National School SCRABBLE Program and School SCRABBLE Championship, and creator of the SCRABBLE All*Stars, the United States' first televised SCRABBLE match. Under his leadership, the NSA raised over a million dollars in prize money for competitors and grew the tournament scene to over two hundred official competitions annually.

Williams has also worked as a writer and producer for both television and film for Nickelodeon, CNN, ESPN, Paramount, TV Land, and MTV Networks, among others. He lives in Greenport, New York, with his wife and business partner, Jane Ratsey Williams.

Set in Linotype Fairfield
Format by Seamus Byrne
Manufactured by American Book–Stratford Press
Published by HARPER & BROTHERS, New York

"John, this is a business. If you want to keep doing this, you have to think more like a marketing person and less like a SCRABBLE player," a senior Hasbro Games executive told me in a meeting.

"John Williams cares nothing about the game and tournament players. I bet he doesn't even play SCRABBLE! He's only in it for the money." That was posted by a West Coast veteran tournament player on a popular gamer website. A quick check of the official tournament statistics page revealed my SCRABBLE rating was almost 200 points higher than hers!

"My wife and I have played a game of SCRABBLE every night for 47 years. I honestly think it's keeping us alive! Thank you," a man from Ohio wrote.

"We have to always remember that this game is bigger than all of us." That was from my wife and business partner, Jane Ratsey Williams.

Okay. That's what some other people have said. Now it's my turn.

FOREWORD

OVER THE YEARS, PEOPLE'S REACTION TO my work has always been a blend of bemusement and bewilderment.

"You may quite possibly have the most random job in the United States," a *Los Angeles Times* reporter once told me.

"I bet you're a really good speller!" at least 372 different people have remarked to their own amusement at various social gatherings.

"I hate you. And if you insist on taking words like *asshole, cunt* and *spic* out of the SCRABBLE® Dictionary, you're going to be sorry. I know where you live, and what you look like." This note was received from a disgruntled—and anonymous—word lover who had read a news story about the proposed "cleansing" of the *Official SCRABBLE Players Dictionary.*

"Dad, next time can you please walk behind me?" That was my thirteen-year-old daughter as we passed three boys from her class on the sidewalk in our small town. "Hi, Mr. SCRABBLE!" the boys had shouted to me.

CONTENTS

to Jane Ratsey Williams and George Merritt

Copyright © 2015 by John D. Williams Jr.

All rights reserved
Printed in the United States of America
First Edition

"Scrabbling over Scrabble" by Stefan Fatsis, from the *New York Times*,
July 14, 2013. All rights reserved. The printing, copying or retransmission of the content without expressed written permission is prohibited.

For information about permission to reproduce selections from this
book, write to Permissions, Liveright Publishing Corporation,
a division of W. W. Norton & Company, Inc., 500 Fifth Avenue,
New York, NY 10110

For information about special discounts for bulk purchases, please
contact W. W. Norton Special Sales at specialsales@wwnorton.com
or 800-233-4830

Manufacturing by Quad Graphics Fairfield
Book design by Ellen Cipriano Design
Production manager: Julia Druskin

ISBN 978-0-87140-773-3

Liveright Publishing Corporation
500 Fifth Avenue, New York, N.Y. 10110
www.wwnorton.com

W. W. Norton & Company Ltd.
Castle House, 75/76 Wells Street, London W1T 3QT

1 2 3 4 5 6 7 8 9 0

Dispatches from
the Games, Grammar,
and Geek Underground

JOHN D. WILLIAMS JR.

LIVERIGHT PUBLISHING CORPORATION

A DIVISION OF W. W. NORTON & COMPANY

New York · London

Also by John D. Williams Jr.

Everything SCRABBLE ® *(with Joe Edley)*

doesn't weaken the hurricane. In fact, it may continue to intensify. Global warming heats both the sea surface and the deep water, thus creating ideal conditions for a hurricane to survive and thrive in its long journey from tropical depression to category 4 or 5 super-storm.

After Katrina, Georgia Tech scientists reexamined the historical hurricane and SST data using "a methodology based on information theory, isolating the trend from the shorter term natural modes of variability." They looked at four factors that can affect hurricane intensity: atmospheric humidity, wind shear (which can rip storms apart), rising SSTs, and large-scale air-circulation patterns. "Results show that the increasing trend in the number of category 4 and 5 hurricanes for the period 1970–2004 is directly linked to the trend in SSTs; other aspects of the tropical environment, while influencing shorter term variations in hurricane intensity, do not contribute substantially to the observed global trend."

The evidence gives us a high level of confidence that statement number 2 is true: Average hurricane intensity increases with increasing tropical sea-surface temperature.

3. THE FREQUENCY OF THE MOST INTENSE HURRICANES IS INCREASING GLOBALLY

Three major articles published in mid-2005 pointed out that intense hurricanes had become more common in recent decades. These analyses spawned a whirlwind of media attention because the authors were highly credible and because the articles happened to come out in the weeks before and just after Katrina.

Dr. Kevin Trenberth, head of the Climate Analysis Section of the National Center for Atmospheric Research (NCAR), published the first, in *Science,* two months before Katrina. He began by noting that in 2004 "an unprecedented four hurricanes hit Florida; during the same season in the Pacific, 10 tropical cyclones or typhoons hit Japan (the previous record was six)." What we call hurricanes in America are called cyclones or typhoons in other parts of the world. They all have maximum sustained surface winds of at least 74 mph. Trenberth explained that theory suggests global warming will increase the intensity of hurricanes and the rainfall they bring. He noted that from 1995 to 2004, Atlantic hurricane seasons were abnormally active, as measured by the Accumulated Cyclone Energy Index, which tracks "the collective intensity and duration of tropical storms and hurricanes" during each season.

Kerry Emanuel, a professor of atmospheric sciences at MIT, published next, in *Nature*, a few weeks before Katrina hit. Emanuel, one of the world's leading hurricane experts, created a measure of hurricane destructiveness, which he called the *power dissipation index*. This is essentially the maximum sustained wind speed cubed (raised to the third power)—a measure of hurricane intensity that correlates well with the "actual monetary loss in windstorms"—integrated over the storm's life. He then used the best available data from all sources for hurricanes and sea-surface temperature in both the North Atlantic and the western North Pacific.

Emanuel found a sharp increase in the index in the last thirty years and a close correlation between the power dissipation index and SST in both oceans. Tropical cyclones in both oceans have increased both their peak wind speed and their duration substantially since 1949.

Finally, in September, scientists from Georgia Tech (Peter Webster, Hai-Ru Chang, and Judith Curry) and NCAR (Greg Holland) published in *Science* a detailed analysis of hurricanes in six different ocean regions, including the North Atlantic. They examined the record for the past thirty-five years, the period when high-quality satellite data became available. During this time, SSTs increased about 0.5°C. They found a large increase in the number of super-hurricanes (categories 4 and 5) in every region. Comparing the

1975–1989 period with the 1990–2004 period, they found a more than 50 percent increase in super-hurricanes overall and in the North Atlantic. They concluded that "global data indicate a 30-year trend toward more frequent and intense hurricanes, corroborated by the results of the recent regional assessment [Emanuel's 2005 study]."

THE FUTURE IS NOW

The terms *hypothesis* and *theory* are often used interchangeably, but for scientists, a theory is "a hypothesis that has been confirmed or established by observation or experiment, and is propounded or accepted as accounting for the known facts; a statement of the general laws, principles, or causes of something known or observed," as the *Oxford English Dictionary* defines it. Theories have heft. They have credibility. The germ-theory of disease and human-caused global warming are well-established scientific theories.

For a hypothesis like "Greenhouse warming is causing an increase in global hurricane intensity" to be elevated to theory status, it must pass three additional tests, beyond accounting for the observed data. A theory must make accurate predictions, survive scrutiny by critics, and beat out competing theories, as Judith Curry has written. Let's consider the theory's predictive value.

The three papers described above, arguing that an increase in SST was causing an increase in intense hurricanes, were all based on data through 2004. Since 2005 turned out to be the warmest year on record, with high June–November SSTs in the Atlantic and Gulf of Mexico, it is valuable to examine some of the remarkable records set that year, courtesy of the National Oceanic and Atmospheric Administration:

- Twenty-seven named tropical storms—from Arlene to Wilma, Alpha to Zeta—formed during the 2005 season. This is the *most* named storms in a single season, breaking the old record of 21 set in 1933.

- Fifteen hurricanes formed during the 2005 season (a post-storm analysis in 2006 upgraded Cindy from a tropical storm to a hurricane). This is the *most* hurricanes in a single season, breaking the old record of 12 set in 1969.
- Seven category 3 or higher hurricanes formed during the 2005 season. This *ties* the season record for such hurricanes, first set in 1950.
- Four category 5 hurricanes formed during the 2005 season (Emily, Katrina, Rita, and Wilma). This is the *most* category 5 hurricanes recorded in a single season, breaking the old record of 2 set in 1960 and 1961.
- Seven named storms made United States landfall during 2005. This puts the 2005 season in a *tie* for second place for landfalling storms, behind the 1916 and 2004 seasons where eight named storms made landfall. An eighth storm brushed the coast of North Carolina in 2005 but did not make an official landfall.
- The 2005 season was the *most* destructive for United States landfalling storms, largely due to Katrina. Damage estimates for the 2005 season are over $100 billion.
- Dennis became the *most* intense hurricane on record before August when a central pressure of 930 mb was recorded.
- Emily *eclipsed* Dennis's record for lowest pressure recorded for a hurricane before August when its central pressure dropped to 929 mb. Emily's strength was revised in 2006, so it became "*the earliest-forming Category 5 hurricane on record* in the Atlantic basin and the only known hurricane of that strength to occur during the month of July."
- Vince was the *first* tropical cyclone in recorded history to strike the Iberian Peninsula. Vince was the farthest north and east a storm has ever developed in the Atlantic basin.

In the end, 2005 was not just the warmest year on record, it had the most intense and long-lasting hurricane season, as measured by the Accumulated Cyclone Energy Index. One hurricane season cannot, however, confirm or disprove this hypothesis (or competing hypotheses). Hurricane seasons are subject to enormous year-to-year variability because of factors such as the El Niño weather pattern, which tends to weaken Atlantic hurricane seasons. But we should expect a general upward trend in the intensity and length of Atlantic hurricane seasons, and we should expect more and more records to be smashed.

A strong hypothesis is hard to criticize effectively and objectively; a weak one is not. Let's see how this one fares. The critique offered by meteorologists in particular is worth exploring in detail because it sheds light on the national global-warming debate and on how the nation is likely to respond to the growing evidence of climate change over the next decade or two.

The first major critique of the theory and the 2005 studies supporting it was "Hurricanes and Global Warming," published in the November 2005 issue of the *Bulletin of the American Meteorological Society*. Among its coauthors were three leading public critics of the warming-hurricane connection—Max Mayfield, director of NOAA's National Hurricane Center, Christopher W. Landsea of NOAA's Hurricane Research Division, and Roger Pielke Jr. of the University of Colorado at Boulder—together with two other NOAA hurricane experts. A subhead that begins the article, "An interdisciplinary team of researchers survey the peer-reviewed literature to assess the relationships between global warming, hurricanes, and hurricane impacts," is followed by:

Debate over climate change frequently conflates issues of science and politics. Because of their significant and visceral impacts, discussion of extreme events is a frequent locus of such

conflation. Linda Mearns, of the National Center for Atmospheric Research (NCAR), aptly characterizes this context:
"There's a push on climatologists to say something about extremes, because they are so important. But that can be very
dangerous if we really don't know the answer."

Wow! I have read hundreds of literature-survey articles by scientists over the years, and not a single one began like that. You don't
have to be a scientist to realize that objective surveys don't start by
questioning the character of those they disagree with—their mo-
tives and their scientific method. These authors suggest that Emanuel and the others have a political agenda, and rather than presenting
sound analysis, they have been pushed to say things they can't support.

You would never know from this article (four of whose authors
work at NOAA) that a division of NOAA, the National Climatic
Data Center, had been repeatedly publishing articles and an index
showing that extreme events are in fact becoming more frequent.
You would also never know from this article that there is a strong
consensus among climate scientists that global warming leads to
more extreme weather events. The authors never report that information or even discuss the subject. They just imply that those who
make such arguments are not practicing pure science.

While claiming to be an up-to-date survey, the article bases
most of its critique on old studies that largely predate the recent
surge in SSTs and hurricane intensity examined in the new studies.
When it does examine the new studies, it focuses primarily on Atlantic hurricanes, even though the second *Science* paper found that
"the largest increase [in category 4 and 5 hurricanes] occurred in
the North Pacific, Indian, and Southwest Pacific Oceans." There is
no explanation for this omission. For the specific matter of the
North Atlantic, the authors assert that "much of the recent upward
trend in Atlantic storm frequency and intensity can be attributed to

large multidecadal fluctuations," although the authors never define "much."

This brings us to the competing hypothesis: Atlantic SSTs and hurricanes come in natural multidecadal cycles. This hypothesis deserves attention because the natural-cycles argument is repeated widely in the media, with arguments such as "We had some big hurricanes in the 1940s" used to imply that what we are seeing today is not evidence of human-caused climate change.

NATURAL CYCLES VERSUS GLOBAL WARMING

We have two battling hypotheses. In one corner is the global-warming theory, which says that forcings (natural and human-made) explain most of the changes in our climate and temperature. The natural forcings include fluctuations in the intensity of sunlight (which can increase or decrease warming) and major volcanoes that inject huge volumes of gases and aerosol particles into the stratosphere (which tend to block sunlight and cause cooling). The biggest forcings caused by humans are the greenhouse gases we generate, particularly carbon dioxide from burning coal, oil, and natural gas. But we humans also put significant sulfate aerosols into the atmosphere from burning coal and diesel fuel without advanced emissions controls.

Global warming explains the vast majority of the recent warming in North Atlantic SSTs and most, if not all, of the rise in hurricane intensity in all oceans. A 2006 article in the *Bulletin of the American Meteorological Society* by six leading climatologists noted that recent research "specifically shows an increase [in hurricane intensity] in all ocean basins and an overall global increase, which is the type of signature that would be expected from global warming changes."

In the other corner, we have the natural-cycles hypothesis. This hypothesis offers little or no explanation for the rising hurricane activity in the North Pacific, Indian, and southwestern Pacific Oceans. Nor can it account for most of the rise in North Atlantic SSTs over the past three decades. Its advocates claim it can explain much of the high level of Atlantic hurricane activity in the 1940s, 1950s, and early 1960s and now again in the past decade.

The natural cycle in the Atlantic is called the Atlantic multi-decadal oscillation. Consider figure 3, which is a plot of average sea-surface temperatures for June–November in the North Atlantic's hurricane-forming region. You can just make out what looks like a 60- to 70-year cycle with positive peaks around the 1880s and 1950 (and possibly 2005) and negative peaks around the early 1910s and the mid-1970s. As you can see, however, the dip around the early 1910s is much deeper than the little dip centered in the mid-1970s. Similarly, the peak of each cycle keeps getting higher. Not surprisingly, the 1995–2005 period has had considerably more total tropical storms, hurricanes, and category 4 and 5 hurricanes—the city destroyers—than the peak years from the last cycle of Atlantic hurricane activity (1945–1955).

When I first began researching hurricanes, I believed, like many scientists, that global warming made hurricanes more intense *and* that hurricanes followed a natural oscillation six to seven decades long. I knew that climate scientists had an excellent understanding of the shape of the entire temperature record, including the temperature peak in midcentury, as detailed in several recent modeling studies of the various natural and human-made forcings. But I never connected the dots.

Then, at an October 2005 seminar of the American Meteorological Society, MIT's Kerry Emanuel pointed out that the downswing in temperature and hurricane activity in the 1960s and 1970s may not have been "a natural fluctuation," adding that "a lot of what I thought was natural I now think was forced." Also, Judith Curry from Georgia Tech presented slides showing a stunning parallel be-

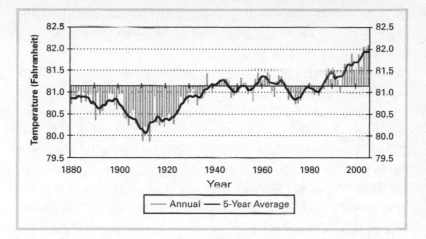

Figure 3. The average sea-surface temperature in °F for June–November in the North Atlantic's hurricane-forming region, since 1880. A 5-year mean is also provided to smooth out annual fluctuations. The data is from NOAA.

tween SSTs and hurricane intensity in the Atlantic over the last century.

As I talked with more climate experts and reviewed the literature, I saw that the dots—the multiple forcings of the past hundred years together with the temperature and hurricane trends—formed a clear picture. Why the temperature dip centered in the early 1910s? A series of six major volcanoes erupted from 1875 to 1912 all around the globe: in Iceland in 1875, Indonesia (Krakatoa) in 1883 (the largest explosion ever recorded), New Zealand in 1886, Guatemala in 1902, Kamchatka in 1907, and Alaska in 1912. The aerosols emitted by these awesome volcanoes kept the planet cooler than it would have been during this time.

The subsequent rise in global temperatures and Atlantic sea-surface temperatures is also well explained by forcings—a slow but steady increase in human-generated greenhouse gases, a slight increase in solar intensity, and the absence of any major volcano eruptions that might otherwise have blocked these trends. The rise in number and intensity of hurricanes in midcentury occurred at the same time as this rise in Atlantic SSTs.

But what explains the drop in SSTs and hurricanes from the mid-1960s through the early 1990s that some critics (mistakenly) believe undercuts the global-warming theory? Not coincidentally, that drop began just around the time of the 1963 eruption of Mount Agung in Indonesia, which "produced the largest stratospheric dust veil in the Northern Hemisphere in more than 50 years." Not coincidentally, the drop also came during a three-decade stretch when humans were emitting unprecedented amounts of industrial aerosol and sulfate. Not coincidentally, the drop continued through the 1982 El Chichon eruption in Mexico and the 1991 Mount Pinatubo eruption in the Philippines, which "produced very large stratospheric aerosol clouds and large climatic effects." Multiple major sun-blocking events all worked together to give us a false sense of security, to shield us from the full impact of the rapid growth in atmospheric carbon dioxide concentrations. And they cooled the air and the seas, resulting in fewer intense hurricanes.

Not coincidentally, temperatures (and hurricanes) rebounded strongly after the major volcanic eruptions ended and the human-made aerosol emissions by the industrial nations dropped sharply thanks to clean-air regulations, even as human emissions of greenhouse gases continued to soar and utterly overwhelmed the aerosol cooling effect.

With all these variables, no wonder this picture took climate scientists so long to bring into focus. This complexity helps explain why many meteorologists, most of whom have little training in global-warming science, keep standing by their flawed natural-cycles hypothesis.

The view that this is not all a grand coincidence gains credence from a 2006 study by American and British climatologists and meteorologists led by the Lawrence Livermore National Laboratory.

They concluded: "Volcanically induced cooling of the ocean surface penetrated into deeper layers, where it persisted for decades after the event." The research makes clear that the combination of natural and human-made forcings, correctly modeled, can explain the key trends in both SSTs and subsurface ocean temperatures for the past 120 years. Subsurface temperatures can be as important to hurricane intensity as sea-surface temperatures.

When I posed all this to MIT's Kerry Emanuel in February 2006, he replied, "It would appear that Atlantic hurricanes are a kind of global thermometer, following closely the trend in global (and especially Northern Hemispheric) temperatures produced by volcanic activity, solar variations, sulfate aerosols, and greenhouse gases. *I think the 'natural cycles' argument will prove to be largely false.*"

In 2006, Emanuel coauthored a study that concluded that the Atlantic multidecadal oscillation (AMO) trend has been overestimated and that "there is no evidence that natural climate oscillations such as the AMO contributed to long-term tropical North Atlantic SST variations." Global warming is now clearly the dominant force behind SSTs in the Atlantic's hurricane-forming region and will become more and more dominant in the future.

Higher SSTs have helped cause the rapid intensification of hurricanes like Katrina, as the post-Katrina report by the National Climatic Data Center explained. And the day before Katrina struck, the *New Orleans Times-Picayune* reported, "The northern Gulf of Mexico is unusually warm," likely "the result of *relentless high temperatures in recent weeks* along Louisiana's Gulf Coast," according to National Hurricane Center meteorologist Eric Blake.

Global warming also increases the incidence of such heat waves and makes them more intense and long-lasting. And it puts into the atmosphere more warm, moist air—the stuff hurricanes are made of. Shortly before Katrina, NOAA's Christopher Landsea said, "The warmer the sea-surface temperature and the more warm, moist air that is available, the stronger a hurricane can become." After Katrina, Max Mayfield, then director of the Tropical Prediction Center at the National Hurricane Center, told CBS's Bob Schieffer, "We think the best correlation [with hurricane activity] we have here is with the sea-surface temperatures." Yet Mayfield testified to Congress in September 2005, "The increased activity since 1995 is due to natural fluctuations/cycles of hurricane activity, driven by the Atlantic Ocean itself along with the atmosphere above it and not enhanced substantially by global warming."

This conclusion is "untenable," said a major 2006 study by climate scientists from NASA, Columbia University, Yale University, MIT, Lawrence Berkeley National Laboratory, and Argonne National Laboratory. They concluded that "to the degree that hurricane intensification of the past decade is a product of increasing SSTs in the Atlantic Ocean and the Gulf of Mexico, human-made greenhouse gases probably are a substantial contributor."

Yet untenable critiques from meteorologists can seem very credible to the public, as can critiques from those with little training in or knowledge of global-warming research. So it is no wonder we do not seem close to achieving the consensus needed to avert catastrophic climate change. Many major media outlets, including CNN, *USA Today,* and the *Chicago Tribune,* bought this story line— proving you can spin hurricanes backward—and the combined mantras of "It's a natural cycle" and "Those who say otherwise have a political agenda" may keep the public, the media, and policy makers confused for years to come.

Even though only a small fraction of hurricanes make landfall, the global-warming signal is starting to show up. Emanuel notes that "a trend in landfalling intensity is already apparent" when one looks at hurricanes worldwide. Significantly, the National Climatic Data Center developed a measure for the "strength and frequency" of tropical storms and hurricanes striking this country for its Climate Extremes Index. That index had an average value of 20 over the past ninety-five years. The two highest values this measure has seen were in 2004 and 2005, at 80 and 92 respectively. No year before 1985 exceeded 65.

"More than half the total hurricane damage in the U.S. (normalized for inflation and populations trends) was caused by just five events," explains Emanuel. Storms that are category 4 and 5 at landfall (or just before) are what destroy major cities like New Orleans and Galveston with devastating winds, rains, and storm surges. We have seen a more than 50 percent increase in category 4 and 5 storms both globally and in the Atlantic. Where precisely such storms make landfall is random on a year-to-year basis, but over time, more and more will inevitably strike this country, especially as the Gulf gets warmer. And that is without considering the combined impact of more intense hurricanes and sea-level rise.

Tropical cyclones are threshold events—if SSTs are below 80°F, they do not form. Some analysis even suggests there is an SST "threshold [close to 83°F] necessary for the development of major hurricanes." Global warming may actually cause some hurricanes to develop or intensify that otherwise would not have (by raising SSTs above the threshold at the right place or time).

For now, we can't know with confidence whether global warming has caused a specific hurricane to develop or intensify. But we can know with very high confidence that global warming has increased the intensity and rainfall of recent hurricane seasons.

The destruction of New Orleans by Katrina, particularly the breaching of the levees, might have been avoided if the storm had been a little less severe and generated a little less wind and rain. In the case of Katrina, the added intensity from global warming may have been the straw that broke the camel's back, as NCAR's Kevin Trenberth put it in October 2005, the extra push that brought the poorly built levees down.

2000–2025: REAP THE WHIRLWIND

For they have sown the wind, and they shall reap the whirlwind.

—Hosea

How will the rest of this era play out? Why did I advise my brother not to rebuild on the Gulf Coast? Why should New Orleans not be rebuilt unless the levees protecting it are built to withstand a category 5 hurricane?

"I don't see any reason why the power of hurricanes wouldn't continue to increase over the next 100 to 200 years," said MIT's Emanuel. Hurricanes can get much, much bigger than we have so far seen in the Atlantic. The most intense Pacific storm on record was Super Typhoon Tip in 1979, which reached maximum sustained winds of 190 mph near the center. On its wide rim, gale-force winds (39 mph) extended over a diameter of an astonishing 1,350 miles. It would have covered nearly half the continental United States.

No wonder ABC News reported in 2006 that hurricane scientists are considering adding a category 6 for hurricanes above 175 miles per hour. Ultimately, they may become common.

If we don't reverse our emissions paths quickly, global temperatures will rise faster and faster through 2100 and beyond. This will translate into warmer oceans in all three dimensions: Warmth will spread over wider swaths of the ocean as well as deeper below the surface—we've already seen that in the first known tropical cyclone in the South Atlantic (2004) and the first known tropical cyclone to strike Spain (2005). That means we will probably see stronger hurricanes farther north along the U.S. Atlantic coast in the coming decades.

More intense storms will be seen earlier and later in the season. The 2005 hurricane season was the most striking example of that trend, with Emily, "the earliest-forming Category 5 hurricane on record in the Atlantic" in July, and Zeta, the longest-lived tropical cyclone to form in December and cross over into the next year, where it became the longest-lived January tropical cyclone. We have already seen a statistically significant increase in the length of the average hurricane season over the last several decades, according to a 2006 analysis. The data from the past century indicate that a 1°F increase in SSTs leads to an extra five tropical storms a year in the Atlantic—an ominous statistic in a world taking no actions to stop a projected 2°F increase in sea-surface temperatures by midcentury, and more than double that by century's end.

At the same time, the inland United States will heat up at an even faster rate, so the Mississippi River will not be such a cool stream of water pouring into the Gulf. As the sea level rises, the protective outer delta of the Mississippi will continue to disappear and storm surges will penetrate deeper inland. Hurricanes weaken rapidly over land. Even a foot of shallow delta water can dramatically reduce this weakening effect, allowing hurricanes to reach deeper inland with their destructive force.

So not only will we see increased category 4 and category 5 hurricanes, but sooner or later—probably sooner—one of the hurricanes that enters the Gulf will ride a wide and deep mass of warm water straight to the shore, and rather than weakening as it approaches the shore, like Katrina did, it will maintain its strength. Then a category 5 super-hurricane will bring havoc back to New Orleans and the Gulf Coast.

Americans should plan on the 2004 hurricane season—with its four super-hurricanes (category 4 or stronger)—becoming the norm over the next few decades. But if 2004 is the norm, we should not be surprised if as many as a quarter of the hurricane seasons in this era are as severe as those of 2005 with its five super-hurricanes. After all, the ocean and the entire planet are just going to get warmer.

As of the end of 2005, *this decade has already had five of the six hottest years on record* (the other being an El Niño–boosted 1998), so it will no doubt be the hottest decade in thousands of years. As will the next decade. And the decade after that. And on and on and on. Such is the nature of global warming on a planet that refuses to take serious action.

CHAPTER THREE

2025–2050: PLANETARY PURGATORY

Obviously, if you get drought indices like these, there's no adaptation that's possible.
—David Rind, NASA climate scientist, 2005

We're showing warming and earlier springs tying in with large forest fire frequencies. Lots of people think climate change and the ecological responses are 50 to 100 years away. But it's not 50 to 100 years away— it's happening now in forest ecosystems through fire.
—Thomas Swetnam, University of Arizona climate scientist, 2006

Imagine if the climate changed and extreme weather became so constant that it was no longer considered extreme. Mammoth heat waves like the one that killed 35,000 Europeans in 2003 would occur every other year. Mega-droughts and widespread wildfires, like those of the record-breaking 2005 wildfire season, which ravaged 8.5 million acres, would be the norm. This new climate would wipe out whole forests, including virtually every pine tree in British Columbia. The Arctic would have little or no summer ice, and the Greenland ice cap would melt, eventually raising sea levels by 20 feet.

If we permit this Planetary Purgatory to occur, the nation and the world would be forced to begin a desperate race against time—a race against the vicious cycles in which an initial warming causes changes to the climate system that lead to more warming, which makes adapting to climate change a never-ending, ever-changing, expensive, exhausting struggle for our children, and their children, and on and on for generations.

This chapter will focus on (1) the impacts of accelerated warming, especially drought and wildfires, and (2) the fatal feedbacks that will probably start to kick into overdrive during this era and complicate any effort to stop the Greenland Ice Sheet from melting.

HELL AND NO WATER

By the end of the Planetary Purgatory era, 2050, Earth will probably be hotter than it has been in 125,000 years. By then, the planet is likely to be warming 0.6°F (0.33°C) *per decade* or more, even if global-emissions growth slows somewhat from its current pace. Every three decades, the earth will warm more than it has in the past century. The temperature over much of the inland continental United States will likely rise nearly 1°F per decade (and in Alaska even faster). This unprecedented rate of temperature change could continue for decades.

The first brutal impacts will be marathon heat waves that last for weeks over many states. Americans have not experienced this type of extreme extended heat wave, but Europe did in August 2003. The oppressive heat brought temperatures in the upper 90s or higher across much of the continent for three weeks, and killed 15,000 people in France, 7,000 in Germany, 4,200 in Italy, and more than 2,000 in Great Britain, which on August 10 recorded its first-ever temperature over 100°F.

Scientists have studied this torrid heat wave extensively. A 2004 study in *Nature*, by British scientists from Oxford University and the Hadley Centre for Climate Prediction and Research, examined the role of greenhouse gas emissions. It concluded that human influence more than doubled the risk of such a deadly heat wave. If we stay on our current emissions trajectory, more than half of European summers will be hotter than 2003 within the next four decades. By the end of the century, "2003 would be classed as an anomalously *cold* summer relative to the new climate," the study notes.

Particularly worrisome will be shortages of water, which is essential to human life and agriculture. And large parts of the world already suffer water shortages. Moreover, many proposed solutions to our energy needs, including biofuels and hydrogen production, require huge quantities of water.

THE PRESENT IS PROLOGUE

To see what is likely to happen during Planetary Purgatory, let's look at what has happened already. Since the 1970s, the number of "very dry areas" on the planet, as defined by the widely used Palmer Drought Severity Index, has more than doubled, to about 30 percent of the global land. As a major study by the National Center for Atmospheric Research concluded, "These results provide observational evidence for the increasing risk of droughts as anthropogenic [human caused] global warming progresses and produces both increased temperatures and increased drying."

Not surprisingly, but rarely reported in context, wildfires have been on the rise worldwide for half a century. Every decade since the 1950s has seen an increase in major wildfires in the United States and around the world.

Large parts of the country have been getting hotter and drier, and suffering extended droughts. "The period since 1999 is now officially the driest in the 98 years of recorded history of the Colorado

River, according to the United States Geological Survey," noted a 2004 *New York Times* article. In March 2006, Phoenix set a record with more than 140 consecutive rainless days. "The average temperature for the continental United States from January through June 2006 was the warmest first half of any year since records began in 1895," reported NOAA's National Climatic Data Center. In June, 45 percent of the contiguous United States was in a moderate-to-extreme state of drought. By July, the figure was 51 percent.

Although the 2005 wildfire season, which ravaged 8.5 million acres, was record-breaking, the record it broke was from 2000, when wildfires consumed 8.25 million acres. From 2000 through 2005, wildfires destroyed nearly 30 million acres, some 47,000 square miles—an area *the equivalent of Pennsylvania.* Stunningly, 2006 has already broken the record set in 2005, with 8.7 million acres burned by mid-September.

Not only do drought and high temperatures increase the number of wildfires, they also lead to a greater range of pests that feast on trees whose defenses have been weakened by heat and lack of water. Trees from the Southwest up to Alaska are dying by the millions.

A 2005 study led by the University of Arizona, with the Los Alamos National Laboratory and the U.S. Geological Survey, examined a huge 3-million-acre die-off of vegetation in 2002–2003 "in response to drought and associated bark beetle infestations" in the Four Corners area (Arizona, New Mexico, Colorado, and Utah). This drought was not quite as severe as the one that region experienced in the 1950s, but it was much warmer, hence it fit the global-warming model. The recent drought had "nearly complete tree mortality across many size and age classes," whereas "most of the patchy mortality in the 1950s was associated with trees [more than] 100 years old."

Most of this tree death was caused by bark beetle infestation, and "such outbreaks are tightly tied to drought-induced water stress." Healthy trees defend themselves by drowning the tiny pine beetles in resin. Without water, weakened, parched trees are easy meals for bugs.

"We're seeing changes in [mountain pine beetle] activity from Canada to Mexico," said Forest Service researcher Jesse Logan in July 2004, "and the common thing is warming temperatures." According to the Department of Forest Resource Management at the University of British Columbia, the beetle infestation has spread to higher and more northern regions thanks in large part to climate change. And milder winters since 1994 have reduced the winter death rate of beetle larvae in Wyoming from 80 percent per year to under 10 percent.

In a February 2006 speech on climate change, Senator Lisa Murkowski of Alaska pointed out that the tremendous recent warming had opened the door to the "voracious spruce bark beetle," which devastated more than 3 million acres in Alaska, "providing dry fuel for outbreaks of enormous wild fires." Half of the wildfires in the record-breaking 2005 season were in Alaska.

I have been focusing on U.S. impacts, but the grim reality in British Columbia is too stunning to ignore. The Canadian and British Columbia Forest Service have reported that as of 2004, the mountain pine beetle infestation had killed 280 million cubic meters (10 billion cubic feet) of stately British Columbia pine trees, of which 170 million cubic meters would have been harvestable. By 2014, they project the beetle will have killed 80 percent of the harvestable pine trees—more than 800 million cubic meters. By 2025, virtually all may be gone over a region the size of North Dakota or Washington State. That is especially likely now that "it has become apparent that B.C. is facing the 'worse-case scenario,'" according to the University of British Columbia. So Canada will now log the pines as fast as possible: "Harvest levels in the region will be increased significantly over the next decade." Even so, the infestation may well spread, and then "forests across Canada may be at risk."

The authors of the 2005 study on vegetation die-off warn that the recent drought in the Four Corners "may be a harbinger of future global-change-type drought throughout much of North America and elsewhere, in which increased temperatures in concert with multidecadal drought patterns" cause unprecedented changes in ecosystems. In 2005 climatologist Jonathan Overpeck noted that this study, together with the recent evidence that temperature and annual precipitation are headed in opposite directions, raises the question of whether we are at the "dawn of the *super-interglacial drought.*"

The increased risk of severe drought we are seeing today was predicted back in 1990 by scientists at NASA's Goddard Institute of Space Studies. Their model also suggested that, in the second half of this century, severe drought, which was already occurring with about 5 percent frequency by 1990, will occur *every other year*—and more frequently in the West. The huge population growth in the western United States during the twentieth century happened to coincide with relatively wet weather in the region, weather that will likely prove to be an anomaly. One 2004 newspaper article noted, "The development of the modern urbanized West—one of the biggest growth spurts in the nation's history—may have been based on a colossal miscalculation."

Global warming also reduces the snowpack, and "snow is our water storage in the West," notes Philip Mote, climatologist for the state of Washington. States such as Montana see only 18 inches of precipitation a year. Portland gets 36 inches a year, but only one-tenth of that is during the summer. Snowmelt comprises 75 percent of all water in western streams. The warming of the last few decades has already reduced snowpacks at five out of six western snow-measurement sites. Many have suffered a 15 to 30 percent decline. And warming has moved up the peak of the annual spring runoff. In California's Sierra Nevada, streams peak as much as three weeks earlier than they did only a few decades ago.

By midcentury, warming is likely to reduce western snowpacks *by up to 60 percent* in regions such as the Cascade Range of Oregon and Washington. Summertime stream flows are projected to drop 20 to 50 percent. By century's end, the Cascades might be snow-free by April 1, and western streams might peak two months earlier than they once did. This will inevitably lead to more wildfires. A 2006 study led by the Scripps Institution of Oceanography found that the greatest increases in wildfires since 1970 were associated with warmer temperatures and earlier snowmelts, which reduce humidity and expose forests to the full effect of arid summers.

What will wildfires be like during the Planetary Purgatory era and beyond? The 2006 Scripps study compared the period 1987–2003 with the period 1970–1986. The researchers found that the active wildfire season in the West has increased 78 days and that major fires now burn 37 days—nearly five times as long as they did in the first period. And yet the average spring and summer western temperatures rose only 0.87°C (1.6°F) from the earlier period to the recent one. With current emissions trends, the West is likely to see June–August temperatures rise between 2°C and 5°C over the next half-century—suggesting we can expect a dramatic increase in fires.

Researchers at the U.S. Forest Services Pacific Wildland Fire Sciences Lab looked at past fires in the West to create a statistical model of how future climate change may affect wildfires. Their work suggests that "the area burned by wildfires in 11 Western states could double . . . if summer climate warms by slightly more than a degree and a half" centigrade. On our current emissions path, this is likely to happen by midcentury. By century's end, states such as Montana, New Mexico, Washington, Utah, and Wyoming could see burn areas increase *five times*.

If we don't change course soon, the West faces a scorching climate—Hell and No Water—with summers that are far hotter and drier, longer wildfire seasons with more ferocious fires, and, at the same time, far less water for agriculture and hydropower.

THE NEED FOR SYSTEMS THINKING

Global warming is so challenging and so potentially devastating because it is a systems problem. Although the basic definition of a system is simple—"any set of interconnected elements"—many systems, such as our climate, are exceedingly complicated.

The word *environment* comes from Old French, *viron,* meaning "circle." Since the word *cycle* also derives from *circle,* let's call the environment the cycle of life. I have not centered this book on the environment per se—on the destruction of the coral reefs or the threat to the polar bears—because so many good books have already done so and because my focus here is on the risk to the health and well-being of current and future generations of Americans.

I am a physicist who has studied and written about systems. Systems are dominated by unexpected and nonintuitive behavior because they have feedbacks, thresholds, delays, and nonlinearities. To understand the climate system, it is critical to recognize the distinction between atmospheric *concentrations* of CO_2 (the total stock of CO_2 already in the air) and annual *emissions* of CO_2 (the yearly new flow into the air). A 2002 study led by John Sterman, director of the System Dynamics Group at the MIT Sloan School of Management, found that even "highly educated graduate students" held many myths about the climate system.

Many believe temperature responds immediately to changes in CO_2 emissions or concentrations. Still more believe that stabilizing emissions near current rates would stabilize the climate, when in fact emissions would continue to exceed removal, increasing GHG [greenhouse gas] concentrations and [planetary heating]. Such beliefs support "wait and see" policies, but violate basic laws of physics.

In fact, until annual carbon dioxide *emissions* drop to about one-fifth of current levels, *concentrations* of heat-trapping carbon dioxide will continue to rise, and with rising *concentrations*, the pace of climate change will continue to accelerate.

During the Planetary Purgatory era, the painful reality of global warming will touch the lives of all Americans. We will be forced to begin a desperate scramble, together with other nations, to stop the planet's temperature rise before the Greenland Ice Sheet melts. All Americans will become expert on both annual CO_2 emissions and total atmospheric CO_2 concentrations—two quantities that will ultimately determine the fate of the next fifty generations of Americans. I predict they will eventually be reported with as much fanfare as the gross domestic product.

As an important aside, scientists and government agencies often use carbon, C, rather than carbon dioxide, CO_2, as a metric. Carbon dioxide is the greenhouse gas. Carbon is found in fossil fuels and soils and trees. The global carbon cycle is what many scientists study. You need familiarity with both quantities to follow the scientific and political debates about climate science and climate solutions. The key relationship to remember is:

1 ton carbon, C, equals 3.67 tons carbon dioxide, CO_2

Thus 11 tons of carbon dioxide equals 3 tons of carbon, and a price of $30 per ton of carbon dioxide equals a price of $110 per ton of carbon.

In 2005, fossil fuel combustion released into the air more than 26 billion tons of CO_2 (more than 7 billion tons of carbon). This is five times the annual rate of emissions from the 1940s. For the past decade, annual emissions have been rising about 2 percent per year, in large part driven by China and the United States. This rate of growth seems likely to continue through 2015 and possibly through

2025, barring a sudden reversal of U.S. (and Chinese) climate and energy policy. In 2005, the U.S. Department of Energy forecast that global annual emissions would exceed 30 billion tons of CO_2 in 2010 and, in 2025, 38 billion tons of CO_2 (more than 10 billion tons of carbon). Such rapid *emissions* growth by 2025 would make *concentrations* soar and take the nation and the world to the very edge of catastrophe.

While emissions might be thought of as the water flowing into a bathtub, atmospheric concentrations are the water level in the bathtub. Emissions are analogous to the federal budget deficit we incur each year, and concentrations are analogous to the total national debt that has been accumulated.

In 2005, atmospheric concentrations of carbon dioxide were 380 parts per million, about a third higher than the preindustrial average of about 280 ppm. In recent years, the rate of growth of concentrations has doubled. Concentrations are now climbing more than 2.5 ppm a year. By 2025, concentrations are projected to be 420–430 ppm. During Planetary Purgatory, concentrations are projected to rise an average of 3 ppm a year. In this scenario, by 2050, atmospheric concentrations would hit 500 ppm. Yet once we get much past 500 ppm, the complete melting of the Greenland ice sheet and the resulting 20-foot sea-level rise become all but inevitable.

Now it begins to be clear how desperate we will be in Planetary Purgatory. Suppose that America takes no serious action on climate while George W. Bush is president, and we successfully block any serious efforts by other nations. Suppose that then, starting about 2010, we take some wishy-washy actions to slow our emissions growth, while China and other developing nations continue their booming growth largely unchecked (thanks to growing populations, industrialization, and a rapidly expanding middle class). Suppose we continue making modest investments in developing new technology. Near 2020, America starts to get more serious, and we organize international commitments that slow global emissions growth *by half.*

Finally, in 2025, the entire world wakes up to the full gravity of global warming. Now we adopt the aggressive five-decade effort to deploy the best existing energy technology described in chapter 1 (modified from the analysis by Princeton's Stephen Pacala and Robert Socolow). From 2025 through 2075, the world achieves eight remarkable changes:

1. We launch a massive performance-based efficiency program for homes, commercial buildings, and new construction.
2. We launch a massive effort to boost the efficiency of heavy industry and expand the use of cogeneration (combined heat and power).
3. We capture the CO_2 from 800 new large coal plants and store it underground.
4. We build 1 million large wind turbines (or the equivalent in renewables like solar power).
5. We build 700 new large nuclear-power plants while shutting down no old ones.
6. We require every car to have an average fuel economy of 60 mpg.
7. We enable every car to run on electricity for short distances (requiring another half-million large wind turbines) before reverting to biofuels (requiring one-twelfth the world's cropland).
8. We stop all tropical deforestation, while doubling the rate of new tree planting.

Pacala and Socolow call these "wedges," since each starts slowly but then rises in impact over the 50 years and ultimately avoids the emission of 1 billion tons of carbon per year.

Had we started these eight wedges in 2010, global carbon emissions would have remained frozen at 8 billion metric tons per year. But because we delayed, because we started in 2025, they will merely *slow* emissions growth, so that global carbon emission will rise from 10 billion metric tons per year in 2025 to 12 billion metric tons per year in 2075. Finally, suppose that, starting in 2075, we adopt even more aggressive use of advanced energy technologies, and global emissions actually start *dropping* 1.5 percent per year.

In this scenario, carbon dioxide concentrations would exceed 600 ppm in 2100—and perhaps exceed 750 ppm, given the likely effect of the climate system's vicious cycles, as we will see shortly—and continue to rise. The temperature rise from current levels to 2100 would be a whopping 2.5°C or more. The outcome: We caused an eventual 20-foot sea-level rise, and we probably caused an eventual 80-foot rise. We didn't prevent a century or more of super-hurricanes and mega-droughts. We were insufficiently desperate and poorly led. We waited for new technology to show up in 2025 instead of deploying existing technology at once.

And if we do wait until 2025, the relatively painless technology-driven solutions that are available in 2007 or 2010 will no longer be sufficient to avoid climate catastrophe. Our actions will have to be far more desperate and aggressive. Just how desperate and aggressive critically depends on the myriad feedback loops in the climate system that will almost certainly punish any unwise delay in taking global warming seriously.

CLIMATE REALITY VERSUS CLIMATE MODELS

The earth's climate system is "far from being self-stabilizing," in the words of climatologist Wallace Broecker, but is "an ornery beast which overreacts even to small nudges." Push it too hard in one direction, you get an ice age, in another direction, you get 80-foot-higher sea levels. This suggests that the climate system has one or more vicious cycles, in which a little warming causes a change that speeds up warming, as when warming melts highly reflective Arctic ice, replacing it with the blue sea, which absorbs far more sunlight and hence far more solar energy, causing the Arctic Ocean to heat up more, melting more ice, and so on. Vicious cycles are often called "positive feedbacks" in the scientific literature, because these feedbacks add to and increase the effect. It is not a term I will use much here because it has a positive connotation in general usage—everybody wants to get positive feedback—whereas everybody should want to avoid the vicious cycles of the climate system.

The models that tell us how much warming we will get from a certain level of carbon dioxide emissions do not fully account for all of the vicious cycles. Thus, these models almost certainly significantly *underestimate* the climate's likely response to our emissions of greenhouse gases, a view shared by a number of recent studies and most of the climate scientists I talked to, such as Harvard's Dan Schrag. Let's look briefly at three studies from 2006.

Scientists analyzed data from a major expedition to retrieve deep marine sediments beneath the Arctic to understand the Paleocene-Eocene Thermal Maximum, a brief period some 55 million years ago of "widespread, extreme climatic warming that was associated with massive atmospheric greenhouse gas input." This study, published in *Nature,* found Artic temperatures almost beyond imagination—above 23°C (74°F)—temperatures far warmer than current climate models had predicted when applied to this period. The three dozen authors conclude that existing climate models are missing crucial factors that can significantly amplify polar warming.

A second study looked at temperature and atmospheric changes during the Middle Ages. The study found that the effect of vicious cycles in the climate system—where global warming boosts atmospheric CO_2 levels—"will promote warming by an extra 15 percent to 78 percent" compared with typical estimates by the U.N.'s Intergovernmental Panel on Climate Change. The study notes that these results may even be conservative because they ignore other green-house gases such as methane, whose levels will likely be boosted as temperatures warm.

The third study looked at temperature and atmospheric changes during the past 400,000 years. It found evidence for significant increases in both CO_2 and methane (CH_4) levels as temperatures rise. The conclusion: If our current climate models correctly accounted for such vicious cycles, "we would be predicting a significantly greater increase in global warming than is currently forecast over the next century and beyond"—as much as 1.5°C warmer this century alone.

Let's look at some key vicious cycles that climate modelers are missing or underestimating.

THE FOUR (POTENTIAL) SOURCES OF THE APOCALYPSE

For the last few decades, nearly 60 percent of the carbon dioxide that we have been adding to the atmosphere has stayed there. Where did the rest go? The other 40 percent has been absorbed by several "sinks"—the ocean, soils (including permafrost), and vegetation. They are called sinks because they absorb carbon and remove it from the ecosystem. Returning to the bathtub analogy, a carbon sink is just like the drain in your bathtub. The sources, including cars, factories, and power plants, are like faucets. As long as the sources generate more carbon dioxide than the sinks can drain, atmospheric concentrations (the water level in the bathtub) will continue to rise.

This is called the *global carbon cycle.* At some threshold of carbon dioxide concentrations and temperature rise, most scientists believe that one or all of these sinks will saturate—like clogged-up drains, they will not be able to absorb any more. Some carbon sinks may actually turn into *sources* of greenhouse gases. Preliminary evidence suggests that may be starting to happen already. I think we will know for certain by the 2025–2050 era. Let's look at four key sinks that could drive vicious cycles: oceans, soils, permafrost, and vegetation.

First, the oceans. According to a 2005 report by the United Kingdom's Royal Society, ocean warming leads to a "decreased mixing between the different levels in the oceans." That, in turn, "would reduce CO_2 uptake, in effect, reducing the oceanic volume available to CO_2 absorption from the atmosphere." In other words, if surface water that has absorbed CO_2 does not switch places with deeper water, the ocean will absorb less and less CO_2 over time and more will stay in the atmosphere. The increased ocean stratification would also tend to separate some phytoplankton from their nutrients, "leading to a decline in oceanic primary production," which would also reduce the ocean's ability to take up carbon, which means more CO_2 would stay in the air, and on and on. Finally, on our current CO_2 emissions trend, the ocean will become so acidic that coral reefs and other sea life will be devastated, further reducing the ocean's ability to absorb carbon.

Second, the soils. Warming can cause soils to stop taking up CO_2 and, ultimately, to start releasing it. A 2002 study of Texas grasslands found that as CO_2 concentrations increase, the ability of the soil to take up carbon slowed more rapidly than expected, "indicating that we are currently at an important threshold." The study notes that "the ability of soils to continue as sinks is limited." British soil experts have been monitoring their soil at several thousand sites in England and Wales since 1978. In 2005, they reported that the soils are releasing their carbon. The net carbon content has been dropping 0.6 percent per year—a huge amount considering that the

CO_2 released from British soils would be enough to erase the industrial-emissions reductions the country has achieved so far with its enlightened energy policies.

Third, the tundra, Arctic permafrost, and frozen peat. The permafrost is soil that stays below freezing (0°C or 32°F) for at least two years. Peat is basically mulch, or organic matter that is partially decomposed. It is found around the globe, but it is frozen near the poles. Normally, plants capture carbon dioxide from the atmosphere during photosynthesis and slowly release that carbon back into the atmosphere after they die. But the Arctic acts like a freezer, and the decomposition rate is very low. So frozen peat is "a locker of carbon," as UCLA scientist Laurence Smith explained at an American Meteorological Society seminar in February 2006.

How much? According to a June 2006 *Science* article by Russian and American scientists, nearly 1,000 billion metric tons of carbon (some 3,600 billion metric tons of carbon dioxide) are locked up in the Arctic's permafrost. That exceeds all the carbon dioxide currently in the atmosphere. The permafrost may contain more than a third of all carbon stored in soils globally, much of it in the form of methane. The problem: Global warming is melting the top layer of permafrost, creating the possibility of large releases of soil carbon, and that is a potentially devastating vicious cycle. We are defrosting the tundra freezer—and at an unprecedented rate.

A 2006 study by Alaska researchers finds rapid degradation to key elements of the permafrost "that previously had been stable for 1000s of years." The study, titled "Abrupt Increase in Permafrost Degradation in Arctic Alaska," concludes that this recent degradation exceeds changes seen earlier in the twentieth century by a factor of ten to a hundred.

New Scientist magazine reported in August 2005 that in western Siberia a frozen peat bog the size of France and Germany combined is turning into "a mass of shallow lakes," some almost a mile wide. In the past 40 years, the region has warmed by 3°C, greater warming than almost anywhere else in the world, in part because of the vicious cycle described earlier: Warming melts highly reflective ice and replaces it with dark soils, which absorb more sunlight and warm up, melting more ice, and on and on.

Russian botanist Sergei Kirpotin describes an "ecological landslide that is probably irreversible and is undoubtedly connected to climatic warming." The entire western Siberian sub-Arctic region is melting, and it "has all happened in the last three or four years," according to Kirpotin, who believes we are crossing a critical threshold. The peat bogs formed near the end of the last ice age some 11,000 years ago. They generate methane, which, up until now, has mostly been trapped within the permafrost, and in even deeper ice-like structures called clathrates. The Siberian frozen bog is estimated to contain 70 billion tons of methane (CH_4). If the bogs become drier as they warm, the methane will oxidize and the emissions will be primarily CO_2. But if the bogs stay wet, as they have been recently, the methane will escape directly into the atmosphere.

Either way we have a dangerous vicious cycle, but the wet bogs are worse because methane has twenty times the heat-trapping power of carbon dioxide. Some 600 *million* metric tons of methane are emitted each year from natural and human sources, so if even a small fraction of the 70 *billion* tons of methane in the Siberian bogs escapes, it will swamp those emissions and dramatically accelerate global warming. Researchers monitoring a single Swedish bog, or mire, found it had experienced a 20 to 60 percent increase in methane emissions between 1970 and 2000. In some methane hot spots in eastern Siberia, "the gas was bubbling from thawing permafrost so fast it was preventing the surface from freezing, even in the midst of winter."

Even if the tundra carbon is all emitted as carbon dioxide instead of methane, the consequences would be disastrous. Carbon emissions from human activity already exceed 7 billion tons a year, and we are on track to be at 10 billion tons a year by 2025. But as we have already seen, if we exceed annual emissions levels of 10 billion tons for any significant length of time, we will have no chance of avoiding catastrophic warming.

A major 2005 study led by NCAR climate researcher David Lawrence found that virtually the entire top 11 feet of permafrost around the globe could disappear by the end of this century. Using the first "fully interactive climate system model" applied to study permafrost, the researchers found that if we somehow stabilize carbon dioxide concentrations in the air at 550 ppm, permafrost would plummet from more than 4 million square miles today to 1.5 million. If concentrations hit 690 ppm, permafrost would shrink to just 800,000 square miles.

While these projections were done with one of the most sophisticated climate-system models in the world, the calculations *do not yet include the feedback effect of the released carbon from the permafrost.* That is to say, the CO_2 concentrations in the model rise only as a result of direct emissions from humans, with no extra emissions counted from soils or tundra. Thus they are conservative numbers—or *overestimates*—of how much CO_2 concentrations have to rise to trigger *irreversible* melting.

David Lawrence told me that NCAR's climate model will not incorporate these feedbacks for many years. And most major climate models do not include these crucial feedbacks (one exception is below). Thus, the *Fourth Assessment Report* by the Intergovernmental Panel on Climate Change, coming out this year (2007), almost certainly *underestimates* greenhouse gas forcings and climate change this century. In short, we have a much tougher task than the U.N.'s consensus-based process has been telling us.

By the end of Planetary Purgatory, most of the tundra may be unsavable.

Fourth, the tropical forests. Tropical forests store carbon, and destroying them releases that carbon. Intact tropical forests serve as a carbon sink for slightly more than 1 billion metric tons of carbon a year. A 2006 article by British scientists reviewing the current state of knowledge on tropical forests and carbon dioxide estimated that tropical deforestation released emissions "at the higher end" of the reported range of 1 to 3 billion metric tons of carbon a year.

Unfortunately, we do not appear prepared to stop current deforestation trends, while the carbon sink is likely to shrink because of increased drought, wildfires, and temperatures. The mechanisms are deadly enough individually, but when they interact synergistically the effects are multiplied and create a classic vicious cycle.

We've already seen how high temperatures and drought have combined to create record wildfires in the United States, but the situation is far worse in other parts of the world. The global fires of 1997–1998 "may have released carbon equivalent to 41 percent of worldwide fossil fuel use," according to a 2003 *Nature* article. Over Southeast Asia and Latin America alone, acreage equal to half of California burned out of control. While Indonesia lost more than double the acreage the United States lost in its record-breaking 2005 wildfire season, that developing country spends only about 2 percent of what we do on fire suppression. The article concluded grimly, "Pan-tropical forest fires will increase as more damaged, less fire-resistant, forests cover the landscape."

In Indonesia, both rain forests and peat lands burned. Carbon-rich tropical peat deposits can be more than 60 feet deep. A 2002 *Nature* article reported, "The extensive fire damage caused in 1997 has accelerated changes already being caused in tropical peatlands by forest clearance and drainage." Using satellite images to compare logging activity for the years 1997 and 2000, the authors found that "logging had increased by 44 percent," which made the remaining forests "more susceptible to fire in the future." Absent a major effort to address the problem, "tropical peatlands will make a significant contribution to global carbon emissions for some time to come."

In 2005, the Amazon was suffering a brutal drought—in many regions the harshest since records began a hundred years ago. By October, the governor of Amazonas State had declared a "state of public calamity." The threat to the Amazon forest is grave. The Woods Hole Research Center in Santarém on the Amazon River reported in 2006 that the "forest cannot withstand more than two consecutive years of drought without breaking down." Dr. Dan Nepstad of Woods Hole expects "mega-fires" to sweep across the jungle if it gets too dry.

Today, about 20 percent of the rain forest has been chopped down, and another 22 percent has been hurt enough by logging that sufficient sunlight can reach the forest floor to dry it out. Models suggest that when 50 percent of the forest is destroyed—which some models project for 2050—it will have crossed a "tipping point" beyond which its destruction cannot be stopped. In the coming decades, drought and heat will combine to devastate the rain forest and its canopy, reducing local rainfall and further accelerating the drought and local temperature rise, ultimately causing the release into the atmosphere of huge amounts of carbon currently locked in Amazon soils and vegetation, another fearsome feedback loop at work.

CROSSING THE POINT OF NO RETURN

Global warming is on the verge of dramatically transforming the global carbon cycle, causing the release of carbon from some soils, tundra, and forests, while slowing the uptake of carbon by the ocean and other carbon sinks.

The United Kingdom's Hadley Centre for Climate Prediction and Research has one of the few climate models that incorporates a significant number of carbon-cycle feedbacks, particularly in soils and tropical forests. In a 2003 study, they found that a typical fossil fuel emissions scenario for this century, which would have led to carbon dioxide concentrations in 2100 of about 700 ppm *without* feedbacks, led instead to concentrations of 980 ppm *with* feedbacks, a huge increase. Even ignoring feedbacks, keeping concentrations below 700 ppm requires the United States and the world to start slowing carbon dioxide emissions from coal, oil, and natural gas significantly by 2015 and to stop the growth almost entirely after 2025.

In 2006 the Hadley Centre, working with other British researchers, published an important study, "Impact of Climate-Carbon Cycle Feedbacks on Emissions Scenarios to Achieve Stabilisation," which included both ocean and terrestrial carbon-cycle feedbacks (though they do not specifically model carbon emissions from defrosting tundra). The study found that such feedbacks reduce the amount of fossil fuel emissions we can release by 21 percent to 33 percent.

We have no room for error. The Hadley study finds that just to stabilize at 650 ppm, annual emissions this century will have to *average* under 9 billion tons of carbon, a level that emissions will probably achieve by 2015. Absent the feedbacks, annual emissions this century could have averaged nearly a third more.

There appears to be a threshold beyond which it becomes more and more difficult for us to fight the feedbacks of the carbon cycle with strong energy policies that reduce fossil fuel emissions into the air. While the threshold is not known precisely today, it appears to be somewhere between 450 ppm and 650 ppm, based on my review of the literature and conversations with climate scientists. By 2025, we'll know much better where it is. Unfortunately, on our current path, the world's emissions and concentrations will be so high by 2025 that the "easy" technology-based strategy will not be able to stop us from crossing the very high end of the threshold range.

That's why I am calling the second quarter of this century Planetary Purgatory. Barring a major reversal in U.S. policies in the very next decade, come the 2020s, most everyone will know the grim fate that awaits the next fifty generations. But the only plausible way to avoid it will be a desperate effort to cut global emissions by 75 percent in less than three decades—a massive, sustained government intervention into every aspect of our lives on a scale that far surpasses what this country did during World War II. That would indeed be punishment for our sins of inaction.

Failing that desperate effort, we would end up at midcentury with carbon emissions far above current levels, and concentrations at 500 ppm, rising 3 to 4 ppm a year—or even faster if the vicious cycles of the climate system have kicked in.

We have passed the point of no return.

CHAPTER FOUR

2050–2100: HELL AND HIGH WATER

We could get a meter [of sea-level rise] easy in 50 years.
—Bob Corell, chair, Arctic Climate Impact
    Assessment, 2006

The peak rate of deglaciation following the last Ice Age was . . . about one meter [39 inches] of sea-level rise every 20 years, which was maintained for several centuries.
—James Hansen, director, Goddard Institute for
    Space Studies (NASA), 2004

Sea-level rise of 20 to 80 feet will be all but unstoppable by mid-century if current emissions trends continue. The first few feet of sea-level rise alone will displace more than 100 million people worldwide and turn all of our major Gulf and Atlantic coast cities into pre-Katrina New Orleans—below sea level and facing super-hurricanes.

How fast can seas rise? For the past decade, sea levels have been rising about 1 inch a decade, double the rate of a few decades ago. The *Third Assessment Report* of the U.N. Intergovernmental Panel on Climate Change (IPCC), released back in 2001, projected that sea levels would rise 12 to 36 inches by 2100, with little of that rise coming from either Greenland or Antarctica. Seas rise mainly because ocean water expands as it gets warmer, and inland glaciers melt, releasing their water to the oceans.

Sea-level rise is a lagging indicator of climate change, in part because global warming also increases atmospheric moisture, as we've seen. More atmospheric moisture probably means more snowfall over both the Greenland and Antarctica ice sheets, which would cause them to gain mass in their centers even as they lose mass at the edges. Until recently, most scientists thought that the primary mechanism by which these enormous ice sheets would lose mass was through simple melting. The planet warms and ice melts—a straightforward physics calculation and a very slow process, with Greenland taking perhaps a thousand years or more to melt this way, according to some models.

Since 2001, however, a great many studies using direct observation and satellite monitoring have revealed that both of the two great ice sheets are losing mass at the edges much faster than the models had predicted. We now know a number of physical processes can cause the major ice sheets to disintegrate faster than by simple melting alone. The whole idea of "glacial change" as a metaphor for change too slow to see will vanish in a world where glaciers are shrinking so fast that you can actually watch them retreat.

The disintegration of the Greenland and Antarctic ice sheets is a multistage process that starts with the accelerated warming of the Arctic.

THE END OF THE ARCTIC AS WE KNOW IT

Global warming tends to occur faster at high latitudes, especially in the Arctic. That is called polar amplification. Arctic warming is amplified for several synergistic reasons, as explained in the most comprehensive scientific survey completed to date, the December 2004

Arctic Climate Impact Assessment, by leading scientists from the eight Arctic nations—Canada, Denmark/Greenland, Finland, Iceland, Norway, Russia, Sweden, and the United States:

1. Warming melts highly reflective white ice and snow, which is replaced by the dark blue sea or dark land, both of which absorb far more sunlight and hence far more solar energy.
2. In the Arctic, compared with lower latitudes, "more of the extra trapped energy goes into warming rather than evaporation."
3. In the Arctic, "the atmospheric layer that has to warm in order to warm the surface is shallower."
4. So, when the sea ice retreats, the "solar heat absorbed by the oceans in summer is more easily transferred to the atmosphere in winter."

And this leads to more snow and ice melting, further decreasing Earth's reflectivity (albedo), causing more heating, which the thinner Arctic atmosphere spreads more quickly over the entire polar region, and so on and so on.

We can witness this classic feedback loop today at the North Pole, where the summer ice cap has shrunk more than 25 percent from 1978 to 2005, a loss of 500,000 square miles of ice, an area twice the size of Texas. The Arctic winters were so warm in both 2005 and 2006 that sea ice did not refreeze enough to make up for the unprecedented amount of melting during recent summers. A synthesis report in August 2005 by twenty-one leading climate scientists, supported by the U.S. National Science Foundation's Arctic Systems Science Program, described the future in terms that were unusually stark for a group of scientists:

At the present rate of change, a summer ice-free Arctic Ocean within a century is a real possibility, *a state not witnessed for at least a million years.* The change appears to be driven largely

by *feedback-enhanced global climate warming,* and there seem
to be few, if any, processes or feedbacks within the Arctic system that are capable of altering the trajectory toward this
"super interglacial" state. [Emphasis added.]

We appear to be crossing a threshold in the Arctic, one that existing models did not predict would happen so fast. "The recent sea-
ice retreat is larger than in any of the (19) IPCC [climate] models,"
Tore Furevik pointed out in a November 2005 talk on climate-system
feedbacks. He is deputy director of Norway's Bjerknes Centre for
Climate Research. Once again, the models on which the IPCC bases
its conclusions appear to be "too conservative," either underestimating or missing entirely relevant climate feedbacks. Most models suggest that the Arctic Ocean will see ice-free summers by 2080 to 2100.
At our current pace, this will happen long before then.

According to a 2005 *Science* article, key Arctic landmasses have
warmed "0.3° to 0.4°C per decade since the 1990s," double the rate
of the previous two decades. A 2005 study led by the Institute of Arctic Biology at the University of Alaska at Fairbanks and the U.S.
Geological Survey, estimated that the reduced snow cover and albedo in the summertime Arctic landscape, caused by global warming, added local atmospheric heating comparable to what a doubling
of CO_2 levels (to 550 ppm) would do over many decades to the global
atmosphere. In short, the dramatic climatic changes in the Arctic
today are a warning to us of both the pace and degree of change
America will experience early in the second half of this century.

The study also noted that "the continuation of current trends
in shrub and tree expansion could further amplify this atmospheric
heating by two to seven times." As the permafrost thaws, creating a
moist, nutrient-rich environment for vegetation, polar amplification will accelerate. We have very few climate models that incorporate the impact of such changes in vegetation, which again indicates
how likely it is that we are underestimating the future warming of

the Arctic. The scientific evidence is simply accumulating too fast to model adequately.

New research suggests that the summer Arctic could be ice-free far sooner than anyone ever imagined. Simply looking at the shrinking *area* of the Arctic ice misses an even more alarming decline in its thickness and hence its *volume*. At a May 2006 seminar sponsored by the American Meteorological Society, Dr. Wieslaw Maslowski of the Oceanography Department at the Naval Postgraduate School reported that models suggest that the Arctic lost one-third of its ice volume from 1997 to 2002. He made an alarming forecast: "If this trend persists *for another 10 years*—and it has through 2005—we could be ice-free in the summer" (emphasis added).

The loss of Arctic ice has little effect on sea levels because the ice is floating on the Arctic Ocean. Like a floating ice cube in a glass of water, when it melts, it doesn't change the water level. Why, then, should we be worried? Because in the Arctic, the accelerating warming of the land, air, and ocean sets the stage for one of the severest impacts of climate change facing our country—extreme sea-level rise from the disintegration of the Greenland Ice Sheet.

THE END OF GREENLAND—AND COASTAL LIFE—AS WE KNOW IT

> *Models indicate that warming over Greenland is likely to be of a magnitude that would eventually lead to a virtually complete melting of the Greenland ice sheet, with a resulting sea-level rise of about seven meters (23 feet).*
>
> —Arctic Climate Impact Assessment, 2004

The Greenland Ice Sheet extends over some 1.7 million square kilometers (more than 650,000 square miles). It is as large as the entire state of Alaska and almost as big as Mexico. It is 3 kilometers (nearly 2 miles) at its thickest. It contains nearly 3 million cubic kilometers (750,000 cubic miles) of ice. Unlike the Arctic ice cap, Greenland's landlocked ice, when it returns to the ocean, causes sea levels to rise.

Current climate models project that the entire ice sheet will melt if Greenland warms only about 4.5°C (8.1°F). Since Greenland is currently warming much faster than the planet as a whole, that is likely to occur when the planet warms more than 3°C compared with levels of the late 1800s. Exceeding such warming by 2100 is a near certainty if greenhouse gas concentrations significantly exceed 550 parts per million, a doubling from preindustrial levels. On our current path, we may hit 550 by midcentury.

Once the warming passes this threshold, the melting may become almost unstoppable. As climatologist Jonathan Gregory has pointed out, melting lowers the altitude of the ice-cap surface, which leads to more warming and reduced snowfall, another vicious cycle. Until recently, the conventional wisdom was that Greenland would take a thousand years or more to lose its ice sheet. But that assumed that the loss in mass would come exclusively from simple melting. We now know, however, that melting is anything but simple.

A team led by NASA and MIT scientists reported in 2002 that the ice was flowing in parts of Greenland much faster during the summer melting season than the winter. They concluded that some of the water flows to the ice-bedrock interface at the bottom of the glacier and acts as a lubricant for the entire glacier to slide and glide on. This "provides a mechanism for rapid response of the ice sheets to climate change," a factor that has been given "little or no consideration in estimates of ice-sheet response to climate change."

Scientists have observed another crucial change to Greenland's glaciers in recent years—the outlet glaciers have been speeding up, thinning, and disintegrating. The Greenland Ice Sheet drains into the sea through dozens of large glaciers, although roughly half the discharge "is through 12 fast-flowing outlet glaciers, most no more than 10 to 20 kilometers across at their seaward margin, and each fed from a large interior basin of about 50,000 to 100,000 square kilometers," reported a 2006 review article in *Science.* The outlet glaciers have ice shelves or floating tongues of ice that can extend tens of kilometers past the point where the glaciers are supported by the ground. The front face of the ice shelves are hundreds of meters thick and calve or break off icebergs into the ocean.

For many years, scientists have been studying Jakobshavn Isbrae, Greenland's largest outlet glacier, which drains some 6.5 percent of the entire ice sheet's area. From 1950 to 1996, the glacier's terminal point, or calving front, was stable, fluctuating about 2.5 kilometers back and forth around its seasonal average. This multi-decadal stability may have been due to "resistance from the fjord walls and pinning points" that helped secure the outlet glacier.

The outlet glacier is like a cork in a champagne bottle—and humanity, with our ever-increasing emissions of heat-trapping gases, has been frantically shaking this bottle. So it should not be a total surprise that a study of the Jakobshavn Isbrae glacier using satellite images found that "in October 2000, this pattern [of stability] changed when a progressive retreat began that resulted in *nearly complete disintegration of the ice shelf* by May 2003." The cork popped. Freed from this barrier that had been holding it back, the glacier's speed increased dramatically to 12.6 kilometers (7.8 miles) a year. Ice discharge nearly doubled. The authors concluded that "fast-flowing glaciers can significantly alter ice-sheet discharge at sub-decadal timescales and that their response to climate change has at least the potential to be rapid."

Jakobshavn Isbrae's sudden behavior change is no random event. A 2006 study found a similar change in two East Greenland outlet glaciers—Kangerdlugssuaq and Helheim, which are about 200 miles apart. In both glaciers, "acceleration and retreat has been sudden, despite the progressive nature of warming and thinning over some years." The top surface height of Helheim dropped more than 150 feet in two years. The surface of Kangerdlugssuaq dropped more than 250 feet. The two glaciers together drain about 8 percent of Greenland's ice sheet. They have nearly doubled the ice transport to the sea from this area of Greenland, to 100 cubic kilometers a year, up from about 50. The authors conclude that "the most plausible sequence of events is that the thinning eventually reached a *threshold*, ungrounded the glacier tongues and subsequently allowed acceleration, retreat and further thinning." This represents a step change in ice dynamics "not included in current models." The authors warn that given such behavior in three disparate outlet glaciers, "we should expect further Greenland outlet glaciers to follow suit."

How fast do Greenland glaciers move these days? Using Global Positioning System equipment, researchers have clocked Helheim at speeds exceeding 14 kilometers per year, nearly triple its 2001 speed. That flow rate equals an inch a minute. In 2005, Jakobshavn Isbrae was clocked at a similar speed. You can watch these glaciers move. That isn't "glacial change"—Greenland's glaciers are moving far faster than America's climate policy.

While 2002 had been the record for surface-area melting in Greenland since 1979 (the year systematic satellite monitoring began), 2005 topped that easily. A major 2006 study led by NASA's Jet Propulsion Laboratory found that "accelerated ice discharge in the west and particularly in the east doubled the ice sheet mass deficit in the last decade from 90 to 220 cubic kilometers per year." (Los Angeles uses about 4 cubic kilometers of fresh water a year.) The study's lead author, Eric Rignot, said in 2006, "In the next 10 years, it wouldn't surprise me if the rate doubled again."

Whereas glacier acceleration was widely found below 66° north latitude between 1996 and 2000, that line had shifted to 70° north by 2005. The authors conclude, "As more glaciers accelerate farther north, the contribution of Greenland to sea-level rise will continue to increase." In short, global warming is rapidly speeding up the disintegration of the entire Greenland Ice Sheet, and if we stay on our current emissions path until the 2050–2100 era, the loss of the Greenland Ice Sheet could become irreversible, according to NASA's Jay Zwally.

The IPCC's *Third Assessment Report* in 2001, which is used as the standard by most nations for impact assessment, projected a half-meter (20-inch) sea-level rise by 2100, with a worst case of 1 meter. But that assessment assumed Greenland would contribute little to sea-level rise by 2100. The startling changes now observed in Greenland alone would suggest 20 inches is a best-case scenario for 2100—and we should plan on much worse. If glacier acceleration continues, then by itself Greenland could easily generate sea-level rise of 5 inches or more *per decade* during Hell and High Water—and for centuries to come.

Greenland is not, however, the only major ice sheet showing signs of unexpected disintegration. So is Antarctica.

THE END OF ANTARCTICA—AND CIVILIZATION— AS WE KNOW IT

> *The last IPCC report characterized Antarctica as a slumbering giant in terms of climate change. I would say it is now an awakened giant.*
> —Chris Rapley, head of the British Antarctic Survey, 2006

Antarctica is bigger than the United States, and its ice sheet has locked away more than *eight times* as much ice as Greenland's. It holds 90 percent of Earth's ice. As recently as the *Third Assessment Report* in 2001, many scientists were not very worried about an Antarctic contribution to sea-level rise in this century. Antarctica is 99 percent covered by ice that is on average about 2 kilometers (1.2 miles) thick. It is one huge freezer. Until recently, scientists believed that warming-induced increases in snowfall over central Antarctica would just about counterbalance whatever melting occurred along the edges.

But as with Greenland, "in the last decade, our picture of a slowly changing Antarctic ice sheet has radically altered," explained a 2005 report by the Ice Sheet Mass Balance and Sea Level committee, a group of leading climate scientists and glaciologists. As with Greenland, global warming is causing outlet glaciers to thin and disintegrate while ice flow accelerates.

The Antarctic Peninsula, which juts out in the direction of South America, is warming the fastest—about 2.0°C in the past half-century, a rate unprecedented for at least two millennia. In 2002, much of the peninsula's Larsen B Ice Shelf disintegrated in spectacular fashion. The shelf, which had probably been in existence since the end of the last ice age, lost an area larger than the state of Rhode Island in a matter of weeks. After the collapse, glaciers flowing into it sped up two- to eightfold. One glacier's surface dropped 38 meters (125 feet) in six months, leading to an additional mass loss of 27 cubic kilometers per year, just from this small part of Antarctica.

In 2005, the British Antarctic Survey and U.S. Geological Survey reported the results of a comprehensive analysis of the glaciers that drain the peninsula's ice sheet. Of 244 glaciers, 212 have retreated since the earliest positions recorded five decades ago, and they have retreated far greater distances than the few advancing glaciers have expanded. Moreover, the line of retreating glaciers has moved steadily southward during this time, toward the South Pole, suggesting the influence of global warming. The authors conclude that "the cumulative loss of ice at the fronts of these glaciers may be leading to an increased drainage of the Antarctic Peninsula that is more widespread than previously thought."

The peninsula is not the only area of Antarctica with glaciers that are warming up—and speeding up. A 2004 study in *Geophysical Research Letters* noted that over the previous decade, the grounded Amundsen Sea portion of the West Antarctic Ice Sheet has been losing 50 cubic kilometers of volume each year "due to an imbalance between snow accumulation and ice discharge." Satellite measurements reveal that the ice shelves in one major outlet glacier, Pine Island Bay, have been thinning by up to 5.5 meters per year during this time. The reason appears to be ocean currents averaging 0.5°C warmer than freezing. The Pine Island and Thwaites glaciers enter the Amundsen Sea at Pine Island Bay. They are discharging ice three times faster than they were just ten years earlier. The study concludes that "the drawdown of grounded ice shows that Antarctica is more sensitive to changing climates than was previously considered."

A major 2004 study led by NASA researchers using satellite and aircraft laser altimeter surveys found that glaciers in this sector of the ice sheet are "discharging about 250 cubic kilometers of ice per year to the ocean," much more ice than is accumulating in the areas that feed these glaciers. The glaciers are thinning far faster than they were even a decade ago. As noted, that mass loss is partly counterbalanced by increased snowfall over the rest of Antarctica, and in 2001 the IPCC projected that Antarctica would *gain* mass this century. Only three years later, the data showed otherwise.

In a surprising finding, University of Colorado at Boulder researchers reported in 2006 that Antarctica as a whole was *losing* up to 150 cubic kilometers of ice annually. They used twin satellites to measure the mass of the entire Antarctic ice sheet as part of the Gravity Recovery and Climate Experiment (GRACE). That Antarctica is rapidly losing ice was confirmed by another 2006 study, the most comprehensive survey ever undertaken of the ice sheets, led by NASA's Zwally.

Perhaps the most important, and worrisome, fact about the

West Antarctic Ice Sheet (WAIS) is that *it is fundamentally far less stable than the Greenland Ice Sheet* because most of it is grounded far below sea level. The WAIS rests on bedrock as deep as 2 kilometers underwater. The 2004 NASA-led study found that most of the glaciers they were studying "flow into floating ice shelves over bedrock up to hundreds of meters deeper than previous estimates, providing exit routes for ice from further inland if ice-sheet collapse is under way." A 2002 study in *Science* examined the underwater grounding lines—the points where the ice starts floating. Using satellites, the researchers determined that "bottom melt rates experienced by large outlet glaciers near their grounding lines are far higher than generally assumed." And that melt rate is positively correlated with ocean temperature.

The warmer it gets, the more unstable WAIS outlet glaciers will become. Since so much of the ice sheet is grounded underwater, rising sea levels may have the effect of lifting the sheet, allowing more—and increasingly warmer—water underneath it, leading to further bottom melting, more ice-shelf disintegration, accelerated glacial flow, further sea-level rise, and so on and on, another vicious cycle. The combination of global warming and accelerating sea-level rise from Greenland could be the trigger for catastrophic collapse in the WAIS.

Were the Antarctic Peninsula to disintegrate, sea levels would rise globally by half a meter (20 inches). The Pine Island and Thwaites Glaciers could add another 1-meter rise. A collapse of the entire WAIS would raise sea levels 5 to 6 meters, perhaps over the course of a century. Combined with the disintegration of Greenland's ice sheet, that could raise the oceans more than 12 meters (40 feet).

If the planet warms enough, it could experience an even greater sea-level rise, since the East Antarctic Ice Sheet is about eight times larger in volume than the WAIS. Some 3 million years ago, when the earth was a little more than 3°C warmer than preindustrial levels (about 2.2°C warmer than today), Antarctica had far less ice and sea levels were a stunning 25 meters (80 feet) higher than today. If we stay on our current emissions path, the planet will almost certainly be that warm by century's end.

"A warming of this magnitude would risk 'the end of civilisation as we know it by the end of this century,'" said Peter Barrett, director of Victoria University's Antarctic Research Centre in Wellington, at the Royal Society of New Zealand's awards dinner in 2004, where he won the New Zealand Association of Scientists' Marsden Medal for lifetime achievement.

2050-2100: THE TRIPLE THREAT

How much the seas rise—and how fast—depends on how hot the planet gets. If we could avoid doubling carbon dioxide concentrations from preindustrial levels, we would have a very good chance of avoiding the worst of sea-level rise and might even avoid melting most of Greenland and Antarctica.

The scenario I put forward in the last chapter assumes that emissions will continue at current growth rates for another decade, then the growth rate slows by half for a decade, and then we aggressively adopt the seven low-carbon technological wedges for five decades (and stop tropical deforestation), and finally emissions start dropping in 2075. Because vicious cycles kick in, this scenario leaves concentrations at more than 800 ppm in 2100 (nearly a tripling of preindustrial levels), with average global temperatures more than 3°C higher than today *and still rising.*

What precisely happens to our coastal cities in a tripled-CO_2 world? You will not find many detailed studies on the subject, for two main reasons. First, most scientists have based their efforts to model climate impacts on a doubling of CO_2 concentrations because they (and their funders) have expected the world to wake up and take action. Second, most climate scientists did not expect the kind of accelerated flow and disintegration of the ice sheets we are now witnessing.

But in a tripled-CO_2 world, the United States should plan on the melting of Greenland and the West Antarctic Ice Sheet (ultimately augmented by ice loss from East Antarctica) to begin fueling a significant sea-level rise this century and beyond. We should plan for a 0.5- to 1.0-meter (20- to 40-inch) sea-level rise by 2050 and a 1.5- to 2.0-meter (60- to 80-inch) sea-level rise by 2100. How likely is this to happen? My interviews with leading climate scientists indicate that these numbers are emerging as the top of the likely range, even for a world of just 700 ppm. You can cut these numbers in half if you are of the cross-your-fingers-and-hope-for-the-best school of disaster planning.

We also need to plan for the probability that, by 2050, the hurricane season we experienced in 2005 will have become fairly typical. Also, the *rate* of sea-level rise by the end of the century is likely to be several inches a decade, and it could be more than a foot a decade. Thus, we are not trying to adapt to a static situation where sea level jumps 3 feet and stops, as so many analysts seem to have assumed. This amount of static sea-level rise has been well studied, but the impact of a constantly rising sea level has not, nor has the synergistic effect of increasing hurricane intensity.

A 1991 study led by the U.S. Environmental Protection Agency (EPA) noted that any significant sea-level rise "would inundate wetlands and lowlands, accelerate coastal erosion, exacerbate coastal flooding, threaten coastal structures, raise water tables, and increase the salinity of rivers, bays, and aquifers." The first 1 meter of sea-level rise inundates about 35,000 square kilometers (13,000 to 14,000 square miles) of U.S. land, roughly half wetlands and half dry land. Many shores would retreat rapidly, with beaches likely to "erode 50–100 meters from the Northeast to Maryland; 200 meters along the Carolinas; 100–1,000 meters along the Florida coast; and 200–400 meters along the California coast."

As sea-level rise increases, the impacts multiply. One 2001 analysis reported that 22,000 square miles of land just on the Atlantic and Gulf coasts are at less than 1.5 meters elevation. While some of that might be salvageable if sea levels rose that high and stopped, in the post-2050 world, steadily rising sea levels would quickly lead to the abandonment of far more area.

Abandonment is particularly likely because the states that have the most area in jeopardy are, in order, Louisiana, Florida, North Carolina, and Texas—Hurricane Alley. By 2100, Louisiana could lose an area the size of Vermont to the sea. Florida could lose a Connecticut. North Carolina and Texas could each lose a Delaware. These numbers are conservative in that they don't consider the impact of tides, storm surges, coastal erosion, or land subsidence. Today, the part of our coast that hasn't been eroded by storm and tide has generally been toughened up by them. Sea-level rise exposes parts of the shore to storms and tides that are not so strengthened.

Now imagine that sea levels keep rising 5 inches a decade or more at the same time that the Gulf of Mexico, Florida, and the South Atlantic coasts are battered year after year by hurricane seasons similar to, or even worse than, what they experienced in 2004 and 2005. There's no chance New Orleans could survive the century. Indeed, the city seems unlikely to survive the next category 4 or 5 hurricane whenever it comes, because so far the U.S. government appears unwilling to foot the bill for designing levees to protect it from such storms—let alone from such storms in a world where sea levels are considerably higher.

If our government won't spend the money to protect New Orleans sufficiently today, what are the chances we will spend the money to protect dozens of coastal cities post-2050, once everyone knows that sea levels will keep rising and intense hurricanes will occur relentlessly? Consider also that by then, we will be devoting huge resources to desperately cutting our greenhouse gas emissions, to figuring out how to reverse catastrophic warming, and to dealing with the devastating consequences of drought, wildfires, and massive relocations. *Protecting* dozens of major coastal cities from future flooding will be challenging enough—*rebuilding* major coastal cities destroyed by super-hurricanes will be an almost impossible task.

This will be the beginning of the era of urban triage. New Orleans, the Outer Banks of North Carolina, the Florida Keys and South Florida, Galveston, and other low-lying Texas cities, Biloxi and other low-lying Gulf Coast cities, will be the first to go. Some will be abandoned before being hit by a category 4 or 5 hurricane. Others, afterward.

In this scenario, most of our coasts, especially along the Gulf and South Atlantic, will be designated permanent (or, more accurately, semipermanent) wetlands and will no doubt be uninsurable for building. Some major ports and cities, such as Houston and Miami, would likely be the subject of major preservation efforts. But I have not seen one estimate of the cost of designing levees and other protections for such large cities against rapidly rising sea levels and a category 5 hurricane.

And this is not the worst case.

The authors of a 2005 study, "Global Estimates of the Impact of a Collapse of the West Antarctic Ice Sheet," led by the University of Southampton in England, point out that theirs is the first paper to consider the global impacts of a 5- to 6-meter (16- to 20-foot) sea-level rise. A 1980 paper by the National Center for Atmospheric Research that considered a similar sea-level rise focused only on the United States. Both these studies are "optimistic" in that they assume that after the ice sheet collapses, the sea-level rise will return to a very slow rate. They also didn't consider how hurricanes will change the cost of any protection measures in Hurricane Alley, or how governments and individuals would perceive the viability of building in those regions.

The 2005 paper's worst-case scenario has some 6 meters of sea-level rise from 2030 to 2130, based on a collapse of the West Antarctic Ice Sheet, with little or no contribution from Greenland. Given recent scientific studies, I believe a more plausible version of the same events might be a steadily accelerating loss of mass from Greenland coupled with periodic collapses of parts of the West Antarctic Ice Sheet, creating much uncertainty and fear.

In their scenario, by 2100, some 400 million people worldwide will be exposed to the rising seas. A total land area of more than 4 million square kilometers will be flooded (absent any protective measures), roughly one-half the area of the continental United States. Low-lying countries such as Bangladesh would be utterly inundated. Trillions of dollars of assets would be at risk. In scenarios where the sea level rises and then stops or slows dramatically (and there is no significant increase in coastal storms), adaptation is straightforward if expensive, and a large fraction of the most populated and valuable coastal lands might well be protected. But if people believed that sea levels would simply continue rising more than a foot a decade, any significant defense of coastal cities would seem untenable, especially in hurricane-prone regions.

In this country, one-quarter of Florida would be submerged—and one-third would be underwater when sea-level rise hit 7.6 meters (25 feet). If one or more category 4 or 5 hurricanes struck what was left of the state on a regular basis, perhaps every other year, how could any significant portion of the state be protected for human population and commerce?

Louisiana would be in the same capsized boat, flooded up to Baton Rouge. In Texas, Galveston, Corpus Christi, Beaumont, and Port Arthur would be submerged. Houston would be seriously at risk and difficult to protect from the combination of rising sea levels and super-hurricanes. Savannah, Georgia, Charleston, South Carolina, Virginia's major coastal cities, one-fourth of Delaware, most land along the Chesapeake Bay, and huge sections of such cities as Washington, D.C., New York, and Boston would be flooded. Large parts of the San Francisco Bay and Puget Sound would also be, although in general the West Coast would be better off since it has fewer low-lying coastal areas and no hurricane risk.

If Americans in 2100 came to see 12 meters (40 feet) sea-level rise as inevitable by 2200, who can even begin to fathom how the nation would respond?

I have focused in this chapter on the "high water" part of the scenario, but let's not overlook the hellish heat we would experience. A November 2005 study in the *Proceedings of the National Academy of Sciences* is one of the few to look at the extreme temperatures that a near tripling of carbon dioxide concentrations would have on United States weather in the last quarter of this century (from 2071 to 2095).

A vast swath of the country would see the average summer temperature rise by a blistering 9°F. Houston and Washington, D.C., would experience temperatures exceeding 98°F for some 60 days a year. Oklahoma would see temperatures above 110°F some 60 to 80 days a year. Much of Arizona would be subjected to temperatures of 105°F or more for 98 days out of the year—14 full weeks. We won't call these heat waves anymore. As the lead author, Noah Diffenbaugh of Purdue University, said to me, "We will call them normal summers." They will be accompanied by extreme droughts on a recurring basis, some in the West lasting for many years at a time, with two to five times the wildfire devastation, as discussed in chapter 3. And temperatures would continue to rise relentlessly into the next century, accompanied by declines in soil moisture over much of this country. Much of the Southwest would be at risk of desertification.

Hell and High Water is not our certain future, but it is the future we should expect and plan for if we do not sharply reverse our energy and environmental policy in the next two decades. As with the avian bird flu, doing nothing would make disaster inevitable.

Scientists once hoped that some as yet unidentified mechanism in the climate system might avert catastrophe, but if climate models have any gaps today, they are gaps that *underestimate* the speed and severity of future impacts.

In any case, even if the worst case of several meters' sea-level rise by 2100 doesn't come to pass, our likely future on a tripled-CO_2 planet Earth is still almost unimaginably grim.

I have left out details of the other impacts scientists see as possible or likely. For example, in a tripled-CO_2 world, the oceans become so warm and acidic that virtually all coral reefs die. In fact, much of the world's oceans, especially in the Southern Hemisphere, become inhospitable to many forms of marine life. Globally, more than a quarter of all species may die, since they are far less capable of adapting than we humans are, especially to such a rapid climate change. In a tripled-CO_2 world, tropical diseases find fertile ground over much larger portions of the planet.

I have focused on impacts in the United States, largely because so many people I talk to mistakenly believe we Americans will not be severely affected by climate change, or at least not anytime soon. But not only will this rich country suffer, poor countries will suffer greatly. Imagine what will happen in Africa, a continent already afflicted with persistent, widespread drought and a shortage of safe drinking water. One 2006 study reported in *Science* found that by 2100, climate change could dry up lakes and streams in one-quarter of the African continent.

Much attention has been given to the possibility that the ocean-circulation patterns could change dramatically, especially by the melting of the Greenland Ice Sheet injecting fresh water into the North Atlantic, which in turn might shut down the so-called thermohaline current that helps warm Europe. This scenario, carried to an absurd extreme in the movie *The Day After Tomorrow*, supposedly plunges the planet into an ice age. This is, as James Hansen put it to me, "the implausible worst-case scenario." While the current may be weakening, a complete collapse is considered very unlikely this century and in any case would be unlikely to put much of a dent in the extreme warming most of the planet is going to experience on our current emissions path.

Some, including James Lovelock, have raised the prospect of a runaway greenhouse effect with ever-accelerating increases in greenhouse gas emissions, which might kill hundreds of millions of people by the end of this century. That view does not find much support in the scientific literature, and I regard it about as implausible as *The Day After Tomorrow*.

The possibility, however, that the thawing tundra might release a large fraction of its carbon in the form of methane is quite genuine, and so we could end up in a quadrupled-CO_2 world (carbon dioxide concentrations of 1,100 ppm) by 2100 or soon thereafter. Such a world is vastly grimmer than anything I have described here.

In a quadrupled-CO_2 world, average temperatures over much of the inland United States would be a scorching 20°F hotter. Soil moisture would drop 50 percent or more over much of the country. Prolonged drought would ravage much of our cropland, turning breadbaskets into dust bowls. Sea-level rise of 80 feet or more would be inevitable. We would exceed global temperatures before the Antarctic ice sheet formed, when sea levels were 70 meters (230 feet) higher on our planet. Humanity would be faced with centuries of suffering from a continuously worsening climate.

Scientists have given us more than enough serious and credible warnings of the consequences of our current path. The IPCC's *Fourth Assessment Report* this year (2007) will present a much stronger consensus and a much clearer and darker picture of our likely future than the *Third Assessment*—but it will almost certainly still underestimate the likely impacts. The *Fifth Assessment*, due around 2013, should include many of the omitted feedbacks, like that of the defrosting tundra, and validate the scenarios described on these pages, especially if we haven't yet sharply reversed our current energy policies. At that point, exceeding a doubling of carbon dioxide concentrations in our air will be a near certainty, and a tripling will be quite likely.

The IPCC process tends to produce an underestimation of worst-case scenarios for two reasons—because it is consensus-based and because it encompasses many greenhouse gas scenarios that assume far stronger action on emissions reduction than the United States or the world seems prepared to embrace.

PART II

THE POLITICS AND
THE SOLUTION

CHAPTER FIVE

HOW CLIMATE RHETORIC
TRUMPS CLIMATE REALITY

The scientific debate is closing (against us) but not yet closed.
—Frank Luntz, conservative strategist, 2002

Global warming is real (conservatives secretly know this).
—David Brooks, *New York Times* columnist, 2005

The global-warming problem is no longer primarily a scientific matter. Science has told us what we need to know about how life on this planet will be ruined if we stay on our current greenhouse gas emissions path. Global warming is also not a technological problem. We have the technologies to avoid the disasters that await us if we keep doing nothing.

Today, global warming is a problem of politics and political will. We lack the will to take the necessary actions—and many of the actions we are poised to take are either inadequate or ill conceived. The great political tragedy of our time is that conservative leaders in America have chosen to use their superior messaging and political skills to thwart serious action on global warming, thereby increasing the chances that catastrophic climate change will become a reality.

Global warming should not be a partisan issue—not when the health, well-being, and security of the next fifty generations of Americans are at stake. But it has become partisan, at least in this country. In order to determine how to create the politics of action in the next decade, we must understand what the politics of inaction has caused in the past decade. That's what this chapter is about.

AMERICA VERSUS THE WORLD

The United States is almost alone in opposing mandatory action to reduce greenhouse gas emissions. The rest of the developed world (other than Australia) believes that the threat posed by warming is so great that they ratified the 1997 Kyoto Protocol, an international climate treaty that requires strong action—reducing emissions to about 5 percent below 1990 levels by 2008–2012. It was a politically difficult move for many of those countries to make given their knowledge that the United States, the world's biggest emitter, would probably not join.

Moreover, the rest of the industrialized world embraced the Kyoto Protocol even though it did not restrict the emissions from developing countries such as China and India, which many in our country see as a fatal flaw in the agreement and a major reason not to vote for it. Yet that flawed agreement is viewed instead in most other countries as a critical first step to solving the climate problem.

British prime minister Tony Blair said in February 2003, "It is clear Kyoto is not radical enough," given the scale of the climate problem. That same year Blair announced that "for Britain, we will agree to the Royal Commission [on Environmental Pollution] target of a 60 percent reduction in emissions by 2050. And I am committed now to putting us on a path over the next few years towards that target," despite the fact that this would force a dramatic change in how England uses energy in transportation, industry, and buildings. In September 2004, Blair gave a speech in which he reiterated Britain's commitment to deep emissions reductions, saying that the accelerating rate of global warming has become "simply unsustainable in the long-term." He went on to explain:

> And by long-term I do not mean centuries ahead. I mean within the lifetime of my children certainly; and possibly within my own. And by unsustainable, I do not mean a phenomenon causing problems of adjustment. I mean a challenge so far-reaching in its impact and irreversible in its destructive power, that it alters radically human existence. . . .
>
> There is no doubt that the time to act is now.

British environmental politics is far, far removed from ours: After the speech, Conservative Party leader Michael Howard accused Blair (the Labor Party leader) of not taking strong enough action and of "squandering the chance to lead efforts against climate change."

The United States has been headed in exactly the opposite direction. President George W. Bush not only rejected the Kyoto Protocol, he has worked feverishly to block other countries from taking any further action to reduce emissions, and he opposes any mandatory action by this country. A major Senate bill from John McCain (Republican) and Joe Lieberman (Democrat) that would put an absolute cap on U.S. greenhouse gas emissions received just 38 votes in the summer of 2005—5 fewer than it received the first time it was offered in 2003—even though its restrictions had been weakened to try to attract support.

"The United States is not going to ratify this process because the U.S. Congress is not going to allow them to do so, even if the

Administration would sign up to it," said John Shanahan, senior counsel to Senate Committee on Environment and Public Works chair James Inhofe (Republican), in February 2006. Shanahan also predicted, "You need 60 votes in the U.S. Senate to pass anything. They have got 38 right now. And they may go for something 'super light' to win a few more symbolic votes. *But they will never get 60*" (emphasis added).

In 2005, Tony Blair convened a climate conference with dozens of the world's top climate scientists. In 2006 he released a major scientific report, *Avoiding Dangerous Climate Change,* which included more than forty peer-reviewed papers. In his foreword, Blair stated, "It is clear from the [scientific] work presented that the risks of climate change may well be greater than we thought," but he noted, "action now can help avert the worst effects of climate change."

In the United States, climate science is not treated seriously. As many newspaper stories have related, and as a number of scientists confirmed, the U.S. government routinely undermines the ability of government scientists to communicate their ideas to the American public. The administration edits their work and blocks their access to the media. I will return to this point shortly.

In 2006, Fred Barnes, executive editor of *The Weekly Standard,* wrote of Bush's opposition to the Kyoto global-warming treaty:

Though he didn't say so publicly, Bush is a dissenter on the theory of global warming. . . . He avidly read Michael Crichton's 2004 novel *State of Fear,* whose villain falsifies scientific studies to justify draconian steps to curb global warming. Crichton himself has studied the issue extensively and concluded that global warming is an unproven theory and that the threat is vastly overstated. Early in 2005, political adviser Karl Rove arranged for Crichton to meet with Bush at the White House. They talked for an hour and were in near-total agreement.

Bush ignores every major study by the world's leading climate scientists, ignores his strong ally Tony Blair, yet instead reads Crichton's fiction thriller and spends an hour chatting with him. Apparently, science fiction trumps science fact.

Senator Inhofe praised Crichton for "a compelling presentation of the scientific facts of climate change" and actually invited him to be a witness at a 2005 Senate hearing on the role of science in environmental policy. Crichton took that opportunity to accuse the entire scientific community of fudging the science of climate change, a charge he also makes in his book, and one that meteorologist William Gray made at the same hearing.

THE CONSERVATIVE CONSENSUS ON CLIMATE

Those who deny that global warming is an urgent problem and those who seek to delay strong action to reduce greenhouse gas emissions have been more persuasive than climate scientists. I call these people the Denyers and Delayers, and they have been particularly persuasive among conservatives, who currently hold much of the political power in this country. Let's explore a few examples from the conservative media, blogs, pundits, think tanks, and politicians. I've chosen them to show that the misinformed skepticism about climate science among conservative political and intellectual leaders runs deep and wide.

In February 2006, *New York Times* columnist John Tierney wrote: "Scientists agree that the planet seems to be warming, but their models are so crude that they're unsure about how much it will heat up or how much damage will be done. There's a chance the warming could be mild enough to produce net benefits."

Tierney has packed a great deal of misinformation into two sentences.

The overwhelming majority of scientists agree the planet *is* warming—not "seems to be"—the data itself is beyond dispute.

The models are not crude. On the contrary, the models have become very sophisticated and even predictive. If there is an appearance of uncertainty about how much the planet will heat up or how much damage will be done, it's because of the uncertainty of how much greenhouse gases we humans are going to release into the atmosphere. Scientists spend a great deal of time analyzing and publicly discussing scenarios that include both very low growth and very high growth in human-caused emissions and concentrations. That means scientists talk about a wide range of potential impacts, which may look to some like uncertainty. Tragically, however, the low-emission scenarios have become more unlikely with each passing year of political inaction—inaction driven in large part by influential but misinformed people such as Tierney.

Similarly, it is a dangerous myth that global warming could be mild enough to provide net benefits. This possibility has died because we did not seize the moment, thanks in part to those such as Tierney who have successfully argued for inaction based on the myth itself. For warming to be mild and even beneficial requires first that the climate's sensitivity to forcing by greenhouse gases be on the very low side—a possibility that has been all but eliminated by a stream of studies in recent years. It requires the United States and the world to stabilize atmospheric carbon dioxide *concentrations* at levels low enough to avoid starting the vicious cycles of the carbon system, well below 550 parts per million (ppm). Unfortunately, we are headed to well over 700 ppm. As we saw in the last chapter, exceeding 700 ppm would probably mean another sizzling 3°C or more of warming *this century,* widespread droughts, and an eventual sea-level rise of 40 to 80 feet or more, an outcome neither mild nor beneficial.

Those stark facts mean we must start reducing the amount of U.S. greenhouse gas *emissions* immediately. Yet Tierney opposes "spending large sums to avert biblical punishments that may never come." On Tierney's path of inaction, the only real scientific question becomes, How bad will the impact of global warming be—very serious or irreversibly apocalyptic?

Second, consider the late commentator Jude Wanniski. In May 2005 he wrote an open letter to *The New Yorker*, expressing his disapproval of Elizabeth Kolbert's three-part series "The Climate of Man," which he labeled "Un-Journalism." The only scientific critique he offered was that the series begins by "announcing that the scientific community has now concluded that mankind in a significant way is producing the carbon dioxide that is cooking the atmosphere" and then shows pictures of melting glaciers, "although the reader cannot tell from looking that the glacier is melting because too many of us are driving SUVs or because solar activity in the last part of the 19th century heated up the earth by a degree or two, and the icecaps are still melting as a result."

In fact, scientists have studied solar activity for decades and have concluded that its contribution to recent warming is at most very small. Even stranger, the planet *cooled* slightly in the last part of the nineteenth century, primarily due to multiple volcanic eruptions, including that of Krakatoa, whose particulates helped block out the sun. It's surprising that a smart man like Wanniski would trot out an old and discredited argument—and that he would so easily believe that the entire scientific community had missed this important contribution to the earth's climate. This is just one example of the Denyers ignoring the thousands of studies disputing their position and instead grasping onto notions that have been widely refuted by scientists.

Third and fourth, consider columnists Charles Krauthammer and George Will on the subject of hurricanes and climate change. Krauthammer proclaimed on September 9, 2005, "There is no relationship between global warming and the frequency and intensity of Atlantic hurricanes. Period." He provided no evidence in support of this statement.

On the September 25, 2005, broadcast of ABC's *This Week*,

George Stephanopoulos and David Gergen discussed the recent scientific evidence linking hurricane intensity to global warming. Then Gergen, who is so well known for his political moderation that he has served both Democratic and Republican presidents, said, "It does seem to me under these circumstances this is a wake-up call to take global warming and climate change more seriously." George Will was ready with a sarcastic reply:

> I have an alternative theory. I think these two hurricanes were caused by the prescription drug entitlement. You will say, "How can you say that? The entitlement hasn't even started." There's no conclusive evidence that global warming, that is to say, an unprecedented, irreversible, and radical change has started. You will say, "There's no scientific proof." Same answer. You will say, "Aren't you embarrassed, Mr. Will, to be attaching your political agenda to a national disaster?" Yeah, I'm embarrassed, but everyone else is doing it.

This may well be the most antiscientific statement Will has ever uttered, if not the silliest, equating a serious cause-and-effect relationship put forward by leading scientists using a widely accepted scientific theory with a causation that is sheer nonsense. Once again comes the accusation that anyone who raises this issue has a "political agenda," when clearly those who dismiss it have the agenda.

Strangely, neither Krauthammer nor Will comes from the wing of the conservative movement that reflexively dismisses key scientific theories, such as evolution. Quite the reverse. Within weeks of their global-warming comments, both wrote strong op-eds against those who embrace the "phony theory," as Krauthammer put it, of intelligent design over evolution. Will's reply to school board members who endorsed a proclamation that "evolution is not a fact" was "But it is."

How can such ardent defenders of the science of evolution be such ardent rejecters of the science of global warming? How can people, even those who question the science underlying evolution, embrace the warnings of scientists that avian bird flu could evolve into a powerful human pandemic but reject warnings from climate scientists? How can so many conservatives dismiss the consensus of thousands of the world's top climate scientists?

The answer is that ideology trumps rationality. Most conservatives cannot abide the *solution* to global warming—strong government regulations and a government-led effort to accelerate clean-energy technologies into the market. According to Jude Wanniski, Elizabeth Kolbert's *New Yorker* articles did nothing more "than write a long editorial on behalf of government intervention to stamp out carbon dioxide." His villain is not global warming; it is the threat to Americans from government itself.

George Will's review of Michael Crichton's *State of Fear* says:

> Crichton's subject is today's fear that global warming will cause catastrophic climate change, a belief now so conventional that it seems to require no supporting data. . . .
>
> Various factions have interests—monetary, political, even emotional—in cultivating fears. The fears invariably seem to require *more government subservience to environmentalists* and *more government supervision of our lives.* [Emphasis added.]

Conservatives such as Will are so opposed to government regulations that they are skeptical of anyone who identifies a problem that requires regulatory solutions— and they are inherently accepting of those who downplay such problems.

George Will believes that advocates for action on climate want more government supervision of our lives. But if we hold off on modest government action today, we will almost guarantee the need for much more extreme government action in the post-2025 era. Only Big Government—which conservatives don't want—can relo-

cate millions of citizens, build massive levees, ration crucial resources such as water and arable land, mandate harsh and rapid
reductions in certain kinds of energy—all of which will be inevitable necessities if we don't act now.

THE ART OF POLITICAL PERSUASION

> *Of all the talents bestowed upon men, none is so pre-*
> *cious as the gift of oratory. He who enjoys it wields a*
> *power more durable than that of a great king.*
> —Winston Churchill

Anyone who wants to understand the politics of global warming,
and anyone who wants to change the politics of global warming,
must understand why the Denyers are so persuasive in the public
debate and why scientists are not. Science and logic are powerful
systematic tools for understanding the world, but they are no match
in the public realm for the twenty-five-century-old art of verbal
persuasion: rhetoric.

While logic might be described as the art of influencing minds
with the facts, rhetoric is the art of influencing both the hearts and
minds of listeners with the figures of speech. The figures are the
catalog of the different, effective ways that we talk, including
alliteration and other forms of repetition, metaphor, irony, and the
like. The goal is to sound believable. As Aristotle wrote in *Rhetoric,*
"Aptness of language is one thing that makes people believe in the
truth of your story."

The figures of speech have been widely studied by marketers
and social scientists. They turn out to "constitute basic schemes by
which people conceptualize their experience and the external
world," as one psychologist put it. We think in figures, and so the
figures can be used to change the way we think. That's why political

speechwriters use them. To help level the rhetorical playing field in the global-warming debate, I will highlight the three rhetorical elements that are essential to modern political persuasion.

First, simple language. Contrary to popular misconception, rhetoric is not big words; it's small words. "The unreflecting often imagine that the effects of oratory are produced by the use of long words," a precocious twenty-three-year-old Winston Churchill wrote in an unpublished essay on rhetoric. "All the speeches of great English rhetoricians . . . display a uniform preference for short, homely words of common usage." We hear the truth of his advice in the words that linger with us from all of the great speeches: "Judge not that ye be not judged," "To be or not to be," "Lend me your ears," "Four score and seven years ago," "blood, toil, tears and sweat," "I have a dream."

In short, simple words and simple slogans work.

Second, repetition, repetition, repetition. Repetition makes words and phrases stick in the mind. Repetition is so important to rhetoric that there are four dozen figures of speech describing different kinds of repetition. The most elemental figure of repetition is *alliteration* (from the Latin for "repeating the same letter"), as in "compassionate conservative." Repetition, or "staying on message," in modern political parlance, remains the essential rhetorical strategy. As Frank Luntz, a leading conservative-message guru and political strategist, has said, "There's a simple rule: You say it again, and you say it again, and you say it again, and you say it again, and you say it again, and then again and again and again and again, and about the time that you're absolutely sick of saying it is about the time that your target audience has heard it for the first time."

Third, the skillful use of tropes (from the Greek for "turn"), figures that change or turn the meaning of a word away from its literal meaning. The two most important tropes, I believe, are metaphor and irony. "To be a master of metaphor," Aristotle writes in *Poetics,* is "a sign of genius, since a good metaphor implies intuitive perception of the similarity in dissimilars." When Bush said in 2006 that the nation was "addicted to oil," he was speaking metaphorically. Curing an addiction, however, requires far stronger medicine than the president proposed: America could become energy-independent, but only through a series of government-led policies identical to the ones needed to avoid catastrophic climate change.

SCIENCE, CLIMATE, AND RHETORIC

Rhetoric works, and it works because it is systematic. As Churchill wrote, "The subtle art of combining the various elements that separately mean nothing and collectively mean so much in an harmonious proportion is known to very few." Unfortunately, the major player in the climate debate, the scientific community, is not good at persuasive speech. Scientists might even be described as anti-rhetoricians, since they avoid all of its key elements.

Few scientists are known for simple language. As the physicist Mark Bowen writes in *Thin Ice,* his book about glaciologist Lonnie Thompson: "Scientists have an annoying habit of backing off when they're asked to make a plain statement, and climatologists tend to be worse than most."

Most scientists do not like to repeat themselves because it implies that they aren't sure of what they're saying. Scientists like to focus on the things they *don't* know, since that is the cutting edge of scientific research. So they don't keep repeating the things they *do* know, which is one reason the public and the media often don't hear from scientists about the strong areas of consensus on global warming.

Scientific training, at least as I experienced it, emphasizes sticking to facts and speaking literally, as opposed to figuratively or metaphorically. Scientific debates are won by those whose theory best explains the facts, not by those who are the most gifted speakers. This view of science is perhaps best summed up in the motto of the Royal Society of London, one of the world's oldest scientific academies (founded in 1660), *Nullius in verba:* take nobody's word. Words alone are not science.

Scientists who are great public communicators, such as Carl Sagan and Richard Feynman, have grown scarcer as science has become increasingly specialized. Moreover, the media likes the glib and the dramatic, which is the style most scientists deliberately avoid. As Jared Diamond, author of *Collapse,* has written, "Scientists who do communicate effectively with the public often find their colleagues responding with scorn, and even punishing them in ways that affect their careers." After Carl Sagan became famous, he was rejected for membership in the National Academy of Sciences in a special vote. This became widely known, and, Diamond writes, "Every scientist is capable of recognizing the obvious implications for his or her self-interest."

Scientists who have been outspoken about global warming have been repeatedly attacked as having a "political agenda." As one 2006 article explained, "For a scientist whose reputation is largely invested in peer-reviewed publications and the citations thereof, there is little professional payoff for getting involved in debates that mix science and politics."

Not surprisingly, many climate scientists shy away from the public debate. At the same time, the Bush administration has muzzled many climate scientists working for the U.S. government, as we will see. As a result, science journalists, not practicing scientists, are almost always the ones explaining global warming to the public. Unfortunately, the media is cutting back on science reporting in general and finds reporting climate science particularly problematic.

It is not surprising, then, that the American public is so uninformed about global warming, so vulnerable to what might be called the conservative crusade against climate. I say conservative, rather than Republican, because many moderate Republicans have been as strong on climate as Tony Blair, most notably California governor Arnold Schwarzenegger, who said in 2005, "I say the debate is over. We know the science, we see the threat, and the time for action is now." He then committed the state to reduce greenhouse gas emissions to 80 percent below 1990 levels by 2050—precisely the reductions needed to ensure that the Greenland Ice Sheet does not melt. And in 2006, he signed a law crafted with the help of Democratic state legislators that requires a 25 percent reduction in California's carbon dioxide emissions by 2020.

A NOTE ON SKEPTICISM

The people I call global-warming Delayers and Denyers are also called "climate skeptics" or "contrarians." I think those terms are misused here. All scientists are skeptics. Hence the motto "Take nobody's word." Skeptics can be convinced by the facts; Denyers cannot. Skeptics do not continue repeating arguments that have been discredited. Denyers do.

A contrarian is "one who takes a contrary view or action, especially an investor who makes decisions that contradict prevailing wisdom." Contrarians may have a good strategy for making money in the stock market, but how many have a hidden agenda to undermine faith in the stock market itself? Moreover, if the scientific consensus somehow reversed itself, the Denyers wouldn't suddenly reverse themselves. They aren't contrarians.

The Denyers and Delayers, as I use the terms, are those who aggressively embrace one or both parts of a twofold strategy. First, they deny the strong scientific consensus that the climate change we are witnessing is primarily human-caused and likely to have serious negative impacts if we don't reverse our greenhouse gas emissions trends. Second, they work to delay this country from taking any serious action beyond perhaps investing in new technology.

Their beliefs were well articulated by Michael Crichton in a 2006 interview: "If you just look at the science, I, at least, am underwhelmed. This may or may not be a problem, but it is far from the most serious problem. If you want to do something, [limiting emissions] is not what to do. We don't at this moment have good technology to do this, if, in fact, it's necessary to do it."

Such is the road to ruin. Those who advance such a view, including President Bush, deserve a strong label. No doubt many Denyers and Delayers are sincere in their beliefs, but the quotes of Luntz and Brooks suggest that some are not. Sincere or insincere, they spread misinformation or disinformation that threatens the well-being of the next fifty generations of Americans. Denyers and Delayers are also not content merely to dispute the work of climate scientists—they are actively engaged in smearing those scientists' reputations.

THE CONSERVATIVE BATTLE PLAN

The Denyers and Delayers do not just have messaging skills superior to scientists (and environmentalists and most progressive politicians), they also have a brilliant strategy, a poll-tested plan of attack. A 2002 memo from the Luntz Research Companies explains precisely how politicians can sound as if they care about global warming without actually doing anything about it. It focuses in particular on casting doubts about the science. The memo can be found on the web, and anyone who cares about the future of America should read it.

Luntz's team has "spent the last seven years examining how best to communicate complicated ideas and controversial subjects." A big fan of rhetorical devices, Luntz specifically urges conservatives to "use rhetorical questions" whenever discussing the environment.

Like any good rhetorician, Luntz says that "it can be helpful to think of environmental (and other) issues in terms of a 'story.'" His next line is stunning: "A compelling story, even if factually inaccurate, can be more emotionally compelling than the dry recitation of the truth."

Luntz explains, *The three words Americans are looking for in an environmental policy . . . are 'safer,' 'cleaner' and 'healthier,'* (emphasis in original throughout). So people who want to seem to care about the environment should use those very words often. He also notes:

> *"Climate change" is less frightening than global warming.* As one focus group participant noted, climate change "sounds like you're going from Pittsburgh to Fort Lauderdale." While global warming has catastrophic connotations attached to it, climate change suggests a more controllable and less emotional challenge.

Focus groups are nothing new in politics, nor is coming up with the best spin for your ideas. But rarely has it been done with such callous disregard for the gravity of a scientific matter.

Luntz's lessons have been taken to heart in more places than you might imagine. An e-mail message sent in July 2005 from NASA headquarters to the Jet Propulsion Laboratory in Pasadena, California, criticized a web presentation that used the phrase "global warming," stating that it is "standard practice" in the agency to use the phrase "climate change." At the insistence of political appointees, the NASA press office had "a general understanding that when something in this field was written about that it was to be described as climate change and not global warming," as one retired press officer put it in 2006.

Interestingly, "climate change" has become for some conservatives, such as Senator Lisa Murkowski, a phrase to describe the obvious changes in climate we are observing in places like Alaska that (in their thinking) may or may not be caused by human activity, whereas "global warming" is reserved for change that is caused by human emissions of greenhouse gases. Like most scientists, I use the terms interchangeably.

Luntz writes, *"The most important principle in any discussion of global warming is your commitment to sound science.* Americans unanimously believe all environmental rules and regulations should be based on sound science and common sense." Luntz did not invent the phrase "sound science"—a good history can be found in Chris Mooney's book, *The Republican War on Science.* Luntz's strong suit is identifying what phrases work and then convincing conservatives to repeat those phrases over and over. "Sound science" works not only because of its alliteration but because it makes the speaker seem to care about science, even when he or she is actually peddling unsound science.

In theory, "sound science" means genuine peer-reviewed and widely corroborated science, as opposed to speculative Soviet-style "politicized science." In the case of global warming, virtually every single piece of peer-reviewed science supports humans as the primary cause, and as we've seen repeatedly the recent literature strongly suggests the impacts will be somewhere between serious and catastrophic if we don't change course soon.

Luntz's central point is the height of cynicism: *"You need to continue to make lack of scientific certainty a primary issue in the debate. . . . The scientific debate is closing (against us) but not yet closed. There is still a window of opportunity to challenge the science."*

This is one of the great tragedies of our times: For Luntz and a large number of conservatives, global warming is strictly a partisan political issue. He acknowledges that the science is moving against his position, but this does not persuade him. He suggests that conservatives muddy the waters, by providing people with information that supports an erroneous view, so that serious action on global warming can be delayed for as long as possible.

Do conservative political and intellectual leaders truly understand that they are on the wrong side of the scientific debate? *New York Times* columnist David Brooks wrote these astonishing words in 2005: "Global warming is real (conservatives secretly know this)." Delay, delay, delay. That is the goal. But we know that with just one more decade of delay, the only way to be sure the Greenland Ice Sheet doesn't melt would be onerous government action.

The Luntz strategy isn't new. One 1969 tobacco-industry memo famously states, "Doubt is our product since it is the best means of competing with the 'body of fact' that exists in the mind of the general public. It is also the means of establishing a controversy." Other, less famous lines are eerily prescient about global warming: "Doubt is also the limit of our 'product.' Unfortunately, we cannot take a position directly opposing the anti-cigarette forces and say that cigarettes are a contributor to good health. No information that we have supports such a claim."

The Denyers and the Delayers are luckier than the cigarette makers because they feel free to tout the "fact" that global warming might have benefits, as John Tierney did in the quote above, or as George Will does when he wrote in December 2004 that the climate models don't tell us "how much warming is dangerous—or perhaps beneficial." This sales pitch—combining doubt with the false hope of potential benefit—is one the tobacco companies could only dream of.

DENY, DENY, DELAY, DELAY

In a box labeled "Language That Works," Luntz recommends lines for Republican speeches that have been repeated endlessly in various forms by the Delayers:

> *"We must not rush to judgment before all the facts are in. We need to ask more questions. We deserve more answers. Until we learn more, we should not commit America to any international document that handcuffs us either now or into the future."*

In science, the facts are never completely in, making this a highly effective rhetorical strategy in any scientific debate. And this line of attack can be used equally well in ten or twenty years, or forever, because "*all* the facts" are never in. If we must wait until the painful reality of mega-droughts and rapid sea-level rise are upon us, the point of no return will have long passed.

Paula Dobriansky, the Bush administration's under secretary of state for global affairs, justified U.S. efforts to block further action on climate change at a December 2004 international conference with these words: "Science tells us that we cannot say with any certainty what constitutes a dangerous level of warming, and therefore what level must be avoided."

Apply this "certainty" test to all public policy, and we would never take any action to avoid any future problem. The Pentagon cannot say with any certainty what constitutes a dangerous level of opposing forces. Epidemiologists cannot say with any certainty what constitutes a dangerous number of birds infected with avian flu. Doctors cannot say with certainty what constitutes a dangerous weight. Does that mean we have no army? No avian flu policy? That a 300-pound patient with health problems shouldn't be put on a weight-loss regimen?

A core element of the White House's climate strategy has been to call for more research into climate change, but here we clearly see the administration saying one thing and doing the opposite. The Government Accountability Office reviewed the administration's research effort and in April 2005 came to the stunning conclusion that the effort was missing a major piece required by law—a plan to assess the impact of global warming on "human health and welfare," agriculture, the environment, energy, and water.

The White House's constant call for more research is nothing but a smokescreen. The Bush team has systematically worked to hold back the results of such research, to censor the information about the real dangers of global warming that its own agencies are supposed to provide to the public. For instance, since the 1990s, the U.S. Global Change Research Program had been working on a "U.S. National Assessment of the Potential Consequences of Climate Variability and Change." The Competitive Enterprise Institute (CEI), a conservative think tank funded in part by ExxonMobil, sued the Bush White House, under the little-known Federal Data Quality Act, to remove this comprehensive peer-reviewed study from circulation, labeling the report "junk science." A Freedom of Information Request revealed in 2003 that the White House had secretly asked CEI to sue it to get the nation's premier climate assessment withdrawn.

In short, the White House conspired with an oil-company-funded think tank to block a major government scientific report that sought to spell out the dangers of climate change to Americans. The failure of our government to warn us of the dangers, to provide our people with a national assessment of the potential consequences of climate change, denies Americans the information they need to make decisions.

The White House heavily edited a 2003 report from the U.S. Environmental Protection Agency, removing several paragraphs that described the dangers posed by rising temperatures, as the *New York Times,* CBS News, and other media outlets reported. It actually removed a reference to key findings of the National Academy of Sciences, a study that the president himself had commissioned. Ultimately every substantial conclusion in the EPA report was gutted. Even the sentence "Climate change has global consequences for human health and the environment" was considered too strong to be left in and it was removed.

The White House actually hired Philip Cooney, a former lobbyist for the American Petroleum Institute, to do its scientific censoring.

Much of what we have learned about the censoring comes from a whistleblower, Rick Piltz, a senior associate from the government office that coordinates federal climate-change programs, who resigned in March 2005. His documents showed that the White House had systematically edited reports by government scientists to make the otherwise strong scientific conclusions and consensus seem doubtful. Two days after Piltz's story broke, Cooney resigned from the White House. Within days, he was hired by ExxonMobil, which has devoted millions of dollars to supporting groups that advance the Denyer and Delayer agenda.

More recently, we have learned the shocking extent of the administration's censorship efforts, thanks to reports in the *New York Times*, *The New Republic*, and *60 Minutes*. The Bush administration has been engaged for a number of years in muzzling government scientists, according to a number of scientists inside and outside the government. I myself have spoken to many scientists—some of whom are afraid of speaking out publicly—and they confirm this. Rick Piltz has launched a website, www.climatesciencewatch.org, that regularly reports on government censorship of climate research.

Political appointees at NASA put in place a policy to limit media access to James Hansen—director of NASA's Goddard Institute for Space Studies—and all NASA climate scientists. After Hansen reported the NASA data showing that 2005 was the warmest year on record, and after he began giving lectures warning that we have at most a decade to sharply reverse our greenhouse gas emissions trends, NASA's public-affairs staff was ordered to review his forthcoming lectures, journal articles, web postings, and media contacts. Hansen was told he would face "dire consequences" if he continued to speak out about climate change.

After Hansen went public with his charges in early 2006, NASA seems to have changed its public-affairs policy, but the muzzling has continued at other government agencies. Interview requests from the media have been routinely rejected. And at agencies such as the National Oceanic and Atmospheric Administration, those media interviews that are granted can occur only if public-affairs staff monitors the conversation. As Hansen said in February 2006, "On climate, the public has been misinformed and not informed."

As we saw in chapter 2, some NOAA meteorologists have been publicly advocating an untenable scientific position—that recent increases in hurricane intensity have been well correlated with recent increases in sea-surface temperatures, but that the temperature increases have nothing to do with global warming. The NOAA meteorologists who take this position seem to have unfettered access to the press, even though few of them are experts on global warming. On the other hand, we rarely hear from the numerous global-warming experts at NOAA, many of whom disagree with the agency's official position. "Scientists who don't toe the party line are being intimidated from talking to the press," says MIT climatologist Kerry Emanuel. "I think it is a very sad situation. I know quite a few people who are frightened, but they beg me not to use their name."

The man in charge of NOAA is Vice Admiral Conrad Lautenbacher, a Bush appointee with a Ph.D. in applied mathematics and forty years of Navy service. At a December 2003 conference in Milan, for instance, he repeated the standard rhetoric: "I do believe we need more scientific info before we commit to a process like Kyoto." But it isn't clear what "scientific info" would impress him. In

2005 remarks shortly after Katrina hit New Orleans, he said of the connection between hurricane intensity and global warming: "People have hunches, certainly everybody can have a hunch, but the information is not there at this point that would allow you to make that connection. We have no direct link between the number of storms and intensity versus global temperature rise."

Lautenbacher describes the scientific studies that disagree with his view as merely "hunches." He then repeats the argument that the increase in hurricane intensity is just part of a natural cycle, completely unaware that the natural-cycle explanation is itself closer to a hunch than a proven theory, as we've seen. In February 2006, Lautenbacher wrote a letter to NOAA staff stating that "a few recent media reports have (incorrectly) asserted that some NOAA scientists have been discouraged from commenting on the question of whether human-caused global warming may be influencing the number or intensity of hurricanes." In reply, Jerry Mahlman, former director for sixteen years of NOAA's Geophysical Fluid Dynamics Laboratory, wrote:

Contrary to Dr. Lautenbacher's assertions, I state emphatically that climate scientists within NOAA have indeed recently been systematically prevented from speaking freely. A number of NOAA scientists have directly and openly disagreed with Lautenbacher's statements that deny his direct connection with censorship of climate science.

Mahlman further notes that "the ideologically driven distortion of the truth about the relationship between hurricane intensity increases and warming ocean temperatures has been thoroughly refuted" in the scientific literature.

A great many people and businesses are making major investments and plans based on their understanding of the risk that the Gulf region could get hit by another powerful hurricane. Everyone, from those rebuilding the Gulf Coast and the levees to insurance companies to home owners like my brother, are trying to make plans—plans that involve the lives, the life savings, and the livelihoods of millions of people. They must have good information. They all rely on NOAA for the most objective scientific analysis and projections. Repeating over and over again the scientifically untenable claim that the recent spate of intense hurricanes is just a "natural cycle" with no link to global warming is dangerously misleading. Mahlman noted to me: "What value is there in obscuring the truth or flat-out lying about it?"

The global-warming Denyers and Delayers wish to do far more than just stop the public from learning the truth; they attack the credibility of those who try to tell the facts. The most virulent of them is Senator James Inhofe. In July 2003 he said, "With all of the hysteria, all of the fear, all the phony science, could it be that man-made global warming is the greatest hoax ever perpetrated on the American people? It sure sounds like it." Why would climate scientists pull such a horrible hoax? At his 2005 Senate hearing with Michael Crichton and meteorologist Bill Gray, Inhofe and his witnesses repeated the smear that climate scientists fudge their results in order to satisfy their funders and convince them to hand over more money.

Some of these attacks are very sophisticated and use the best rhetorical tricks. In his 2002 strategy memo, Frank Luntz recommends this attack:

> Scientists can extrapolate all kinds of things from today's data, but that doesn't say anything about tomorrow's world. You can't look back one million years and say that proves that we're heating the globe now hotter than it's ever been. After all, just 20 years ago scientists were worried about the new Ice Age.

Let's look at the worries of scientists 20 years ago. A 1977 report by the National Academy warned that uncontrolled greenhouse gas emissions might raise global temperatures 10°F and sea levels 20 feet. A 1979 academy report warned that "a wait and see policy may mean waiting until it is too late." A 1983 report from the Environmental Protection Agency warned that "substantial increases in global warming may occur sooner than most of us would like to believe," and the result of inaction might be "catastrophic." Twenty years ago, the leading American scientists were worried about global warming.

Michael Crichton repeats this attack in his novel *State of Fear*, in which he has one of his fictional environmentalists say, "In the 1970s all the climate scientists believed an ice age was coming." Snookered, columnist George Will picked this up in his glowing review and then repeated it on the March 26, 2006, edition of ABC TV's *This Week* with George Stephanopoulos. This clever and popular attack tries to make present global-warming fears seem faddish, saying current climate science is nothing more than finger-in-the-wind guessing.

The Denyers insist that climate scientists used to believe in cooling and now they believe in warming. Like all good attacks, this one is built around a partial truth, in this case, a milli-truth, one part in a thousand of the truth. Global warming leveled off between 1940 and 1975. As explained in chapter 2, this was largely a result of dust and aerosols sent by humans (and volcanoes) into the atmosphere, which temporarily overwhelmed the already well-understood warming effect from greenhouse gases. In the 1970s, a few scientists wondered whether the cooling effect from aerosols would be greater than the heating produced from greenhouse gases, and some popular publications ran articles about a new ice age. Most climate scientists were far more worried about the long-term greenhouse gas trends, even in the midst of short-term cooling—and they proved to be right.

The aerosol effect was fully explained in the 1980s and became part of scientific modeling "that is in remarkable agreement with the observations," as Tom Wigley, a leading climatologist with the National Center for Atmospheric Research, wrote in a 2003 letter to the U.S. Senate. Ignoring the science, the Denyers keep repeating the fiction as if it were the latest argument, sounding a bit like flat-earthers but much more dangerous. Senator Inhofe used this smear in his 2005 Senate hearing with Crichton, and George Will wrote, "Thirty years ago the fashionable panic was about global *cooling*," and then he cited a number of quotes that seem to support him. In January 2005 the website realclimate.org debunked the whole notion in a post titled "The Global Cooling Myth." They showed that Will's quotes from scientific magazines are misattributed or taken out of context in a way that nearly reverses their meanings.

Since Inhofe, Crichton, and Will are not scientists, they won't get drummed out of their community for repeating what is factually untrue.

A spring 2003 workshop of top atmospheric scientists in Berlin concluded that the shielding effect of aerosols may be far greater than previously estimated. Nobel laureate Paul Crutzen said, "It looks like the warming today may be only about a quarter of what we would have got without aerosols." This conclusion would suggest the planet may be far more susceptible to warming than previously thought. Crutzen noted that aerosols "are giving us a false sense of security right now." A 2005 study led by researchers at the National Oceanic and Atmospheric Administration concluded, "Natural and anthropogenic aerosols have substantially delayed and lessened the total amount of global ocean warming—and therefore of sea level rise—that would have arisen purely in response to increasing greenhouse gases."

The real irony here is that the aerosol-shielding issue, fully explained, gives the public *greater* reason to act preemptively on climate, not less. The entire record of climate science, rather than being a narrative based on fickle fads, is one of relentless, hard-nosed, continual progression of knowledge, which is characteristic of science, as opposed to politics or propaganda.

TRUTHINESS OR CONSEQUENCES

I believe the most effective piece of propaganda on global warming is Michael Crichton's 2004 novel, *State of Fear*. Everywhere I speak, I am asked questions based on unsubstantiated assertions in his book. More than any other single document published on global warming, the book captures the essence of Frank Luntz's vision: "A compelling story, even if factually inaccurate, can be more emotionally compelling than the dry recitation of the truth." In 2005, Comedy Central's Stephen Colbert introduced the word *truthiness* to describe emotional appeals that sidestep the facts. "Truthiness is what you want the facts to be as opposed to what the facts are," says Colbert. "What feels like the right answer as opposed to what reality will support." He might have coined the term for Crichton.

Although a work of fiction, *State of Fear* has a clear political agenda, as evidenced by Crichton's December 7, 2004, press release:

> STATE OF FEAR raises critical questions about the facts we believe in, without question, on the strength of esteemed experts and the media. Although the story is fiction, Michael Crichton writes from a firm foundation of actual research challenging common assumptions about global warming.

In an appendix titled "Why Politicized Science Is Dangerous," Crichton draws a direct and lengthy analogy between climate science and eugenics and Soviet biology under Lysenko, where all dissent to the party line was crushed and some Soviet geneticists were executed. With no evidence whatsoever, he claims that in climate science, "open and frank discussion of the data, and of the issues, is being suppressed." With this he is using an old trick—accuse your opponent of the same nefarious thing you yourself are doing.

Modern science is by nature open and frank. Any country and any laboratory can conduct any research it wants, and can publish it in one of hundreds of serious journals around the world. The scientific community conducts peer reviews of arguments on their merits—that's the gold standard. Just before the mistake-riddled, global-warming-will-cause-an-ice-age movie *The Day After Tomorrow* came out, the journal *Science* published an article by two environmental scientists that concluded, "In light of the paleoclimate record and our understanding of the contemporary climate system, it is safe to say that global warming will not lead to the onset of a new ice age." I have yet to see a critique of Crichton's book by the global warming Denyers and Delayers, even though it is seriously flawed, as we will see.

Crichton's book deserves a brief review here, since it has become a rallying cry for the Denyers and Delayers. On TV, in interviews, and in talks around the country, Crichton continues to cast doubt on the seriousness and urgency of global warming. He thinks the scientific and environmental communities have fabricated the threat and that efforts to manage the emissions of greenhouse gases are misguided. To make his case, Crichton accuses the scientific community of bad faith, as noted, and he distorts the science. He creates a scientist-hero, Dr. John Kenner, who outdebates the book's environmentalists.

Kenner says that real-life climatologist Jim Hansen manipulated the media in a 1988 congressional hearing, and that he's discredited because "Hansen overestimated [global warming] by three hundred percent." Had Crichton checked primary sources, he would have found Hansen's prediction came very close to being exactly accurate. The smear Crichton now cites was created ten years later, when global warming Denyer Pat Michaels shamefully misrepresented Hansen's testimony. Michaels is a visiting scientist with the Marshall Institute and a senior fellow at the Cato Institute—organizations that receive funds from ExxonMobil to advance the Denyers/Delayers agenda.

A full factual debunking of the book can be found on real climate.org. It's a fascinating tale of how misinformation is spread. Crichton even spreads truthiness in his bibliography, mischaracterizing the landmark 2002 National Research Council report, *Abrupt Climate Change,* as follows: "The text concludes that abrupt climate change might occur sometime in the future, triggered by *mechanisms not yet understood.*" This is simply not true. The report concludes plainly, "Abrupt climate changes were especially common when the climate system *was being forced to change most rapidly.* Thus, greenhouse warming . . . may increase the possibility of large, abrupt, and unwelcome regional or global climatic events" (emphasis added).

Why would Crichton mischaracterize the report in his bibliography? Because one of his main goals in the book is to undermine the case that global warming causes *abrupt* climate change and *extreme* weather events. In his story, a mainstream environmental group is plotting to create extreme weather events that will cause the deaths of thousands of people timed to coincide with a conference on abrupt climate change in order to trick the public into accepting global warming as truth. In a bizarre coincidence, the book's climax has the evil environmentalists carefully plan a seismic tsunami—just weeks before an actual tsunami devastated Southeast Asia.

But the truth is stronger than fiction. Seismic tsunamis are caused by earth tremors. *They are not caused by global warming.* Any climate scientist knows that. This is a stunning blunder by Crichton, calling into question his claim to have any understanding of global warming.

Senator Inhofe, Michaels, and other Denyers have actually accused the environmental community of blaming the Indian Ocean tsunami on global warming. The environmentalists did nothing of the kind. "I am appalled that environmentalists are trying to ride on the backs of 160,000 dead people to push their global-warming agenda without any factual basis," Pat Michaels told the online magazine *Grist* in January 2005. He issued his own press release, saying, "Michael Crichton should sue environmentalists who blame the massive death toll from the Indian Ocean's tragic tsunamis on sea level rise for plagiarism."

In a January 2005 piece titled "The Tsunami Exploiters," columnist James Glassman said that Tony Juniper of Friends of the Earth in Britain had said of the tsunami, "Here again are yet more events in the real world that are consistent with climate change predictions." In fact, Juniper was talking about an increase in 2004 of *other kinds* of natural disasters that may be related to global warming. He had already put out a press release explaining that his remarks were made *before* the tsunami had even hit.

A few environmentalists had pointed out that rising sea levels (caused by global warming) coupled with the decline in natural barriers such as coral reefs (caused at least in part by global warming) had made the area more susceptible to the ravages from a seismic tsunami (caused by earthquakes). They had also pointed out that current climate trends could make future tsunamis even more deadly. Every one of those statements is, unfortunately, true. A *Grist* headline summed up the phony attack with biting rhetoric: "Right-Wingers Exploit Tsunami by Accusing Enviros of Exploiting Tsunami."

The smear about the tsunami is part of a systematic, decade-long effort by the Denyers to change the discourse in the media and the environmental community about the connection between extreme weather events and climate change—and to keep advocates of strong action on the rhetorical defensive. Tragically, their efforts have been all too successful.

THE DEATH OF ENVIRONMENTAL MESSAGING

When a group is so thoroughly beaten rhetorically, its members begin to bicker internally, often self-destructively. In 2004, two environmental strategists, Michael Shellenberger and Ted Nordhaus, released a bombshell essay, "The Death of Environmentalism: Global Warming Politics in a Post-Environmental World," based in part on interviews with twenty-five environmental leaders. Their essay started a virulent debate. Anybody who cares about the environment and global warming should hear both sides.

The original essay is passionately argued but supremely misguided. Interestingly, one of the authors' central arguments concerns rhetoric at its most basic.

> Most environmentalists don't think of "the environment" as a mental category at all—they think of it as a real "thing" to be protected and defended. They think of themselves, *literally*, as representatives and defenders of this thing. Environmentalists do their work as though these are *literal* rather than *figurative* truths. They tend to see language in general as representative rather than constitutive of reality. This is typical of liberals who are, at their core, children of the enlightenment who believe that they arrived at their identity and politics through a rational and considered process. They expect others in politics should do the same and are constantly surprised and disappointed when they don't.
>
> The effect of this orientation is a certain *literal-sclerosis*—the belief that social change happens only when people speak a *literal* "truth to power." *Literal*-sclerosis can be seen in the assumption that to win action on global warming one must talk about global warming instead of, say, the economy, industrial policy, or health care.

Had the authors gone on to make a compelling case that a figurative approach to global warming was superior to a literal approach, these paragraphs might have been a powerful launching point. But ironically, they instead play right into the hands of the political masters of figurative language, the global warming Denyers and Delayers. While figurative language certainly makes for more persuasive messaging—a central point of this chapter—wise public policy, at least in the environmental realm, *must* be based on scientific literalism.

Their thirty-page paper argues three main points:

1. Environmentalists, even after spending "hundreds of millions of dollars" in the previous decade and a half "combating global warming," have "strikingly little to show for it."
2. Environmentalists' efforts to enact policy measures to reduce greenhouse gas emissions through regulation (caps on greenhouse gas emissions and higher fuel-economy standards for cars) have failed and are therefore wrongheaded.
3. Environmentalists are mired in group think and "policy literalism," which makes them unable to see that the true solution to global warming is a visionary technological fix, the New Apollo Project, a proposal to spend $30 billion a year for ten years on clean-energy technologies, developing and deploying renewable energy and hydrogen cars.

The first point is self-evidently true. The authors, however, spend virtually no time trying to analyze *why* the message has failed. They simply assume that the message was wrong. They do not discuss at all the brilliant rhetorical seduction by the Denyers and Delayers. This is like trying to understand why John Kerry lost without examining the Bush team's strategy.

The authors also do not notice that global warming has a key difference compared with previous issues on which the environmental community has been successful—clean air and clean water, for instance. Those issues were dramatically visible (terrible smog in our big cities, Lake Erie catches fire), directly affected people's health at the time, and the solutions, though costly, could be put into place relatively quickly with very visible results. The signs of global warming are less visible (especially since much of the environmental community and media stopped talking about those signs, such as extreme weather, until recently), the major impact is a few decades away, and strong action now will not provide quick visible results. What strong action in the next decade will do—and only strong action can do it—is avoid catastrophic climate change. But that is hardly as sellable—with literal or figurative language—as avoiding tens of thousands of deaths next year by cutting smog.

On the second point, environmentalists have indeed utterly failed to get the United States to put even the mildest cap on greenhouse gas emissions or establish stronger fuel-economy standards. Does the failure to achieve these policies prove they are the wrong policies? Not at all.

The fact that the environmental community is bad at messaging should not be mistaken for proof that its message is bad—particularly in the case of an environmental problem unprecedented in human history and in the face of opponents with vastly superior language intelligence and resources. The industrialized nations, including all of Europe, have made serious commitments to reduce greenhouse gas and are putting into place a cap on carbon dioxide emissions. Those countries all have tougher fuel-economy requirements or much higher gasoline taxes or both than does the United States.

America absolutely needs an aggressive technology strategy similar to the New Apollo Project (minus the push for hydrogen cars). Mandatory reduction targets, such as a cap on carbon dioxide emissions, without aggressive technology programs will slow economic growth. But technology programs without mandatory targets won't solve our climate problem. They are a seductively attractive false hope. That's why the Denyers and Delayers are among the biggest supporters of technology programs without mandatory targets.

CHAPTER SIX

THE TECHNOLOGY TRAP AND THE
AMERICAN WAY OF LIFE

*There is no doubt that the time to act is now. It is
now that timely action can avert disaster. It is now
that with foresight and will such action can be taken
without disturbing the essence of our way of life, by
adjusting behaviour, but not altering it entirely.*
—Tony Blair, 2005

*It's important not to get distracted by chasing short-
term reductions in greenhouse emissions. The real
payoff is in long-term technological breakthroughs.*
—John H. Marburger III,
president's science adviser, 2006

The mantra of the Delayers is "technology" and "technology
breakthroughs." Their technological fix to the greenhouse gas
problem is, unsurprisingly, not imminent. It is "long-term." But as
we have seen earlier, failing to act in the near term—now—will
bring about such drastic conditions that soon our only choice will
be to react with extremely onerous government policies.

In 2005, British prime minister Tony Blair described the crucial
two-prong strategy we must adopt: "We need to invest on a large

scale in existing technologies *and* to stimulate innovation into new low-carbon technologies for deployment in the longer term." Future technology will be able to help preserve our way of life in the long term *if and only if* we have already moved "on a large scale" to technologies that already exist. Over the next few decades, we must rapidly deploy available technologies that stop global carbon dioxide emissions from rising. *Then,* in the second half of this century, we must sharply reduce global greenhouse gas emissions by deploying all the new technologies we have developed.

The time to act is now.

VOLUNTARY WARMING

It is hard to imagine that people will use low-carbon technologies on the vast scale needed until they see a financial return for cutting carbon, and that will not happen until spewing out carbon has a significant financial cost. But for carbon to have a cost, the government must either tax carbon dioxide emissions or create a market that establishes a price for emitting carbon dioxide. This second approach would be similar to the system used to trade emissions of sulfur dioxide under the Clean Air Act administered by the EPA. I prefer the trading system. The Bush administration strongly opposes both.

During the 2000 presidential campaign, George W. Bush promised to regulate greenhouse gas emissions in the electric-utility sector by putting a mandated cap on carbon dioxide emissions that would be modeled on what his father put into place in 1990 regarding sulfur dioxide emissions. This helped blur the distinction between Bush and his opponent, Al Gore, who was well known for advocating action on global warming. Many thought this was a sign that Bush was a moderate on the environment, like his father. Not surprisingly, he has not carried through on this promise, and there have been no regulations of any kind on greenhouse gas emissions during his presidency.

"What will never fly is a mandatory cap on carbon," said James Connaughton in a February 2004 briefing. He is the chair of the White House Council on Environmental Quality and thus is supposed to be one of the administration's *advocates* for the environment. In December 2004 the *Financial Times* reported that U.S. climate negotiators had actually worked "to ensure that future additions to the Kyoto protocol on climate change should avoid committing nations to reducing their carbon dioxide emissions." This must be the first time in U.S. history that a presidential candidate promised a particular environmental remedy and four years later his aides had not only ruled it out but were actively undermining other countries' efforts to adopt it.

Conservative message makers such as Frank Luntz realized that it could be politically dangerous to oppose *any* action on global warming, even if their efforts to obfuscate the climate science were successful. Luntz lays out a clever solution to this conundrum in his 2002 "Straight Talk" memo on climate-change messaging:

> *Technology and innovation are the key in arguments on both sides.* Global warming alarmists use American superiority in technology and innovation quite effectively in responding to accusations that international agreements such as the Kyoto accord could cost the United States billions. Rather than condemning corporate America the way most environmentalists have done in the past, they attack us for lacking faith in our collective ability to meet any economic challenges presented by environmental changes we make. This should be our argument. We need to emphasize how voluntary innovation and experimentation are preferable to bureaucratic or international intervention and regulation.

This pro-technology pitch is quite a reversal for conservatives. In the early 1980s the Reagan administration cut funding for energy efficiency and renewable-energy technology and innovation programs by 70 to 90 percent. The Clinton administration began reversing some of those cuts, but in 1995 the conservative Congress under House Speaker Newt Gingrich refused to fund any increases. In fact, the House of Representatives even pursued legislation that tried to shut down all applied research into low-carbon energy technologies. In April 1996, Deputy Energy Secretary Charles Curtis and I wrote "Mideast Oil Forever," an article for *The Atlantic* explaining "how the congressional attack on energy research is threatening the economy, the environment, and national security."

Ultimately, we were able to stave off the worst of the cuts by demonstrating that the Department of Energy's technology-development efforts had achieved a remarkable payback for the country. My old office at the Department of Energy (DOE) is exceedingly good at developing clean-energy technologies and then getting people to use more efficient versions of existing technology (lighting, motors, heating and cooling). Those energy-efficiency efforts, which cost taxpayers a few hundred million dollars, were verified by the National Academy of Science as having saved businesses and consumers $30 billion in energy costs. But, tragically, while we were able to beat back the most brutal cuts, we did not meet our goal of significantly increasing funding for low-carbon and oil-reducing technologies.

By the time Bush took office, Luntz and other conservative strategists realized that since they opposed genuine action on global warming, they needed a way to sound like they were doing something. The result was the dual strategy of advocating voluntary action and touting new technology.

Luntz counsels conservatives that while the wait-for-new-technology strategy is important, "you will still fall short unless you emphasize the voluntary actions and environmental progress already underway." In February 2002, after a year of sustained criticism from Democrats and others for failing to take any action on global warming, the Bush administration set a voluntary target for the nation to reduce greenhouse gas *intensity* by 18 percent by 2012.

The word *intensity* is often dropped in media coverage, because it is a complex concept that means little to most people. But without the word *intensity*, it sounds like the Bush administration actually made a commitment to *reduce* total U.S. greenhouse gas emissions, rather than to *increase* them, which in fact is what they did. Even with the word *intensity*, U.S. emissions are permitted to increase enormously. *Intensity* here means "the amount per unit of economic activity, as measured by gross domestic product (GDP)." Bush's double-talk committed the nation to reduce greenhouse gas emissions per dollar of GDP by 18 percent over a ten-year period, which by the administration's own calculation would lead to an *increase* in total emissions of 14 percent during that ten-year period—since GDP was projected to rise about 32 percent.

The intensity rhetoric also allowed the administration to say that it was trying to do something when it wasn't. The nation's "greenhouse gas intensity" had been dropping at a faster rate than in the Bush proposal (while absolute emissions kept rising). So the administration was able to generate positive public relations for a commitment that actually allowed greater growth in greenhouse gas emissions than would otherwise have occurred.

Greenhouse gas intensity is a misleading metric because what threatens us is the total amount of greenhouse gases in the atmosphere, not the amount of gases relative to our GDP. Greenhouse gas intensity can drop every year forever, and concentrations will still increase enough to raise sea levels 80 feet.

At negotiations in Montreal in November 2005 to develop a follow-up to the Kyoto Protocol, the chief U.S. negotiator, Harlan Watson, continued the administration's steadfast opposition to mandatory controls. He shamelessly claimed that Bush's strategy had led to genuine environmental progress and had cut emissions from the year 2000 to 2003. But that period includes a recession and 9/11, which severely reduced economic activity and travel-related emissions. Also, Bush did not begin his presidency until 2001 and didn't start his "voluntary" strategy until 2002. Since 2002, U.S. emissions have *risen* at a rate of 1 percent per year.

As compelling as voluntary innovation and experimentation may sound, they simply do not bring about an absolute reduction in emissions, although well-designed efforts funded at high levels *can* slow the growth rate, as discussed below. I know this all too well because for five years in the 1990s I helped develop, oversee, and run the DOE programs aimed at technology development and voluntary greenhouse gas reductions.

In 1992, President George H. W. Bush signed an agreement saying that the United States would adopt policies that would return greenhouse gas emissions to 1990 levels by 2000. The so-called Rio climate treaty came into force in March 1994. In its early days, the Clinton administration thought that an aggressive set of voluntary programs, combined with an energy tax, would stop emissions growth. Personally, I didn't like the energy tax, because energy is not the problem, greenhouse gas emissions are. Congress didn't like the energy tax either and killed it.

After the 1994 midterm elections, the Gingrich Congress began canceling or cutting the funds for most of the voluntary programs. By "voluntary programs" I am referring to efforts that were aimed not at developing new technologies but at accelerating their deployment into the U.S. market. Such market-entry programs involve public education or working with businesses, cities, and states to lower the many barriers to new technology. This key distinction between technology *development* and technology *deployment* may seem mundane, but it is one that will prove critical to whether or not this nation can avoid catastrophic global warming without devastating its economy.

TECHNOLOGY AND THE DELAYERS

"The United States is neither ashamed of its position on Kyoto nor indifferent to the challenges of climate change," then secretary of energy Spencer Abraham said in 2003. "The United States is investing billions of dollars to address these challenges." Following the Luntz script, Abraham continued:

> Either dramatic greenhouse gas reductions will come at the expense of economic growth and improved living standards, or breakthrough energy technologies that change the game entirely will allow us to reduce emissions while, at the same time, we maintain economic growth and improve the world's standards of living.

His Energy Department further reported, "Abraham said no technologies currently exist to significantly cut emissions of gases linked to global warming."

Astonishing double-talk, especially considering that Abraham made it in Berlin to a group of European climate-policy experts, and every single European country had already agreed to dramatic greenhouse gas reductions under Kyoto.

Luntz's memo states that the "scientific breakthroughs" argument works best for the Delayers. He recommends saying that "as a nation, we should be proud. We produce . . . virtually all the world's health and scientific breakthroughs, yet we produce a fraction of the world's pollution." A very large fraction—we Americans produce one-quarter of the world's greenhouse gases, which is presumably more than what he means by "a fraction."

Luntz urges politicians to say, "America has the best scientists, the best engineers, the best researchers, and the best technicians in the world." When Bush launched his hydrogen-car proposal during his 2003 State of the Union address, he said, "With a new national commitment, our scientists and engineers will overcome obstacles to taking these cars from laboratory to showroom, so that the first car driven by a child born today could be powered by hydrogen, and pollution-free."

A hydrogen car available for a child born in 2003 will not be available in time to stop the climate crisis, even if hydrogen cars actually could help reduce greenhouse gas emissions in the 2020s, which they cannot.

Luntz recommends that when supporters of environmental regulations argue, "We can do anything we set our sights on" and "American corporations and industry can meet any challenge," Denyers and Delayers should "immediately agree" but then argue that we don't need "excessive regulation" or an "international treaty with rules and regulations that will handcuff the American economy" (Luntz's favorite metaphor). Republicans, he says, should argue that we can achieve environmental goals with good old American technology alone.

A 2005 Luntz strategy document, "An Energy Policy for the 21st Century," again argues *"Innovation and 21st-century technology should be at the core of your energy policy,"* repeating the word *technology* thirty times. In an April 2005 speech describing his proposed energy policy, Bush repeated the word *technology* more than forty times. This time *Business Week* recognized that Bush was following Luntz's script and noted, "What's most striking about Bush's Apr. 27 speech is how closely it follows the script written by Luntz earlier this year." The article also pointed out "the President's failure to propose any meaningful solutions."

In his 2006 State of the Union address, Bush announced that America was addicted to oil and the solution was a push for breakthrough technologies, especially in advanced batteries for cars, bio-fuels, and renewable energy. He proposed his "Advanced Energy Initiative—a 22-percent increase in clean-energy research." But the 2005 federal budget had actually *cut* energy R&D by 11 percent compared with that of the year before. And three years earlier, in his 2003 address, Bush had said the answer to our energy and environmental problems was hydrogen cars, and he *cut* the budget for renewable energy and bioenergy to pay for that unjustifiable program.

At a February 2006 speech at the National Renewable Energy Laboratory in Colorado, Bush repeated the word *technology* two dozen times. A few reporters noted that two weeks earlier, the lab had laid off a number of people, including top researchers in areas that the president said were now a priority. Bush blamed this on "a budgeting mix-up," saying, "Sometimes, decisions made as the result of the appropriations process, the money may not end up where it was supposed to have gone." A more reasonable explanation: Technology rhetoric is nothing more than rhetoric.

For the Delayers, the technology pitch is win-win-win. It makes them sound like they're doing something, even while global-warming emissions keep rising. The strong pitch for developing new technology leaves the false impression that existing technology cannot solve our problems—the absurd point former energy secretary Abraham made in the 2003 Berlin speech. And the Delayers can even reap the rhetorical rewards of touting technology as our solution to global warming without actually spending more money on the key technologies.

The technology mantra seductively plays to the American people's optimism, while stealing the argument from optimists who believe, as I do, that our technology is precisely the reason why we *can* agree to cap greenhouse gas emissions. The pitch has boxed progressive politicians (and scientists and environmentalists) into a corner. Both sides—those who want to delay on global warming and those who want action now—say they advocate technology, but in this narrative only the stick-in-the-mud progressives want onerous rules and regulations. No wonder those pursuing action today have had so much difficulty getting political traction—and no wonder the Delayers repeat their mantra so much.

Like the best seductions, the technology pitch contains a half-truth: We *do* need to invest in technology—but we *must* couple that investment with mandatory emissions-reduction targets or else global-warming pollution will continue its dangerous rise.

It is not just delaying politicians who use the technology trap as a strategy—corporate Delayers love it too. One of the biggest funders of efforts to convince the public that global warming is not occurring has been ExxonMobil. Since the president announced his hydrogen-car initiative, the oil and gas company has also funded significant advertising about its research into hydrogen-related technologies. It also helped fund a $100 million clean-technology research program at Stanford University. In an April 2005 *Washington Post* ad, ExxonMobil proclaimed:

> We're now making the largest ever investment in independent climate and energy research that is specifically designed to look for new breakthrough technologies. The world faces enormous energy challenges. There are no easy answers. It will take straightforward, honest dialogue about the hard truths that confront us all.

Sounds so reasonable, except ExxonMobil has been as much a champion of "honest dialogue" as the Luntz memo is about "Straight Talk." ExxonMobil has pumped more than $8 million into think tanks, media-outreach organizations, and consumer and religious groups that advance the Denyer and Delayer agenda, including the Competitive Enterprise Institute, the Hoover Institution, the Hudson Institute, the George C. Marshall Institute, the Tech

Central Science Foundation, and the Center for the Study of Carbon Dioxide and Global Change, which calls CO_2 emissions "a force for good." Exxon also participated in discussions involving a 1998 fossil fuel industry proposal "to depict global warming theory as a case of bad science."

The leading opponent of fuel-economy standards is General Motors. It has spent millions lobbying Congress to make sure the company is not required to build more fuel-efficient vehicles—cars that competitors like Toyota are selling briskly today because they saw the inevitability of rising oil prices and growing customer concern about the environment. GM is also the leading U.S. car company that advocates hydrogen cars, and it spends millions on ads asserting that these cars are right around the corner—absurdly claiming in April 2005 that we are actually at the "endgame" of GM's hydrogen strategy. What a pity that GM's promises ring hollow, and not just because hydrogen cars are decades away from being a plausible greenhouse gas reduction strategy.

When I was at the U.S. Department of Energy in the 1990s, we partnered with GM, Ford, and Chrysler to speed the introduction of hybrid gasoline-electric cars, since increased fuel efficiency was (and remains) clearly the best hope for cutting vehicle greenhouse gas emissions by the year 2025. This partnership was part of an informal deal between the Clinton administration and the car companies in which we did not pursue fuel-economy standards and in return the car companies promised to develop a triple-efficiency car (80 mpg) by 2004. Ironically, in the mid-1990s, the car companies were actively lobbying to *cut* funding for hydrogen-car development and to shift that money into near-term technologies such as hybrids. Even more ironically, the main result of our government-industry partnership (which had excluded foreign automakers) was to motivate the Japanese car companies to develop and introduce their own hybrids first.

In one of the major blunders in automotive history, GM walked away from hybrids as soon as it could—when the Bush administration came in—after taxpayers had spent $1 billion on the program. The result: Toyota and Honda walked in. *GM, which had had a technological lead in electric drives, let its number one competitor, Toyota, achieve a stunning 7-year head start* in what will likely be this century's primary drivetrain. GM was publicly criticizing the future of hybrid technology as late as January 2004, and finally announced later in that year a halfhearted effort to catch up to Toyota.

Let this history give pause to anybody who promotes a purely technology-based solution to greenhouse gas emissions (and gasoline consumption) in the transportation sector. GM and President Bush have it exactly backward. It's not, as they have argued incessantly, fuel-economy standards that cost American jobs and market share. It's the lack of them. And because the future is one of constrained oil supplies, inevitable oil price shocks, and the urgent need to reduce greenhouse gases in the transportation sector, the car companies that will have the most success are the ones that can deliver a practical, fuel-efficient vehicle, especially efficient dual-fuel vehicles that can run on low-carbon alternatives to petroleum. Toyota and Honda figured this out, but GM insists on fighting the future. As a result, it has been hemorrhaging cash and market share, both of which are being claimed by smarter competitors.

Yes, joint government–auto industry research and development makes sense, and yes, perhaps even a subsidy to support switching automakers' manufacturing base to hybrids is warranted, but *only* together with legislation that sharply tightens fuel-economy standards and caps carbon dioxide emissions.

BREAKING THE BREAKTHROUGH MYTH

What technology breakthroughs in the past three decades have transformed how we use energy today? The answer: There really haven't been any. We use energy today roughly the same way we did

30 years ago. Our cars still run on internal combustion engines that burn gasoline. Alternatives to gasoline such as corn ethanol make up under 3 percent of all U.S. transportation fuels—and corn ethanol is hardly a breakthrough fuel. Fuel economy did double from the mid-1970s to the mid-1980s, *as required by government regulations,* but in the last quarter-century, the average fuel economy of American consumer vehicles has remained flat or even declined slightly.

The single biggest source of electricity generation, by far, is still coal power, just as it was 30 years ago. The vast majority of all power plants still generate heat to make steam turn a turbine, and the average efficiency of our electric power plants is about what it was 30 years ago. We did see the introduction of the highly efficient natural gas combined-cycle turbine, but that was not based on a breakthrough from the past three decades—and constrained natural gas supply in North America severely limited growth in gas-fired power, so the share of U.S. electricity generated by natural gas has grown only modestly in 30 years. Nuclear power was about 10 percent of total U.S. electric power 30 years ago, and now it's about 20 percent. But the nuclear energy "breakthrough" occurred long before the 1970s, and we haven't built a new nuclear power plant in two decades, in large part because that power has been so expensive.

We do have many more home appliances, but they still haven't fundamentally changed *how* we use energy. Interestingly, home energy use per square foot has not changed that much even with all those new electronic gadgets, for two reasons. First, my old office at the DOE developed major advances in key consumer technologies, including refrigeration and lighting. Second, efficiency standards for appliances have made the use of those efficient technologies widespread. From the mid-1970s until today, refrigerator electricity use has dropped a whopping three-quarters. Perhaps that should be called a breakthrough, especially because some of the savings came from remarkable improvements in the guts of the refrigerator from

Oak Ridge National Laboratory. But we still use refrigerators pretty much as we did, so in that sense these breakthroughs didn't change how we use energy.

One of the most widely publicized energy-technology break-throughs occurred in 1986 when researchers at IBM Zurich Research Laboratory discovered a material that conducted electricity with no resistance at considerably higher temperatures than previous conductors. Over the next few years a series of breakthroughs in these high-temperature superconductors were announced. This technology generated great excitement because it held the promise of superefficient electric motors and loss-free long-distance electric transmission lines. Yet all these years later, you may ask, where are all the high-temperature superconductors? They have had very little impact on either electric motors or power transmissions.

"Typically it has taken 25 years after commercial introduction for a primary energy form to obtain a 1 percent share of the global market" (emphasis added). So noted Royal Dutch/Shell, one of the world's largest oil companies, in its 2001 scenarios for how energy use is likely to evolve over the next five decades. Note that this tiny toehold comes 25 years after *commercial* introduction. The first transition from scientific breakthrough to commercial introduction may itself take decades. Consider fuel-cell cars, which get a lot of hype today. Yet fuel cells were invented in 1839, and more than 165 years later we still don't have a single commercial fuel-cell car. We barely have any viable commercial fuel cells for stationary electric power generation.

I tend to think that Shell's statement is basically true, although I believe we could in some instances speed things up—but only with the kind of aggressive technology-deployment programs and government standards that conservatives do not like. Given that we must dramatically reverse greenhouse gas emissions trends over the next 25 years, we *must* focus on technologies that are either commercial or nearly commercial *today*.

Why don't never been-seen-before breakthroughs change how we use energy? Why don't breakthrough energy technologies enter the market the way breakthroughs in consumer electronics and telecommunications seem to? If we focus on the two most important sectors for global warming, transportation and electricity generation, the answer is fairly straightforward: The barriers to market entry for new technologies are enormous. The entire electric grid—from power plant to transmission line to your house—represents hundreds of billions of dollars in investment, much of which has long since been paid off. We have coal plants and hydropower plants that are several decades old and still running. This keeps electricity widely available, and much lower in price here than in almost any other industrialized country. And it keeps competing technologies at a permanent disadvantage.

The entire gasoline-fueling delivery infrastructure—refineries, pipelines, gasoline stations, and the like—also represents hundreds of billions of dollars of investment that assures widespread availability, low price, and very tough competition for any potential alternative fuel. A comparable investment has been made in automobile manufacturing plants, a key reason why we have not seen a new American car company successfully launched for a very long time.

Perhaps the best example of a breakthrough that is changing the vehicle market is the nickel metal hydride battery currently being used in virtually every hybrid gasoline-electric car today. The key to making hybrids work is the battery. Research on nickel metal hydrides began in the 1970s. In the early 1980s, a U.S. company, Ovonics, introduced nickel metal hydride batteries into the market for consumer electronics. At the DOE we were interested in hybrids in the mid-1990s because a few years earlier Ovonics had developed a version of the battery for cars under a partnership with the government in the U.S. Advanced Battery Consortium.

Hybrids were introduced into the U.S. car market by the Japanese car companies Toyota and Honda in 1997. Sales began to soar after 2000, thanks to improved engineering, high gasoline prices, and government incentives. Even so, in 2005, 8 years after they were introduced, hybrids were only slightly more than 1 percent of new-car sales in the United States. But here we want to know how long before a breakthrough significantly affects how we use energy or how much energy we use. So the question is, How long before hybrids reduce U.S. gasoline consumption?

Consider first that the average car now lasts for nearly 20 years, making it difficult for any breakthrough technology to have a rapid impact on the market. Second, consider that engine technology has gotten dramatically more efficient in the past two decades, but the average vehicle on the road has not. Why not? The efficiency gains have been offset by increased performance (faster acceleration) and the increased weight of the average car (thanks to the growing popularity of sport-utility vehicles and light trucks).

How soon will hybrids begin reducing U.S. gasoline consumption? The best answer is, "Maybe never." Why should hybrids increase the average efficiency of the U.S. cars and light trucks any more than the steady advances in engine efficiency of the past two decades did? The good news is that hybrid drivetrains provide enough efficiency improvement and their electric motors develop such high acceleration that automakers have used the technology to raise both horsepower and fuel economy simultaneously. But a number of hybrid models have been introduced that achieve only a very modest efficiency gain. Moreover, vehicle efficiency must rise significantly over the next two decades just to keep gasoline consumption—and hence greenhouse gas emissions—constant, simply to make up for the increases that would otherwise come from more and more people buying more and more cars and driving farther and farther.

If we want to reduce U.S. oil consumption and greenhouse gas emissions from cars, the most obvious strategy is the one that we already employed successfully to double the fuel economy of our cars from the mid-1970s to the mid-1980s—tougher government mileage standards. No other strategy has ever worked for this country.

The Denyers and Delayers remain tragically stuck with their "we must wait for new technology" rhetoric. Perhaps the most egregious example of this came in January 2006, after six former EPA administrators—five of them Republican, including EPA chiefs for Nixon, Ford, and Reagan—urged the Bush administration to impose mandatory greenhouse gas emissions controls as a way to address global warming. In response, EPA's administrator, Stephen Johnson, said the administration policy is to pursue voluntary programs and technological innovation, rather than mandates and standards. He then said: *"Are we going to tell people to stop driving their cars, or do we start investing in technology [to cut emissions]? That's the answer, investing in those technologies"* (emphasis added).

This astonishing false choice—invest in technology or force people to stop driving their cars—comes from our country's top person for protecting the environment. Johnson can't seem to grasp that today's *existing* technology was yesterday's new technology. Hybrids were once new; now they aren't. They can substantially reduce U.S. greenhouse gas emissions if government standards require them to do so. Technology is no substitute for standards. Technology is what makes standards practical and affordable.

The Delayers don't believe in technology—they believe only in *new* technology, that is, until it is no longer new. The Bush administration not only opposes significantly higher national mileage standards for cars, it is even opposing in court a law passed by the state of California requiring that car companies use existing technologies to cut carbon dioxide emissions per vehicle by 30 percent. The administration argues that carbon dioxide is not a pollutant California can regulate and that this law illegally preempts federal authority in setting mileage standards for cars.

If the Delayers were truly serious about new technology offering the only possible strategy for dealing with global warming, they would propose a far larger budget to develop it. Yet the Bush administration has never increased the total energy R&D budget for the federal government. And worse, when we take out programs that offer little hope in the first half of this century (such as the hydrogen car program), and we subtract the notorious congressional earmarks that have run rampant since 2000 (which often divert funds from well-designed technology programs to pork-barrel projects), we have seen a substantial decline in money for development of clean-energy climate solutions.

Our bill for *imported* oil alone now exceeds $250 billion a year. In total, Americans spend nearly $1 trillion a year on energy. The global-warming damages this country will sustain could run into the trillions of dollars. The core of any strategy to reduce greenhouse gas emissions and oil consumption is energy efficiency and renewable energy. The R&D budget for those technologies (minus hydrogen and earmarks) is a paltry few hundred million dollars a year and has dropped steadily since 2000. The federal government is spending less than $2 per American per year on the best technologies for avoiding 80-foot sea-level rise.

The scale of the global-warming problem warrants spending equivalent to that of the Manhattan Project or the Apollo program or even the Pentagon's current technology program for developing a missile defense. That would give us an advanced energy-technology program of about $10 to $20 billion per year. One way we know that the Delayer "technology only" strategy is empty rhetoric: The funding levels they suggest cannot deal with the problem—and they block all efforts to increase funding.

ADAPTATION AND GEO-ENGINEERING

Two other technology-based strategies for dealing with global warming—or, rather, not dealing with it—are adaptation and geo-engineering. I haven't written much about how we would adapt to Hell and High Water, for several reasons.

For the foreseeable future, the primary focus of our climate policy today must be avoiding that grim outcome. Also, making adaptation a major focus of U.S. climate policy presupposes a political consensus that climate scientists are correct about current and future impacts. Otherwise, how could politicians agree to spend hundreds of billions of dollars adapting to a large rise in sea levels or an increased number of super-hurricanes or the growing risk of mega-droughts? But if we had such a consensus, then the only moral choice would be to direct the vast majority of our resources to avoiding this catastrophe in the first place.

Many Delayers use the idea of adaptation to argue against action now, to create the false hope that global warming will be of a pace and scale that our children and their children can deal with—which, ironically, would be true only if we ignored their advice and took aggressive mitigation action now. After all, how do you adapt to sea levels rising a foot or more a decade until oceans are 80 feet higher or more? How do you adapt to widespread, ever-worsening global mega-droughts—especially in a world that will need as much water and arable land as possible by midcentury to feed perhaps 9 billion people and grow vast amounts of zero-carbon energy crops?

Of course we should develop drought-resistant crops and new levee technology and better desalinization technology. But for the foreseeable future, avoiding global warming should receive ten to one hundred times the funds of any adaptation effort.

Interestingly, when I was at the Energy Department, we tried to launch an effort aimed at both mitigation *and* adaptation, called "Cool Communities." Most cities have dark surfaces and less vegetation than their surroundings, making them as much as 5°F warmer. Reducing this "heat island" effect would cut greenhouse gas emissions from air-conditioning and offset some of the increase in

urban temperatures from global warming—and it would even reduce smog formation.

Cooling a city means planting shade trees for buildings and
putting light-colored surfaces on buildings, roads, and parking. The
government has a key role to play in research and testing to help
identify and develop the best roofing and paving materials, in funding computer models for determining the optimal approach to
cooling a city, and in disseminating information. Yet even though
Cool Communities was probably the most cost-effective adaptation
program ever devised, the Republican Congress killed it because it
was part of Clinton's plan to reduce global-warming emissions.

I also don't plan to devote much discussion to how we might
geo-engineer our way out. Geo-engineering is "the intentional
large-scale manipulation of the global environment" to counteract
the effects of global warming. Such a strategy presupposes a political consensus that climate scientists are correct about current and
future impacts. How else could politicians agree to spend the vast
sums of money needed to, say, put in place thousands of satellites
around the earth with mirrors to reflect the sunlight, as some have
proposed?

Geo-engineering also presupposes that politicians and scientists and the public share a high degree of certainty about all aspects
of climate science. Any human-induced engineering project large
enough to affect Earth's climate, such as seeding the upper atmosphere with massive amounts of aerosols, is just as likely to have
unintended consequences that make things worse. If we had such
certainty and consensus about climate science at any time in the
foreseeable future, it would *still* be better to focus the vast majority
of our resources on reducing emissions, since that strategy carries
far less risk.

"The 'geo-engineering' approaches considered so far appear to
be afflicted with some combination of high costs, low leverage, and
a high likelihood of serious side effects," concluded John Holdren,

director of the Woods Hole Research Center and president of the American Association for the Advancement of Science, in 2006.

Moreover, unlike adaptation, which a country can undertake by itself, geo-engineering is necessarily a planetwide strategy that would certainly require approval and coordination by the United Nations. Yet if the United States has not reversed its energy and climate policy by the 2020s, and joined the world community in an aggressive effort to reduce emissions—if the richest, most polluting nation on earth has refused to devote even 2 percent of its enormous wealth to spare the planet from millennia of misery—we will be a pariah nation. We will hardly be in a position to work with other nations in a desperate gamble to reengineer the planet's climate back to what it was before we engineered it into ruins with our emissions.

One might imagine an internationally sanctioned geo-engineering effort that began with small-scale tests and slowly worked up to planetwide deployment in the second half of this century. If we sharply reverse emissions trends in the next decade, we would minimize both the amount of geo-engineering we might need to do and the speed with which we needed to do it, giving us time to get much smarter and making the effort far less risky. If we hit 500 ppm of carbon dioxide in 2050, however, we will probably be on the verge of crossing a threshold that simply cannot be undone by geo-engineering.

Geo-engineering, like adaptation, might be an important post-2050 strategy, but it seems unlikely to be of much value unless we keep concentrations close to, or, preferably, well below, 550 ppm through 2100. And that requires the aggressive deployment of existing and near-term technology in the electricity and transportation sectors, starting immediately.

CHAPTER SEVEN

THE ELECTRIFYING SOLUTION

This analysis suggests that the United States could reduce its greenhouse gas emissions by between 10 and 40 percent of the 1990 level at very low cost. Some reductions may even be a net savings if the proper policies are implemented.

—U.S. National Academy of Sciences, 1991

What are the winning strategies for avoiding climate catastrophe, for avoiding Hell and High Water? This chapter examines the solutions for the power sector. Amazingly, with the right technology strategy over the next two decades, we could cut U.S. carbon dioxide emissions by two-thirds without increasing the total electric bill of either consumers or businesses.

In previous chapters I have touched on a number of aggressive low-carbon strategies or "wedges" we need to achieve over the next five decades to stabilize concentrations below a doubling. Each wedge ultimately avoids the emission of 1 billion metric tons of carbon a year. These are the ones aimed at reducing emissions from electricity and heavy industry:

1. Launch a massive performance-based efficiency program for homes, commercial buildings, and new construction.

2. Launch a massive effort to boost the efficiency of heavy industry and expand the use of cogeneration (combined heat and power).
3. Capture the CO_2 from 800 new large coal plants and store it underground.
4. Build 1 million large wind turbines (or the equivalent in renewables such as solar power).
5. Build 700 new large nuclear power plants while shutting down no old ones.

The biggest climate threat in the power sector comes from traditional coal plants. That's because coal contains more carbon than any other fossil fuel, and a typical coal plant converts only about one-third of the energy in the coal to electricity. The rest is wasted.

As of 2002, we had nearly 1,000 gigawatts (GW) of coal plants worldwide, which was about 40 percent of total global electricity generation. A typical large coal plant is about one gigawatt, or 1,000 megawatts (MW), in size. By 2030, the world is projected to double that to 2,000 GW of coal electricity.

More than a third of the new coal plants are expected to be built in China, but one in six will be here in the United States. Natural-gas plants had been the preferred new U.S. power plant, in part because they are far more efficient and less polluting than coal plants. But high prices for natural gas have made them much more expensive to operate than coal plants.

The coal plants that will be built from 2005 to 2030 will release as much carbon dioxide as all of the coal burned since the industrial revolution more than two centuries ago. On this emissions trajectory, the world would be emitting 10.5 billion metric tons of carbon (38 billion metric tons of carbon dioxide) in 2030. To stabilize atmospheric carbon dioxide concentrations below a doubling of what they were in preindustrial times, we need to keep *average* annual emissions to only 7 billion metric tons during this century.

So if we build these plants, we need to shut them down within two decades. Considering they represent a capital investment of more than $1 trillion, that doesn't seem likely. The only alternative in 2030 would be to retrofit the plants to capture and store the carbon dioxide they release. But virtually all of the planned coal plants are unsuitable for such retrofits.

CARBON CAPTURE AND STORAGE

Carbon capture and storage (CCS), also called carbon sequestration, is an attractive idea across the political spectrum because it might allow us to continue using a major fossil fuel, coal, but in a way that does not destroy the climate. Everyone from the Natural Resources Defense Council to the Bush administration loves carbon sequestration, although not in quite the same way.

Here's what is involved: To permanently store carbon, to keep it out of our atmosphere forever, the carbon dioxide from all power plants must be removed and stored somewhere forever. The carbon dioxide can be captured either before or after combustion—although capturing it before is far easier and cheaper. Coal can be gasified and the resulting syngas can then be chemically processed to generate hydrogen-rich gas and carbon dioxide. The hydrogen-rich gas can be combusted directly in a combined-cycle power plant. The carbon dioxide can be piped to a sequestration site. The whole process is called integrated gasification combined cycle (IGCC).

IGCC technology costs more than traditional coal plants. The total extra costs for this process, including geological storage in sealed underground sites, are currently quite high, $30 to $80 a ton of carbon dioxide, according to the DOE. As the National Coal Council reported in 2003, "Vendors currently do not have an adequate economic incentive" to pursue the technology because "IGCC may only become broadly competitive with" current coal and natural-gas power plants "*under a CO_2-restricted scenario.*" Thus, "power companies are not likely to pay the premium to install today's IGCC designs in the absence of clear regulatory direction on the CO_2 issue." Unless we promptly put into place restrictions on CO_2 emissions, carbon sequestration will be pushed much farther into the future. Before carbon capture and storage can become a significant factor, we must have a government policy that puts a cap on emissions.

In February 2003 the DOE announced the billion-dollar, ten-year FutureGen project to design, build, construct, and demonstrate a 275-megawatt prototype plant that would cogenerate electricity and hydrogen and sequester 90 percent of the carbon dioxide. The goal is to "validate the engineering, economic, and environmental viability of advanced coal-based, near-zero emission technologies that by 2020" will produce electricity that is only 10 percent more expensive than current coal-generated electricity.

The administration's strategy is either doubly pointless or doubly cynical, depending on your perspective. First, by the time this technology is ready to commercialize in the early 2020s, the world will have built or begun construction on more than a 1,000 GW of coal plants, using traditional technology that is not designed for CCS. Second, we will still need a mandatory cap on carbon emissions to make FutureGen plants viable because they will be more expensive than traditional plants even in the 2020s. Since the Bush administration opposes a mandatory cap, the whole R&D effort looks like another delaying action.

People in the energy business call it NeverGen.

Sequestration has another problem, one that must be solved if carbon capture and storage is going to be a major contributor to greenhouse gas reductions any time soon: where to put the carbon dioxide. The largest potential physical reservoir is the deep oceans. But ocean sequestration poses serious environmental risks and is unlikely to be viable. After all, the oceans are already storing a large portion of the CO_2 we have poured into the atmosphere. And their ability to store CO_2 is likely to diminish this century (a bad outcome we do not wish to hasten), and the increased acidification of the ocean is already posing a threat to marine life.

Tens of millions of tons of carbon dioxide have already been injected into oil fields to enhance recovery of oil—that's one reason we know CCS works. But using carbon dioxide to increase recovery of oil does not help reduce net greenhouse gas emissions, since the oil itself is ultimately burned, releasing CO_2.

Research is focusing on pumping highly compressed liquid carbon dioxide, called supercritical CO_2, into huge geological formations, such as deep underground aquifers. A 2003 workshop on carbon management by the National Academy of Sciences noted, "Less dense than water, CO_2 will float under the top seal atop the water in an aquifer and could migrate upward if the top seal is not completely impermeable."

What's the problem here? Even tiny leakage rates undermine the environmental value of sequestration. If we are trying to stabilize CO_2 concentrations at twice preindustrial levels, a mere 1 percent annual leakage rate could add $850 billion *per year* to overall costs by 2095, according to an analysis by Pacific Northwest National Laboratory. If we cannot be certain that leakage rates are well below 1 percent, the study concludes, "the private sector will find it increasingly difficult to convince regulators that CO_2 injected into geological formations should be accorded the same accounting as CO_2 that is avoided," meaning that you would not be able to give the same economic value to CO_2 injected underground as to CO_2 that was never generated (because of technologies such as wind or efficiency). The analysis notes, "There is no solid experimental evidence or theoretical framework" for determining likely leakage rates from different geological formations.

The flow of CO_2 *into* the ground from 800 GW of coal plants would equal the current flow of oil *out* of the ground. If we are going to store that huge amount of CO_2 inside deep underground aquifers, exhaustive testing will have to be done. Each potential site will need intensive monitoring to guarantee it can store CO_2 with no leaks. Very sensitive and low-cost in situ monitoring techniques must be developed to provide confidence that leakage rates are exceedingly low. The geologic stability of storage sites—think earthquakes—is especially important because a massive release of carbon dioxide could suffocate a huge number of people if it hit a populated area.

To start sequestering a significant amount of carbon dioxide in the 2020s, we must immediately begin identifying, testing, and certifying sites. This will not be easy; after spending billions of dollars and conducting more than two decades of scientific study, we have identified only one site in this country as a safe, permanent repository for nuclear waste—Yucca Mountain in Nevada—and even in that case, we have been unable to achieve the consensus needed to start storing waste in it.

If sequestration proves feasible on a large scale, there is a glimmer of good news: Analysis suggests carbon capture and storage could eventually eliminate much of U.S. electric-sector coal emissions for between $20 and $40 a ton of carbon dioxide. If we had such a price today—and a major effort to identify and certify storage sites—we *might* see significant sequestration start by 2020. Absent such policies, it will be delayed a decade or more. In the meantime, we must avoid building traditional coal plants. The best strategy for that is certainly energy efficiency.

THE TECHNOLOGY STRATEGY THAT WILL WORK

Our top two priorities in energy policy should be to minimize the need for new coal-fired power and to free up inefficiently used natural gas for high-efficiency power generation. Energy efficiency remains by far the single most cost-effective strategy for achieving these goals, for minimizing carbon dioxide emissions into the air.

Most buildings and factories can cut electricity consumption by more than 25 percent right now with rapid payback (under four years). I have worked with companies from Johnson & Johnson to IBM to Nike who have demonstrated this over and over again. My 1999 book, *Cool Companies,* describes a hundred case studies of companies that have cut their consumption substantially, making a great deal of money in the process and reaping other, unexpected benefits as well. Many companies that have pursued efficiency have found gains in productivity, because better-designed buildings improve office-worker productivity and redesigned industrial processes typically also reduce waste and increase output. So why doesn't every profit-seeking outfit do likewise? There are many reasons why most companies do not do what the best companies do, including inertia and lack of information. Also, I found that companies tend to be far more aggressive about efficiency when there are comprehensive government programs helping them.

We have more than two decades of broad experience with very successful state and federal energy-efficiency programs. In short, we know what works.

Perhaps the most cost-effective federal strategy would simply be to replicate, nationally and globally, California's myriad energy-efficiency programs and standards for homes and commercial buildings. From 1976 to 2005, electricity consumption per capita grew 60 percent in the rest of the nation, while it stayed flat in high-tech, fast-growing California. This astonishing achievement is shown in figure 4, which compares electricity consumption in California (in megawatt-hours per person) with that in the rest of the country since 1960.

How was California able to keep per capita electricity consumption flat for three decades? By adopting an aggressive, performance-based energy-efficiency strategy. By performance-based I mean one targeted toward efforts that deliver the most bang for the buck.

Most of the money came from California utilities. One key reg-

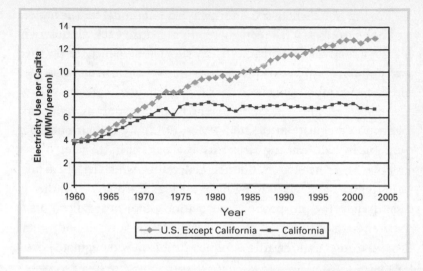

Figure 4. What energy efficiency can really do.

ulatory change was critical. Most utilities in this country can make money only by selling more power, and they lose profits if they sell less. Needless to say, they have little motivation to help their customers cut their electricity bills by using energy more efficiently. California changed the regulations so that utilities' profits are not tied to how much electricity they sell. It has also allowed utilities to take a share of any energy savings they help consumers and businesses achieve. The bottom line is that California utilities can make money when their customers save money.

If it is cheaper to satisfy growing demand with energy efficiency than with new power plants, utilities can still grow their profits. Efficiency strategies today include energy audits, outreach and education, training, technical assistance, and rebates for purchasing energy-efficient products. The California Energy Commission also directly supports efforts to boost energy efficiency, including building codes that specify efficiency requirements for new construction.

You may ask whether California is a good model for the nation, given the troubles it had deregulating its electric-utility industry in the 1990s and the resulting electricity shortages. In fact, the botched deregulation is precisely what convinced Californians that they needed to redouble efforts on energy efficiency.

How had things become botched up? As soon as California began to deregulate in the mid-1990s, utilities cut their efficiency funding in half, causing electricity use per capita to rise. Worse, utilities were forced to sell off their generators, which left them hostage to greedy energy-trading firms such as Enron. Even earlier in that decade, the prospect of deregulation put a near halt to planning and construction of new power plants because nobody knew what the rules and rewards would be in this new deregulated marketplace.

I was at the U.S. Department of Energy at the time, and we warned California that in a deregulated market no one would have an incentive to keep much surplus capacity. Normally, public utility commissions require a lot of spare capacity to ensure that the juice keeps flowing to consumers during the kind of rare long-lasting and widespread heat waves that drive summer air-conditioning demand to extreme levels. Most of the time that spare "peak demand" capacity goes unused, making it relatively unprofitable for companies to maintain. But by the late 1990s, global warming was making those once rare mammoth heat waves commonplace (and in 2006, California would suffer its worst heat wave ever, blanketing the state in 100°F temperature for weeks, killing more than one hundred people and sending electricity demand soaring).

Moreover, California imports a great deal of electricity. In the 1990s, the state failed to anticipate that the rapid growth of neighboring states meant that when the demand crunch came, those imports would dry up. With demand growing faster than expected and supply slowing down, with summers getting hotter and power surpluses shrinking, and with crooked companies like Enron controlling the trade of electricity and natural gas, the day of reckoning was inevitable.

The crisis hit in 1999 and 2000, with shortages and blackouts. The state raised prices and launched a massive efficiency program, the amazing results of which are now in. From 2000 to 2004, California utilities spent $1.4 billion. The average cost of the electricity saved was 2.9 cents per kilowatt-hour—far cheaper than what new peak power generation in the state costs, 16.7 cents per kilowatt-hour, and half the price of building base-load power (generators that run all the time), 5.8 cents per kilowatt-hour. Helping people use electricity more wisely is far cheaper than building new power plants, and that's without even counting the benefits of avoided global-warming pollution and healthier air to breathe.

The utility programs became steadily more effective over time. By 2004, the average cost of the efficiency programs had dropped in half, to under 1.4 cents per kilowatt-hour, cheaper than any form of new power supply in this country—*and far cheaper than any carbon-free power,* including renewable energy and nuclear plants. And it is not just California that has achieved these results. A 2006 report by the Western Governors' Association confirmed that a variety of energy-efficiency programs in western states have delivered savings at similarly low cost.

One of the leaders in California's energy-efficiency push is Dr. Arthur Rosenfeld, the world-class physicist who launched the Center for Building Sciences at Lawrence Berkeley National Laboratory in the 1970s. He helped develop many of the energy-efficiency programs for the state and many of the efficient technologies used around the nation, including windows and lighting. I worked with him at the Department of Energy, and he later became a California energy commissioner, helping guide the state through its crisis.

Rosenfeld told me that California was so satisfied with the efficiency effort that it was going to ramp up funding. Rather than keeping electricity per capita flat, they want to cut it 0.5 percent to 1 percent a year. He notes that the state's efficiency efforts, from the 1970s through 2004, have lowered the energy bill of Californians by $12 billion a year, which comes to a whopping $1,000 a family—even accounting for the extra cost of the efficiency products, services, and programs. The total investment has, on average, paid for itself in energy savings in less than three years and then just keeps generating profits for Californians. *And it is avoiding the emissions of more than 10 million metric tons of carbon dioxide every year.* This is the program to copy—around the country and the world.

I asked Dr. Rosenfeld how much it would cost to duplicate California's program nationwide. His answer: The total effort costs about 2 percent of the revenues of electric utilities, which translates into $6 billion a year nationwide (since the nation's electric bill is about $300 billion). Because parts of United States have more air-conditioning demand than California, he thought the United States might want to invest closer to $9 billion a year, if the goal is to keep electricity consumption per capita flat. Now, that would be a bargain, when America's 100 million households save some $1,000 each year!

Most important, these programs focus on *existing* technology, on getting those technologies into the marketplace, into the homes and offices of consumers and businesses, as quickly as possible. The California Energy Commission has an R&D program to develop new technology, but only so that it can then be sped into the marketplace. In California, efforts to deploy existing energy-efficiency technologies have maintained support through Democratic and Republican administrations alike.

Most conservative politicians do not like energy-efficiency programs, especially ones aimed at accelerating the market entry of new technologies. The Gingrich Congress cut or eliminated most of the deployment programs that the Clinton Energy Department launched in the early 1990s. The Bush administration has sharply cut the funding for the most historically effective efficiency efforts so that they can make room for hydrogen-fuel-cell R&D, which has no realistic prospect of seeing significant marketplace success for several decades.

The Bush administration has relentlessly cut funding for technology deployment. Especially counterproductive is the administration's move to shut down the DOE's regional offices in Boston, Philadelphia, Atlanta, Chicago, Denver, and Seattle. These were set up in the 1970s to help the nation learn how to save energy. They are, or were, the primary national effort to deliver technical and financial assistance to communities, states, industries, and other energy users. The president is shutting them down just when we need them the most.

NATURAL-GAS EFFICIENCY

Since 2000, the United States has suffered through repeated price spikes for natural gas. Between 1999 and 2002 we added some 138 gigawatts in natural-gas-fired capacity, but the increased demand for gas—no surprise—led to a price increase. North American natural-gas supply is limited. Worse, Canadian natural-gas exports to the United States are projected to decline in coming years as Canada uses more and more of the gas for its own purposes, including producing oil from the Alberta tar sands.

High natural-gas prices have driven increases in demand for coal electricity and for new coal plants. High prices have led many politicians to advocate spending tens of billions of dollars on facilities to bring in liquefied natural gas (LNG), even though LNG tankers and terminals are widely seen as a major terrorist target and even though that would increase the nation's dependence on imported energy. About 58 percent of the world's natural-gas reserves are in Iran, Russia, and Qatar—hardly bastions of democracy or stability, hardly the kind of countries we want to be beholden to.

Rather than a major effort to increase our dependence on

foreign-energy supplies, a superior national strategy is more efficient use of our domestic natural gas. As with electricity, most buildings and factories can cut natural-gas consumption by more than 25 percent right now with rapid payback (under four years), after which the savings become profits forever.

A major focus should be on more efficient use of steam, which is crucial for production in energy-intensive industries such as chemicals, food products, plastics, primary metals, pulp and paper, textiles, and petroleum refining. It is generated mainly by natural gas. Steam accounts for $24 billion a year of U.S. manufacturing energy costs and 40 percent of U.S. industrial carbon dioxide emissions. Expanding state and federal efforts to use steam far more efficiently, such as the DOE's Best Practices Steam Program, would cut those numbers sharply.

The energy-intensive industries are not only major consumers of natural gas, they account for 80 percent of energy consumed by U.S. manufacturers and 90 percent of the hazardous waste. They represent the best chance for increasing efficiency while cutting pollution. Many are major emitters of greenhouse gases other than carbon dioxide. A 1993 analysis for the DOE found that a 10 to 20 percent reduction in waste by American industry would generate a cumulative increase of $1.94 trillion in the gross domestic product from 1996 to 2010. By 2010 the improvements would be generating 2 million new jobs, or roughly 1.5 percent of employment in that year.

For these reasons, in the 1990s, the Energy Department began forming partnerships with energy-intensive industries to develop clean technologies. We worked with scientists and engineers to identify areas of joint research into technologies that would simultaneously save energy, reduce pollution, and increase productivity. The Bush administration has slashed funding for this program by 50 percent—and wants to shut it down entirely. This is especially baffling from an administration that opposes environmental regulations, because funding for pollution prevention technology is by far the best way for the nation to minimize the need for such regulations. But that's why it's always important to remember that the new-technology-is-the-only-answer pitch is just empty rhetoric, no matter how many times the administration repeats it.

An important companion strategy to natural-gas efficiency would be a major national effort to encourage the simultaneous generation of both electricity and heat, called *cogeneration,* or combined heat and power. Cogen provides large opportunities to save both energy and carbon dioxide. Right now, fossil fuels burned at large central-station power plants generate most of the electricity used by U.S. companies. These plants are typically quite inefficient, converting *only about one-third* of the energy in fossil fuels into electricity. The waste heat generated by that combustion is literally thrown away, and then more energy is lost transmitting the electricity from the power plant to the factory or building. The total energy wasted by U.S. power generators each year equals the total energy Japan uses each year. More fossil fuels are then burned in our buildings and factories to provide heat, hot water, and steam. The average building boiler converts *only about two-thirds* of its fossil fuels to useful heat or steam.

By generating electricity and capturing the waste heat in a cogeneration system, much energy and pollution can be saved. *Overall system efficiencies can exceed 80 percent.* Total greenhouse gas emissions can be cut in half.

Many studies have shown that the potential market for cogen is enormous. For instance, a 2000 study for the DOE found that the market potential for combined heat and power at commercial and institutional facilities alone was 75,000 megawatts, about one-tenth of current U.S. power-generation capacity. The remaining potential in the industrial sector is about 88,000 megawatts.

Cogen and other *on-site* power systems, such as solar panels, are called distributed energy as opposed to large central-station power plants, like coal or nuclear. Their market penetration is limited by barriers that have nothing to do with their cost or performance—especially the countless obstacles and fees that major utilities can place in their way. In the late 1990s, the DOE launched a study of these barriers, looking at sixty-five distributed-energy projects. The result was a July 2000 report that offered a variety of recommendations we should embrace:

- Adopt uniform standards for interconnecting distributed power to the grid.
- Adopt testing and certification procedures for interconnection equipment.
- Accelerate development of distributed power-control technology and systems.
- Develop tools for utilities to assess the value and impact of distributed power.
- Develop new regulatory principles compatible with distributed-power choices.
- Adopt regulatory tariffs and utility incentives to fit a distributed-power model.

The strategies we need to avoid climate catastrophe are not about imposing the heavy hand of government on the marketplace; rather they are about leveling the playing field and giving an extra push to low-carbon technologies. How much carbon dioxide could an efficiency and cogen strategy save the country? Before answering that, let's look at the potential for renewable power.

THE RENEWABLES REVOLUTION

Energy efficiency can stop the runaway growth of electricity demand. Cogeneration can reduce the carbon emissions of much of the electricity that is generated. Renewable energy can deliver electricity without any carbon emissions. In terms of annual percentage growth, wind and solar energy were the two fastest-growing forms of power in the past two decades. I will focus here on wind because it is the renewable that can meet the most large-scale demand at the lowest price.

Modern wind turbines convert the kinetic energy of the wind into electricity. Wind turbines are often grouped together into "farms" to generate bulk electrical power. Electricity from these turbines is fed into the local utility grid and distributed to customers.

America has exceptional wind resources, especially the central United States from the Texas Panhandle up through the Great Plains. North Dakota alone has enough energy from high-wind resources to supply 36 percent of the electricity of the lower forty-eight states. Much of the available wind, however, is not located near the consumer. Therefore, if wind were to become a significant portion of the generation mix, additional investments in transmission and distribution infrastructure would be needed.

Over the past 15 years, major aerodynamic improvements in blade design have cut the cost of electricity from wind power by 10 percent *per year*. New, utility-scale wind projects are being built all around the country today, delivering electricity at prices as low as 4 cents per kilowatt-hour in the best wind sites. Media attention has been focused on the few public disputes over wind-farm locations, such as the offshore wind farm planned near Cape Cod, but most of the country has been embracing wind enthusiastically; aggregated installed wind in the United States is roughly 9,000 megawatts as of the end of 2005—five times the installed capacity of 1999.

The next-generation wind turbine is projected to bring costs down to 3 cents per kilowatt-hour over the next several years (including the wind-production tax credit). Since wind is an intermittent electricity generator and does not provide power on an as-needed basis, it loses some value on a per-kilowatt-hour basis, compared with traditional generation that can provide steady base-load power. On the other hand, wind can more than make up for this lost value by providing benefits in terms of reduced emissions and elimination of fuel risk (such as seen by natural-gas plants).

While wind now provides less than 1 percent of U.S. electricity generation, it represents up to 40 percent of electricity in regions of Germany, Spain, and Denmark. And wind is only one of several renewable technologies that are near-competitive with grid electricity. As a major 2004 report by the International Energy Agency concluded: "Under the best conditions—optimized system design, site and resource availability—electricity from biomass, small hydropower, wind and geothermal plants can produce electricity at costs ranging from 2–5 cents/kilowatt-hour."

Note that geothermal energy made that list. Geothermal power converts the earth's own deep energy into heat and electricity. It remains a very attractive power source. But in 2006, when Bush proposed his "Advanced Energy Initiative—a 22-percent increase in clean-energy research," he needed to find money to fund it. He found it by zeroing out all federal funding for geothermal research.

Renewable-energy power plants typically have high capital costs, but their operating costs are low, because they don't consume fuel on a daily basis. While most forms of renewable energy are not competitive with current wholesale electricity prices, it is well to remember that

1. Many traditional power plants have long since paid off their capital costs, so that their electricity cost comes only from fuel and operating costs. New fossil fuel power plants don't have that price advantage.
2. Many renewables have not yet achieved their ultimate cost reduction from either improvements in technology or manufacturing economies of scale at higher volume.

3. Carbon dioxide emissions have no economic cost to the producer and are never counted in the comparisons of true energy costs.

So new renewables will be increasingly competitive with new fossil fuel plants, especially when we properly account for the real cost of global-warming emissions, which, as we have seen, threatens to bring about almost incalculable damage to the next fifty generations of Americans.

It is then no surprise to learn that by 2005, some two dozen states and more than forty countries had a national target for their own renewable-energy supply, including all twenty-five countries in the European Union. The E.U. has set a target of having 21 percent of its electricity come from renewables by 2010.

Our Congress, however, refuses to adopt a renewable standard that would require even 10 percent of U.S. power to be delivered by renewable energy. Yet a standard requiring *20 percent* of U.S. electricity to be renewable by 2020 has very little net cost to the country, but brings the huge benefit of reducing future natural-gas prices and future greenhouse gas emissions. Under such a standard, electricity prices would be *lower* in 2020 than they are today, according to a 2001 Department of Energy study.

POWER SWITCH

What could this country achieve with an energy policy based on existing technology and the most successful strategies used by states and other countries to get those technologies into the marketplace? In 2003 I coauthored a study on "The Path to Carbon-Dioxide-Free Power," which focused on the three technology areas I have been discussing: energy efficiency, cogeneration, and renewables.

The results were very promising. They showed that with a set of innovative and ambitious policies the U.S. electricity sector could cut CO_2 emissions in half by 2020. The price of carbon dioxide never exceeds about $15 a ton ($55 a ton of carbon), which translates into slightly more than 1.5 cents per kilowatt-hour added to the cost of a traditional coal plant. Electricity rates rise slightly, but at the same time we will be using electricity more efficiently, which will cause bills to drop substantially. The net savings would be about *$20 billion per year* from 2004 to 2020 and would exceed $80 billion a year after 2020.

The country would see only a small increase in electricity generation from current levels, and natural-gas use stays roughly flat, even while the U.S. population rises 20 percent and industrial output increases 75 percent. Yet consumers and businesses would receive the same or better energy services in 2020 than in the business-as-usual case. The power system would become more reliable and less vulnerable to external disruption, including terrorist attack.

As an added benefit, Americans would see a sharp decline in air pollution and a resulting improvement in health. Utility mercury emissions, which threaten the health and developmental ability of children, would drop 90 percent. Emissions of oxides of nitrogen and sulfur dioxide, which are linked to respiratory and other health problems in humans, drop by two-thirds or more.

Many studies before and since this one have shown similar results, including two major studies by our national laboratories. In fact, *Policy Implications of Greenhouse Warming*, a 1991 study by the National Academy of Sciences, concluded, "This analysis suggests that the United States could reduce its greenhouse gas emissions by between 10 and 40 percent of the 1990 level and at very low cost. Some reductions may even be a net savings if the proper policies are implemented."

American conservatives (and many economists) do not believe such emissions reductions are possible without a very high cost. They do not accept that the economy now operates inefficiently, nor do they believe government technology policies would have much value. Their studies typically ignore the possibility of efficiency and cogeneration, and, with tunnel vision, they assume the only way to achieve the proposed reductions is with very high prices for carbon dioxide in electricity.

If we do nothing for the next two decades, U.S. carbon dioxide emissions will rise another 20 percent or more, and we will have invested hundreds of billions of dollars in another generation of inefficient and carbon-intensive technologies and power plants. If we then try to reduce emissions to 60 percent below 1990 levels by 2050, the cost of energy would probably have to double and the government would probably have to simply mandate shutting down most of our coal plants, with devastating consequences for consumers and businesses. The Delayers believe that action on global warming will hurt the U.S. economy and require onerous government mandates. Ironically, their way of thinking could become a self-fulfilling prophecy.

Having worked with dozens of companies to design profitable emissions-reduction strategies, and having carefully reviewed more than a hundred specific case studies of buildings and factories that employed energy efficiency, cogeneration, and renewable energy, I have no doubt that the United States could dramatically reduce its carbon emissions per kilowatt-hour without raising its overall energy bill.

But you don't have to take my word for this. Nor do you have to wade into the dull details of either the technologies or the economics. Just consider California. In 2004 the state consumed about 7,000 kilowatt-hours per person, whereas the rest of the country consumed about 13,000 kWh per person. California's electricity rates (cents per kWh) are about 50 percent higher than the national average, yet its annual electric bill per person is about the same as the rest of the nation because it wastes less electricity. Its rates are higher partly because California is paying for the legacy of its flawed deregulation in the 1990s, and that portion of the extra rate should decrease over time. Its rates are also higher because it has much cleaner power generation, using more renewables and natural gas than the rest of the country. Californians decided that they value the reduction of unhealthful air pollution.

The result is that each kilowatt-hour consumed in California generates only about half the carbon dioxide emissions of the national average. Combine that fact with the more efficient use of electricity, and you get a startling statistic. In terms of electricity consumption, *the average California generates under one-third of the carbon dioxide emissions of the average American while paying the same annual bill.*

NUCLEAR POWER

The lack of knowledge about energy by even the most senior politicians is scary. Consider Senator John McCain's comments in a March 2006 interview, in which he stated he would demand legislation to expand U.S. nuclear power as part of his efforts to reduce greenhouse gas emissions: "It's the only technology presently available to quickly step up to meet our energy needs," he said.

Wrong on both counts: Nuclear is not the only technology, nor is it the quickest. The licensing and construction process for nuclear plants takes many years, and it should, given that the plants are expensive, carry many safety and environmental risks, and have been given limited liability by Congress in case of an accident. An energy-efficiency strategy would be much faster.

McCain's comment reflects a common misconception that some never-named entity is mysteriously holding back the expansion of nuclear power in this country. What has really been holding back nuclear power is the economic and other risks it poses to utilities and financiers—Wall Street.

Nuclear energy is mostly carbon-free power. Yet it is not a slam-dunk solution to global warming. A major 2003 study by MIT, "The Future of Nuclear Power," highlighted many of the "unresolved problems" that have created "limited prospects for nuclear power today." The study found that "in deregulated markets, nuclear power is not now cost competitive with coal and natural gas." The public has significant concerns about safety, environmental, health, and terrorism risks associated with nuclear power. The study also found that "nuclear power has unresolved challenges in long-term management of radioactive wastes." It described possible technological and other strategies for addressing these issues but noted that "the cost improvements we project are plausible but unproven."

Peter Bradford, a former member of the Nuclear Regulatory Commission (NRC), told the *New York Times* in May 2005, "The abiding lesson that Three Mile Island taught Wall Street was that a group of NRC-licensed reactor operators, as good as any others, could turn a $2 billion asset into a $1 billion cleanup job in about 90 minutes."

Nuclear power may well be one important piece of the climate-stabilization puzzle, which is why I have included it as one of the eight wedges. Achieving one nuclear wedge means building a nuclear power plant somewhere in the world every month for the next fifty years, while maintaining current nuclear capacity.

But nuclear power is hardly a fledgling technology that needs even more targeted support from the U.S. government. Nuclear already gets countless subsidies. For instance, the Price-Anderson Act limits liability in the event of a nuclear disaster. And the Energy Policy Act of 2005 gives the industry billions of dollars more in subsidies—even authorizing more than $1 billion to build a nuclear plant solely for the purpose of making hydrogen, an especially pointless subsidy, as we will see in the next chapter.

The nation needs to put into place mandatory carbon dioxide controls. If a significant price for carbon makes nuclear power attractive to utilities and financiers, and if the plants meet the necessary safety and environmental codes, and if the country can finally agree on a place to put the nuclear waste, then new nuclear plants may well make a significant contribution to reducing greenhouse gas emissions in this country. I certainly wouldn't shut down any existing nuclear plants that are run safely. Nor would I discourage other countries from pursuing nuclear power, as long as it is done under the proper international controls to prevent the proliferation of nuclear weapons.

California, however, achieves its remarkably low per capita carbon dioxide emissions from electricity while getting a lower share of its power from nuclear energy than the national average. That's why federal electricity policy should focus on establishing a price for carbon dioxide, promoting energy efficiency, cogeneration, and renewable energy, and accelerating coal gasification together with carbon capture and storage. Those strategies can take us as far as we need to go on emissions reductions in the utility sector for the next few decades.

We will need a similarly aggressive and intelligent set of technology policies to deal with the other major CO_2-producing sector of the U.S. economy—transportation.

CHAPTER EIGHT

PEAK OIL, ENERGY SECURITY, AND THE CAR OF THE FUTURE

We have a serious problem. America is addicted to oil, which is often imported from unstable parts of the world.
—President George W. Bush, 2006

In the absence of revolutionary changes in energy policy, we are risking multiple disasters for our country that will constrain living standards, undermine our foreign-policy goals, and leave us highly vulnerable to the machinations of rogue states.
—Senator Richard Lugar, 2006

Our ever-worsening addiction to oil makes America less secure. Since 1990, we have fought two wars in the Persian Gulf. We suffered a major terrorist attack funded largely by Persian Gulf oil money. Every year we send more than $250 billion overseas because we import most of our oil. Oil prices keep spiking above $70 a barrel, and gasoline above $3 a gallon. The economic lifeblood of our country is held hostage to countries that are antidemocratic and politically unstable—and to terrorists who keep targeting the world's oil infrastructure. Price spikes above $100 a barrel (and $4 a gallon) are all but inevitable in the coming years. And many fear we may be close to seeing worldwide oil production peak and then decline, which will bring an era of steadily rising oil and gasoline prices.

It's no wonder that politicians—even those who don't worry about global warming—keep talking about oil. So why haven't we taken any serious action on oil for decades? The answer is simple—reducing U.S. oil consumption requires a major government-led effort, such as much tougher mileage standards, and our political leaders have rejected such efforts (except for ones that are merely cosmetic).

The astonishing January 2006 statement by President Bush's EPA administrator, Stephen Johnson, bears repeating: "Are we going to tell people to stop driving their cars, or do we start investing in technology? That's the answer, investing in those technologies." This false choice leaves the nation with no oil policy except strong, empty rhetoric suggesting that the cure for our addiction to oil can be found in happy talk about future technology. Here's what President Bush said the next month, in February 2006:

> Our nation is on the threshold of new energy technology that I think will startle the American people. We're on the edge of some amazing breakthroughs—breakthroughs all aimed at enhancing our national security and our economic security and the quality of life of the folks who live here in the United States.

The president has actually misdirected more than a billion dollars toward the development of hydrogen cars, a solution that will not address either our oil or climate problems in our lifetime, as we will see. I also examine in this chapter why the peak in global oil production is less of a threat to our way of life than is widely perceived, and why peak oil won't avert catastrophic climate change.

We will see why the win-win policies needed to avoid Hell and High Water would also make this nation energy-independent by midcentury, even with declining domestic oil supplies. Finally, this chapter describes the car and fuel of the future. Let's start with some background.

TRANSPORTATION AND OIL

About two-thirds of U.S. oil consumption is in the transportation sector, the only sector of the U.S. economy almost wholly reliant on oil. The energy price shocks of the 1970s helped spur growth in natural-gas use for home heating. It also drove the electric utility sector and the industrial sector to sharply reduce their dependence on petroleum. But roughly 97 percent of all energy consumed by our cars, sport-utility vehicles, vans, trucks, and airplanes is still petroleum-based.

Over the past two decades, cleaner engines and reformulated gasoline have worked together to cut vehicular emissions of noxious urban air pollutants, especially the oxides of nitrogen that are a precursor to ozone smog and particulates, the stuff that does so much damage to our hearts and lungs. But the contribution to global warming by cars and light trucks, such as SUVs, has risen steadily. In the 1990s the transportation sector saw the fastest growth in carbon dioxide emissions of any major sector of the U.S. economy. And the transportation sector will generate nearly half of the 40 percent rise in U.S. carbon dioxide emissions forecast for 2025.

Internationally, the situation is equally fearful. As Claude Mandil, executive director of the International Energy Agency (IEA), said in May 2004, "In the absence of strong government policies, we project that the worldwide use of oil in transport will nearly double between 2000 and 2030, leading to a similar increase in greenhouse gas emissions." If by 2050 the per capita energy consumption of China and India were to approach that of South Korea, and if the Chinese and Indian populations increase as predicted, those two supergiant countries *by themselves* would consume more oil than the entire world used in 2003.

"It took us 125 years to use the first trillion barrels of oil," says a Chevron oil-company ad. "We'll use the next trillion in 30." This computes to an average of about 33 billion barrels of oil a year, which is 91 million barrels of oil a day or *A Thousand Barrels a Second,* the title of a 2006 book by energy economist Peter Tertzakian. World demand hit about 84 million barrels a day in 2005, up from 78 million in 2002—a torrid pace of demand growth that slowed only somewhat when prices spiked above $60 and even $70 a barrel in 2005 and 2006.

Since oil is a finite, nonrenewable resource, many analysts have tried to predict when global production will peak and then start declining, just as U.S. oil production in the lower forty-eight states did three decades ago. Some experts believe this peak will occur by 2010. Princeton geophysicist Kenneth Deffeyes wrote in 2001, "There is nothing plausible that could postpone the peak until 2009. Get used to it." Royal Dutch/Shell, a company that has downgraded its own oil-reserve estimates, adds only two or three decades to this forecast. According to Shell, "A scarcity of oil supplies—including unconventional sources and natural gas liquids—is very unlikely before 2025. This could be extended to 2040 by adopting known measures to increase vehicle efficiency and focusing oil demand on this sector." As we will see, Shell's hedges—"unconventional sources and natural gas liquids" as well as "known measures" to increase vehicle efficiency—will largely decide how the peaking of global oil production will affect the climate and our way of life.

"Conventional" oil means the liquid crude petroleum that is extracted from the ground using the traditional method, an oil well. Experts do not agree on how much "ultimately recoverable" oil remains in the ground, in part because they use different definitions for conventional oil and in part because they disagree about how much technology advances will enable more oil to be found and extracted. Also, the peak-oil "pessimists" simply don't believe the claims by some Middle East governments as to how much conventional-oil reserves they have.

Resolving that dispute is beyond the scope of this book, but a few points are critical to understand. The vast majority of the world's conventional-oil reserves are in unstable regions, such as the Middle East, guaranteeing extreme oil-price volatility for decades to come. The rapid growth in demand for oil by developing countries, especially China and India, coupled with the refusal by the United States to adopt strong policies to restrain or reverse our own growing demand, ensure that conventional oil will almost certainly peak and then decline sometime in the next quarter-century. The world is in fact running out of conventional oil. What about unconventional oil?

PEAK OIL AND GLOBAL WARMING

Unfortunately, *most forms of unconventional oil will make global warming worse*—and some of them will make Hell and High Water all but inevitable. Ironically, global warming is making it easier to explore and drill for oil in the Arctic because the sea ice is vanishing at an ever-increasing rate. The amount of undiscovered oil in the Arctic has been estimated at 200 to 400 billion barrels—enough to supply the world for seven to fourteen years at current usage. Let's look at some of the major unconventional sources.

First, we have a number of viscous oils called bitumen, heavy oil, and tar sands (or oil sands). There is more recoverable heavy oil in Venezuela than there is conventional oil in Saudi Arabia, and Canada has even more recoverable oil in its tar sands. Tar sands are pretty much the heavy gunk they sound like, and making liquid fuels from them requires huge amounts of energy for steam injection and refining. Canada is currently producing about a million barrels of oil a day from the tar sands, and that is projected to triple over the next two decades.

The tar sands are doubly dirty. On the one hand, the energy-intensive conversion of the tar sands directly generates two to four times the amount of greenhouse gases per barrel of final product as the production of conventional oil. On the other hand, Canada's increasing use of natural gas to exploit the tar sands is one reason that its exports of natural gas to the United States are projected to shrink in the coming years. So instead of selling clean-burning natural gas to this country, which we could use to stop the growth of carbon-intensive coal generation, Canada will provide us with a more carbon-intensive oil product to burn in our cars. That's lose-lose.

From a climate perspective, fully exploiting the tar-sands resource would make Canada's climate policy as immoral as ours.

Second, even more oil can probably be recovered from shale, a claylike rock, than from the tar sands. Most of the world's shale is found in the United States, and most of our shale, a trillion tons, is found in Colorado and Utah. After the oil shocks of the 1970s, billions were spent exploring the possibility of shale oil, but those efforts were abandoned in the 1980s when oil prices collapsed. Shale does not contain much energy—per pound, it has one-tenth the energy of crude oil and one-fourth that of recycled phone books. Converting shale to oil requires a huge amount of energy—possibly as much as 1,200 megawatts of generating capacity to produce only 100,000 barrels per day. If those were fossil-based megawatts, we would be spewing millions of tons of greenhouse gases into the air every year just to create a fuel that itself would spew more greenhouse gases into the air when burned in a car. But then it would be equally crazy to use renewable energy to make shale, when we critically need that zero-carbon power to displace coal electricity.

We simply must leave the shale in the ground.

Third, the recovery of conventional oil from a well can be enhanced by injecting carbon dioxide (CO_2) into the reservoir. Estimates for potential recovery are 300 to 600 billion barrels. A 2005 study, "Peaking of World Oil Production," led by Science Applications International Corporation (SAIC) explained:

> CO_2 flooding can increase oil recovery by 7–15 percent of original oil in place. Because EOR (enhanced oil recovery) is relatively expensive, it has not been widely deployed in the past. However, as a way of dealing with peak conventional oil production and higher oil prices, it has significant potential.

The SAIC study might also have noted that in a world where carbon capture and storage from coal generation becomes commonplace—which might occur as soon as two decades from now—we may be awash in carbon dioxide that could be diverted to EOR. What a double tragedy it would be if that carbon dioxide were not put into deep underground aquifers (permanently reducing the amount of heat-trapping gas in the atmosphere) but instead was used to extract more fossil fuels from the ground (which would ultimately release carbon dioxide into the atmosphere when burned in internal combustion engines).

Fourth, coal and natural gas can be converted to diesel fuel using the Fischer-Tropsch process. During World War II, coal gasification and liquefaction produced more than half of the liquid fuel used by the German military. America has so much coal, it could replace all imported oil with liquid fuel from coal—and keep generating electricity from coal—for more than 100 years. China has nearly as much coal as we do. The Chinese are launching a huge coal-liquefaction effort and plan to generate 300,000 barrels of oil a day from coal by 2020.

The process is incredibly expensive. You need to spend $5 billion or more just to build a plant capable of producing only 80,000 barrels of oil a day (the United States currently consumes more than 21 million barrels a day). You need about 5 gallons of water for every gallon of diesel fuel that's produced—not a particularly good long-term strategy in a world facing mega-droughts and chronic water shortages. Worse, the total carbon dioxide emissions from coal-to-diesel are about double that of conventional diesel. You can capture the carbon dioxide from the process and store it underground permanently. But that will make an expensive process even more expensive, so it seems unlikely for the foreseeable future, certainly not until carbon dioxide is regulated and has a high price, and we have a number of certified underground geologic repositories.

More important, even if you capture the CO_2 from the Fischer-Tropsch process, you are still left with diesel fuel, a carbon-intensive liquid that will release carbon dioxide into the atmosphere once it is burned in an internal combustion engine. A great many people I have spoken to are confused about this point; they think that capturing and storing the CO_2 while turning coal to diesel is as good an idea as capturing the CO_2 from the integrated gasification combined-cycle process for turning coal into electricity. No. The former process still leaves you with a carbon-intensive fuel, whereas the latter process leaves you with zero-carbon electricity. Worse, some people propose taking the captured CO_2 and using it for enhanced oil recovery, which, as we've seen, is the equivalent of not capturing the carbon dioxide at all.

Coal-to-diesel is a bad idea for the planet. If the United States or China pursues it aggressively, catastrophic climate change will be all but unavoidable. Turning natural gas into diesel is not as bad an idea, at least from the perspective of direct emissions, because natural gas is a low-carbon fuel. But it represents a tremendous misuse of natural gas, which could otherwise be used to displace coal plants and sharply reduce future greenhouse gas emissions.

A 2006 study by the University of California at Berkeley found that meeting the future demand shortfall from conventional oil with unconventional oil, especially coal-to-diesel, could increase annual carbon emissions by 2 billion metric tons (7.3 gigatons of carbon dioxide) for several decades. That would certainly be fatal to any effort to avoid 20 to 80 feet of sea-level rise.

We are simply running out of time, and we no longer have the luxury of grossly misallocating capital and fuels. That's why significantly exploiting unconventional sources of liquid fossil fuel such as coal, tar sands, and shale is the road to ruin. And that's why the Bush administration efforts to push hydrogen-fuel-cell cars make so little sense.

THE HYPE ABOUT HYDROGEN

> *Forget hydrogen, forget hydrogen, forget hydrogen.*
> —Former CIA director James Woolsey, 2006

The promise of hydrogen cars as a simple techno-fix, a deus ex machina to solve our environmental problems painlessly, and without regulations, is a cornerstone of the Bush administration's climate policy. In his January 2003 State of the Union address, the president pledged "$1.2 billion in research funding so that America can lead the world in developing clean, hydrogen-powered automobiles." He then said that "the first car driven by a child born today could be powered by hydrogen, and pollution-free."

The president didn't tell the public that more than 98 percent of the hydrogen made in this country today must be extracted from fossil fuel hydrocarbons—natural gas, oil, and coal—and that process releases huge amounts of carbon dioxide. "It is highly likely that fossil fuels will be the principal sources of hydrogen for several decades," concluded a prestigious National Academy of Sciences panel in 2004. In fact, hydrogen as a transport fuel might even *in-*

crease greenhouse gas emissions rather than reduce them. That was the conclusion of a January 2004 study by the European Commission and European oil companies and car companies.

The only way hydrogen cars could be "pollution-free" is for the hydrogen to be made from pollution-free sources of energy, like wind power. But the administration and Congress won't even pass a law requiring that 10 percent of U.S. electricity be renewable by 2020—so what are the chances that children born in 2003 will be driving a car in 2020 with pollution-free hydrogen?

Making hydrogen for use in cars is a terrible use of pollution-free power. Instead, we should build renewable-power plants to avoid the need to build new coal plants and save *four times as much carbon dioxide at less than one-tenth the cost* of using that same renewable power to make hydrogen to run a car. Study after study has shown that it makes no sense to squander renewable power to make hydrogen for cars until the electric grid is itself virtually greenhouse-gas-free—and that is at least four decades away. That's 40 years from now, even if we are able to reverse our current energy policy the day after Bush leaves office.

And this analysis assumes that hydrogen cars will actually become practical for consumers any time soon. But that is highly unlikely. They simply require too many scientific breakthroughs. For starters, a pollution-free hydrogen car requires a fuel cell for efficiently converting hydrogen into useful energy without generating pollution. Fuel cells are small, modular electrochemical devices, similar to batteries, except that they can be continuously fueled. They take in hydrogen and oxygen and put out only water plus heat and electricity, which runs an electric motor.

Unfortunately, fuel cells for cars currently cost about $2,000 per kW, which is about fifty times greater than the cost of an internal combustion engine. A major breakthrough will be required to make fuel cells affordable and practical.

Yet another major breakthrough is needed to solve the storage problem. Hydrogen is the most diffuse gas there is. No known material can store enough of it in a practical way to give people the kind of driving range they want. A March 2004 study by the American Physical Society concluded that "a new material must be discovered" to solve the storage problem.

Another problem: Currently hydrogen from pollution-free renewable sources would cost the equivalent of $6 to $10 a gallon of gasoline. So we'll need another major breakthrough that will drop the cost by a factor of three.

Hydrogen cars need three major breakthroughs—in fuel cells, storage, and renewable hydrogen—within the next decade or so, in a world where game-changing energy-technology breakthroughs hardly ever happen. And if those three happened, we would still need someone to spend more than $500 billion to build the fueling infrastructure needed to make hydrogen available throughout the country. An analysis in the May 2004 issue of *Scientific American* stated, "Fuel-cell cars, in contrast [to hybrids], are expected on about the same schedule as NASA's manned trip to Mars and have about the same level of likelihood."

When Bill Reinert, the U.S. manager of Toyota's advanced technologies group, was asked in 2005 when fuel-cell cars would replace gasoline cars, he answered, "If I told you 'never,' would you be upset?" A 2004 MIT study concluded that hydrogen-fuel-cell cars would be unlikely to achieve significant market success until the year 2060, far too late to help.

And yet in spite of all this, the Bush administration keeps pumping money into the budget for hydrogen. In its 5-year budget outlook released in 2006, the hydrogen-technology budget rose to a stunning $323 million in fiscal year 2011 (out of $1.13 billion for all energy efficiency and renewable energy) from a requested $196 million in 2007 (out of $1.18 billion). The tragedy of this is a 20 percent drop in funding for technologies that actually hold some promise of helping to reduce greenhouse gas emissions in the first half of this century.

In April 2005, Energy Secretary Samuel Bodman announced that he was disbanding the department's primary independent advisory board on scientific and technical matters, a board that has existed in some form since 1978. Bodman is uninterested in outside scientific advice. A department spokesman claimed Bodman was doing this because he is a chemical engineer by training and "the secretary has an understanding of science and scientific processes." But Bodman's 5-year budget plan grossly misdirects more than a billion dollars of the department's research-and-development funds, suggesting that he doesn't understand at all.

THE WIN-WIN OIL POLICY

> *My message is that the balance of realism has passed from those who argue on behalf of oil and a laissez-faire energy policy that relies on market evolution, to those who recognize that in the absence of a major reorientation in the way we get our energy, life in America is going to be much more difficult in the coming decades.*
> —Senator Richard Lugar, 2006

If neither hydrogen cars nor the peak and subsequent drop in global oil production are going to save us from endlessly rising greenhouse gas emissions, what will?

I have described a variety of aggressive low-carbon strategies or "wedges" we need to achieve over the next five decades. Each wedge ultimately avoids 1 billion metric tons of carbon emissions a year.

The last chapter looked at the five wedges needed to reduce

emissions from electricity, buildings, and heavy industry. The two wedges needed in the transportation sector are:

- Every car and SUV achieves an average fuel economy of 60 miles per gallon.
- Every car can run on electricity for short distances before reverting to biofuels.

How do we ensure that the *average* car on the road in 2060 gets 60 mpg, when the current average is about one-third that? Some push for high gasoline taxes. European countries such as the United Kingdom and Germany have taxes of more than $2 per gallon, which is five times more than the U.S. tax. Yet the average fuel economy of European Union vehicles is nowhere near 60 mpg. Oil and gasoline prices will probably trend higher over the next two decades by themselves as demand continues to grow in the face of supply constraints, and as terrorism and instability cause price spikes and oil-market jitters. When this country gets serious about global warming, we will put in place a carbon-trading system that will increase the price of gasoline somewhat, though far less than European gas taxes do today. I don't think higher gas taxes are the best way to get 60-mpg cars.

Another, more obvious strategy is tougher fuel-efficiency standards. After all, corporate average fuel economy (CAFE) standards, enacted in 1975, were used successfully in this country to double the fuel efficiency of our cars while making them safer, mandating that new cars have a fuel efficiency of 27.5 miles per gallon. In a 2002 report to President Bush, the National Academy of Sciences concluded that automobile fuel economy could be increased by up to 42 percent for large SUVs with technologies that would pay for themselves in fuel savings. That study did not even consider the greater use of diesels and hybrids. The report was ignored.

Studies by the national laboratories, by MIT, and by the Pew

Center on Global Climate Change have concluded that even greater savings could be cost-effective while maintaining or improving passenger safety. In a comprehensive 2005 study of fuel economy and traffic fatalities in industrialized nations, Robert Noland of the Centre for Transport Studies at Imperial College in London found that "average fleet fuel economy has no effect on traffic fatalities." The conclusion: "Policies aimed at improving fuel economy," whether to reduce dependence on imported oil or to reduce carbon dioxide emissions, "will most likely not have adverse safety consequences." Indeed, greater use of hybrid technology should *increase* vehicle safety. *Automotive Engineering International,* which named the Toyota Prius hybrid "Best Engineered Vehicle 2004," explained that the Prius has a variety of safety features, including an electronic brake-by-wire system and a skid-control computer that coordinates with the hybrid system control computers. Hybrid electronics hold the promise of far more controllability, quicker response, and greater safety.

Even with their much higher gasoline prices, the Europeans have still insisted on a voluntary agreement with automakers to further reduce carbon dioxide emitted per mile by about 25 percent from 1996 to 2008 for the average light-duty vehicle, which equates to a vehicle fuel efficiency of about 44 mpg. Japan has a mandatory target with similar goals. Even China has a far tougher standard than we do, plus a 20 percent tax on the most inefficient cars. The car of the future is definitely fuel-efficient.

Our own federal law is a large obstacle—it still requires that the average new car get 27.5 miles per gallon (the same level we had in 1985). The average SUV must get a mere 20.7 miles per gallon (up a tad from 19.5 mpg in 1985). Worse, the National Highway Traffic Safety Administration uses data from unrealistic tests of vehicle efficiency to judge how well car companies have met the CAFE standard. The result is that in 2005, *Consumer Reports* found that the fleet of 2003-model passenger cars they tested averaged only a pitiful 22.7 mpg, far below the 27.5 the law requires (and even farther below the 29.7 mpg that National Highway Transportation Safety Administration had somehow calculated for those models) The light trucks they tested measured a meager 16 mpg, far below the law's 20.7.

We could design the standards more flexibly, and many groups, including the bipartisan National Commission on Energy Policy, have suggested improvements to CAFE. In 2005 the Center for American Progress proposed that the government offer to help U.S. car companies with their legacy health-care costs in return for a commitment to steady improvements in vehicle fuel efficiency. The climate challenge is so enormous that we will certainly need creative deals and bargains like that if we are to have any chance of avoiding catastrophe.

Another worthwhile strategy would be vehicle standards that reduce carbon dioxide emissions from the tailpipe, which in the short run would increase vehicle efficiency but in the long run would include low-carbon alternative fuels. California has put forward just such a carbon dioxide standard, and ten other states have followed. Tragically, those standards have been strongly opposed by both the Bush administration and the auto companies.

In 2006, Bush did slightly increase the fuel-economy standards for SUVs, and included huge gas-guzzling SUVs that exceed 8,500 pounds, such as GM's Hummer H2, which had previously been exempt from such regulations. But the change was minor and left open a huge loophole that exempts large pickup trucks. In the year 2025, the new standards will save the nation about *two weeks' worth of oil*. Hardly a treatment for a serious addiction. Also, the change appears to have been introduced not to have cleaner energy but to allow the administration to better argue in court that its new federal standards preempt California's much stronger proposed standards.

All that said, requiring improved vehicle efficiency, by itself, cannot achieve the greenhouse gas reductions we will need—

because if the world's population and economies continue their rate of growth, the number of cars on the road will triple by mid-century. So we will also need one or more zero-carbon alternative transportation fuels. Those alternative fuels will have to be electricity and biofuels.

THE CAR AND FUEL OF THE FUTURE

With a straightforward improvement to current hybrids, they can be plugged in to the electric grid and run in an all-electric mode for a limited range between recharging. If the initial battery charge runs low, these plug-in hybrids can run solely on gasoline.

We Americans use our cars mainly for relatively short trips, such as commuting—half of American cars travel less than 30 miles a day—followed by extended periods when the vehicle could be recharged. So an all-electric range of 20 to 30 miles would allow these plug-in hybrid vehicles to replace a substantial portion of gasoline consumption and tailpipe emissions. If the electricity came from CO_2-free sources, these vehicles would dramatically reduce net greenhouse gas emissions.

A conventional car costs about 12 cents a mile to operate, for gasoline costing $2.50 a gallon. In contrast, a plug-in hybrid could run on electrons at 3 cents a mile, using electricity that costs about 8 cents a kilowatt-hour, the current average residential rate. Battery improvement—especially the next generation of lithium-ion batteries that will be available by 2010—will lead to increased functionality for plug-in hybrids. The larger battery of a plug-in hybrid, coupled with a higher-powered electric motor, allows significant downsizing of the gasoline engine and other related mechanical systems. Engineers at the University of California at Davis have built several plug-in hybrid prototypes that can travel 60 miles on electricity alone, with engines that are less than half the size of standard engines.

Plug-in hybrids avoid many of the barriers that have plagued alternative-fuel vehicles and that make hydrogen-fuel-cell cars so impractical. Plug-in hybrids do not have a limited range. They do not have a high fueling cost compared with gasoline. In fact, the per-mile fueling cost of running on electricity is about one-third the per-mile cost of running on gasoline. The key infrastructure dilemma—who will build the new hydrogen-fueling infrastructure until the cars are a success, but who will buy the cars if there aren't thousands of fueling stations already built—is minimized because electricity is widely available and charging is straightforward.

The plug-in hybrid will have a higher first cost, but this will be paid back by the lower fuel bill. One 2006 study found that with gasoline at $3 a gallon—probably the low end of the price range by the time we could begin a broad transition to plug-ins in a decade—the extra cost of the vehicle will be returned in five years, even if electricity prices rise 25 percent from current levels.

The remarkably low fueling cost of the best current hybrids (like the Toyota Prius) and future plug-in hybrids are a major reason why I don't worry as much about peak oil as some do. James Kunstler, for instance, argues in his 2005 book, *The Long Emergency*, that after oil production peaks, suburbia "will become untenable" and "we will have to say farewell to easy motoring." But suppose Kunstler is right. Suppose oil hits $160 a barrel and gasoline goes to $5 a gallon in, say, 2015. That price would still be lower than many Europeans pay today. You could just go out and buy the best hybrid and cut your fuel bill in half, back to current levels. Hardly the end of suburbia. And suppose oil hit $280 a barrel and gasoline rose to $8 dollars a gallon in 2025. You would replace your hybrid with a plug-in hybrid, and those trips under 30 miles that have made suburbia what it is today would actually *cut* your fuel bill by a factor of more than ten—even if all the electricity were from zero-carbon sources like wind power—*to far below what you are paying today.*

I expect commercial plug-in hybrids to be available within a few years. And as battery technology improves and gasoline prices rise in the coming decade, plug-ins will become increasingly popular. Growing concern over global warming will only serve to accelerate the transition.

THE CAR OF THE FUTURE IS CLIMATE-FRIENDLY

Environmentally, plug-in hybrids have an enormous advantage over hydrogen-fuel-cell vehicles in utilizing zero-carbon electricity because of the inherent inefficiency of generating hydrogen from electricity, transporting hydrogen, storing it aboard the vehicle, and then running it through the fuel cell. The overall efficiency of a hydrogen-fuel-cell vehicle's ability to use renewable electricity is a meager 20 to 25 percent. The efficiency of charging an onboard battery and then discharging it to run an electric motor in a plug-in hybrid, however, is 75 to 80 percent.

Replacing half of the U.S. ground-transport fuels (gasoline and diesel) with hydrogen from wind power by 2050, for example, might require 1,400 gigawatts of advanced wind turbines or more. However, replacing those fuels with electricity (for plug-in hybrids) might require less than 400 GW. That 1,000-GW difference is an insurmountable obstacle for hydrogen fuel especially because the United States will need hundreds of gigawatts of wind and other zero-carbon power sources just to sharply reduce greenhouse gas emissions in the electricity sector, as we have seen.

Another advantage of plug-ins is that they hold the potential to make intermittent renewable power, like wind, more cost-effective. Wind delivers power only when the wind is blowing, and this is not as valuable to electric utilities as base-load power plants that provide power available all the time. But most cars stay parked for more than twenty hours a day. We can imagine that an electric utility might lease a plug-in hybrid to a consumer or business willing to leave the vehicle connected when it was not on the road and to permit the utility to control when the vehicle's battery was charged and discharged depending on its generation or voltage-regulation needs. Such an arrangement would help utilities with load balancing. It would also allow utilities to do most of the charging when the wind was blowing, eliminating the need for costly electricity storage that high levels of wind power might otherwise need. One reason the municipal utility Austin Energy has helped launch a national campaign for the plug-in hybrid is that they have so much West Texas wind power available at night.

CELLULOSIC ETHANOL

Biomass can be used to make a zero-carbon transportation fuel, such as ethanol, which is now used as a gasoline blend. Today, the major U.S. biofuel is ethanol made from corn, which yields only about 25 percent more energy than was consumed to grow the corn and make the ethanol. A considerable amount of R&D is being spent on producing ethanol that can be made from far less energy-intensive sources. Called cellulosic ethanol, it can be made from agricultural and forest waste and also from dedicated energy crops, such as switchgrass or fast-growing poplar trees, which can be grown and harvested with minimal energy consumption, so that overall net emissions are near zero.

Ethanol's advantage over alternative fuels like hydrogen gas is that it is a liquid fuel and thus much more compatible with our existing fueling system. Existing oil pipelines, however, are not compatible with ethanol, so significant infrastructure spending would still be required before ethanol could become the major transportation fuel. And ethanol production will require technological advances before it can match the price of (untaxed) gasoline on an equivalent energy basis. Carnegie Mellon University researchers note that cellulosic ethanol costs the equivalent of "$2.70 per gallon in order to get as much energy as in a gallon of gasoline."

Thus, if oil prices in, say, 2020 are consistently higher than $70 a barrel, cellulosic ethanol could be a competitive alternative fuel. This is particularly true because by that time we will inevitably have a price for carbon, further improving the cost of cellulosic ethanol relative to gasoline.

Probably the biggest barrier to biofuels, and to biomass energy in general, is that biomass is not very efficient at converting and storing solar energy, so large land areas would be needed to plant enough crops to provide a significant share of transportation energy. One 2001 analysis by ethanol advocates concluded that to provide enough ethanol to replace the gasoline used in the light-duty fleet alone, "it would be necessary to process the biomass growing on 300 million to 500 million acres, which is in the neighborhood of one-fourth of the 1.8 billion acre land area of the lower 48 states" and is roughly equal to the total amount of U.S. cropland in production today. That amount of displaced gasoline represents about 60 percent of all U.S. transportation-related carbon dioxide emissions today but under 40 percent of what is projected for 2025 under a business-as-usual scenario. Given the vast acreage needed, using so much land for fuel would obviously have dramatic effects—environmental, political, and economic.

If ethanol is to represent a major transportation fuel in the coming decades, then U.S. vehicles will need to become far more fuel-efficient. A fleet of 60-mpg cars would substantially reduce the biomass acreage requirements. And putting cellulosic ethanol blends into plug-in hybrids would further reduce acreage requirements, especially since there are plausible strategies for cogeneration of biofuels and biomass electricity.

In the long term, biomass-to-energy production could be exceedingly efficient with "biorefineries" that produce multiple products. Dartmouth engineering professor Lee Lynd described one such future biorefinery where cellulosic ethanol undergoes a chemical pretreatment, then fermentation converts the carbohydrate content into ethanol, as CO_2 bubbles off. The residue is mostly lignin (a polymer found in the cell walls of plants). Water is removed, and the biomass residue is then gasified to generate electricity or to produce a stream of hydrogen and CO_2. The overall efficiency of converting the energy content of the original biomass into useful fuel and electricity would be an impressive 70 percent, even after accounting for the energy needed to grow and harvest the biomass. The CO_2 can be sequestered. Also, this process could be used to generate biodiesel. This is a futuristic scenario, one that is the subject of intense research and that could make ethanol directly competitive with gasoline, and biomass electricity competitive with other zero-carbon alternatives, especially when there is a price for reducing CO_2 emissions.

ENERGY SECURITY AS A SIDE BENEFIT

Because of the abundance of unconventional oil and low-cost alternative fuels, peak oil is not the major energy problem that threatens the American way of life. Yes, if we don't aggressively pursue fuel efficiency and low-carbon alternative fuels *now*, the nation certainly faces oil price shocks and steadily increasing prices over the next quarter-century. But if we fail to pursue those crucial strategies, then Planetary Purgatory and 20-foot sea-level rise becomes all but inevitable, and we face the multidecade struggle to avoid the worst of Hell and High Water. Even if conventional oil peaks within two decades, the growing use of dirty, unconventional oil, along with rapidly rising natural-gas and coal consumption, will generate far too much carbon dioxide.

Global warming is the energy problem that threatens the American way of life. Over the next few decades, we need to triple the efficiency of our cars and SUVs, and have them also be flexible-fuel plug-in hybrids that run mostly on zero-carbon electricity and cellulosic ethanol. Whether your primary concern is peak oil and our energy insecurity or global warming, it is important to recognize that sharply reducing our reliance on oil will not happen with the Bush administration strategy. Their strategy is *rhetoric* about our oil addiction plus the *reshuffling* of some of our federal R&D dollars while at the same time blocking national efforts to boost the use of renewable power and opposing state efforts to boost vehicle fuel efficiency.

Triple-efficiency vehicles will be the norm by 2050 only with much higher mileage standards of the kind that most other countries, including China, are embracing (or with tailpipe-emissions standards for carbon dioxide, as California and ten other states propose). If we fail to embrace such standards nationally, the rest of the world will lead in advanced automotive technology, and GM and Ford will continue to bleed market share and jobs. The standard should be written in such a way as to encourage companies to meet them with hybrid technology, because that will help make cars safer and jump-start the shift to plug-in hybrids.

A successful transition to alternative fuels also requires government standards. Indeed, the only reason Brazil has been so successful in replacing gasoline with ethanol is that the government required minimum levels of ethanol blends and then required all gasoline stations to have at least one ethanol pump. We need such sensible policies in the United States. Here are two from the National Commission on Energy Policy:

- Develop the first six pioneer cellulose-to-energy plants between 2008 and 2012 using production or investment incentives.
- Modify agricultural subsidies to include energy crops without increasing total farm subsidies or decreasing farm income.

We should sharply increase federal investments in biofuels and advanced batteries while cutting the hydrogen program by more than half. We should adopt a renewable-fuels standard whereby 25 percent of our gasoline would be replaced with cellulosic ethanol by 2025. We should also launch a major effort to have at least 10 percent of our new cars be plug-in hybrids by 2025.

These strategies would not only sharply reduce greenhouse gas emissions from cars but would do so without raising the nation's fuel bill for transportation. As huge side benefits, we could achieve genuine energy security, sharply lower our trade deficit, revitalize our domestic auto industry, create countless jobs, and increase our national security, because we would no longer be beholden to undemocratic governments in the Middle East or have our economy repeatedly subject to price shocks from political instability or terrorist attacks.

CHAPTER NINE

THE U.S.–CHINA SUICIDE PACT ON CLIMATE

The "international fairness" issue is the emotional home run. Given the chance, Americans will demand that all nations be part of any international global warming treaty. Nations such as China, Mexico and India would have to sign such an agreement for the majority of Americans to support it.

—Frank Luntz, 2002

We don't need an international treaty with rules and regulations that will handcuff the American economy or our ability to make our environment cleaner, safer and healthier.

—Frank Luntz, 2002

What country's insatiable thirst for oil imports is most responsible for the tightening world market since the mid-1990s? Hint: It's not China. From 1995 to 2004, China's annual imports grew by 2.8 million barrels a day. Ours grew 3.9 million. China now sucks up about 6 percent of all global oil exports. We demand 25 percent, even though China has a billion more consumers.

In what year will China's total contribution to climate change from burning fossil fuels surpass ours? Hint: Climate change is driven by rising atmospheric concentrations of greenhouse gases, and those concentrations have been driven by cumulative emissions since the dawn of the industrial revolution. While China's *annual* CO_2 emissions may well exceed ours by 2025, its *cumulative* emissions might not surpass ours until after 2050.

Not only are we the richest nation in the world, but for many decades to come we will be the one most responsible for global warming. No wonder the Chinese and Indians and others in the developing world expect us to take action first, just as we did to save the ozone layer. No wonder the rest of the industrialized world embraced the Kyoto restrictions on greenhouse gas emissions, even knowing the emissions from developing countries such as China and India were not restricted.

One can only marvel at a strategist like Frank Luntz for his ability to appeal to Americans who "will demand that all nations be part of any international global warming treaty," while, in the same breath, reaching out to Americans who oppose "an international treaty with rules and regulations that will handcuff the American economy." Such a rhetorical flimflam strategy by the global-warming Denyers and Delayers is politically very savvy, but it is the sure road to Hell and High Water.

That said, China's emissions *are* growing at an alarming rate. In 2000 the government walked away from the California-style energy-efficiency effort it had embraced since 1980. For the past few years, it has been building one major dirty-coal plant *almost every week*. The climate problem cannot be solved if China and other rapidly developing countries do not take steps to restrain their emissions growth. But if the United States maintains its position that we will not take strong action until China does, neither country is likely to act in time. This chapter explores how the United States and China might avoid destroying the climate and, with it, our way of life.

A BRIEF HISTORY OF TIMETABLES

> *Perhaps the most extraordinary aspect of the Montreal Protocol [on Substances that Deplete the Ozone Layer] was that it imposed substantial short-term economic costs in order to protect human health and the environment against speculative future dangers—dangers that rested on scientific theories rather than on proven facts. Unlike environmental agreements of the past, this was not a response to harmful developments or events, but rather preventive action on a global scale.*
>
> —Richard Benedick, former ambassador, 2005

The ozone layer shields life on Earth from the sun's harmful ultraviolet rays. In 1974, climate scientists warned us that chlorofluorocarbons (CFCs) were destroying Earth's ozone layer, threatening to bring about a sharp increase in skin cancer. Within only 5 years, the United States voluntarily banned their use in spray cans, and CFC production began to decline. But other uses for CFCs, as refrigerants and solvents, began driving the demand up again by the early 1980s.

In 1985, scientists discovered a hole in the ozone shield over Antarctica. As the National Academy of Sciences wrote, this was "the first unmistakable sign of human-induced change in the global environment. . . . Most scientists greeted the news with disbelief. Existing theory simply had not predicted it."

Chlorine concentrations had been increasing over Antarctica for decades, up from the natural level of 0.6 parts per billion. Yet as Richard Benedick, President Ronald Reagan's chief negotiator at the Montreal conference, explained in a 2005 Senate hearing, "no effect on the ozone layer was evident until the concentration exceeded two parts per billion, which apparently triggered the totally unexpected collapse." His ominous lesson for today: "Chlorine concentrations had *tripled* with no impact whatsoever on ozone until they crossed an unanticipated threshold." As we have seen repeatedly, Earth's climate system has many such thresholds.

The stunning revelation of an ozone hole drove the world to negotiate the Montreal Protocol. The 1987 agreement called for a 50 percent cut in CFC production by 1999. Significantly, the protocol's targets and timetables *slowed the rate of growth of concentrations only slightly* and would still have led to millions of extra skin cancer cases by midcentury. Further, the protocol allowed developing countries to delay implementing the control measures for about ten years and required rich countries to give them access to alternative chemicals and technologies together with financial aid.

Nevertheless, President Reagan endorsed the protocol, and the Senate ratified it. By the end of 1988, twenty-nine countries and the European Economic Community—but not China or India—had ratified it. The treaty came into effect the next year, but it took many more years of negotiations, continuous strengthening of the scientific consensus, and significant concessions to developing countries in both technology transfer and financial assistance, before amendments to the treaty were strong enough and had enough support from rich and poor countries alike to ensure that CFC *concentrations* in the air would be reduced.

The analogy of the ozone layer and the Montreal Protocol to global warming and the Kyoto Protocol is far from perfect—greenhouse gases are more integral to modern life than CFCs ever were. American politics have changed in two decades, and the terms of the Montreal Protocol would no doubt be viewed today as wholly inadequate and politically unacceptable, especially without ratification by China and India. Yet this small first step by the rich nations jump-started a multiyear process that saved the ozone layer and prevented millions of cases of skin cancer. It also set an example of how the world could come together to tackle the climate problem.

For many decades, scientists have been warning us about the dangers of greenhouse gases. By the late 1970s, the National Academy of Sciences, the nation's most prestigious scientific body, had warned that uncontrolled greenhouse gas emissions might raise global temperatures 10°F and cause sea levels to rise catastrophically. The discovery of the ozone hole in 1985—an unexpected climate impact from an unanticipated emissions threshold—made us more aware of how we have affected the climate and helped push the nations of the world into an international effort to control greenhouse gas emissions.

In 1992, President Bush's father signed the United Nations Framework Convention on Climate Change (UNFCCC), also called the Rio climate treaty, and that year the Senate ratified it unanimously. The convention's goal was to set up an international process to stabilize "greenhouse gas concentrations in the atmosphere at a level that would prevent dangerous anthropogenic [human-made] interference with the climate system." The UNFCCC did not establish what that level was but did establish a nonbinding target that called for developed countries to return their emissions of greenhouse gases to 1990 levels. Perhaps most significant, the signatories to the treaty recognized "that the largest share of historical and current global emissions of greenhouse gases has originated in developed countries, that per capita emissions in developing countries are still relatively low and that the share of global emissions originating in developing countries will grow to meet their social and development needs." The Rio treaty recognized the "common but differentiated responsibilities and respective capabilities" of each nation and established a core principle: "Accordingly, *the developed country Parties should take the lead in combating climate change* and the adverse effects thereof" (emphasis added).

Unfortunately, supporters of action on climate change, including those in the Clinton administration, never fully explained to the American people how and why the rich countries had promised to take the lead in combating climate change. As a result, the U.S. Senate passed a resolution in 1997, offered by Senators Robert Byrd (Democrat) and Chuck Hagel (Republican), with a vote of 95–0, stating a "sense of the Senate" that the United States should not sign any protocol to the UNFCCC that would "mandate new commitments to limit or reduce greenhouse gas emissions for the [industrialized countries], unless the protocol or other agreement also mandates new specific scheduled commitments to limit or reduce greenhouse gas emissions for Developing Country Parties within the same compliance period."

Probably the Clinton administration's biggest political mistake on the climate issue was making no serious effort to stop that 95–0 outcome. This meant that the 1997 Kyoto Protocol, which set targets and timetables only for the emissions of rich countries, was dead before it got to the U.S. Senate—even though it was similar in most important respects to the Montreal Protocol, which had passed the Senate a decade earlier and had saved the ozone layer and the lives of countless Americans.

When you talk to people from China, India, or other developing countries, they don't understand our politics at all. They don't understand how the country that became the richest by spewing greenhouse gases that are now destroying everybody's climate would refuse to use some of that wealth to prevent catastrophic warming. They find it absurd that American politicians argue for delay by saying we must wait for the poorest countries to make commitments at the same time.

In the 1997 Byrd-Hagel amendment that helped kill the protocol, the senators stated their objection: "whereas greenhouse gas emissions of Developing Country Parties are rapidly increasing and are expected to surpass emissions of the United States and other

OECD countries as early as 2015." That language sounds so reasonable. As Luntz wrote, *"The 'international fairness' issue is the emotional home run."*

But remember that the key metric is not *annual* emissions but *cumulative* emissions. Cumulative emissions are what drive up carbon dioxide concentrations, and concentrations are what determine how much the planet warms. Developed countries had four times the cumulative emissions of developing countries from 1850 to 1995. The rich countries' total emissions from fossil fuel consumption would exceed that of the poor countries through midcentury. Even in the year 2000, the average American emitted nine times the carbon dioxide of a typical Chinese and twenty times that of a typical Indian. And, of course, the rich countries were (and still are) far, far, richer, especially on a per capita basis. That's why few developing countries are likely to agree to serious restrictions on their greenhouse gas emissions until and unless the developed countries go first, which is what we agreed to under the Rio treaty. And that's why virtually every developed country (other than the United States) agreed to the terms of the Kyoto Protocol.

THE CHINA SYNDROME

China's energy history can be divided into several phases, as we learn from Dr. Mark Levine, cofounder of the Beijing Energy Efficiency Center. The first phase (1949–1980) was a "Soviet-style" energy policy characterized by subsidized energy prices, no concern for the environment, and energy use that rose faster than economic growth (GDP).

The second phase (1981–1999) was "California on steroids," when the country embraced an aggressive push on energy management and energy efficiency, surpassing the efficiency efforts California has achieved since the mid-1970s. This came about as a result of Deng Xiaoping heeding the advice of leading academic experts who suggested a new approach to energy. Chinese strategies included

- factory energy-consumption quotas and energy-conservation monitoring
- efficient technology promotion and closing of inefficient facilities
- controls on oil use
- low interest rates for efficiency project loans
- reduced taxes on efficient-product purchases
- incentives to develop new efficient products
- monetary awards to efficient enterprises
- strategic technology development and demonstration
- national, local, and industry-specific technical efficiency service and training centers

During the mid-1990s, China also began dramatic energy-price reforms, which led to higher prices for coal, oil, and electricity. China's policies kept energy growth to a modest level during a time of explosive economic growth. For instance, from 1990 to 2000, its economy more than doubled, but carbon dioxide emissions rose by only one-fourth. Remarkably, *during the 1990s, the United States actually increased its annual emissions of carbon dioxide more than China did.*

Unfortunately, toward the end of the last decade, China scaled back or eliminated many of its efficiency efforts, leading to the third phase of the country's energy history (2000–present), "energy crisis." China's energy demand began soaring again, rising much more rapidly than GDP. Recently, the country has been adding the equivalent of California's entire generating capacity every year. Most of the new power is from traditional coal plants, none of which can be easily retrofitted to capture carbon dioxide. As of 2005, China was burning twice as much coal as the United States. China now consumes more than twice as much steel as the United States and produces nearly as much cement as the rest of the world.

Oil demand has also been exploding, albeit beginning from a relatively low base. As of 2005, China still used less than one-third the oil that we do. And it has much higher fuel-economy standards than we do, as well as a 20 percent tax on the biggest gas-guzzling vehicles. But China has an exploding middle class, its passenger-car market increased tenfold in the 1990s, and it has been adding highways so fast that their total length is now second only to that of the United States. Worse still, China is pursuing several coal-to-diesel demonstration projects, and plans to replace 10 percent of projected oil imports in 2020 with that most carbon-intensive of liquid fossil fuels.

A 2005 study by the National Center for Atmospheric Research looked at our large and growing trade deficit with China. The study found that if the United States had produced domestically all the products that it had imported from China, our emissions in 2003 would have been 6 percent higher and China's would have been 14 percent lower. Also, America's rate of growth in CO_2 emissions would have been nearly 50 percent higher from 1997 to 2003—which means we are exporting to China a huge fraction of our growth in greenhouse gas emissions. And since our manufacturing system is more efficient and less coal-intensive than China's, total global CO_2 emissions from 1997 to 2003 would have been lower by a stunning 720 million metric tons had we made the products we bought from China during that short period.

China, the United States, and the world are at a crossroads.

One path, the current path, leads to catastrophe. In 2004, China's carbon dioxide emissions rose an alarming 15 percent. If its recent emissions trend—and ours—continue unchecked, our two countries alone will be responsible for half of all growth in global carbon dioxide emissions from 2000 to 2025.

At a 2005 U.S.-China conference on coal sponsored by Harvard University, a senior Chinese official told me, "We hope your government will delay action" on climate change since "we benefit from your government policy." America's climate policy gives political cover to those in China who wish to continue their recent explosive growth in carbon emissions.

The Bush administration has not been content merely blocking domestic efforts to cut greenhouse gas emissions but has been actively trying to block international negotiations aimed at developing mandatory reduction targets beyond what Kyoto would require. Worse, the administration has been working hard to woo developing countries away from the UNFCCC Kyoto Protocol effort to develop global mandatory targets. It has launched the Orwellian-named Asia-Pacific Partnership on Clean Development and Climate, which rejects clean development. That partnership, whose members include the United States, Australia, China, India, Japan, and South Korea, explicitly rejects all mandatory efforts to reduce emissions, including caps.

Not surprisingly, the partnership endorses a strategy of voluntary action and technology development. It claims its strategy will reduce annual carbon emissions in 2050 from "reference case" levels of 22 billion tons down to 17 billion tons. But that "reference case" is the most extreme emissions trend line imagined by the Intergovernmental Panel on Climate Change. It represents a world with economic growth that is both very rapid and fossil fuel intensive. If carbon emissions in 2050 are 17 billion tons, we would be on the irreversible path to 80 feet of sea-level rise—even if there were no vicious cycles in the carbon system such as methane released from the melting tundra. With those powerful vicious cycles, we must keep global carbon emissions well below 10 billion tons in 2050.

The Asia-Pacific Partnership is a climate suicide pact. It is playing Russian roulette with six bullets in your gun.

America and the world must quickly jump off this path and onto a very different one. China must return to its strong efficiency efforts from the 1980s, while at the same time embracing a low-carbon strategy, including massive amounts of renewable energy and carbon capture and storage. The choking pollution in major Chinese cities, coupled with the energy bottlenecks and frequent blackouts found in most provinces, should be motivation enough—even ignoring the benefits of avoiding catastrophic sea-level rise and climate change that will devastate the country, with so much of its wealth along the coasts, with so much susceptibility to droughts and water shortages.

But as in our country, China's leaders operate under the misguided belief that they can pollute all they want during this time of rapid growth, then use their *future* wealth to solve their environmental problems. While that paradigm has worked in America for polluted rivers and smoggy cities, it is fatally flawed for dealing with the threat posed by irreversible climate impacts, such as the disintegration of the Greenland Ice Sheet or the release of the carbon and methane locked in the frozen tundra.

Most of the rest of the industrialized world is prepared to go down the only effective alternative path and has already made a baby step in the right direction by ratifying Kyoto. But as with restrictions on CFCs and the Montreal Protocol, the developing world will embrace the necessary mandatory restrictions on greenhouse gas emissions if and only if the United States leads the way forthrightly, and only if there is a broad-based strategy for the rich countries to help the poor countries embrace low-carbon development. So the next president of the United States must be a strong leader who makes climate the overriding priority.

In 2009, America must start with very strong domestic actions both to save ourselves and to send a clear signal to the rest of the world that we take moral responsibility for being by far the single biggest contributor to climate change. Second, we must then quickly bring together all the nations of the world to establish appropriate targets and timetables, ones that will distinguish between rich and poor countries, ones that keep atmospheric concentrations of carbon dioxide below 550 ppm. Any other course for this nation is self-destructive.

CHAPTER TEN

MISSING THE STORY OF THE CENTURY

In the end, adherence to the norm of balanced reporting leads to informationally biased coverage of global warming. This bias, hidden behind a veil of journalistic balance, creates . . . real political space for the US government to shirk responsibility and delay action regarding global warming.
> —Maxwell Boykoff and Jules Boykoff, 2004

This is no time for men who oppose Senator McCarthy's methods to keep silent. We can deny our heritage and our history, but we cannot escape responsibility for the result.
> —Edward R. Murrow, March 9, 1954

If we do not avert Hell and High Water, global warming will be the news Story of the Millennium. In a world where sea levels are rising a foot or more every decade for centuries, our coasts are ravaged by superstorms, and we face endless mega-droughts, global warming won't be the most important story—it will be the only story.

If we do avert catastrophe, global warming will still be the Story of the Century. Starting very soon, and for many decades to come, the top news will focus on the country coming together to embrace an aggressive government-led effort to preserve the American way of life by changing everything about how we use energy—on a scale that dwarfs what the nation achieved during World War II.

While the media has begun providing more coverage of global warming, that coverage is still a long way from adequately informing the public about the urgency of the problem and the huge effort needed to avert catastrophe. The media's miscoverage of global warming makes it much less likely that the country will act in time, and it is a key reason why only a third of Americans understand that global warming will "pose a serious threat to you or your way of life in your lifetime," according to a March 2006 Gallup Poll.

We don't have any Edward R. Murrows today, at least not on the climate issue. What we do have is a declining number of science reporters, and only a handful of those are dedicated to covering climate. Worse, the media has the misguided belief that the pursuit of "balance" is superior to the pursuit of truth—even in science journalism. The result is that global warming and its impacts are systematically underreported and misreported.

WHEN BALANCE ISN'T BALANCED

In November 2005, *Meet the Press* with Tim Russert held a remarkable discussion on the threat of avian bird flu. Russert began with a quote from Senate Majority Leader Bill Frist, a physician, who laid out an ominous scenario of "a fast-moving highly contagious disease that wipes out 5 percent of the world population," which the senator said had already happened once, in 1918. The Frist quote ends: "This glimpse into the past might be a preview to our future. An avian flu pandemic is no longer a question of if but a question of when."

Russert then spent a half hour discussing bird flu with Michael Leavitt, President Bush's secretary of Health and Human Services; Michael Ryan, director of the World Health Organization's Epi-

demic and Pandemic Alert and Response Department; Dr. Julie
Gerberding, director of the Centers for Disease Control and Prevention; and Dr. Anthony Fauci, director of the National Institute
of Allergy and Infectious Diseases. All four of these experts expressed great concern about avian bird flu and the urgent need for
preemptive action.

Russert did not interview anyone who felt that the threat from
bird flu had been exaggerated (and such experts do exist). He did
not interview anyone who questioned the science of evolution, even
though this bird flu can't become a pandemic unless the virus mu-
tates to allow easy human-to-human transmission and even though
the Bush administration itself has questioned the teaching of evolution in schools. As one evolutionary biologist wrote in 2005, "If
we're unlucky, this virus will give us a nasty demonstration of evolution in action."

Russert asked Fauci how much of a possibility a pandemic flu
really was and how worried should people be. Fauci, one of the
country's most respected medical experts, pointed out that it wasn't
a high-probability event, then added, *"But when you're dealing with
preparing for something in which the consequences are unimaginable,
you must assume, A, the worst-case scenario, and B, that it's going to
happen"*(emphasis added).

That is precisely how we should think about global warming.
The threat it poses to our nation and our planet is certainly as grave
as that posed by avian flu, and potentially much more devastating.
The consequences may be longer-term, but the time to start acting
is equally short. And the scientific consensus about global warming
is as strong as or stronger than that surrounding the possibility of a
bird flu pandemic. Yet there has never been a *Meet the Press* devoted
to global warming with four experts all warning the public of the
looming danger and the urgent need for action.

I discussed the strong consensus on global warming in chapter 1. To repeat the key point, as *Science* editor in chief Donald Kennedy said back in 2001, "Consensus as strong as the one that has developed around this topic is rare in science." A 2004 analysis of nearly 1,000 peer-reviewed scientific studies concluded that "politicians, economists, journalists, and others may have the impression of confusion, disagreement, or discord among climate scientists, but that impression is incorrect."

This remarkable consensus creates a very large problem for the media when they choose to cover a scientific matter as a political debate and give equal time to "both sides." As long as a handful of U.S. scientists, most receiving funds from the fossil fuel industry, get equal time with hundreds of the world's leading climate scientists, the public inevitably ends up with a misimpression about the state of our scientific understanding. Nor can that ever change as long as the Denyers refuse to alter their views in the face of the evidence and the media keep refusing to weigh the evidence or present the consensus accurately.

This isn't real balance. It is the media putting its thumb on the scale.

Sadly, even the most respected newspapers fall into this trap, as seen in the study "Balance as Bias: Global Warming and the U.S. Prestige Press," which analyzed more than 600 hard-news articles published from 1990 to 2002 in the *New York Times, Washington Post, Los Angeles Times,* and *Wall Street Journal.* The study found that

- 53 percent of the articles gave roughly equal attention to the views that humans contribute to global warming and that climate change results exclusively from natural fluctuations
- 35 percent emphasized the role of humans while presenting both sides of the debate
- 6 percent emphasized doubts about the claim that human-caused global warming exists

- Only 6 percent emphasized the predominant scientific view that humans are contributing to Earth's temperature increases

The authors found a "significant difference between the scientific community discourse and the US prestige press discourse." As an example of balance as bias, consider these lines from an April 2001 *Los Angeles Times* article:

The issue of climate change has been a topic of intense scientific and political debate for the past decade. Today, there is agreement that the Earth's air and oceans are warming, but disagreement over whether that warming is the result of natural cycles, such as those that regulate the planet's periodic ice ages, or caused by industrial pollutants from automobiles and smokestacks.

Notice how science and politics become merged, and the reader is left with the distinct impression that there is an intense scientific disagreement about whether the warming has a natural or a human-made cause. But there is no such disagreement. Few climate scientists doubt that most of the warming is human-caused and, equally important, that human-caused warming will increasingly dwarf all natural trends.

The media's pursuit of "balance," coupled with their growing desire for drama and entertainment, has left them vulnerable to targeted campaigns of misinformation. To create doubt on any scientific issue, all you have to do is find a few credible-sounding people to present your side, and no matter how many people are on the other side, you've got instant debate. This exploitable flaw in the coverage of science has not gone unnoticed by the global-warming Delayers. As the *New York Times* reported in April 1998, the fossil fuel industry developed a draft plan "to spend millions of dollars to convince the public that the [Kyoto] environmental accord is based on shaky science." Its major strategy was "a campaign to recruit a cadre of scientists who share the industry's views of climate science and to train them in public relations so they can help convince journalists, politicians and the public that the risk of global warming is too uncertain to justify controls on greenhouse gases like carbon dioxide."

The amount of media coverage of global warming has improved in the last few years, likely because the weight of scientific evidence plus the consensus about the dangers of inaction have become too strong to ignore. Yet most articles on climate are still confusing or misleading or both. Let's look at a few 2006 articles from the *Washington Post,* a newspaper that has done some of the media's best reporting on global warming.

Consider a short January 23 article on a *Nature* paper that "suggests that melting mountain glaciers and ice caps, which account for about a quarter of the expected sea level rise, will produce about half the level of sea level rise by 2100 others have predicted." You might expect the article would be balanced with an expert explaining why scientists are far more concerned with observations of accelerated disintegration of the Greenland and Antarctic ice sheets, which contain far more ice and which this study doesn't examine at all. Instead, the article quotes Pat Michaels, of the Marshall and Cato Institutes, both funded by ExxonMobil to advance the Denyers' agenda.

Michaels is quoted saying the *Nature* paper "is one of many recent papers pointing towards reductions in sea level rise in this century due to more refined models of ice balance"—a claim that is best described as the opposite of the truth. Indeed, six days later, on January 29, the *Post* itself got the story straight and published a front-page article noting, "Most scientists agree human activity is causing Earth to warm," so "the central debate has shifted to whether climate change is progressing so rapidly that, within decades, humans may be helpless to slow or reverse" key impacts such as "dramatic sea level rise by the end of the century that would take tens of thousands of years to reverse."

A July 2006 coal-industry memo revealed how the industry is funding Michaels as part of its strategy to stop action on global warming. The Associated Press led its story, "Coal-burning utilities are passing the hat for one of the few remaining scientists skeptical of the global warming harm caused by industries that burn fossil fuels." That article also explained how Michaels misrepresented James Hansen's testimony in an effort to discredit him (see chapter 5).

Consider a May 3, 2006, *Washington Post* article on how the new conservative government in Canada is cutting programs to reduce greenhouse gas emissions. The article explained that in the Kyoto Protocol, countries "pledged to meet quotas to reduce the carbon dioxide emissions that many scientists believe are warming Earth, melting glaciers and brewing more intense storms." Such misleading sentences serve only to confuse the public. The overwhelming majority of scientists believe carbon dioxide emissions are warming the earth and melting glaciers, as the earlier January 29 *Post* article had noted. And the scientific literature is clear that global warming makes storms more intense; the debate on this issue is primarily over *how much* more intense.

The article balances quotes from Canadians who believe the country should take action on climate change with quotes from Morten Paulsen of Friends of Science, a group of Delayers and Denyers with links to the fossil fuel industry. According to Paulsen, "We shouldn't be spending billions of dollars fighting a problem that may not be there." The article states, "He said that arguments that global warming is caused by carbon dioxide are unproven and that 'we believe they are a white elephant.'"

Arguments that global warming is caused by carbon dioxide are *not* unproven. Countless studies have been published on this, all major scientific bodies that have looked at the question acknowledge this as a fact, and it would be hard to find 1 scientist in 10,000 who would agree with Paulsen's claim. Would the *Post* quote someone denying that we had landed on the moon? Would the *Post* quote a tobacco-company lobbyist saying, "Arguments that cancer is caused by cigarette are unproven"?

Consider another *Washington Post* article from the same day, May 3, on a major government study that "undermines one of the key arguments of climate change skeptics, concluding that there is no statistically significant conflict between measures of global warming on the earth's surface and in the atmosphere." For more than a decade the Denyers have argued that global warming could not be happening because the measured warming of the earth's surface was apparently not matched by the satellite measurements of the atmosphere's temperature—measurements first analyzed and reported by University of Alabama researchers led by John Christy. Christy's analysis had suggested a temperature *decrease* in the satellite data. As one encyclopedia notes, however, other scientists "over the years have shown errors in his interpretation of the data which has slowly and consistently increased his results."

Christy, like Michaels, is among a handful of scientists regularly quoted by the media for "balance." While the number of scientists reporting evidence of human-induced climate change multiplies with each passing year, the "balancers" remain a group small enough to fit into a typical home bathroom. Or even its shower. Christy contributed to a 2002 book called *Global Warming and Other Eco-Myths*, published by the Competitive Enterprise Institute, which is funded by ExxonMobil.

Science magazine begins its article on that same 2006 government study: "Global warming contrarians can cross out one of their last talking points." *Science*'s headline trumpets the news: "No Doubt About It, the World Is Warming." Such a stunning vindication for climate scientists needs no quote from Denyers for phony balance. The *Post*, however, spends nearly half the article quoting James Inhofe and John Christy dismissing the relevance of the blockbuster report. Inhofe's spokesman repeats the discredited natural-cycles argument, which the *Post* article does not rebut. Christy claims the earth isn't heating up rapidly enough for him to be very worried, an assertion the article also chooses not to rebut. So an article that should read as a crushing blow to global-warming Denyers instead becomes a vehicle for them to rehash dubious and discredited arguments, with little or no check by the newspaper.

The *Science* article isn't quite perfect. It says the new report, though commissioned by the Bush administration, "will not change White House policy." It then paraphrases a White House spokesperson: "President George W. Bush believes that greenhouse gas emissions can be brought down through better use of energy while the understanding of climate science continues to improve." If Bush really believes that, he has never publicly stated it, nor has he pursued a single policy to achieve reductions in emissions through better use of energy. The spokesperson, or the reporter, may have been confused or mistaken—or meant that Bush believes greenhouse gas emissions *intensity* (per unit GDP) can be brought down through better use of energy. Either way, someone reading the article would be left with the mistaken impression that Bush is actually pursuing energy strategies that reduce emissions.

I can't see why serous news outlets would quote Michaels or Christy on climate science. Those that do quote Michaels should follow AP's lead in explaining that he has been intentionally misleading and is heavily subsidized by the coal industry. Those that quote Christy should explain how he consistently misanalyzed key data and then trumpeted his mistaken conclusions as proof that global warming wasn't happening, long after other scientists explained that he was wrong.

Then there is meteorologist Bill Gray, who testified at a 2005

Senate hearing that we will be headed back into a period of global cooling in a few years and that climate science is just a hoax created by the scientific community to get more funding. Gray is typically described as a great hurricane forecaster, as in a 2006 *Washington Post Magazine* cover story. You would never know from such coverage that shortly after the 2004 hurricane season, he predicted, "We probably won't see another season like this for a hundred years." He was off by only 99 years.

How consistently wrong do you have to be before the media stops quoting you as an expert?

"If your mother says she loves you, check it out" was the adage journalists like my father were schooled on. Be skeptical of even the most obvious truths and check your facts, yes, but nowhere does the motto say to ignore the truth or assume there is none. Today the media's motto seems to be "If your mother says she loves you, get a quote from the neighborhood bully."

EVERYBODY TALKS ABOUT THE WEATHER

One area of media miscoverage in this country deserves particular mention. The key message about what is happening has been muffled. That message is: Climate change is a driving force behind the increasing amount of extreme weather we are experiencing.

Consider a *New York Times* article from July 2003, "Records Fall as Phoenix All but Redefines the Heat Wave," highlighting daytime temperatures of 117°F and nighttime temperatures of 96°F—"the hottest night in Phoenix history." The article never suggests even the possibility that global warming has contributed to redefining the heat wave or that scientists expect such heat waves to become not only more commonplace but more severe.

Consider a *Washington Post* article from the same month, "Coastal Louisiana Drowning in Gulf: Encroaching Salt Water Is

Threatening the State's Economy and Homes." The article discusses a variety of reasons Louisiana annually loses more than 25 square miles of coastland to the Gulf of Mexico, such as efforts to control the flow of the Mississippi River. Nowhere does the article mention even the possibility that climate change has contributed to the problem or that future sea-level rise, left unchecked, may undermine all efforts to find a long-term solution.

Consider a January 2006 NBC News report on extreme weather titled "Meltdown." The report starts in New York, which in midwinter was experiencing springlike weather with temperature in the 50s. It shows reporter Mike Taibbi hitting golf balls in a short-sleeve shirt and getting advice from a golfing pro. After jumping to footage of unusual weather around the country and the world, Taibbi talks to NBC meteorologist Jeff Ranieri:

TAIBBI: But the unseasonable weather isn't restricted to the Northeast. With twenty-five straight days of downpour, Seattle and the Pacific Northwest are approaching rainfall records. Extreme heat and lack of rain have fed the wildfires tormenting parts of Oklahoma and Texas. Rare ocean tornadoes have been seen off the Florida coast. And in usually frigid Chicago, kids eating ice cream cones watch flamingos and giraffes take the sun. . . . Around the world, more extreme weather; the snowiest winters in generations in parts of Japan and China. The cause of all this?

RANIERI: *I wouldn't say that this is, uh, a long-term pattern that we're stuck in. It's just . . . it's Mother Nature and it's just how* it's working in the beginning of January.

TAIBBI: Back to the *thoroughly enjoyable extreme weather* in New York . . . [Emphasis added.]

Wrong, wrong, and wrong. As the chapter 2 discussion of the U.S. Climate Extremes Index makes clear, it *is* a long-term pattern.

The pattern is *not* what we expect from Mother Nature, but it is precisely what we *do* expect from global warming. And while it may be enjoyable in wintertime for New Yorkers, it is catastrophic for those suffering from flooding and wildfires.

If the media's coverage of weather extremes does not improve in the next few years, we will have no chance of avoiding the disintegration of the great ice sheets. Ironically—and as we have seen throughout the book, irony is the defining characteristic of the global-warming debate—the only truly prophetic element of the NBC story was its title, "Meltdown."

Such bad coverage has consequences: Even sophisticated people are left uninformed. Consider Lisa Murkowski, Republican senator from Alaska, the state most strongly hit by the effects of climate change, who sits on the Senate Environment Committee and casts votes that determine the nation's climate policy. Near the end of a September 2005 hearing on climate science, she pointed out that Alaska had experienced "continuous erosion of our coastal villages" and the "warmest summer that we've seen in 400 years." What does she think of all this? "I'm sitting up in Alaska where I can see that we're experiencing climate change. *I'm not going so far as to say it is global warming. But we see climate change*" (emphasis added).

Why take any serious action now if it all might just be a natural event, purely a coincidence that it is occurring at the same time that we're putting into the atmosphere massive amounts of greenhouse gases that scientists predicted would cause these exact changes?

How did the media coverage get so bad? The story should be as simple and logical as the story about avian flu. We have an overwhelming consensus among our leading scientists that global warming is happening and humans are the primary cause. We know that one of the earliest expected impacts of global warming is an increase in extreme weather events. We have a painfully obvious increase in extreme weather.

We even have the federal agency in charge of climatic data, the

National Climatic Data Center, with a comprehensive statistical measure showing that the weather has actually gotten more extreme—and which explained more than ten years ago that the chances that this increase was due to factors *other* than global warming, such as "natural climate variability," was statistically very small.

Yet my guess is that you've never heard of the U.S. Climate Extremes Index, even though it was explicitly created to take a complicated subject ("multivariate and multidimensional climate changes in the United States") and make it more easily understood by American citizens and policy makers. I follow this subject of the connection between climate change and extreme weather very closely, and yet, until 2006, I had not seen a single mention of the index in the media or even in a scientific paper since its original introduction back in 1995.

Story after story in the media appear with no link whatsoever between extreme weather and global warming, no link to the human-made trend that will ultimately transform all our lives. Even the monster U.S. heat wave at the end of July and early August 2006 generated few stories that mentioned global warming. I was actually interviewed by a major national news outlet about this heat wave. They were interested in my work on urban heat islands, whereby dark roofs and asphalt pavement and the loss of shade trees have made cities much hotter than they would otherwise be (see chapter 6). Although I discussed how global warming is making this kind of devastating heat wave more likely and more intense—and combining with the heat-island effect to make cities increasingly inhospitable in the summer—they did not use any of these comments. They wanted only a story on how heat islands affect heat waves.

What are the reasons for this flawed and incomplete reporting?

One reason is that the Delayers have been hard at work criticizing the media for making the link between extreme weather and climate change—and they've succeeded in intimidating them. In his 2004 book, *Boiling Point*, Pulitzer Prize–winning journalist Ross Gelbspan wonders why journalists covering extreme weather events don't use the statement "Scientists associate this pattern of violent weather with global warming." He reports that a few years earlier he had asked "a top editor at a major TV network" why they didn't make this link. The reply was: "We did that. Once. But it triggered a barrage of complaints from the Global Climate Coalition [then the major anti-global-warming lobbying group of the fossil fuel industry] to our top executives at the network."

The lobbyists argued then, as they do now, that you can't prove that any individual weather event is caused by climate change. But that is irrelevant to the two key points: The pattern is exactly what we expect from climate change, and we can expect to see more violent weather events in the future if emissions trends are not reversed soon.

Another reason the media gets the climate extreme-weather link wrong: Most meteorologists in this country, including virtually every TV meteorologist, are not experts on global warming. As one climate scientist explained to me:

> Meteorologists are not required to take a course in climate change, this is not part of the NOAA/NWS [National Oceanic and Atmospheric Administration/National Weather Service] certification requirements, so university programs don't require the course (even if they offer it). So *we have been educating generations of meteorologists who know nothing at all about climate change.* [Emphasis added.]

Asking a meteorologist to explain the cause of recent extreme weather is like asking your family doctor what the chances are for an avian flu pandemic in the next few years or asking a Midwest sheriff about the prospects of nuclear terrorism. The answer might be interesting, but it wouldn't be one I'd stake my family's life on.

A final reason you don't see the link made here in this country as much as you should is that the environmental community itself decided in the mid-1990s to *deemphasize* it. Yes, you read that right. Many environmentalists actually made a conscious decision to stop talking about what are arguably the most visible and visceral signs of warming for most people. A number of senior environmentalists, including those involved with media outreach, told me at the time that they were tired of being beaten up by the other side on this issue. I thought that was a blunder then, and I still do today.

Peter Teague, Environment Program director for the Nathan Cummings Foundation, wrote about this problem in the summer of 2004 after "the fourth in a series of violent hurricanes [had] just bombarded the Caribbean and Florida." He pointed out "no prominent national leader—environmental or otherwise—has come out publicly to suggest that the recent spate of hurricanes was the result of global warming."

But the ever-worsening reality of climate change together with the diligence of leading climate scientists brought the hurricane-warming link roaring back. As noted in chapter 2, leading scientists from MIT, the Georgia Institute of Technology, and the National Center for Atmospheric Research (NCAR) published a series of scientific articles on the rise of intense hurricanes—in what turned out to be the most devastating hurricane season in U.S. history, 2005. And in the months following Katrina, the scientific basis for the connection between global warming and intense hurricanes has grown even stronger.

The media still do not cover the story well. In a major article on climate change in April 2006, the *New York Times* actually claimed, "Few scientists agree with the idea that the recent spate of potent hurricanes, European heat waves, African drought and other weather extremes are, in essence, our fault." Few? That doesn't gibe with the dozens of climate scientists I talked to while researching this book. They all told me what climate scientists have been telling us so many times before—global warming makes extreme weather events more likely and more destructive.

Again, the story is fairly straightforward. Global tropical sea-surface temperature is increasing as a result of greenhouse warming. Average hurricane intensity increases with increasing tropical sea-surface temperature. The frequency of the most intense hurricanes is increasing globally. So greenhouse warming is causing an increase in global hurricane intensity. True, not every scientist agrees with that conclusion, but fewer and fewer are disagreeing, while more and more are speaking out bluntly. "The hurricanes we are seeing are indeed a direct result of climate change, and it's no longer something we'll see in the future, it's happening now," Greg Holland, an NCAR division director, told the American Meteorological Society's 27th Conference on Hurricanes and Tropical Meteorology in April 2006.

That is what I told my brother, to aid in his decision about whether to rebuild or relocate from the Gulf Coast. That is what everyone making such decisions needs to hear to make an informed choice.

THE STORY OF THE CENTURY: BE *VERY* WORRIED

Most of the media do not get global warming—yet. And that extends from TV and radio to newspaper to magazines to even the most sophisticated policy journals such as *Foreign Affairs,* which routinely publishes major articles on subjects like China and energy with virtually no mention of global warming. One publication, however, has consistently delivered timely and powerful stories on global warming, largely unfettered by faux balance—*Time* magazine.

In April 2006, *Time* published a powerful special report on global warming with a warning on the cover in huge letters, "BE WORRIED. BE *VERY* WORRIED. Climate change isn't some vague future problem—it's already damaging the planet at an alarming pace." One of the most interesting things in the issue was a poll in which 1,000 Americans were asked, "Do you think most scientists agree with one another about global warming, or do you think there is a lot of disagreement on this issue?" Only 35 percent said, "Most agree," while 64 percent said, "A lot of disagreement." As *Time* noted, "Most people aren't aware of the broad scientific consensus on warming." But then how could they be, with other media continually misreporting the subject, insisting that as long as there is one global-warming Denyer, that Denyer deserves equal time with the entire rest of the scientific community?

In a fascinating example of intramedia "balance," *Time*'s rival, *Newsweek,* also published an article on global warming that week. Unlike *Time, Newsweek* devoted almost half of its article to quoting various Denyers and Delayers, claiming, "To be fair, neither side has a monopoly on hot air in this debate," falsely equating one or two mild overstatements by advocates of action on global warming with major campaigns to deny the science entirely and delay action indefinitely.

The *Newsweek* article seeks to downplay the growing concern over warming: "But both the [Elizabeth] Kolbert and [Tim] Flannery books are sober, detailed and alarming without being alarmist." Yet Kolbert's book is titled *Field Notes from a Catastrophe,* and the final sentence is "It may seem impossible to imagine that a technologically advanced society could choose, in essence, to destroy itself, but that is what we are now in the process of doing." Flannery's book warns that if we don't act fast enough to limit greenhouse gas emissions, we will "destroy Earth's life-support systems and destabilise our global civilisation." The result: "Humans are thrust into a projected Dark Ages far more mordant than any that has gone before. . . . These changes could commence as soon as 2050."

Both Kolbert's and Flannery's books strike me as alarming *and* alarmist—as befits any sober and detailed examination of the facts.

The subhead on the *Newsweek* article is "Books, Films and a Slick Ad Campaign Make Global Warming the Topic *Du Jour*." No. Global warming is the topic *du siècle*. And if we don't get a lot more stories, and a lot better stories, on the threat and how to stop it, global warming will be the only story that matters to the next fifty generations of Americans.

CONCLUSION

THE END OF POLITICS

The hottest places in Hell are reserved for those who in time of great moral crises maintain their neutrality.
—attributed to Dante

America is great because she is good. If America ceases to be good, America will cease to be great.
—attributed to Alexis de Tocqueville

G lobal warming will change American life forever and end politics as we know it, probably within your lifetime. How might this play out?

In the best case, we immediately start changing how we use energy in order to preserve the health and well-being—the security—of the next fifty generations. The nation and the world embrace an aggressive multidecade, government-led effort to use existing and near-term clean-energy technologies.

The enabling strategy is energy efficiency—since that generates the savings that pays for the zero-carbon energy sources, like wind power and coal with carbon sequestration. Efficiency keeps the total cost low to consumers and businesses. For utilities, we need a California-style energy-efficiency effort nationwide. For cars and light trucks, we need serious federal standards for high-mileage hybrids that can be plugged in to the electric grid. The goal of all these efforts: keeping global emissions at or below 29 billion metric tons of carbon dioxide (8 billion tons of carbon) for the next several decades—and keeping concentrations well below 550 ppm (a doubling of preindustrial levels) this century.

I have called this scenario Two Political Miracles because it would require a radical conversion of American conservative leaders—first, to completely accept climate science, and second, to strongly embrace climate solutions that they currently view as anathema. I have spent nearly two decades working to achieve this clean-energy future and will continue doing so, because it is the best way to preserve the health and well-being of future generations and to boost energy security while creating millions of clean-energy jobs here at home. Yet none of the more than one hundred people I interviewed for this book considers this in the least bit plausible.

They may be right. Tragically, in the face of the stunning recent evidence that climate change is coming faster and rougher than scientists have expected, many conservatives have chosen to redouble their efforts to deny the science and delay serious action. Consider the words of President Bush in May 2006: "In my judgment, we need to set aside whether or not greenhouse gases have been caused by mankind or because of natural effects." That statement is reminiscent of leaders like Herbert Hoover and Neville Chamberlain who were blind to their nation's gravest threats.

President Bush misspoke. The massive surge in greenhouse gas emissions is clearly caused by humankind—that is not even in dispute. What Bush may have meant to say is "climate change" rather than "greenhouse gases," which is the standard rehashing of the long-discredited "climate change is all just natural cycles" argument. We cannot, however, set aside the overwhelming evidence and solid scientific consensus that humankind is to blame for virtually all of recent climate change because that would mean setting aside the possibility of any serious effort to prevent future catastrophic climate change from human emissions.

Consider two ads launched in May 2006 by the Competitive Enterprise Institute, an oil-industry-funded think tank. One claims that the Greenland and Antarctic ice sheets are increasing in mass due to increased snowfall. The ad conveniently ignores the evidence that both ice sheets are now losing ice at the edges faster than they are gaining mass in the center—and doing so much faster than predicted. As recently as 2001, the international scientific community thought that the great ice sheets would not contribute significantly to sea-level rise this century. But as climatologist Richard Alley warned, also in May 2006, "The ice sheets seem to be shrinking 100 years ahead of schedule."

Both ads end with a rhetorical tagline that would be funny if the stakes weren't so deadly serious: "Carbon dioxide—they call it pollution, we call it Life!" Yes, carbon dioxide is needed for life, as is water. But too much of either can be fatal. Just look at New Orleans and the Gulf Coast. The Competitive Enterprise Institute might just as well have ended its ads, "Après nous le deluge" (After us, the deluge)—literally. Under the Competitive Enterprise Institute's banner, we would never take any action whatsoever to reduce carbon dioxide emissions, even to avoid a tripling or quadrupling of preindustrial concentrations. Does the conservative movement really want to side with global-warming pollution over the health and well-being of the next fifty generations?

The conservative Denyers and Delayers are not the only reason America has failed to take up the fight against climate change. "Scientists present the facts about climate change clinically, failing to stress that business-as-usual will transform the planet," leading to as much as 80-feet-higher sea levels, rising "twenty feet or more per century," as NASA's Jim Hansen wrote in 2006.

Progressive politicians have been slow to grasp the overwhelming urgency of the problem. But that is starting to change. Al Gore has launched a major effort to mobilize action, built around his 2006 movie, *An Inconvenient Truth*. Also in 2006, Democrats in both the House and Senate have for the first time introduced legislation that would require reductions in greenhouse gas emissions sufficient to avert catastrophe.

Some major groups that have been on the sidelines, such as evangelical Christians, have begun reconsidering their position on climate. In February 2006, the Evangelical Climate Initiative, a group of more than 85 evangelicals, issued a statement saying, "Human-induced climate change is real," the "consequences of climate change will be significant," and government should immediately pass legislation reducing U.S. carbon dioxide emissions. In response, however, key conservative evangelicals launched the Interfaith Stewardship Alliance, "which has aligned itself with prominent global warming skeptics, including John Christy and . . . Patrick Michaels," as an April 2006 news story explained. In July 2006, the Heritage Foundation hosted an event at which the alliance released a letter, signed by more than 100 evangelicals, questioning the science of climate change; the letter claimed that global warming will have mild and possibly "helpful" consequences and opposed any "government-mandated carbon dioxide emissions reductions," saying they "would cause greater harm than good to humanity."

So I do believe that for all of the failings of the groups seeking strong action on global warming, the conservative Denyers and Delayers are the main reason America lacks the consensus and the political will to take up the fight against catastrophic climate change. They actively spread misinformation. They block those seeking to take action at a state, national, and global level. We will not be able to prevent catastrophic warming without conservatives embracing a dramatically different view of energy policy, international negotiations, and the role of government.

For now, the political success of the global warming Delayers must be acknowledged. No proposal to reduce U.S. greenhouse gas emissions has ever achieved a majority vote in either chamber of Congress. America will almost certainly take no serious action on climate under President Bush, and he may very well block any serious efforts by other nations. Long after Bush leaves office, conservatives in Congress will hold enough strength to block significant action on climate, should they so choose. This suggests that America will at best take some half measures to slow our emissions growth in the next decade, while China and other developing nations continue their breathtaking emissions growth largely unchecked. That will put us on the brink of disaster.

THE RECKONING

Soils, tundra, tropical forests, and oceans currently serve as sinks that absorb nearly half the carbon we are spewing into the atmosphere. The tundra by itself today contains about as much carbon as the atmosphere, much of it in the form of methane, which is more than twenty times as potent at trapping heat as carbon dioxide. At 550 parts per million of atmospheric carbon dioxide concentrations, a doubling of preindustrial levels, we are likely to lose most of the tundra and most of the Amazon rain forest, and with them any hope of avoiding a tripling, which would ruin this planet for the next fifty generations.

But barring the Two Political Miracles, global emissions will hit 37 billion metric tons of carbon dioxide a year in the early 2020s, while global concentrations hit about 430 ppm, rising 3 ppm a year. We will have vastly overshot a safe level of carbon emissions, and misallocated trillions of dollars in capital constructing conventional coal plants, producing unconventional oil, and manufacturing inefficient vehicles. At that point, if we wanted to avoid climate catastrophe while avoiding economic collapse, we would have no choice but to scrap most of this polluting capital long before the end of its natural life, while replacing it with clean, efficient capital at a rapid rate.

This national (and global) reindustrialization effort would be on the scale of what we did during World War II, except it would last far longer. "In nine months, the entire capacity of the prolific automobile industry had been converted to the production of tanks, guns, planes, and bombs," explains Doris Kearns Goodwin in her 1994 book on the World War II home front, *No Ordinary Time*. "The industry that once built 4 million cars a year was now building three fourths of the nation's aircraft engines, one half of all tanks, and one third of all machine guns."

The scale of the war effort was astonishing. The physicist Edward Teller tells the story of how Niels Bohr had insisted in 1939 that making a nuclear bomb would take an enormous national effort, one without any precedent. When Bohr came to see the huge Los Alamos facility years later, he said to Teller, "You see, I told you it couldn't be done without turning the whole country into a factory. You have done just that." And we did it all in less than 5 years.

But of course we had been attacked at Pearl Harbor, the world was at war, and the entire country was united against a common enemy. This made possible tax increases, rationing of items such as tires and gasoline, comprehensive wage and price controls, a War Production Board with broad powers (it could mandate what clothing could be made for civilians), and a Controlled Material Plan that set allotments of critical materials (steel, copper, and aluminum) for different contractors.

Such desperate and undesirable national actions are a long, long way from mandated controls on carbon dioxide emissions or requiring that 20 percent of all power come from renewable sources—neither of which conservatives currently support. The ultimate irony would be if conservative disdain for straightforward government-led solutions *today* forced the country into far more intrusive and onerous government solutions *tomorrow.*

And what happens if the nation and the world fail to take serious action in the 2020s? In the 2030s, record-breaking heat waves and searing droughts will be the norm. Relentless super-hurricane seasons, coupled with the reality of accelerating sea-level rise, will change the landscape of the Gulf Coast and the eastern seaboard. We will simply stop rebuilding most coastal cities destroyed by hurricanes. In this Planetary Purgatory, everyone will realize that the world has but one great task—stopping Greenland and the West Antarctic Ice Sheet from melting, avoiding runaway growth in greenhouse gas concentrations.

Politics as we know it will end. Nonessential efforts, such as the manned space program, will be shut down as politicians direct most of the nation's vast resources toward dealing with the climate. The problem with waiting until the 2030s is that carbon dioxide concentrations are likely to be over 450 ppm and climbing more than 3 ppm a year. At that point, our fate will be largely out of our hands and in the hands of the vicious carbon cycles. Most likely we will be headed irrevocably toward Hell and High Water—a tripling of concentrations or worse, warming of the inland United States of 10°F or worse, sea-level rise exceeding 1 foot a decade, widespread ecosystem collapse, and mass extinctions.

The suffering that my brother and his family and the hundreds of thousands of victims of Hurricane Katrina experienced will be magnified a thousandfold in a world with half a billion environmental refugees, water and food shortages affecting a billion or more people, and worldwide civil strife.

We must pay any price and bear any burden to avoid this fate.

What would have to happen in the next decade to create the political will needed to transform the entire country into a carbon-reducing factory? I see two possibilities. The first requires that a major climatic event or series of events occur. A portion of the West Antarctic Ice Sheet could disintegrate rapidly, raising sea levels 20 inches. Or the country could be hit by the kind of murderous heat wave that overwhelmed Europe in 2003. Or we could experience several more hurricane seasons like 2005. Or, more likely, all of those, since the national and global heat wave of 2006 does not appear to be changing U.S. climate politics.

Second, the public—you—could simply demand change. This is vastly preferable to waiting for multiple disasters. Global warming is the gravest threat to our long-term security. More and more people are coming to this realization every day. When people ask me what they should do, I reply, "Get informed, get outraged, and then get political." I think it is a good idea to take steps to reduce your own greenhouse gas emissions, purchasing a hybrid vehicle, buying Energy Star home appliances, buying renewable power, encouraging your workplace to take action—mainly so that you can see that taking action is not that hard.

You must become a climate champion, a single-issue voter. You must take whatever action you can. You must use whatever influence you have wherever it would make a difference, even if it is only to educate the people around you.

I do believe that if we fail to act in time, it will be the single biggest regret any of us has at the end of our lives.

So you can see why my hair *is* on fire. I hope yours is, too.

ACKNOWLEDGMENTS

While the final judgments in the book are my own, I am exceedingly grateful to everyone who shared their ideas with me: Richard Alley, John Atcheson, Peter Barrett, Bill Becker, Dan Becker, Alec Brooks, Brian Castelli, Joseph Cirincione, Ana Unruh Cohen, Jon Coifman, Bob Corell, Judith Curry, Noah S. Diffenbaugh, Kerry Emanuel, Alex Farrell, Tim Flannery, Louis Fortier, Peter Fox-Penner, Andrew Frank, S. Julio Friedmann, Tore Furevik, David Gardiner, Dean Grodzins, Jason Grumet, Hank Habicht, David Hamilton, Kate Hampton, James Hansen, David Hawkins, Bracken Hendricks, John Holdren, Roland Hwang, Andrew Jones, Chris Jones, Tina Kaarsberg, Dan Kammen, Thomas Karl, David Keith, Henry Kelly, Melanie Kenderdine, Felix Kramer, Kalee Kreider, David Lawrence, Mark Levine, Lee Lynd, Jerry Mahlman, Wieslaw Maslowski, Jan Mazurek, Alden Meyer, Ron Minsk, Ernest Moniz, Philip Mote, Walter Munk, Joan Ogden, Michael Oppenheimer, Jonathan Overpeck, John Passacantando, John Podesta, Arthur Rosenfeld, Doug Rotman, Gavin Schmidt, Stephen Schneider, Dan Schrag, Laurence Smith, Robert Socolow, Kevin Trenberth, Peter Webster, Robert Williams, James Woolsey, Paul Wuebben, and Jay Zwally.

I am grateful to James Fallows for suggesting that I write this book. Special thanks go to those who reviewed all or part of it: Ana Unruh Cohen, Judith Curry, Jay Gulledge, Greg Kats, and Steve Silberstein. I would particularly like to thank Pete O'Connor for his help on research and references, and John Atcheson for his help and support. I would like to thank the Hewlett Foundation for its support of my work.

I owe a permanent debt to my mother for applying her unmatched language and editing skills to innumerable drafts. I am exceedingly grateful to Peter Matson, my agent, for his unwavering efforts on behalf of my work and my writing. He found this book the perfect home.

Henry Ferris, my world-class editor at William Morrow, improved the book tremendously. I would like to thank him and the rest of the staff at William Morrow for their enthusiastic support of this book from the very beginning.

Finally, special thanks go to my wife, Patricia Sinicropi, whose unconditional love and support provide me unlimited inspiration every day. Words cannot express what a remarkable person she is.

NOTES

INTRODUCTION

1 *"We are on"*: James Hansen, "Is There Still Time to Avoid 'Dangerous Anthropogenic Interference' with Global Climate?" (paper presented at the American Geophysical Union, San Francisco, December 6, 2005).

1 *"The ice sheets"*: Richard Alley, American Meteorological Society seminar, Washington, D.C., May 3, 2006.

2 *March 2006 Gallup Poll*: Gallup Poll, March 13–16, 2006, available online at http://www.pollingreport.com/enviro.htm.

5 *advanced acoustic techniques*: Joseph Romm, "Applications of Normal Mode Analysis to Ocean Acoustic Tomography" (Ph.D. diss., Massachusetts Institute of Technology, researched at the Scripps Institution of Oceanography, 1987).

6 *"straw that breaks"*: Kevin Trenberth (American Meteorological Society seminar, Washington, D.C., October 25, 2005).

7 *National Academy of Sciences*: Walter Sullivan, "Scientists Fear Heavy Use of Coal May Bring Adverse Shift in Climate," *New York Times*, July 25, 1977.

CHAPTER ONE: THE CLIMATE BEAST

11 *"The paleoclimate record"*: Wallace S. Broecker, "Cooling the Tropics," *Nature* 376, no. 6357 (July 20, 1995): 212–13.

11 *"The ongoing Arctic"*: Louis Fortier, "The Arctic as a Bellwether for Climate Change" (paper presented at the Arctic Climate Symposium, Washington, D.C., June 15, 2006).

11 *"hypertext history"*: American Institute of Physics website, www.aip.org/history/climate/.

12 *"the stated degree":* National Research Council, *Climate Change Science: An Analysis of Some Key Questions* (Washington, D.C.: National Academies Press, 2001).

12 *"Consensus as strong":* Donald Kennedy, "An Unfortunate U-Turn on Carbon," *Science* 291, no. 5513 (March 20, 2001): 2515. See also S. Fred Singer, "Editor Bias on Climate Change?" and Donald Kennedy's response, *Science* 301, no. 5633 (August 1, 2003): 595–96.

12 Science *published:* Naomi Oreskes, "Beyond the Ivory Tower: The Scientific Consensus on Climate Change," *Science* 306, no. 5702 (December 3, 2004): 1686.

13 *"Evidence of global":* Robert Kunzig, "Turning Point," *Discover,* January 2005: 26–28.

13 *"There can no longer":* James Hansen, "Answers About the Earth's Energy Imbalance," Earth Institute at Columbia University, 2005, available online at www.earthinstitute.columbia.edu/news/2005/story11-04-05_html; James Hansen et al., "Earth's Energy Imbalance: Confirmation and Implications," *Science* 308, no. 5727 (June 3, 2005): 1431–35.

13 *a joint statement:* "Joint Science Academies' Statement: Global Response to Climate Change," June 7, 2005, available online at http://nationalacademies. org/onpi/06072005.pdf.

14 *heat, infrared radiation:* Wikipedia, s.v. "greenhouse effect," http://en .wikipedia.org/wiki/Greenhouse_effect.

15 *ideal for us humans:* Glass greenhouses achieve most of their enhanced warming by physically stopping hot air from leaving the enclosure. The atmospheric greenhouse effect is thus a different type of process, since it relies on gases such as carbon dioxide trapping infrared radiation.

16 *Figure 1:* Jean-Rubert Petit et al., "Historical Isotropic Temperature Record from the Vostok Ice Core," January 2000, Carbon Dioxide Information Analysis Center, Oak Ridge National Laboratory, available online at http:// cdiac.esd.ornl.gov/trends/temp/vostok/jouz_tem.htm, and based on the following studies: Jean Jouzel et al., "Vostok Ice Core: A Continuous Isotope Temperature Record Over the Last Climatic Cycle (160,000 Years)," *Nature* 329, no. 6138 (October 1, 1987): 403–8; "Extending the Vostok Ice-Core Record of Palaeoclimate to the Penultimate Glacial Period," *Nature* 364, no. 6436 (July 29, 1993): 407–12; "Climatic Interpretation of the Recently Extended Vostok Ice Records," *Climate Dynamics* 12, no. 8 (June 1996): 513–21; and Jean-Rubert Petit et al., "Climate and Atmospheric History of the

Past 420,000 Years from the Vostok Ice Core, Antarctica," *Nature* 399, no. 6735 (June 3, 1999): 429–36.

16 *"Recent scientific".* National Research Council, *Abrupt Climate Change: Inevitable Surprises* (Washington, D.C.: National Academies Press, 2002). See also Jonathan Adams et al., "Sudden Climate Transitions During the Quaternary," *Progress in Physical Geography* 23 (March 1999): 1–36.

17 *"in periods as short":* Ibid.

17 *"Abrupt climate changes":* Ibid.

18 *white summer ice cap:* Andrew C. Revkin, "Arctic Ice Cap Shrank Sharply This Summer, Experts Say," *New York Times,* September 28, 2005.

18 *2005 study:* Brian Soden et al., "The Radiative Signature of Upper Tropospheric Moistening," *Science* 310, no. 5749 (November 4, 2005): 841–44.

18 *this is precisely:* Petit et al., "Historical Isotropic Temperature."

18 *The warming appears:* Nicholas Caillon et al., "Timing of Atmospheric CO_2 and Antarctic Temperature Changes Across Termination III," *Science* 299, no. 5613 (March 14, 2003); 1728–31.

19 *Figure 2:* Temperature variation from Petit et al., "Historical Isotropic Temperature Record." CO_2 concentrations from Jean-Marc Barnola et al., *Historical CO_2 Record from the Vostok Ice Core,* January 2003, Carbon Dioxide Information Analysis Center, Oak Ridge National Laboratory, available online at http://cdiac.esd.ornl.gov/ftp/trends/co2/vostok.icecore.co2.

19 *a 2-mile-long:* Urs Siegenthaler et al., "Stable Carbon Cycle–Climate Relationship During the Late Pleistocene," *Science* 310, no. 5752 (November 25, 2005): 1313–17.

19 *"That a number of":* Gavin Schmidt, post on RealClimate website, November 24, 2005, www.realclimate.org/index.php?p=221.

20 *Carbon dioxide levels:* Richard Black, "CO_2 'Highest for 650,000 Years,'" BBC News, November 24, 2005, available online at http://news.bbc.co.uk/2/hi/science/nature/4467420.stm.

20 *Eemian interglacial:* James Hansen, "A Slippery Slope," *Climate Change 68,* no. 3 (February 2005): 269–79; and "Is There Still Time."

20 The last time Earth: Hansen, "A Slippery Slope."

21 *1,100 billion tons:* Gregg Marland, Thomas A. Boden, and Robert I. Andres, "Global, Regional, and National CO_2 Emissions," in *Trends: A Compendium of Data on Global Change,* Carbon Dioxide Information Analysis Center, Oak Ridge National Laboratory, U.S. Department of Energy, available online at http://cdiac.esd.ornl.gov/trends/emis/tre_glob.htm.

21 *more than 26 billion tons:* An additional 4 billion tons of carbon dioxide is released annually from land-use changes (mainly burning and decomposition of forest biomass). See Stephen Bernow et al., *The Path to Carbon Dioxide–Free Power* (Washington, D.C.: Tellus Institute and the Center for Energy and Climate Solutions, for the World Wildlife Federation, June 2003).

21 *2 ppm a year:* National Oceanic and Atmospheric Administration ESRL Global Monitoring Division website, http://www.cmdl.noaa.gov/ccgg/trends/co2_data_mlo.php. Based on Charles David Keeling et al., "Atmospheric Carbon Dioxide Variations at Mauna Loa Observatory, Hawaii," *Tellus* 28 (1976): 538–51; and Kirk W. Thoning, Pieter Tans, and Walter D. Komhyr, "Atmospheric Carbon Dioxide at Mauna Loa Observatory 2: Analysis of the NOAA GMCC Data, 1974–1985," *Journal of Geophysical Research* 94 (1989): 8549–65.

21 *another 0.6°C:* James Hansen et al., "Earth's Energy Imbalance: Confirmation and Implications," *Science* 308, no. 5727 (June 3, 2005): 1431–35, originally published online by *Science* Express, April 28, 2005, www.sciencemag.org/scienceexpress/recent.dtl.

21 *nearly 60 percent:* Hansen, "Is There Still Time."

22 *more than 50 percent:* U.S. Department of Energy, Energy Information Administration, *Annual Energy Outlook 2006,* DOE/EIA 0383 (2006): 71–79, available online at http://www.eia.doe.gov/oiaf/index.html.

22 *2004* Science *magazine article:* Stephen Pacala and Robert Socolow, "Stabilization Wedges: Solving the Climate Problem for the Next 50 Years with Current Technologies," *Science* 305, no. 5686 (August 13, 2004): 968–72.

23 *store that* CO_2 *underground:* Robert Socolow, "Stabilization Wedges: Mitigation Tools for the Next Half-Century" (paper presented at the Global Roundtable on Climate Change, New York, November 14, 2005).

24 *"humanity already possesses":* Pacala and Socolow, "Stabilization Wedges."

26 *climate could be even:* Richard A. Kerr, "Climate Change: Three Degrees of Consensus," *Science* 305, no. 5686 (August 13, 2004): 932–34.

CHAPTER TWO: 2000–2025: REAP THE WHIRLWIND

27 *"I don't see any":* Richard Bradley, "Rain Man," *Plenty,* February/March 2006: 33.

27 *"On our current":* Judith Curry, personal communication, 2006.

28 *On August 28:* The description of Hurricane Katrina in this section is from

Axel Graumann et al., *Hurricane Katrina: A Climatological Perspective*, Technical Report 2005-01, National Climatic Data Center, October 2005, update January 2006; and Richard D. Knabb, Jamie R. Rhome, and Daniel P. Brown, *Tropical Cyclone Report: Hurricane Katrina, 23–30 August 2005*. National Hurricane Center, December 20, 2005.

28 1930s dust bowl: Spencer S. Hsu, "2 Million Displaced by Storms," *Washington Post*, January 13, 2006.

30 *"largely false"*: Kerry Emanuel, personal communication, 2006.

30 *Hurricane seasons:* Here I am defining a super-hurricane as any category 4 or 5 hurricane. This is different from the official term *super-typhoon* for typhoons with winds of 150 mph or higher.

31 *extreme events:* World Meteorological Organization, press release, WMO-no. 695, Geneva, July 2, 2003.

31 *"weather is going haywire"*: "Reaping the Whirlwind," *Independent* (London), July 3, 2003.

31 *35,000 deaths:* Shaoni Bhattacharya, "European Heatwave Caused 35,000 Deaths," NewScientist.com news service, October 10, 2003, http://www. newscientist.com/article.ns?id=dn4259.

31 *Goddard Institute:* NASA says 2005 just edged out 1998, which it calls "notable" because 1998's temperature was "lifted 0.2°C above the trend line by the strongest El Niño of the past century." See "Global Temperature Trends: 2005 Summation" available online at http://data.giss.nasa.gov/gistemp/2005/.

31 *Mumbai:* Steve Connor, "The Worst Weather Ever? At $200bn, It's Certainly the Costliest," *Independent* (London), December 7, 2005.

31 *"the eight months":* National Oceanic and Atmospheric Administration Satellite and Information Service website, http://lwf.ncdc.noaa.gov/oa/climate/research/2006/jun/hazards.html.

31 *worst wildfire season:* Seth Borenstein, "America's Weather Went Wild in 2005," Knight Ridder newspapers, December 30, 2006; and Wikipedia, s.v. http://en.wikipedia.org/wiki/Northeast_Flooding_of_October_2005.

32 *and more intense—precipitation:* Thomas Karl et al., "Trends in U.S. Climate During the Twentieth Century," *Consequences* 1, no. 1 (Spring 1995).

32 *"precipitation, temperature":* Pavel Ya. Groisman et al., "Contemporary Changes of the Hydrological Cycle over the Contiguous United States: Trends Derived from In Situ Observations," *Journal of Hydrometeorology* 5 (February 2004): 64–85.

32 *precisely what is predicted:* Gabriele Hegerl et al., "Detectability of Anthro-

pogenic Changes in Annual Temperature and Precipitation Extremes," *Journal of Climate*, provisionally accepted.

32 *Washington, D.C.:* Capitalweather.com, June 27, 2006, www.capitalweather. com/2006/06/historic-june-2006-flood-day-three.php.

32 *45 percent:* Sarah Goudarzi, "Scorching U.S.: First Half of 2006 Sets Heat Record," livescience.com, July 14, 2006, www.livescience.com/environment/ 060714_record_heat.html.

32 *Climate Extremes Index:* U.S. Climate Extremes Index, available online at www.ncdc.noaa.gov/oa/climate/research/cei/cei.html.

33 Half or more: *Alaska Native Villages*, General Accounting Office, December 2003, GAO-04-142.

33 *Valdez, Alaska:* Borenstein, "America's Weather Went Wild."

34 *Judith Curry and others:* Judith L. Curry et al., "Mixing Politics and Science in Testing the Hypothesis That Greenhouse Warming Is Causing a Global Increase in Hurricane Intensity," *Bulletin of the American Meteorological Society*, August 2006. See also Judith Curry, "Global Warming and Hurricanes," testimony, U.S. House Committee on Government Reform, *Climate Change Hearing*, July 20, 2006.

34 *"There has been":* Graumann et al., *Hurricane Katrina*.

34 twenty times: Sydney Levitus et al., "Warming of the World Ocean," *Science* 287, no. 5641 (March 24, 2000): 2225–29.

34 *matches the predicted warming:* See also James Hansen et al., "Earth's Energy Imbalance: Confirmation and Implications," *Science* 308, no. 5727 (June 3, 2005): 1431–35.

35 *"A warming signal":* Tim P. Barnett et al., "Penetration of Human-Induced Warming into the World's Oceans," *Science* 309, no. 5732 (July 8, 2005): 284–87.

35 *2006 analysis:* James Hansen et al., "Dangerous Human-Made Interference with Climate: A GISS ModelE Study," 2005, submitted to *Journal of Geophysical Research*. See also Nathan P. Gillett and Peter A. Stott, "Detecting Anthropogenic Influence on Tropical Atlantic Sea Surface Temperatures," *Geophysical Research Abstracts* 8, no. 03698 (2006).

36 *"By trapping heat":* Kerry Emanuel, *Divine Wind: The History and Science of Hurricanes* (New York: Oxford University Press, 2005), p. 23.

36 *2006 report on Katrina:* Graumann et al., *Hurricane Katrina*.

37 *"a methodology":* Carlos D. Hoyos et al., "Deconvolution of the Factors

Contributing to the Increase in Global Hurricane Intensity," *Science* 312, no. 5770 (April 7, 2006): 94–97.

37 *the first, in* Science: Kevin Trenberth, "Uncertainty in Hurricanes and Global Warming," *Science* 308, no. 5729 (June 17, 2005): 1753–54.

38 *at least 74 mph:* For a good discussion of the various terminology used around the world, see Emanuel, *Divine Wind,* 23.

38 *Kerry Emanuel:* Kerry Emanuel, "Increasing Destructiveness of Tropical Cyclones Over the Past 30 Years," *Nature* 436, no. 7051 (August 4, 2005): 686–88.

38 *Georgia Tech:* Peter Webster et al., "Changes in Tropical Cyclone Number, Duration, and Intensity in a Warming Environment," *Science* 309, no. 5742 (September 16, 2005): 1844–46.

39 hypothesis: Dave Wilton, "'Theories and Intelligent Design," *A Way with Words: The Weekly Newsletter of Word Origins* 4, no. 12 (June 17, 2005), available online at www.wordorigins.org/AWWW/Vol04/AWWW061705 .html.

39 *National Oceanic and Atmospheric Administration: Climate of 2005: Atlantic Hurricane Season,* National Climatic Data Center, National Oceanic and Atmospheric Administration website, www.ncdc.noaa.gov/oa/climate/ research/2005/hurricanes05.html.

41 *first major critique:* Roger Pielke Jr. et al., "Hurricanes and Global Warming," *Bulletin of the American Meteorological Society,* November 2005. A note indicates "in final form 24 August 2005."

43 *"specifically shows":* Richard Anthes et al., "Hurricanes and Global Warming: Potential Linkage and Consequences," *Bulletin of the American Meteorological Society* May 2006: 623–28.

44 *recent modeling studies:* See, for instance, Hansen et al., "Dangerous Human-Made Interference"; Peter A. Stott et al., "External Control of 20th Century Temperature by Natural and Anthropogenic Forcings," *Science* 290, no. 5499 (December 15, 2000): 2133–37; and Gareth Jones et al., "Sensitivity of Global-Scale Climate Change Attribution Results to Inclusion of Fossil Fuel Black Carbon Aerosol," *Geophysical Research Letters* 32, no. 14 (July 16, 2005).

45 *six major volcanoes:* Alan Robock, "Volcanic Eruptions," in *The Earth System: Physical and Chemical Dimensions of Global Environmental Change,* vol. 1 of *Encyclopedia of Global Environmental Change,* Andrew S.

Goudie and David J. Cuff, eds. (New York: Oxford University Press, 2002), 738–44.

46 *"produced the largest"*: Ibid.

46 *Lawrence Livermore National Laboratory:* Peter Gleckler et al., "Volcanoes and Climate: Krakatoa's Signature Persists in the Ocean," *Nature* 439, no. 7077 (February 9, 2006): 675.

47 *"It would appear"*: Kerry Emanuel, personal communication, 2006. He pointed out that the "tropical North Atlantic ocean temperature follows the whole northern hemisphere rather closely," which argues against any "regional influence," such as the AMO.

47 *"there is no evidence"*: Michael E. Mann and Kerry A. Emanuel, "Atlantic Hurricane Trends Linked to Climate Change," *EOS* 87, no. 24 (June 13, 2006): 233–44. Interestingly, the study notes that the positive or peak phase of the AMO corresponds with the strengthening of the Atlantic's thermohaline circulation, which takes warm and salty water to the coast of western Europe, keeping the continent's climate relatively mild. Some recent evidence suggests that the circulation is weakening, which would mean the AMO is not making a positive contribution to sea-surface temperatures. And that would mean hurricanes are intensifying in spite of—not because of—the AMO.

47 *meteorologist Eric Blake:* Mark Schleifstein, "Katrina Bulks Up to Become a Perfect Storm," *New Orleans Times-Picayune,* August 28, 2005.

47 *"The warmer"*: Chris Carroll, "In Hot Water," *National Geographic,* August 2005, 79.

48 *"We think the best"*: Rush Limbaugh Show, September 26, 2005, transcript, available online at www.rushlimbaugh.com/home/eibessential/enviro_wackos/max_mayfield_shouts_it_s_not_global_warming.guest.html.

48 *"The increased activity"*: Max Mayfield, testimony, *Oversight Hearing on the Lifesaving Role of Accurate Hurricane Prediction,* Senate Committee on Commerce, Science and Transportation Subcommittee on Disaster Prevention and Prediction, 109th Cong., 1st sess. September 20, 2005, available online at www.legislative.noaa.gov/Testimony/mayfieldfinal092005.pdf. See also "NOAA Attributes Recent Increase in Hurricane Activity to Naturally Occurring Multi-Decadal Climate Variability," *NOAA Magazine,* November 29, 2005, available online at www.magazine.noaa.gov/stories/mag184.htm.

48 *a major 2006 study:* Hansen et al., "Dangerous Human-Made Interference."

48 *"a trend in landfalling"*: Kerry Emanuel, "Emanuel Replies," *Nature* 438, no. 7071 (December 22, 2005): E13.

49 *"More than half"*: Emanuel, personal communication.

49 *"threshold"*: Patrick J. Michaels, Paul C. Knappenberger, and Robert E. Davis, "Sea-Surface Temperatures and Tropical Cyclones in the Atlantic Basin," *Geophysical Research Letters* 33, no. 9 (May 10, 2006).

50 *"I don't see"*: Kerry Emanuel quoted in Richard Bradley, "Rain Man," *Plenty,* February/March 2006, 33.

50 *Super Typhoon Tip:* National Weather Service Southern Region website www.srh.weather.gov/srh/jetstream/tropics/tc_structure.htm.

50 *Ultimately:* Bill Blakemore, "Category 6 Hurricanes? They've Happened," ABC News, May 21, 2006, available online at http://abcnews.go.com/GMA/print?id−1986862.

51 *Zeta:* "Tropical Depression Zeta Discussion Number 30," National Weather Service Tropical Prediction Center at the National Hurricane Center, Miami, 4 P.M. EST, January 6, 2006. See www.nhc.noaa.gov/archive/2005/dis/al302005.discus.030.shtml.

51 *1°F increase:* Judith Curry and Peter Webster, "Hurricanes & Global Warming" (paper presented at the EESI Symposium *How Changes in the Arctic Are Affecting the Rest of the World,* Washington, D.C., June 15, 2006).

CHAPTER THREE: 2025–2050: PLANETARY PURGATORY

53 *"Obviously"*: David Rind, quoted in Elizabeth Kolbert, "The Climate of Man," *The New Yorker,* May 2, 2005.

53 *"We're showing"*: Thomas Swetnam, quoted in Tony Davis, "Study: Wildfire Increase Due to Climate Change," *Arizona Daily Star,* July 7, 2006.

53 *Mega-droughts and widespread wildfires:* "NOAA Reports Warmer 2005 for the United States, Near-Record Warmth Globally Hurricanes, Floods, Snow and Wildfires All Notable," *NOAA Magazine,* December 15, 2005, available online at www.noaanews.noaa.gov/stories2005/s2548.htm.

54 *nearly 1°F per decade:* James Hansen et al., "Dangerous Human-Made Interference with Climate: A GISS ModelE Study," 2005, submitted to *Journal of Geophysical Research.*

54 *The oppressive heat:* Shaoni Bhattacharya, "European Heatwave Caused 35,000 Deaths," and "French Heat Toll Tops 11,000," CNN.com, August 29, 2003, www.cnn.com/2003/WORLD/europe/08/29/france.heatdeaths/.

55 *human influence:* Peter Stott et al., "Human Contribution to the European Heat Wave of 2003," *Nature* 432, no. 7017 (December 2, 2004); 610–14.

55 *"These results":* Aiguo Dai et al., "A Global Dataset of Palmer Drought Severity Index for 1870–2002: Relationship with Soil Moisture and Effects of Surface Warming," *Journal of Hydrometeorology* 5 (December 2004): 1117–30.

55 *Every decade:* Millennium Ecosystem Assessment, ed., *Ecosystems and Human Well-Being: Current Status and Trends* (Washington, D.C.: Island Press, 2005), figure 16–8, 449.

55 *"The period since":* Kirk Johnson and Dean Murphy, "Drought Settles In, Lake Shrinks and West's Worries Grow," *New York Times,* May 2, 2004.

56 *Phoenix:* Michael Wilson, "In Phoenix, Even Cactuses Wilt in Clutches of Record Drought," *New York Times,* March 10, 2006. See also "Climate of 2006—June in Historical Perspective," National Climatic Data Center, National Oceanic and Atmospheric Administration website, www.ncdc.noaa .gov/oa/climate/research/2006/jun/jun06.html.

56 *wildfires destroyed:* "Climate of 2005 Wildfire Season Summary" and "Climate of 2006 Wildfire Season Summary," National Climatic Data Center, National Oceanic and Atmospheric Administration website, www.ncdc .noaa.gov/oa/climate/research/2005/fire05.html and www.ncdc.noaa.gov/ oa/climate/research/2006/fire06.html.

56 *A 2005 study:* "Regional Vegetation Die-Off in Response to Global-Change-Type Drought," *Proceedings of the National Academy of Sciences* 102, no. 42 (October 18, 2005): 15144–48. The recent drought had trees dying at rates reaching "90 percent or more" at upper-elevation sites in Colorado and Arizona, whereas the trees that died in the 1950s drought did so mostly at lower elevations.

57 *"We're seeing changes":* Michelle Nijhuis, "Global Warming's Unlikely Harbingers," *High Country News,* July 19, 2004.

57 *thanks in large part:* Kim McGarrity and George Hoberg, "Issue Brief: The Beetle Challenge: An Overview of the Mountain Pine Beetle Epidemic and Its Implications," Department of Forest Resources Management, University of British Columbia, 2005, available online at www.policy.forestry.ubc.ca/ issuebriefs/overview%20of%20the%20epidemic.html.

57 *winter death rate:* "Pine Beetles at 'Epidemic' Levels in Northwest Forests," Associated Press, March 23, 2006, available online at www.signonsandiego. com/news/science/20060323-1411-wst-forestbeetles.html; and The Center

for Health and the Global Environment, *Climate Change Futures* (Harvard Medical School, 2005), available online at www.climatechangefutures.org/pdf/CCF_Report_Final_10.27.pdf.

57 *February 2006 speech:* Senator Lisa Murkowski, "Climate Change: An Alaskan Perspective" (address to Catholic University Law School, Washington, D.C., February 13, 2006), available online at http://murkowski.senate.gov/pdf/Catholic%20U.%20Law%20School.pdf.

57 *Half of the wildfires:* "U.S. Climate Agency Ranks 2005 Near Record for Heat," U.S. Department of State USINFO service, December 16, 2005, available online at http://usinfo.state.gov/gi/Archive/2005/Dec/16-239160.html.

57 *grim reality:* Marvin Eng et al., *Provincial-Level Projection of the Current Mountain Pine Beetle Outbreak: An Overview of the Model (BCMPB v2) and Results of Year 2 of the Project,* for the Mountain Pine Beetle Initiative of the Canadian Forest Service and the British Columbia Forest Service, April 2005, available online at www.for.gov.bc.ca/hre/bcmpb/BCMPB_Main Report_2004.pdf.

57 *"it has become apparent":* McGarrity and Hoberg, "The Beetle Challenge."

57 *"Harvest levels":* Ibid.

58 *"super-interglacial drought":* Jonathan Overpeck, "Warm Climate Abrupt Change—Paleo-Perspectives" (paper presented at the Third Trans-Atlantic Co-operative Research Conference, *Climate, Oceans and Policies—Challenges for the 21st Century,* Washington, D.C., November 1, 2005).

58 *predicted back in 1990:* David Rind et al., "Potential Evapotranspiration and the Likelihood of Future Drought," *Journal of Geophysical Research* 95 (1990): 9,983–10,004 available online at http://pubs.giss.nasa.gov/abstracts/1990/Rind_etal_1.html.

58 *"The development of":* Kirk Johnson et al., "Drought Settles In, Lake Shrinks and West's Worries Grow," *New York Times,* May 2, 2004—through the article makes no mention of global warming.

58 *California's Sierra Nevada:* Robert Service, "As the West Goes Dry," *Science* 303, no. 5661 (February 20, 2004): 1124–27.

59 *2006 study:* Anthony Leroy Westerling, "Warming and Earlier Spring Increases Western U.S. Forest Wildfire Activity," *Science Express,* July 6, 2006, available online at 10.1126/science.1129185.

59 *West is likely:* Steven W. Running, "Is Global Warming Causing More, Larger Wildfires?" (*Science* Express), July 6, 2006, available online at 10.1126/science.1130370.

59 *"the area burned"*: Donald McKenzie et al., "Climatic Change, Wildfire, and Conservation," *Conservation Biology* 18, no. 4 (August 2004): 890–902.

60 *2002 study:* John D. Sterman and Linda Booth Sweeney, "Cloudy Skies: Assessing Public Understanding of Global Warming," *System Dynamics Review* 18, no. 2 (Summer 2002): 207–40.

61 *1 ton carbon:* The fraction of carbon in carbon dioxide is the ratio of their weights. One ton of carbon, C, equals $44/12 = 11/3 = 3.67$ tons of carbon dioxide, CO_2. The atomic weight of carbon is 12, while the weight of carbon dioxide is 44, because it includes two oxygen atoms that each weigh 16. So, to switch from one to the other, use the formula: 1 ton carbon, C, equals $44/12 = 11/3 = 3.67$ tons carbon dioxide, CO_2.

62 *In 2005, the U.S. Department:* U.S. Energy Information Administration, *Annual Energy Outlook 2006*, DOE/EIA 0383 (2006), available online at www.ela.doe.gov/oiaf/index.html.

65 *"positive feedbacks":* The climate system does have negative feedbacks loops, whereby a little warming causes a change that slows down warming. For instance, as sea ice retreats, more ocean area is exposed directly to the atmosphere, which could increase the rate at which the ocean takes up carbon dioxide, thereby slowing the rate at which atmospheric concentrations would otherwise have risen. But as the text indicates, scientific observation and analysis strongly suggests the vicious cycles or positive feedbacks dominate the climate system's response to the kind of greenhouse gas forcings it is now experiencing.

65 *"widespread, extreme climatic":* Appy Sluijs et al., "Subtropical Arctic Ocean Temperatures During the Palaeocene/Eocene Thermal Maximum," *Nature* 441, no. 7093 (June 1, 2006): 610–13.

65 *Middle Ages:* Martin Scheffer et al., "Positive Feedback Between Global Warming and Atmospheric CO_2 Concentration Inferred from Past Climate Change," *Geophysical Research Letter* 33, no. 10 (May 26, 2006).

66 *third study:* Margaret Torn, "Missing feedbacks, asymmetric uncertainties, and the underestimation of future warming," *Geophysical Research Letters* 33, no. 10 (May 26, 2006).

67 *2005 report:* "Oceanic Acidification Due to Increasing Atmospheric Carbon Dioxide," Royal Society (London), June 2005, 7.

67 *more CO_2 would stay:* Jef Huisman et al., "Reduced Mixing Generates Oscillations and Chaos in the Oceanic Chlorophyll Maximum," *Nature* 439, no. 7074 (January 19, 2006): 322–25.

67 *2002 study of Texas:* Richard A. Gill, "Nonlinear Grassland Responses to Past and Future Atmospheric CO_2," *Nature* 417, no. 6886 (May 16, 2002): 279–82.

68 *enlightened energy policies:* John Pickrell, "Soil May Spoil UK's Climate Efforts," *New Scientist* news service, September 7, 2005, available online at http://www.newscientist.com/channel/earth/dn7964-soil-may-spoil-uks-climate-efforts.html; and Pat H. Bellamy et al., "Carbon Losses from All Soils Across England and Wales 1978–2003," *Nature* 437, no. 7056 (September 8, 2005): 245–48.

68 *"locker of carbon":* Laurence Smith, American Meteorological Society seminar, Washington, D.C., February 20, 2006.

68 *nearly 1,000 billion metric tons:* Sergey A. Zimov et al., "Climate Change: Permafrost and the Global Carbon Budget," *Science* 312, no. 5780 (June 16, 2006): 1612–13.

68 *recent degradation:* M. Turre Jorgenson et al., "Abrupt Increase in Permafrost Degradation in Arctic Alaska," *Geophysical Research Letters* 33 (January 24, 2006).

69 *"a mass of shallow lakes":* Fred Pearce, "Climate Warning as Siberia Melts," *New Scientist,* August 11, 2005.

69 *Some 600* million: Wikipedia, s. v. "methane," http://en.wikipedia.org/wiki/Methane.

69 *20 to 60 percent increase:* Torben Christensen et al., "Thawing Sub-Arctic Permafrost: Effects on Vegetation and Methane Emissions," *Geophysical Research Letters* 31 (February 20, 2004).

69 *"the gas was bubbling":* Ian Sample, "Warming Hits 'Tipping Point,' " *Guardian* (London), August 11, 2005.

70 *If concentrations hit 690:* David M. Lawrence and Andrew G. Slater, "A Projection of Severe Near-Surface Permafrost Degradation During the 21st Century," *Geophysical Research Letters* 32 (December 17, 2005); and David Lawrence (American Meteorological Society seminar, Washington, D.C., February 20, 2006). See also Karen E. Frey and Laurence C. Smith, "Amplified Carbon Release from Vast West Siberian Peatlands by 2100," *Geophysical Research Letters* 32 (May 5, 2005).

71 *"at the higher end":* Simon L. Lewis et al., "Tropical Forests and Atmospheric Carbon Dioxide: Current Conditions and Future Scenarios," chapter 14 in *Avoiding Dangerous Climate Change,* eds. Hans Joachim Schellnhuber et al. (Cambridge: Cambridge University Press, 2006).

71 *a 2003* Nature *article:* Mark A. Cochrane, "Fire Science for Rainforests," *Nature* 421, no. 6926 (February 27, 2003): 913–19.

71 *more than 60 feet deep:* Susan E. Page et al., "The Amount of Carbon Released from Peat and Forest Fires in Indonesia During 1997," *Nature* 420, no. 6911 (November 7, 2002): 61–65.

72 *the Amazon was suffering:* Larry Rohter, "A Record Amazon Drought, and Fear of Wider Ills," *New York Times,* December 11, 2005.

72 *Dr. Dan Nepstad:* Fred Pearce, "Amazon Rainforest 'Could Become a Desert,'" *Independent* (London), July 25, 2006.

72 *Models suggest:* Geoffrey Lean, "Dying Forest: One Year to Save the Amazon," *Independent* (London), July 23, 2006.

72 *feedback loop at work:* Peter M. Cox et al., "Amazonian Forest Dieback Under Climate-Carbon Cycle Projections for the 21st Century. *Theoretical and Applied Climatology* 78, no. 1–3 (June 2004): 137–56. See also Richard Betts et al., "The Role of Ecosystem-Atmosphere Interactions in Simulated Amazonian Precipitation Decrease and Forest Dieback Under Global Climate Warming," *Theoretical and Applied Climatology* 78, no. 1–3 (June 2004): 157–75. Tim Flannery, *The Weather Makers: The History & Future Impact of Climate Change* (New York: Atlantic Monthly Press, 2006).

73 *the United States and the world:* Chris D. Jones et al., "Strong Carbon Cycle Feedbacks in a Climate Model with Interactive CO_2 and Sulfate Aerosols," *Geophysical Research Letters* 30 (May 9, 2003): 1479.

73 *important study:* Chris D. Jones et al., "Impact of Climate-Carbon Cycle Feedbacks on Emissions Scenarios to Achieve Stabilisation," chapter 34 in Schellnhuber et al., *Avoiding Dangerous Climate Change* (Cambridge: Cambridge University Press, 2006). This study modeled tundra as if it were any other kind of soil, whereas in fact, as we have seen, it is quite different, especially in its ability to release large amounts of carbon as methane, a far more potent greenhouse gas than carbon dioxide.

CHAPTER FOUR: 2050–2100: HELL AND HIGH WATER

75 *"We could get":* Bob Corell, personal communication.

75 *"The peak rate":* James Hansen, "Defusing the Global Warming Time Bomb," *Scientific American* 290, no. 3 (February 2004): 68–77.

76 *polar amplification:* According to the December 2004 *Arctic Climate Impact Assessment,* a comprehensive report by the leading scientist of the nations that border the Arctic Circle, including ours, over the past 50 years it is

probable, with a confidence level of 66 to 90 percent, that polar amplification has occurred. See also RealClimate website, www.realclimate.org/index.php?p=234.

77 *"solar heat absorbed"*: International Arctic Science Committee (IASC), *Impacts of a Warming Arctic* (Cambridge: Cambridge University Press, 2004), 15.

77 *more than 25 percent*: Andrew Revkin, "In a Melting Trend, Less Arctic Ice to Go Around," *New York Times*, September 29, 2005.

77 *"At the present rate"*: Jonathan Overpeck et al., "Arctic System on a Trajectory to New, Seasonally Ice-Free State," *Eos* 86, no. 309 (2005): 312–13.

78 *"The recent sea-ice"*: Tore Furevik, "Feedbacks in the Climate System and Implications for Future Climate Projections" (presented at "Climate, Oceans, and Policies," the Embassy of Norway's Third Annual Forum Transatlantic Climate Research Conference, Washington, D.C., November 1, 2005).

78 *Most models suggest*: Ola M. Johannessen et al., "Arctic Climate Change—Observed and Modeled Temperature and Sea Ice Variability," *Tellus* 56A, no. 4 (2004): 328–41.

78 *"0.3° to 0.4°C"*: Jonathan A. Foley, "Tipping Points in the Tundra," *Science* 310, no. 5748 (October 28, 2005): 627–28.

78 *A 2005 study*: F. S. Chapin et al., "Role of Land-Surface Changes in Arctic Summer Warming," *Science* 310, no. 5748 (October 28, 2005): 657–60.

79 *"If this trend persists"*: Dr. Wieslaw Maslowski, "Causes of Changes in Arctic Sea Ice" (paper presented at the American Meteorological Society ESSS seminar, Washington, D.C., May 2006).

80 *when the planet warms*: Jonathan M. Gregory and Philippe Huybrechts, "Ice-Sheet Contributions to Future Sea-Level Change," *Philosophical Transactions of the Royal Society* 364, no. 206: 1709–31. Note that some studies project a faster rate of growth of the Greenland temperatures compared to global ones. See, for instance, Petr Chylek and Ulrike Lohmann, "Ratio of the Greenland to Global Temperature Change: Comparison of Observations and Climate Modeling Results," *Geophysical Research Letters* 32, no. 14 (July 21, 2005).

80 *another vicious cycle*: Jonathan Gregory et al., "Threatened Loss of the Greenland Ice-Sheet," *Nature* 428, no. 6983 (April 8, 2004): 616.

80 *NASA and MIT*: Jay Zwally et al., "Surface Melt-Induced Acceleration of Greenland Ice-Sheet Flow," *Science* 297, no. 5579 (July 12, 2002): 218–22.

81 *review article in* Science: Julian A. Dowdeswell, "The Greenland Ice Sheet and Global Sea-Level Rise," *Science* 311, no. 5763 (February 17, 2006): 963–64.

81 *1950 to 1996:* Hong-Gyoo Sohn, Kenneth Jezek, and C. J. van der Veen, "Jakobshavn Glacier, West Greenland: 30 Years of Space-Borne Observations," *Geophysical Research Letters* 25, no. 14 (July 15, 1998).

81 *"in October 2000":* Ian Joughin et al., "Large Fluctuations in Speed on Greenland's Jakobshavn Isbrae Glacier," *Nature* 432, no. 7017 (December 2, 2004): 608–10.

81 *A 2006 study:* Adrian Luckman et al., "Rapid and Synchronous Ice-Dynamic Changes in East Greenland," *Geophysical Research Letters* 33 (February 3, 2006). See also "Glacial Change," *Science News* 168 (December 17, 2005): 387.

82 *14 kilometers per year:* "Glacial Change," *Science News* 168 (December 17, 2005): 387.

82 *"accelerated ice discharge":* Eric Rignot and Pannir Kanagaratnam, "Changes in the Velocity Structure of the Greenland Ice Sheet," *Science* 311, no. 5763 (February 17, 2006): 986–90.

82 *"In the next 10 years":* Eric Rignot quoted in Michael D. Lemonick, "Has the Meltdown Begun?" *Time* (February 27, 2006): 38–39.

83 *NASA's Jay Zwally:* "NASA Survey Confirms Climate Warming Impact on Polar Ice Sheets," NASA press release, March 8, 2006.

83 *"The last IPCC report":* Chris Rapley quoted in Matt Weaver, "PM Issues Blunt Warning on Climate Change," *Guardian* (London), January 30, 2006.

83 *eight times as much:* Chris Rapley, "The Antarctic Ice Sheet and Sea Level Rise," in chapter 3 in *Avoiding Dangerous Climate Change,* eds. Hans Joachim Schellnhuber et al. (Cambridge: Cambridge University Press, 2006).

83 *90 percent of Earth's ice:* "Antarctic Ice Sheet Losing Mass, Says University of Colorado Study," ScienceDaily.com, March 2, 2006.

84 *"in the last decade":* ISMASS Committee, "Recommendations for the Collection and Synthesis of Antarctic Ice Sheet Mass Balance Data," *Global and Planetary Change* 42 (2004): 1–15.

84 *The Antarctic Peninsula:* Hamish Pritchard and David G. Vaughan, "Warmer Summers and Faster Glacier Flow on the Antarctic Peninsula" (poster presentation at the Second ENVISAT summer school, Frascati, Italy, August

2004). See also David G. Vaughan et al., "Recent Rapid Regional Climate Warming on the Antarctic Peninsula," *Climatic Change* 60 (2003): 243–74.

84 *lost an area larger:* "Larsen B Ice Shelf Collapses in Antarctica," National Snow and Ice Data Center, March 18, 2002, available online at http://nsidc .org/iceshelves/larsenb2002/.

84 *One glacier's surface:* Eric Rignot et al., "Accelerated Ice Discharge from the Antarctic Peninsula Following the Collapse of Larsen B Ice Shelf," *Geophysical Research Letters* 31, no. 18 (September 22, 2004); and Ted Scambos et al., "Glacier Acceleration and Thinning After Ice Shelf Collapse in the Larsen B Embayment, Antarctica," *Geophysical Research Letters* 31, no. 18 (September 22, 2004).

84 *"the cumulative loss":* Alison Cook et al., "Retreating Glacier Fronts on the Antarctic Peninsula over the Past Half-Century," *Science* 308, no. 5721 (April 22, 2005): 541–44.

85 *"due to an imbalance":* Andrew Shepherd et al., "Warm Ocean Is Eroding West Antarctic Ice Sheet," *Geophysical Research Letters* 31, no. 23 (December 9, 2004); and Fred Pearce, "Antarctic Glaciers Calving Faster into the Ocean," *New Scientist,* October 18, 2005.

85 *A major 2004 study:* Robert Thomas et al., "Accelerated Sea-Level Rise from West Antarctica," *Science* 306, no. 5694 (October 8, 2004): 255–58.

85 *University of Colorado:* "Antarctic Ice Sheet Losing Mass, Says University of Colorado Study," University of Colorado at Boulder, press release, March 2, 2006.

85 *NASA's Zwally:* NASA press release, March 8, 2006.

86 *it is fundamentally:* "Sea Level, Ice, and Greenhouses—FAQ" available on-line at http://www.radix.net/~bobg/faqs/sea.level.faq.html.

86 *2004 NASA-led study:* Thomas et al. 2004, "Accelerated Sea-Level Rise."

86 *A 2002 study in* Science: Eric Rignot and Stanley S. Jacobs, "Rapid Bottom Melting Widespread Near Antarctic Ice Sheet Grounding Lines," *Science* 296, no. 5575 (June 14, 2002): 2020–23.

86 *another vicious cycle:* As Rapley put it in a 2006 paper, "A combination of accelerated flow and hydrostatic list might cause a runaway discharge." Rapley, "The Antarctic Ice Sheet."

86 *Pine Island and Thwaites:* Pearce, "Antarctic Glaciers."

87 *"A warming of this":* Peter Barrett, "What 3 Degrees of Global Warming Really Means," *Pacific Ecologist* 11 (Summer 2005/06): 6–8.

88 *A 1991 study:* James G. Titus et al., "Greenhouse Effect and Sea Level Rise: The Cost of Holding Back the Sea," *Coastal Management* 19 (1991): 171–204.

88 *The first 1 meter:* James E. Neumann et al., "Sea-Level Rise and Global Climate Change: A Review of Impacts to U.S. Coasts" (prepared for the Pew Center on Global Climate Change, February 2000).

89 *One 2001 analysis:* James G. Titus and Charlie Richman, "Maps of Lands Vulnerable to Sea Level Rise: Modeled Elevations Along the U.S. Atlantic and Gulf Coasts," *Climate Research* 18 (2001): 205–28.

89 *they don't consider the impact:* Stephen Schneider and Robert S. Chen, "Carbon Dioxide Warming and Coastline Flooding: Physical Factors and Climatic Impact," *Annual Review of Energy* 5 (November 1980): 107–40.

89 *a world where sea levels:* Peter Whoriskey, "Post-Katrina Rebuilders Hug Ground, Trust Levees," *Washington Post,* February 26, 2006.

90 *2005 study:* Robert J. Nicholls, Richard S. J. Tol, and Nassos Vafeidis, "Global Estimates of the Impact of a Collapse of the West Antarctic Ice Sheet," January 6, 2004, available online at www.uni-hamburg.de/Wiss/FB/15/Sustain ability/annex6.pdf.

90 *A 1980 paper:* Schneider and Chen, "Carbon Dioxide Warming."

CHAPTER FIVE: HOW CLIMATE RHETORIC
TRUMPS CLIMATE REALITY

99 *"The scientific debate":* Frank Luntz, "Straight Talk" memo (Luntz Research Companies, Washington, D.C., 2002), 131–46, available online at http://www.politicalstrategy.org/archives/001330.php.

99 *"Global warming":* David Brooks, "Running Out of Steam," *New York Times,* December 8, 2005.

100 *Kyoto Protocol:* Different countries have different targets. The 5% figure is the average. See Wikipedia, s. v. "Kyoto Protocol," http://en.wikipedia.org/wiki/Kyoto_Protocol.

100 *"It is clear":* Tony Blair, speech on sustainable development, February 2003, available online at www.number-10.gov.uk/output/Page3073.asp.

101 *"And by long-term":* Tony Blair, speech on climate change, London, September 14, 2004, available online at www.number10.gov.uk/output/page6333.asp.

101 *"squandering the chance":* "UK Must Lead on Climate Change," BBC News, September 13, 2004, available online at http://news.bbc.co.uk/1/hi/uk_

politics/3651052.stm. Also see "UK: PM Gives Dire Warning on Climate," BBC News, September 15, 2004, available online at http://news.bbc.co .uk/1/hi/uk_politics/3656812.stm.

101 *major Senate bill:* McCain-Lieberman climate bill roll-call vote is available online at www.senate.gov/legislative/LIS/roll_call_lists/roll_call_vote_cfm .cfm?congress=109&session=1&vote=00148.

102 *"You need 60":* "US Senate Likely to Reject Future UN Climate Deal—Interview," EurActiv.com, February 15, 2006.

102 *"It is clear":* Tony Blair, Foreword, in *Avoiding Dangerous Climate Change,* eds. Hans Joachim Schellnhuber et al. (Cambridge: Cambridge University Press, 2004).

102 *"Though he didn't":* Fred Barnes, *Rebel-in-Chief: Inside the Bold and Controversial Presidency of George W. Bush* (New York: Random House, 2006).

103 *"a compelling presentation":* Senator James M. Inhofe, "Climate Change Update," Senate floor statement, 109th Cong., 1st sess., January 4, 2005, available online at http://inhofe.senate.gov/pressreleases/climateupdate.htm. See also http://epw.senate.gov/hearing_statements.cfm?id=246814.

103 *"Scientists agree":* John Tierney, "And on the Eighth Day, God Went Green," *New York Times,* February 11, 2006.

105 *"Un-Journalism":* Jude Wanniski, "Un-Journalism at the New Yorker," May 9, 2005, available online at www.wanniski.com/showarticle.asp?articleid= 4350. See also wanniski.com/PrintPage.asp?TextID=3550.

105 *"There is no relationship":* Charles Krauthammer, "Where to Point the Fingers," *Washington Post,* September 8, 2005.

106 *the recent scientific evidence:* "Will Railed About Global Warming-Hurricane Link Claim; Ignored Actual Scientific Data on Hurricane Intensity," *Media Matters for America,* September 26, 2005, available online at http://media matters.org/items/200509260004.

106 *"phony theory":* Charles Krauthammer, "Phony Theory, False Conflict," *Washington Post,* October 18, 2005.

106 *"But it is":* George F. Will, "Grand Old Spenders," *Washington Post,* November 17, 2005.

107 *"Crichton's subject":* George F. Will, "Global Warming? Hot Air," *Washington Post,* December 23, 2004.

108 *"Of all the talents":* Winston Churchill, "The Scaffolding of Rhetoric," unpublished essay, 1897.

108 *"Aptness of language"*: Aristotle, *Rhetoric*, cited in Brian Vickers, *Classical Rhetoric in English Poetry* (Carbondale: Southern Illinois University Press, 1970), 94.

108 *"constitute basic schemes"*: Raymond W. Gibbs, Jr., *The Poetics of Mind* (Cambridge: Cambridge University Press, 1994), 1.

109 *"All the speeches"*: Churchill, "Scaffolding."

109 *"There's a simple"*: Frank Luntz, interview on PBS's *Frontline*, November 9, 2004, available online at www.pbs.org/wgbh/pages/frontline/shows/persuaders/themes/citizen.html.

110 *"Scientists have"*: Mark Bowen, *Thin Ice Unlocking the Secrets of Climate in the World's Highest Mountains* (New York: Henry Holt, 2005), 21.

111 *Words alone:* Royal Society website, www.royalsoc.ac.uk/page.asp?id=1020.

111 *"Scientists who do"*: Jared Diamond, "Kinship with the Stars," *Discover* 18 (May 1997): 44–49.

111 *"For a scientist"*: Judith Curry et al., "Mixing Politics and Science in Testing the Hypothesis That Greenhouse Warming Is Causing a Global Increase in Hurricane Intensity," *Bulletin of the American Meteorological Society,* August 2006.

112 *does not melt:* "Governor Schwarzenegger Announces Landmark GHG Reduction Goals," June 2005, available online at www.climateregistry.org/Default.aspx?TabID=3423&refreshed=true.

112 *"one who takes"*: Answers.com. s.v. "contrarian," www.answers.com/topic/contrarian.

113 *"If you just"*: Michael Crichton, in Michael Crowley, "Michael Crichton's Scariest Creation: Jurassic President," *New Republic,* March 20, 2006.

113 *2002 memo:* Luntz, "Straight Talk."

114 *emphasis in original throughout:* I use italics here and throughout to signify emphasis for Luntz, but he often uses multiple emphases combining italics with boldface, and sometimes combining both of those with underlining.

114 *the phrase "climate change"*: Andrew C. Revkin, "Call for Openness at NASA Adds to Reports of Pressure," *New York Times,* February 16, 2006.

115 *For Luntz and a large:* In 2006, Luntz was asked by the BBC about the memo and replied, "It's now 2006. Now I think most people would conclude that there is global warming taking place, and that the behavior of humans are affecting the climate." But that was true in 2002. And in any case his cynical lines—"The scientific debate is closing (against us) but not yet closed. There is still a window of opportunity to challenge the science."—imply

that he knew he was on the losing side of the issue scientifically but believed the issue could still be won rhetorically. See "Luntz Converts on Global Warming, Distances Himself from Bush," available online at http://think progress.org/2006/06/27/luntz-gw/.

116 *"Doubt is"*: Tobacco memo available online at www.prevention.ch/doubt-is-our-product.pdf.

116 *"how much warming"*: Will, "Global Warming?"

117 *"We must not rush"*: Luntz, "Straight Talk."

117 *"Science tells us"*: Paula Dobriansky, remarks to "The Convention After 10 Years: Accomplishments and Future Challenges," *Tenth Session of the Conference of the Parties (COP) to the U.N. Framework Convention on Climate Change*, Buenos Aires, Argentina, December 15, 2004, available online at www.uspolicy.be/Article.asp?ID=C4A8C67B-E36F-45EA-B557-EEF 7F9A6EB4A.

118 *stunning conclusion:* Government Accountability Office, *Climate Change Assessment: Administration Did Not Meet Reporting Deadline,* report to Senator John McCain and Senator John Kerry, April 14, 2005. See also Andrew C. Revkin, "Climate Research Faulted Over Missing Components," *New York Times,* April 22, 2005.

118 *White House had secretly:* "Group Sues to Enforce Sound Science Law," Competitive Enterprise Institute, press release, August 6, 2003. See also Ross Gelbspan, *Boiling Point: How Politicians, Big Oil and Coal, Journalists and Activists Are Fueling the Climate Crisis—and What We Can Do to Avoid Disaster* (New York: Basic Books, 2004), 56–58.

118 *White House heavily:* "White House Guts Global Warming Study," CBS News, June 19, 2003, available online at www.cbsnews.com/stories/2003/07/24/politics/main564873.shthml; and Andrew C. Revkin and Katharine Q. Seelye, "Report by the E.P.A. Leaves Out Data on Climate Change," *New York Times,* June 19, 2003.

119 *His documents showed:* Climate Change Research Distorted and Suppressed," Union of Concerned Scientists website, at www.ucsusa.org/scientific_integrity/interference/climate-change.html. This page contains excerpts from *Scientific Integrity in Policymaking,* Union of Concerned Scientists, 2004.

119 *More recently:* Andrew C. Revkin, "Climate Expert Says NASA Tried to Silence Him," *New York Times,* January 29, 2006. See also John B. Judis, "The Government's Junk Science: NOAA's Flood," *National Review,* February 20,

2006; and "Rewriting the Science," *60 Minutes,* CBS News, July 30, 2006, available online at www.cbsnews.com/stories/2006/03/17/60minutes/main 1415985.shtml.

120 *"Scientists who don't":* Judis, "The Government's Junk Science."

120 *"I do believe":* Conrad Lautenbacher, quoted in ibid.

121 *"People have hunches":* Conrad Lautenbacher, quoted in Bill Lambrecht, "Missourians Should Heed Storm Lesson, Experts Say," *St. Louis Post-Dispatch,* August 31, 2005.

121 *"a few recent":* "Former NOAA Lab Director: 'Climate Scientists Within NOAA Have Been Prevented from Speaking Freely,'" ClimateScienceWatch post, March 10, 2006, available online at www.climatesciencewatch.org/index.php/csw/details/mahlman-lautenbacher/.

121 *"Contrary to Dr. Lautenbacher's":* Jerry Mahlman, personal communication, 2006.

122 *"With all of the":* Chris Mooney, "Earth Last," *American Prospect,* May 4, 2004.

122 *A 1977 report:* Walter Sullivan, "Scientists Fear Heavy Use of Coal May Bring Adverse Shift in Climate," *New York Times,* July 25, 1977. The rest of the history is available online at www.aip.org/history/climate/Govt.htm.

123 *"In the 1970s":* Michael Crichton, *State of Fear* (New York: HarperCollins, 2004), 315.

123 *George Will picked:* Will, "Global Warming?"

124 *"The Global Cooling Myth":* RealClimate website, http://www.realclimate .org/index.php?p=94. One quote that Will ascribes to the prestigious peer-reviewed journal *Science* actually came from the non-peer-reviewed magazine *Science News.* For a detailed debunking of the notion that scientists were predicting an imminent ice age in the 1970s, see www.wmconnolley .org.uk/sci/iceage/.

124 *A spring 2003 workshop:* Fred Pearce, "Global Warming's Sooty Smoke-screen Revealed," *New Scientist,* June 4, 2003.

124 *A 2005 study:* Thomas L. Delworth et al., "The Impact of Aerosols on Simulated Ocean Temperature and Heat Content in the 20th Century," *Geophysical Research Letters* 32 (December 21, 2005).

125 *"Truthiness":* "The Colbert Report," *60 Minutes,* CBS News, April 30, 2006, available online at www.cbsnews.com/stories/2006/04/27/60minutes/main 1553506.shtml.

125 *"STATE OF FEAR":* "State of Fear," Marich Communications, press release,

December 7, 2004, available online at www.michaelcrichton.com/press/index/html.

125 *geneticists were executed:* Wikipedia, s.v. "Lysenkoism," http://en.wikipedia.org/wiki/Lysenkoism.

126 *"In light of":* Science 304, no. 5669 (April 16, 2004): 400–402.

126 *"Hansen overestimated":* James Hansen, "The Global Warming Debate," NASA website, January 1999, available online at www.giss.nasa.gov/edu/gwdebate.

126 *Michaels is:* Cato Institute website, www.cato.org/people/michaels.html.

128 *The environmentalists did:* "Contextomy Tsunami" at http://www.fallacyfiles.org/archive012005.html; and Bill McKibben, "Stranger Than Fiction," *Mother Jones,* May/June 2005.

128 *"The Tsunami Exploiters":* James Glassman, "The Tsunami Exploiters," Tech Central Station, January 14, 2005, available online at www.techcentralstation.com/011405C.html.

129 *"The Death of Environmentalism":* Michael Shellenberger and Ted Nordhaus, "The Death of Environmentalism," September 2004, available online at www.thebreakthrough.org/images/Death_of_Environmentalism.pdf.

CHAPTER SIX: THE TECHNOLOGY TRAP AND THE AMERICAN WAY OF LIFE

133 *"There is no doubt":* Tony Blair, "The Prime Minister's Speech to the Business and Environment Programme," September 14, 2004, available online at www.g8.gov.uk/servlet/Front?pagename=OpenMarket/Xcelerate/ShowPage&c=Page&cid=1078995903270&aid=1097485779120.

133 *"It's important":* Mark Hertsgaard, "While Washington Slept," *Vanity Fair,* April 17, 2006.

135 *"What will never fly":* Shankar Vedantam, "Senate Impasse Stops 'Clear Skies' Measure," *Washington Post,* March 10, 2005.

135 *"to ensure that":* Fiona Harvey, "U.S. Is Accused of Undermining Kyoto Principles on Emissions," *Financial Times,* December 17, 2004.

138 *"voluntary programs":* Conservatives often use the phrase "voluntary programs" to mean efforts to get industry to make voluntary pledges to reduce emissions.

139 *"The United States is":* Spencer Abraham, quoted in "U.S. Energy Secretary Says New Technologies Needed to Achieve Global Climate Goals," U.S.

Newswire September 17, 2003, available online at http://releases.usnews wire.com/GetRelease.asp?id=20881.

140 *"With a new":* George W. Bush, State of the Union address, January 28, 2003.

140 *A hydrogen car:* Joseph Romm, *The Hype About Hydrogen: Fact and Fiction in the Race to Save the Climate* (Washington, D.C.: Island Press, 2005).

140 *A 2005 Luntz:* Frank Luntz, "An Energy Policy for the 21st Century," *A New American Lexicon,* March 2005, available online at www.politicalstrategy. org/archives/001207.php#1207.

140 *"What's most striking":* "President Discusses Energy at National Small Business Conference," White House press release, April 27, 2005; and John Carey, "Bush Is Blowing Smoke on Energy," *Business Week,* April 28, 2005.

141 *"Sometimes, decisions":* "Bush Blames 'Mixed Signals' for Energy Lab Lay-offs," *USA Today,* February 21, 2006.

143 *"force for good":* "Put a Tiger in Your Think Tank," *Mother Jones,* May/June 2005, available online at www.motherjones.com/news/featurex/2005/05/exxon_chart.html.

143 *"to depict global":* "Industrial Group Plans to Battle Climate Treaty," *New York Times,* April 26, 1998.

146 *Over the next few years:* "High Temperature Superconductors," available online at www.eapen.com/jacob/superconductors/chapter5.html.

146 *"Typically it has":* Global Business Environment, *Energy Needs, Choices and Possibilities: Scenarios to 2050* (London: Shell International, 2001), 22.

146 *We barely have:* Romm, *Hype.*

147 *Research on nickel:* Battery University.com, www.batteryuniversity.com/partone-4.htm.

149 *"Are we going":* Stephen Johnson, quoted in Juliet Eilperin, "Ex-EPA Chiefs Agree on Greenhouse Gas Lid," *Washington Post,* January 19, 2006.

150 *$10 to $20 billion per year:* Daniel N. Kammen and Gregory F. Nemet, "Reversing the Incredible Shrinking Energy R&D Budget," *Issues in Science and Technology* (Fall 2005): 84–88. Missile Defense funding numbers from Missile Defense Agency FY07 budget estimate, available online at www.cdi .org/pdfs/Final%20Budget%20Overview%20FY%202007%20MDA.pdf.

152 *"the intential large-scale manipulation":* David Keith, "Geoengineering Climate," *Elements of Change,* S. J. Hassol and J. Katzenberger, eds. (Aspen, Colo.: Aspen Global Change Institute, 1998), 83–88.

152 *"The 'geo-engineering'"*: John Holdren, "The Energy Innovation Imperative," *Innovations* 1, no. 2 (Spring 2006): 3–23.

CHAPTER SEVEN: THE ELECTRIFYING SOLUTION

154 *"This analysis suggests"*: National Academy of Sciences, *Policy Implications of Greenhouse Warming: Mitigation, Adaptation, and the Science Base* (Washington, D.C.: National Academies Press, 1991).

155 *The coal plants that will:* David G. Hawkins, testimony, U.S. House Committee on Energy and Commerce, Subcommittee on Energy and Air Quality, *Hearing on Future Options for Generation of Electricity from Coal,* 108th Cong., 1st sess., June 24, 2003, available online at www.nrdc.org/global Warming/tdh0603.asp. The new plants amount to some 1,400 GW, which includes 400 GW of plants to replace existing ones that have reached the end of their lifetime.

156 *The total extra costs:* U.S. Department of Energy, Office of Fossil Energy, *Carbon Sequestration R&D Overview,* available online at www.fe.doe.gov/ programs/sequestration/overview.html. This is the cost for large-scale sequestration in places like deep underground aquifers. Small-scale sequestration for enhanced oil and gas recovery is far less expensive.

156 *"Vendors currently"*: *Coal-Related Greenhouse Gas Management Issues,* National Coal Council, Washington, D.C., May 2003.

157 *FutureGen project:* U.S. Department of Energy, Office of Fossil Energy, *FutureGen Fact Sheet,* available online at www.fossil.energy.gov/programs/ powersystems/futuregen/.

158 *"Less dense"*: National Research Council, *Novel Approaches to Carbon Management,* Workshop Report (Washington, D.C.: National Academies Press, 2003), 3.

158 *Pacific Northwest National:* James Dooley and Marshall Wise, "Why Injecting CO_2 into Various Geologic Formations Is Not the Same as Climate Change Mitigation: The Issue of Leakage," Joint Global Change Research Institute (Battelle Pacific Northwest National Laboratory), 2002. See also David Hawkins, "Passing Gas: Policy Implications of Leakage from Geologic Carbon Storage Sites," Natural Resources Defense Council, Washington, D.C., 2002.

159 *Analysis suggests:* See, for instance, Keith and Farrel; and Timothy Johnson and David Keith, "Fossil Electricity and Carbon Dioxide Sequestration," *Energy Policy* 32, no. 4 (March 2004): 367–82. See also Howard Herzog,

"The Economics of CO_2 Separation and Capture," *Technology* 7, supp. 1 (2000): 13–23.

159 *Energy efficiency remains:* See, for instance, Arthur H. Rosenfeld, "Sustainable Development—Reducing Energy Intensity by 2 percent Per Year" (PowerPoint presentation at the International Seminar on Planetary Emergencies, Erice, Italy, August 19, 2003).

160 *This astonishing achievement:* The chart is derived from "Consumption, Physical Units, 1960–2002" for electricity consumption (kWh) and from "Appendix C: Resident Population" of U.S. Department of Energy, "Data Sources and Technical Notes," available online at http://www.eia.doe.gov/emeu/states/_seds.html.

163 *California utilities:* Cynthia Rogers et al., "Funding and Savings for Energy Efficiency Programs for Program Years 2000 through 2004," paper, California Energy Commission Staff, July 2005.

163 *2006 report:* Western Governors' Association, "Energy Efficiency Task Force Report," January 2006, available online at www.westgov.org/wga/initiatives/cdeac/Energy%20Efficiency-full.pdf.

164 And it is avoiding: Personal communications with Art Rosenfeld. See also Audrey Chang, "California's Sustainable Energy Policies Provide a Model for the Nation," Natural Resources Defense Council, Washington, D.C., May 2005. Available online at http://www.e2.org/ext/doc/CASustEnergy Policies.pdf.

165 *increased demand for gas:* Energy Information Administration, *Annual Energy Outlook 2003*, DOE/EIA-0383 (2006): 67.

166 *Steam accounts:* "BestPractices Steam," Alliance to Save Energy website, www.ase.org/section/program/bpsteam. See also Joseph Romm, *Cool Companies: How the Best Businesses Boost Profits and Productivity by Cutting Greenhouse Gas Emissions* (Washington, D.C.: Island Press, 1999).

166 *2 million new jobs:* Joseph Romm and Charles Curtis, "Mideast Oil Forever?" *Atlantic Monthly,* April 1996. According to the study, this is "a relatively large impact considering that the investments driving it were assumed to be made for purposes other than increasing employment."

167 *about 88,000 megawatts:* "The Market and Technical Potential for Combined Heat and Power in the Commercial/Institutional Sector," prepared by Onsite Sycom Energy Corp. for the U.S. Department of Energy, Washington, D.C., January 2000, available online at www.eere.energy.gov/de/pdfs/chp_comm_market_potential.pdf.

168 *July 2000 report:* R. Brent Alderfer et al., *Making Connections: Case Studies of Interconnection Barriers and Their Impact on Distributed Power Projects* (Golden, Colo., National Renewable Energy Laboratory, July 2000).

169 *9,000 megawatts:* John Douglas, "Putting Wind on the Grid," *EPRI Journal* (Spring 2006): 6–15.

170 *"2–5 cents/kilowatt-hour":* *Renewables 2005 Global Status Report: Notes and Reference Companion Document,* Renewable Energy Policy Network for the 21st Century (REN21), October 20, 2005, available online at www.ren21 .net/globalstatusreport/RE2005_Notes_References.pdf.

171 *The E.U. has set:* Ibid, pp. 19–24.

171 *Department of Energy study:* U.S. Department of Energy, Energy Information Administration, *Analysis of Strategies for Reducing Multiple Emissions from Electric Power Plants: Sulfur Dioxide, Nitrogen Oxides, Carbon Dioxide, and Mercury and a Renewable Portfolio Standard,* SR/OIAF/2001-03, July 2001. Electricity prices in 2020 under a 20 percent RPS would be about 4 percent higher than the EIA projects they would be in a business-as-usual scenario, but 2 percent lower than they are today.

171 *"The Path to":* Alison Bailie et al., *The Path to Carbon-Dioxide-Free Power: Switching to Clean Energy in the Utility Sector* (Washington, D.C.: Tellus Institute and Center for Energy and Climate Solutions, Report for the World Wildlife Federation 2003), available online at http://assets.panda .org/downloads/powerswitchfinalusa.pdf.

172 *The net savings:* Net savings included the costs for more energy-efficient equipment and additional cogeneration (plus transfers of revenue from the CO_2 cap and trade program back to the consumers).

174 *"It's the only":* Darren Samuelsohn, "McCain Says White House Run Would Not Change Commitment to Emission Curbs," *E&E News,* March 15, 2006.

174 *Nuclear energy is:* Notwithstanding the fact that uranium enrichment in this country makes use of a highly electricity-intensive process that is almost exclusively powered by coal plants.

175 *2003 study by MIT:* John Deutch et al., *The Future of Nuclear Power* (Cambridge: Massachusetts Institute of Technology, 2003).

175 *"The abiding lesson":* Matthew L. Wald, "Interest in Building Reactors, but Industry Is Still Cautious," *New York Times,* May 2, 2005.

176 *California, however:* Energy Source, CA Total Electric Power Industry Net Generation, U.S. Department of Energy, Energy Information Administra-

tion data table, available online at www.eia.doe.gov/cneaf/solar.renewables/
page/state_profile/rsp_ca_table3.html.

CHAPTER EIGHT: PEAK OIL, ENERGY SECURITY, AND THE CAR OF THE FUTURE

177 *"We have a serious"*: George W. Bush, State of the Union address, January 31, 2006.

177 *"In the absence"*: Senator Richard Lugar, "Energy: The Albatross of National Security," submitted to *Conservative Environmental Policy—Quarterly*, spring 2006, available online at http://lugar.senate.gov/energy/press/articles /060301cepquarterly.html.

178 *"Our nation"*: George W. Bush, quoted in "Bush Pushes Alternative Energy Proposals," Associated Press, February 20, 2006, available online at www .msnbc.msn.com/id/11465801/.

179 *And the transportation sector:* U.S. Department of Energy, Energy Information Administration, *Annual Energy Outlook 2003*, Table A19, DOE/EIA= 0383 (2003). Available online at www.eia.doe.gov/oiaf/archive/aeo03/index .html.

179 *"In the absence"*: "Biofuels for Transport: An International Perspective," International Energy Agency, press release, May 11, 2004, available online at www.iea.org/Textbase/press/pressdetail.asp?PRESS_REL_ID=127.

180 *more oil than the entire world:* Romm and Curtis, "Mideast Oil Forever?" *Atlantic Monthly,* April 1996.

180 *when prices spiked:* Energy Information Administration, *International Petroleum Monthly,* March 2006.

180 *"There is nothing"*: Kenneth Deffeyes, *Hubbert's Peak: The Impending Oil Shortage* (Princeton, N.J.: Princeton University Press, 2001), 158. For the opposing view, see Leonardo Maugeri, "Oil: Never Cry Wolf—Why the Petroleum Page Is Far from Over," *Science* 304, no. 5674 (May 21, 2004): 1114–15.

180 *"A scarcity of oil"*: Global Business Environment, *Energy Needs, Choices and Possibilities: Scenarios to 2050* (London: Shell International, 2001), 18.

181 *200 to 400 billion:* International Energy Agency, *Resources to Reserves,* Paris, September 2005; and David Adam, "Global Warming Sparks a Scramble for Black Gold Under Retreating Ice," *Guardian* (London), April 18, 2006.

181 *heavy oil in Venezuela:* Manik Talwani, "The Orinoco Heavy Oil Belt in Venezuela (or Heavy Oil to the Rescue?)," Rice University, Houston, Texas, September 2002, available online at http://cohesion.rice.edu/natural

sciences/earthscience/research.cfm?doc_id=2819; and *Alberta's Oil Sands 2004*, Government of Alberta, Ministry of Energy, available online at www .energy.gov.ab.ca/docs/oilsands/pdfs/PUB osgenbrf.pdf.

182 *Canada's increasing:* The U. S. Energy Information Administration projects a sharp decline in net imports of Canadian natural gas by 2020. EIA, U.S. Department of Energy, Energy Information Administration *Annual Energy Outlook 2006*, DOE/EIA (2006). See also U.S. DOE, EIA, *Annual Energy Outlook 2004* DOE/EIA (2004), p. 50.

182 *Colorado and Utah:* James R. Udall and Steven B. Andrews, "The Illusive Bonanza: Oil Shale in Colorado," *Energy Bulletin* (October 3, 2005).

183 *"CO₂ flooding":* Robert Hirsch et al., *Peaking of World Oil Production,* Science Applications International Corp., February 2005.

184 *21 million barrels:* Northern Plains Resource Council, *Montana's Energy Future,* 2006; available online at http://www.worc.org/pdfs/Synfuel_Briefing_ Paper.pdf; and David Garman, "Unconventional Liquid Fuels" (PowerPoint presentation to Defense Science Board, U.S. Department of Energy, Washington, D.C., June 2006).

184 *Worse, the total:* Adam Brandt and Alexander Farrell, "Scraping the Bottom of the Barrel: Greenhouse Gas Emission Consequences of a Transition to Low-Quality and Synthetic Petroleum Resources," submitted to *Climatic Change.*

185 *2 billion metric tons:* Ibid.

185 *"Forget hydrogen":* James Woolsey, remarks at Plug-in America press conference, National Press Club, Washington, D.C., January 2006, available online at www.connectlive.com/events/austinenergy/.

185 *"$1.2 billion":* George W. Bush, State of the Union address, 2003, available online at www.whitehouse.gov/news/releases/2003/01/20030128-19 .html.

185 *"It is highly likely":* National Research Council and National Academy of Engineering, *The Hydrogen Economy: Opportunities, Costs, Barriers, and R&D Needs* (Washington, D.C.: National Academies Press, 2004).

186 *January 2004 study: Well-to-Wheels Analysis of Future Automotive Fuels and Powertrains in the European Context,* European Commission Center for Joint Research, EUCAR, and Concawe, Brussels, January 2004.

186 *save four times:* For a longer discussion of hydrogen cars and plug-in hybrids, see Joseph Romm, *The Hype About Hydrogen: Fact and Fiction in the Race to Save the Climate* (Washington, D.C.: Island Press, 2005).

186 *a pollution-free:* Internal combustion engine cars can also be modified to run on hydrogen, although they are considerably less efficient than fuel-cell vehicles and thus have much shorter range and even higher annual fuel bills.

186 *currently cost about $2,000:* U.S. Department of Energy, *Basic Research Needs for the Hydrogen Economy* (Washington, D.C.: Office of Science, 2003).

187 *"a new material":* American Physical Society, "The Hydrogen Initiative," March 2004.

187 *more than $500 billion:* Marianne Mintz et al., "Cost of Some Hydrogen Fuel Infrastructure Options" (Argonne National Laboratory, presentation to the Transportation Research Board, Washington, D.C., January 16, 2002).

187 *"Fuel-cell cars":* Matt Wald, "Questions About a Hydrogen Economy," *Scientific American* 290, no. 5 (May 2004): 66–73.

187 *"If I told you":* Bill Reimert, quoted in Jamie Butters et al., "Fuel-Economy Technologies," *Detroit Free Press,* January 10, 2005.

187 *2004 MIT study:* Nancy Stauffer, *New Vehicle Technologies: How Soon Can They Make a Difference?* (Cambridge: MIT Laboratory for Energy and the Environment, 2005). Available online at http://esd.mit.edu/esd_reports/summer2005/new_vehicle_technologies.html.

187 *5-year budget:* Daniel Whitten, "Barton Rails at Budget Request for Shorting EPACT," *Inside Energy,* March 13, 2006.

188 *Samuel Bodman announced:* Geoff Brumfiel, "Energy Secretary Ditches Science Advisers," *Nature* 440, no. 7085 (April 6, 2006): 725.

188 *"My message":* Lugar, "Energy: The Albatross."

189 *European countries: Transportation Energy Data Book,* edition 22 (Oak Ridge, Tenn.: Oak Ridge National Laboratory, 2002), 5-2, 5-3.

189 *nowhere near 60 mpg:* Feng An and Amanda Sauer, *Comparison of Passenger Vehicle Fuel Economy and Greenhouse Gas Emissions Standards Around the World* (Arlington, Va.: Pew Center on Global Climate Change, December 2004). As of 2002, the average fuel economy of European Union vehicles was 37 mpg, and some of that fuel-economy improvement was achieved not just with high fuel prices but with strong tax incentives to promote diesel vehicles, which are typically more fuel-efficient.

189 *In a 2002 report:* National Research Council, *Effectiveness and Impact of Corporate Average Fuel Economy (CAFE) Standards* (Washington, D.C.: National Academies Press, 2002).

189 *Studies by the national:* Interlaboratory Working Group, *Scenarios of U.S. Carbon Reductions,* Lawrence Berkeley National Laboratory and Oak Ridge National Laboratory, prepared for the Office of Energy Efficiency and Renewable Energy, U.S. Department of Energy, September 1997, pp. 5.44–5.48; David Greene and Andreas Schafer, *Reducing Greenhouse Gas Emissions from U.S. Transportation* (Arlington, Va.: Pew Center on Global Climate Change, May 2003), 13–18; and Malcolm Weiss et al., "On the Road in 2020: A Life-Cycle Analysis of New Automobile Technologies" (Cambridge: MIT, October 2000), tables 5.3 and 5.4.

An Oak Ridge National Laboratory study found that "based on a comparison of fatality data for SUVs to other vehicles, the registered-vehicle-fatality rate (defined as number of fatalities per number of registered vehicles) for SUVs is higher than the registered-vehicle-fatality rate for other vehicles." Stacy Davis and Lorena Truett, *An Analysis of the Impact of Sport Utility Vehicles in the United States,* ORNL (Oak Ridge, Tenn.: Oak Ridge National Laboratory, 2000), 24.

190 *"Policies aimed":* Robert Noland, "Fuel Economy and Traffic Fatalities," *Energy Policy* 33 (2005): 2183–90.

190 *Toyota Prius hybrid:* "Toyota Prius: AEI Best Engineered Vehicle 2004," *Automotive Engineering International,* March 2004: 58–68.

190 *Europeans have still:* An and Sauer, *Passenger Vehicle Fuel Economy.* I have used their normalization so that European mpg can be directly compared with mpg calculated under CAFE.

190 Consumer Reports *found:* "Fuel Economy: Why You're Not Getting the MPG You Expect," *Consumer Reports,* October 2005.

191 *Center for American Progress:* Bracken Hendricks et al., "Strengthening America's Auto Industry," Center for American Progress, Washington D.C., September 13, 2005. Report available online at www.americanprogress.org/autos.

191 *two weeks' worth of oil:* www.hybridcars.com/blogs/brain/fuel-econ-raised.

192 *So an all-electric:* Joseph Romm and Andrew Frank, "Hybrid Vehicles Gain Traction," *Scientific American* 294, no. 4 (April 2006): 72–79.

192 *8 cents a kilowatt-hour:* Ibid.

193 *The plug-in hybrid will: Reducing California's Petroleum Dependence,* Joint Agency Report, California Energy Commission and California Air Resources Board, Sacramento, August 2003.

194 *overall efficiency:* Romm and Frank, "Hybrid Vehicles"; and Alec Brooks,

"CARB's Fuel Cell Detour on the Road to Zero Emission Vehicles," Evworld .com, May 2004.

194 *The efficiency of charging:* Ibid.

194 *1,400 gigawatts:* Joseph Romm, "The Car and Fuel of the Future," Report for the National Commission on Energy Policy, Washington, D.C., June 2005.

194 *less than 400 GW:* Ibid.

195 *overall net emissions:* Lester Lave et al., "The Ethanol Answer to Carbon Emissions," *Issues in Science and Technology* (Winter 2001). See also Lester Lave et al., "Life-Cycle Analysis of Alternative Automobile Fuel/Propulsion Technologies," *Environmental Science and Technology* 34 (2000): 3598–3605.

195 *Existing oil pipelines:* Michael Bryan, "The Fuels Market—Biofuel Penetration and Barriers to Expansion" (paper presented at the Conference on National Security and Our Dependence on Foreign Oil, CSIS, Washington, D.C., June 2002), 13–15.

195 *"$2.70 per gallon":* Lave et al., "Ethanol Answer." This calculation includes a 20-cents-a-gallon tax on ethanol. See also Greene and Schafer, *Reducing Greenhouse Gas Emissions,* 30.

196 *One 2001 analysis:* Lave et al., "Ethanol Answer."

196 *Lee Lynd described:* Personal communications with Lynd.

198 *National Commission:* National Commission on Energy Policy, *Ending the Energy Stalemate: A Bipartisan Strategy to Meet America's Energy Needs,* Washington, D.C., 2004.

CHAPTER NINE: THE U.S.-CHINA SUICIDE PACT ON CLIMATE

200 *"The 'international fairness' issue"* and *"We don't need":* Frank Luntz, "Straight Talk."

200 *2.8 million barrels a day:* Kenneth Lieberthal and Mikkal Herberg, "China's Search for Energy Security: Implications for U.S. Policy," *NBR Analysis* 17, no. 1 (April 2006), available online at www.nbr.org/publications/analysis/pdf/vol17no.1.pdf.

202 *"Perhaps the most":* Richard Benedick, testimony, "The Case of the Montreal Protocol: Science Serving Public Policy," *Hearing on "The Role of Science in Environmental Policy-Making,* U.S. Senate Committee on Environment and Public Works, 109th Cong., 1st sess., September 28, 2005, available online at epw.senate.gov/109th/TestimonyBenedick.pdf.

202 *But other uses:* The history in this section is based on Stephen O. Anderson and K. Madhava Sarma, *Protecting the Ozone Layer* (London: Earthscan, 2002); and Benedick, "Case of the Montreal Protocol."

202 *"first unmistakable sign":* Cheryl Silver with Ruth DeFries (for the National Academy of Sciences), *One Earth, One Future: Our Changing the Global Environment* (Washington, D.C.: National Academies, Press, 1990).

202 *"no effect":* Benedick, "Case of the Montreal Protocol."

204 *National Academy of Sciences:* Walter Sullivan, "Scientists Fear Heavy Use of Coal May Bring Adverse Shift in Climate," *New York Times,* July 25, 1977.

204 *"greenhouse gas concentrations":* U.N. *Framework Convention on Climate Change,* May 1992, full text available online at http://unfccc.int/essential_background/convention/background/items/1349.php.

204 *"Accordingly":* Ibid.

205 *"mandate new commitments":* Byrd-Hagel Resolution, Sen. Res. 98, 105th Cong., 1st sess., *Congressional Record* 143, no. 107 (July 25, 1997): S8113–S8139. Resolution text available online at www.nationalcenter.org/Kyoto Senate.html.

205 *"whereas greenhouse gas":* Ibid.

206 *especially on a per capita basis:* Duncan Austin, José Goldemberg, and Gwen Parker, *Contributions to Climate Change: Are Conventional Metrics Misleading the Debate?* (Washington, D.C.: World Resources Institute, October 1998).

206 *Beijing Energy Efficiency Center:* The discussion of China's energy history is based on Mark D. Levine, "Energy Efficiency in China: Glorious History, Uncertain Future" (remarks at University of California at Berkeley, April 28, 2006); and personal communications with Mark D. Levine.

208 *A 2005 study:* Bin Shui and Robert C. Harriss, "The role of CO_2 Embodiment in U.S.-China Trade," *Energy Policy* (in press).

209 *down to 17 billion tons:* Fiona Harvey and Leora Moldofsky, "U.S. and Australia pledge $128m for climate accord," *Financial Times,* January 12, 2006; and Brian Fisher et al., "Technological Development and Economic Growth, ABARE Research Report" (prepared for the Inaugural Ministerial Meeting of the Asia-Pacific Partnership on Clean Development and Climate, Sydney, January 2006), ABARE, Canberra, available online at www.abare.gov.au/publications_html/climate/climate_06/06_climate.pdf.

CHAPTER TEN: MISSING THE STORY OF THE CENTURY

212 *"In the end"*: Maxwell T. Boykoff and Jules M. Boykoff, "Balance as Bias: Global Warming and the U.S. Prestige Press," *Global Environmental Change* 14 (2004): 125–36.

212 *"This is no time"*: Edward R. Murrow, *See It Now,* March 9, 1954, available online at http://www.spartacus.schoolnet.co.uk/USAmccarthy.htm.

213 *In November 2005: Meet the Press,* MSNBC, November 20, 2005, transcript available online at www.msnbc.msn.com/id/10042399/.

214 *"If we're unlucky"*: Olivia Judson, "Evolution Is in the Air," *New York Times,* November 6, 2005.

215 *"Balance as Bias"*: Boykoff and Boykoff, "Balance as Bias." See also www.fair .org/extra/0411/global-warming.html.

216 *To create doubt:* David Michaels, "Doubt Is Their Product," *Scientific American* 292, no. 6 (June 2005): 96–101.

216 *"to spend millions"*: John Cushman, "Industrial Group Plans to Battle Climate Treaty," *New York Times,* April 26, 1998.

217 *"suggests that melting"*: Juliet Eilperin, "Another Look at Sea Level Rise," *Washington Post,* January 23, 2006.

217 *"is one of many"*: Ibid.

217 *"Most scientists agree"*: Juliet Eilperin, "Debate on Climate Shifts to Issue of Irreparable Change," *Washington Post,* January 29, 2006.

218 *action on global warming:* The memo is available online at http://desmog-blog.com/vampire-memo-reveals-coal-industry-plan-for-massive-propaganda-blitz.

218 *"Coal-burning utilities"*: Seth Borenstein, "Utilities Give Warming Skeptic Big Bucks," Associated Press, July 27, 2006. Available online at www.forbes .com/business/feeds/ap/2006/07/27/ap2910768.html.

218 *May 3, 2006,* Washington Post: Doug Struck, "Canada Alters Course on Kyoto," *Washington Post,* May 3, 2006.

219 *"undermines one of"*: Juliet Eilperin, "Study Reconciles Data in Measuring Climate Change," *Washington Post,* May 3, 2006.

219 *"over the years"*: Wikipedia, s.v. "John Christy," http://en.wikipedia.org/wiki/John_Christy.

219 *"Global warming contrarians"*: Richard Kerr, "No Doubt About It, the World Is Warming," *Science* 312, no. 5775 (May 12, 2006): 825.

221 Washington Post Magazine: Joel Achenbach, "What Global Warming?" *Washington Post Magazine,* May 30, 2006.

221 *"We probably won't"*: "2004 U.S. Hurricane Season Among Worst on Record," *National Geographic News*, November 30, 2004, available online at http://news.nationalgeographic.com/news/2004/11/1130_041130_florida_hurricanes_2004_2.html.

221 *Consider a* Washington Post *article*: Lee Hockstader, "Coastal Louisiana Drowning in Gulf," *Washington Post*, July 13, 2003.

222 *Mike Taibbi*: NBC News, "Meltdown," available online at www.dailykos.com/storyonly/2006/1/13/03957/2447; and "January Could Be Warmest on Record in U.S.," Reuters, January 31, 2006, available online at www.msnbc.msn.com/id/11112822/from/RSS/.

223 *"continuous erosion"*: Senator Lisa Murkowski, statement, *The Role of Science in Environmental Policy Making*," Hearing, U.S. Senate Committee on Environment and Public Works, 109th Cong., 1st sess., September 28, 2005, available online at http://epw.senate.gov/hearing_statements.cfm?id=246814.

224 *Climate Extremes Index*: U.S. Climate Extremes Index available online at www.ncdc.noaa.gov/oa/climate/research/cei/cei.html.

224 *They wanted only*: See, for instance, Don Babwin, "Heat Taxes Utilities, Human Endurance," ABC News, August 1, 2006, available online at http://abcnews.go.com/US/Weather/wireStory?id=2261076; and Jennifer Steinhauer, "In California, Heat Is Blamed for 100 Deaths," *New York Times*, July 28, 2006.

225 *"Scientists associate"*: Ross Gelbspan, *Boiling Point: How Politicians, Big Oil and Coal, Journalists and Activists, Are Fueling the Climate Crisis—and What We Can Do to Avoid Disaster* (New York: Basic Books, 2004), 79–80.

225 *"Meteorologists are not"*: Judith Curry, person communications.

226 *"no prominent national"*: Peter Teague, quoted in Michael Shellenberger and Ted Nordhaus, "The Death of Environmentalism."

226 *"Few scientists agree"*: Andrew C. Revkin, "Yelling 'Fire' on a Hot Planet," *New York Times*, April 23, 2006.

227 *"The hurricanes we"*: Thom Akeman, "Global Warming Behind Record 2005 Storms—U.S. expert," Reuters, April 25, 2006, available online at www.climateark.org/articles/reader.asp?linkid=55586.

227 *"BE WORRIED"*: *Time* 167, no. 14 (April 3, 2006): cover.

228 *"To be fair"*: Jerry Adler, "The New Hot Zones," *Newsweek*, April 3, 2006.

CONCLUSION: THE END OF POLITICS

230 *"America is great":* www.bartleby.com/73/829.html.

231 *"In my judgment":* President Bush (remarks at McCormick Place, Chicago, May 2006), available online at www.whitehouse.gov/news/releases/2006/05/20060522-1.html.

232 *"Scientists present":* James Hansen, "The Threat to the Planet," *New York Review of Books,* 53, no. 12 (July 13, 2006): 12–16.

233 *Evangelical Climate Initiative:* Christians and Climate website, www.christiansandclimate.org/statement.

233 *April 2006 news story:* Lauren Morello, "Evangelical Leaders Take Debate to Capitol Hill," *Greenwire,* April 25, 2006.

233 *"government-mandated":* Interfaith Stewardship Alliance website, www.interfaithstewardship.org/pdf/OpenLetter.pdf.

235 *"In nine months":* Doris Kearns Goodwin, *No Ordinary Time: Franklin and Eleanor Roosevelt: The Home Front in World War II* (New York: Simon & Schuster, 1994), 362.

235 *"You see, I told you":* Edward Teller story told in Richard Rhodes, *The Making of the Atomic Bomb* (New York: Simon & Schuster, 1986), 500.

INDEX